Textbook of Applied Physiology for Nurses - Volume 2

Textbook of Applied Physiology for Nurses - Volume 2

3rd edition

Mario Vaz

MBBS, MD (Physiology)

Former Professor, Department of Physiology

St. John's Medical College, Bangalore

ELSEVIER

ELSEVIER

RELX India Pvt. Ltd.
Registered Office: 818, Indraprakash Building, 8th Floor, 21, Barakhamba Road, New Delhi-110001
Corporate Office: 14th Floor, Building No. 10B, DLF Cyber City, Phase II, Gurgaon-122002, Haryana, India

Textbook of Applied Physiology for Nurses, 3rd edition, Mario Vaz

Publisher's note: Elsevier takes a neutral position with respect to territorial disputes or jurisdictional claims in its published content, including in maps and institutional affiliations.

Previous edition copyrighted 2017, 2022

ISBN: 978-81-312-6928-2
e-Book ISBN: 978-81-312-6929-9

ISBN (Set): 978-81-312-6924-4

Notice

Practitioners and researchers must always rely on their own experience and knowledge in evaluating and using any information, methods, compounds or experiments described herein. Because of rapid advances in the medical sciences, in particular, independent verification of diagnoses and drug dosages should be made. To the fullest extent of the law, no responsibility is assumed by Elsevier, authors, editors or contributors for any injury and/or damage to persons or property as a matter of products liability, negligence or otherwise, or from any use or operation of any methods, products, instructions, or ideas contained in the material herein.

Content Strategist: Deepti Damodaran
Content Project Manager: Shivani Pal
Sr Production Executive: Dhan Singh
Sr Cover Designer: Milind Majgaonkar

Typeset by GW Tech India

Printed in India by Rajkamal Electric Press, Kundli, Haryana.

Preface

This is the third edition of what was formerly the "Textbook of Applied Anatomy & Applied Physiology." In this edition, the anatomy and physiology material are presented as two separate volumes. This serves at least two purposes. First, although it would be ideal for students to learn human biology (i.e. both anatomy and physiology) in an integrated manner, the reality is that anatomy and physiology are taught as two separate subjects within the curriculum. Second, having the original textbook split into two smaller volumes makes it easier for students to carry the books based on their specific time-tables. Nevertheless, the two volumes of anatomy and physiology complement each other and students are encouraged to refer to both of them to better understand the relationship between structure and function of the human body.

In this edition, the material has been extensively reviewed. The language has been simplified where needed but students must recognize that the study of physiology and indeed, medicine, requires a new vocabulary. In order to make the understanding of new medical terms easier, we have provided each chapter with a glossary of terms. Students also find it difficult to read a new subject without a clear outline of the study material. It is for this reason that Specific learning objectives are provided for each chapter and this is supplemented by a few chapter specific questions which allow the student to review what they have learned. Apart from reviewing the written matter of the earlier edition, we have also reviewed the diagrams; some have been modified for greater clarity and new figures have been added where needed.

Each section in Volume II on physiology ends with a chapter on clinical applications related to the particular organ system. This chapter is a bridge between basic physiology and the clinical conditions that nurses are likely to encounter as they proceed with the course, and later, their practice. In keeping with this philosophy, each section has clinical case scenarios that challenge the student to apply their knowledge to the understanding of basic clinical conditions. We also have a brief list of things that a student can learn from a hospital visit. This, we believe is important if the student is to recognize the seamless continuity of learning as they transition from pre-clinical subjects to clinical work. Some of these activities are as simple as reviewing clinical and laboratory investigation forms related to the topics that they are learning about. As a commitment to encouraging the idea of self-learning, essential to professionals becoming lifelong learners, we have also included topics for self-directed learning.

The textbook is accompanied by a workbook. We have added over 300 multiple choice questions to the existing set of varied questions. Answer keys have been provided but in many cases, chapter references are provided to encourage students to review the subject matter for greater clarity.

Writing a textbook is an on-going and continuous exercise. It requires feedback and must continuously evolve to be relevant to its users. In this context, we thank all those who have provided us with comments and suggestions. Our intent is that a thorough understanding of the wonderful workings of the human body inspires students to be the best professionals that they can be, by providing the foundations on which their understanding of the clinical subjects are built.

Preface to the Second Edition

A book is only useful when it serves the needs of its users. At the outset we would like to acknowledge the various reviewers and people who sent us feedback of the first edition. We continue to encourage feedback on the book so that we can address the continued needs of students and teachers.

This edition has been extensively revised in keeping with the revised INC curriculum. New chapters have been written, and old chapters have been updated with new material including tables and diagrams.

Given the rightful need for early clinical exposure, applied aspects of the basic concepts in anatomy and physiology have been addressed at the end of each chapter. These have been written keeping in mind that students are in the first year of their course. In the Physiology section, there are dedicated chapters on Applied aspects of an entire system. These chapters outline common conditions that the students will encounter in their clinical training. Case studies have also been provided that require the student to synthesise learning across chapters of an entire system. Simple suggested activities during hospital visits reinforce the need for early clinical exposure and the integration of the basic medical sciences with clinical medicine.

Nurses, like all other health professionals require to be self-learners. In order to facilitate this, the applied chapters in Physiology have topics for self-directed learning which are not covered in the book, but which encourage students to widen their reading. These topics could be the basis of assignments or student seminars.

This is a combined book of anatomy and physiology. This allows students to better understand structure-function relationships. We have opted to keep the anatomy and physiology sections separate as this is how the subjects are commonly taught and assessed. However, students are encouraged to use the readily available material in this book to cross reference chapters in anatomy and physiology. This will allow for more integrated learning. In order to facilitate this, a ready reckoner of chapter linkages on structure and function is provided.

Students coming into the nursing curriculum often grapple with the new nomenclature and the vast subject material. In order to help students deal with these problems, every chapter has specific learning objectives, a glossary of key terms and a summary at the end of each chapter.

Students are also acutely aware that they have the hurdles of examinations to overcome. In order to address this student need, we have created a workbook that helps students to review and revise the subject matter of the main textbook. This workbook, thus, complements the main textbook and contains short answer questions for rapid review and short and long essay questions. Answer keys to these questions have been provided or in the case of longer questions, references to the main textbook.

We would like to acknowledge the feedback from our own colleagues and students. In particular, we would like to acknowledge Dr Yogitha Ravindran (Anatomy) and Dr Savitha D (Physiology), both of St. John's Medical College for their comments and review.

We trust that this revised edition meets the needs of the students and teachers alike and strongly elicit your comments and feedback to improve the book.

Nachiket Shankar
Mario Vaz

Preface to 1st Edition

Over the years, as teachers, we have seen our nursing students struggle to find an appropriate textbook of Anatomy and Physiology that meets their needs. This book is intended to fulfil that need. In drafting the contents of the book, we paid close attention to the curriculum of the Nursing Council of India, which has prescribed the structure of the book and the chapters. One of the challenges in writing this book was the decision on the 'depth' of the material. We were aware that to write a book that was too sketchy would, in effect, be undermining the worth of nurses. Too detailed a book and the very purpose that we undertook this project would be defeated. We hope that we have provided a 'middle' ground: we are aware that some students may wish to explore the subject matter in greater detail from other reference books. In such a situation we trust that the book provides a solid foundation on which to build on.

We have written the chapters under several headings. Each chapter has specific learning objectives which allow the student to know what they should be able to learn on reading the chapter. A glossary of terms is provided so that students can come to grips with the nomenclature or vocabulary of a new subject. The main body of the chapter addresses the specific learning objectives that have been outlined and is followed by a summary. We have also provided Applications in Nursing, which have been restricted to things that we believe a first-year student would be reasonably expected to understand. Clearly, there are many more applications which the student will appreciate as they move on in the nursing course. Finally, there are review questions which allow the student to quiz themselves on what they have read.

Although primarily written for nurses, this book will also likely serve the needs of those who are enrolled in the allied health sciences.

A textbook is only useful if it meets the needs of students and teachers. We, therefore, would welcome feedback that will allow us to better address these needs in future editions.

Contents

Syllabus Mapper

VOLUME II: APPLIED PHYSIOLOGY	
Syllabus for Applied Physiology	**Chapters/Unit from the Book**
UNIT – I General Physiology-Basic concepts	
Organisation of the Human Body and its Regulatory Systems	Chapter 1
Cell physiology including transportation across cell membrane	Chapter 2
Body fluid compartments, Distribution of total body fluid, intracellular and extracellular compartments, major electrolytes and maintenance of homeostasis	Chapters 3, 4
Cell cycle	Chapter 5
Tissue- formation, repair	Chapter 6
Membranes and glands- functions	See accompanying Anatomy texbook
Application and implication in nursing	Chapter 7
UNIT – II Respiratory system	
Functions of respiratory organs	Chapter 8
Physiology of respiration	Chapter 8
Pulmonary circulation- functional features	Chapter 8
Pulmonary ventilation, Exchange of gases	Chapter 9, 10
Carriage of oxygen and Carbon- dioxide, Exchange of gases in tissue	Chapter 11
Regulation of respiration	Chapter 12
Hypoxia, cyanosis, dyspnoea, periodic breathing	Chapter 13
PFT	Chapter 14
Respiratory changes during exercise	Chapter 15
Aging changes	Chapter 16
Application and implication in nursing	Chapter 17
UNIT – III Digestive system	
Functions of the organs of digestive tract	Chapter 18
Saliva-composition, regulation of secretion and functions of saliva	Chapter 19
Composition and function of gastric juice, mechanism and regulation of gastric secretion	Chapter 19
Composition of pancreatic juice, function, regulation of pancreatic secretion	Chapter 19
Functions of liver, gall bladder and pancreas	Chapter 20
Composition of bile and function	Chapter 20
Secretion and Function of small and large intestine	Chapters 19, 22
Movements of alimentary tract	Chapter 21
Digestion in mouth, stomach, small intestine, large intestine, Absorption of food	Chapter 22
Metabolism of CHO, fat and proteins	Chapter 23

VOLUME II: APPLIED PHYSIOLOGY

Syllabus for Applied Physiology	Chapters/Unit from the Book
Application and implications in nursing	Chapter 24
UNIT – IV Circulatory and lymphatic system	
Functions of heart, conduction system, cardiac cycle, Stroke volume and cardiac output	Chapters 25, 26, 27,
Blood pressure and Pulse	Chapter 28
Circulation- principles, factors influencing blood pressure, pulse	Chapter 28
Coronary circulation, Pulmonary and systemic circulation	Chapters 25, 29
Heart rate-regulation of heart rate,	Chapter 27
Normal value and variations	Chapters 26, 27, 28
Cardiovascular homeostasis in exercise and posture	Chapter 30
Aging changes	Chapter 31
Application and implication in nursing	Chapter 33
UNIT – V Blood	
Blood-Functions, Physical characteristics, Components	Chapter 34
Formation of blood cells	Chapters 35, 36
Erythropoiesis, Functions of RBC, RBC life cycle	Chapter 35
WBC- types, functions	Chapter 36
Platelets-Function and production of platelets	Chapter 37
Clotting mechanism of blood, clotting time, bleeding time, PTT	Chapter 37
Hemostasis –role of vasoconstriction, platelet plug formation in hemostasis, coagulation factors, intrinsic and extrinsic pathways of coagulation	Chapter 37
Blood groups and types	Chapter 38
Functions of reticulo- endothelial system, Immunity	Chapter 39
Application in nursing	Chapter 40
UNIT – VI The Endocrine system	
Functions and hormones of Pineal Gland, Pituitary gland, Thyroid, Parathyroid, Thymus, Pancreas and Adrenal glands.	Chapters 41,42,43, 44, 45,
Other hormones	Chapter 41
Alterations in disease	Chapters 42,43, 44, 45, 46
Application and implication in nursing	Chapter 46
UNIT – VII The Sensory Organs	
Functions of skin	Chapter 47
Vision, hearing, taste and smell	Chapter 48, 49, 50
Errors of refraction, aging changes	Chapter 48, 49, 50, 51
Application and implications in nursing	Chapter 51
UNIT – VIII Musculo-skeletal system	
Bones- Functions, movements of bone s of axial and appendicular skeleton, Bone healing	See accompanying Anatomy textbook
Joints and joint movements	See accompanying Anatomy textbook
Alteration of joint disease	See accompanying Anatomy textbook
Properties and Functions of skeletal muscles – mechanism of muscle contraction	Chapters 52, 53, 54
Structure and properties of cardiac muscles and smooth muscles	Chapter 55
Application and implication in nursing	Chapter 56

Continued

VOLUME II: APPLIED PHYSIOLOGY

Syllabus for Applied Physiology	Chapters/Unit from the Book
UNIT – IX Renal system	
Functions of kidney in maintaining homeostasis	Chapter 57
GFR	Chapter 58
Functions of ureters, bladder and urethra	Chapter 58
Micturition	Chapter 58
Regulation of renal function	Chapter 58
Application and implication in nursing	Chapter 59
UNIT – X The Reproductive System	
Female reproductive system- Menstrual cycle, function and hormones of ovary, oogenesis, fertilization, implantation, Functions of breast	Chapters 60, 61, 62
Male reproductive system- Spermatogenesis, hormones and its functions, semen	Chapter 63
Application and implication in providing nursing care	Chapter 64
UNIT – XI Nervous system	
Overview of nervous system	Chapter 65
Review of types, structure and functions of neurons	Chapter 66
Nerve impulse	Chapter 67
Review functions of Brain- Medulla, Pons, Cerebrum, Cerebellum	Chapter 65
Sensory and Motor Nervous system	Chapters 69,70
Peripheral Nervous system	Chapter 65
Autonomic Nervous system	Chapter71
Limbic system and higher mental Functions- Hippocampus, Thalamus, Hypothalamus	Chapter 72
Vestibular apparatus	Chapter 70
Functions of cranial nerves	Chapter 73
Autonomic functions	Chapter 71
Physiology of Pain- somatic, visceral and referred	Chapter 69
Reflexes	Chapter 74
CSF formation, composition, circulation of CSF, blood brain barrier and blood CSF barrier	Chapter 68
Application and implication in nursing	Chapter 75

1

SECTION

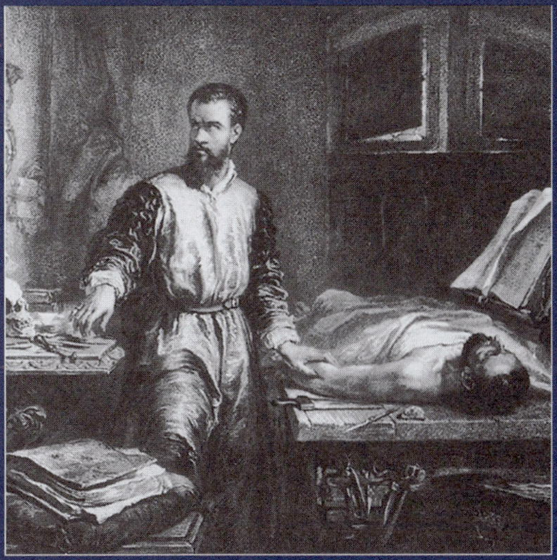

General Physiology – Basic Concepts

Section Outline

SECTION 1

General Physiology – Basic Concepts

CHAPTER 1

Organization of the Human Body, Its Regulatory Systems and Homoeostasis

SPECIFIC LEARNING OBJECTIVES

At the end of this chapter, the student should be able to:

- Describe the levels of organization of the human body.
- Define homoeostasis with examples.
- Define a hormone.
- Differentiate between the terms endocrine, paracrine and autocrine.
- Differentiate broadly between endocrine and nervous regulation.
- Describe the concept of negative feedback with examples.
- Describe the concept of positive feedback.

GLOSSARY OF TERMS

- **Homoeostasis:** the maintenance of the internal environment
- **Endocrine:** related to hormones
- **Hormone:** a chemical messenger secreted by ductless glands in small quantities which acts at a distance from the site of its secretion
- **Paracrine:** when a chemical messenger secreted by a cell acts on neighbouring cells
- **Autocrine:** when a cell secretes a chemical messenger which acts on itself (the same cell)
- **Neurotransmitter:** a chemical messenger released from nerve endings
- **Negative feedback:** when a stimulus acts to reverse (reduce) its own activity
- **Positive feedback:** when a stimulus acts to enhance (increase) its own activity

This chapter introduces the ideas and concepts which will be repeated and expanded in other parts of the book.

THE CELL AND ORGANIZATION OF THE HUMAN BODY

The basic unit of the human body is the cell (Fig. 1.1). A cell needs nutrients to survive and uses energy for its functions. Each living cell performs certain functions. Some functions are general and some are specific. Some cells divide and grow faster than others and some are unable to divide at all.

A cell contains various organelles. These are components of the cell that perform specific functions. Table 1.1 summarizes the various functions of the basic organelles of a cell. This is not a complete list; for other details about the structure and function of the cell, see Chapter 3 of the accompanying text book. You will learn about other organelles and functions in subsequent chapters.

Many cells of the same type form a **tissue**. Examples of tissues include epithelial tissue (which covers the body and lines the organs), connective tissue (which binds various structures together) and muscle tissue (which contracts), among others.

Tissues make up an **organ** which is a structural and functional unit within the body. Examples of organs are the heart, lungs, kidneys and liver.

At yet a higher level is the **organ system**. Our bodies are made up of various organ systems. They include, for instance, the respiratory system, the digestive system, the circulatory and lymphatic system, the endocrine system, the nervous system, the musculoskeletal system, the renal system and the reproductive system.

HOMOEOSTASIS

In order to function well and together, cells, organs and organ systems need to be regulated or controlled. This is important because the body undergoes all kinds of stress. Different regulatory systems maintain the internal environment of the body constant. A scientist named Walter Cannon coined the term

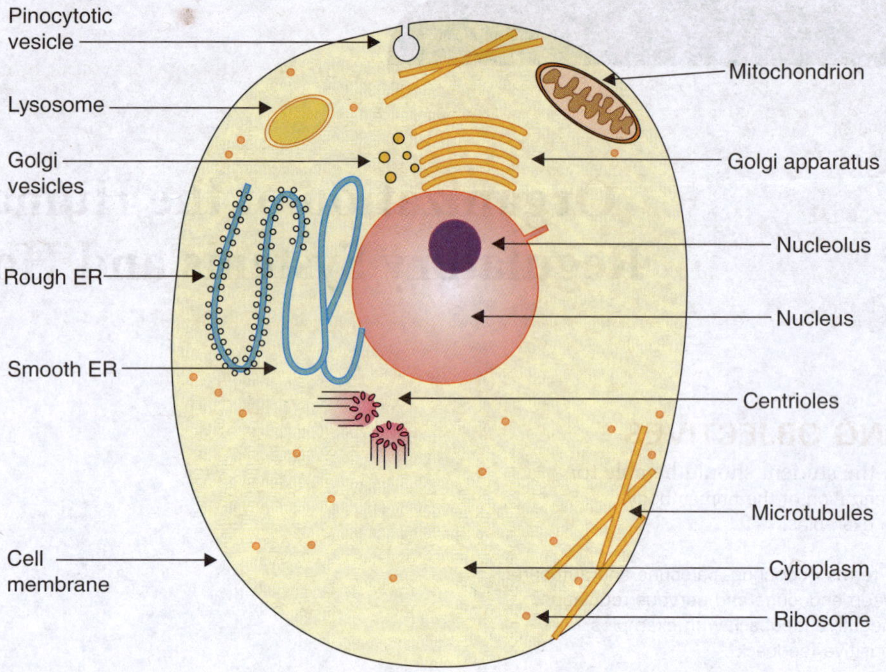

FIG. 1.1 Structure of a typical cell.

Table 1.1 Functions of Some of the Parts of a Cell

Organelle	Function
Cell membrane	• Maintains the structure of the cell • Transports substances into and out of the cell
Nucleus	• Contains the genetic material of the cell (genes, in the form of DNA) • Cell division • Regulation of cell function
Ribosomes	• Protein synthesis
Mitochondria	• The 'powerhouse' of the cell; produces energy as adenosine triphosphate (ATP) through oxidative phosphorylation
Endoplasmic reticulum	• ROUGH: Attachment of ribosome (important for protein synthesis) • SMOOTH: Steroid synthesis
Golgi bodies	• Modification and packaging of proteins before secretion
Lysosomes	• Digestion of large molecules

homoeostasis to describe this constancy of the environment. What this means is that various parameters are kept constant in our body. As examples, body temperature is normally maintained at around 37°C, the pH of blood is maintained around 7.4 and blood pressure is maintained at around 120/80 mm Hg. There are many other examples. Each parameter is maintained constant around a certain range. As an example, pH may vary between 7.35 and 7.45 normally. The aim of homoeostasis is to allow the body to respond to the various stresses that it is exposed to, appropriately. Thus, we are able to maintain our body temperature constant on a very cold day or a very hot day.

REGULATORY SYSTEMS

Two major **regulatory systems** that control our body are the endocrine system and the nervous system.

Endocrine System

The **endocrine system** consists of a number of endocrine glands which secrete chemical messengers called **hormones**. The endocrine glands do not have ducts and secrete small quantities of the hormones directly into the blood. They are then carried to organs at some distance away from the endocrine gland where they have their action. They bring about their action by acting on specific proteins called receptors. There are a large number of hormones in the body, for example, growth hormone, thyroxine, parathormone, glucocorticoids and insulin. These are described in greater detail in Section 6.

In summary, the characteristics of hormones are as follows:

1. They are secreted by ductless glands.
2. They are secreted in small quantities.
3. They are carried in circulation.
4. They have their action some distance away from the endocrine gland.
5. They act on specific receptors.

The cells in the body are also regulated by chemical messengers that are secreted close to the target cell or by the target cell itself.

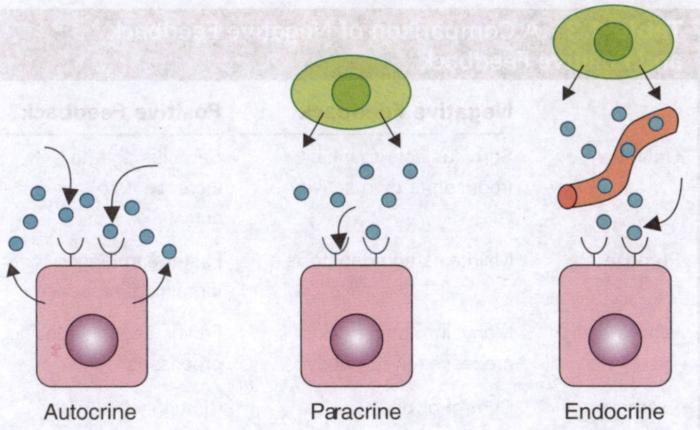

FIG. 1.2 Autocrine, paracrine and endocrine secretions.

Paracrine action occurs when a chemical messenger secreted by a cell acts on neighbouring cells (para = beside).

Autocrine action occurs when a cell secretes a messenger which acts on itself (auto = self). Examples of these will be given later in the book.

The three mechanisms by which chemical messengers act, which have been described earlier, that is, endocrine, paracrine and autocrine, are illustrated in Fig. 1.2.

Nervous System

The **nervous system** is the other major regulatory system in the body. The nervous system regulates how we move (motor system), how we sense our surroundings (sensory system) and how we control the heart, the various organs and various metabolic processes (autonomic nervous system,). These are discussed in greater detail in Section 11. The brain has many other functions which are discussed later.

The nervous system is made up of nerves(neurons). These neurons release chemical messengers called **neurotransmitters** from the nerve endings. There are many different types of neurotransmitters; some excite (stimulate) the cells and some inhibit (slow down) the cells. Examples of neurotransmitters are acetylcholine, norepinephrine, glycine and glutamate.

While both the endocrine system and nervous system help to regulate the body, there are important differences in how they do this. This is summarized in Table 1.2.

Table 1.2 Comparison of the Endocrine System and Nervous System

	Endocrine System	Nervous System
Organization	Multiple ductless glands	Central and peripheral nervous systems
Chemical messenger	Hormone	Neurotransmitter
Transmission of the messenger	Bloodstream	Neuron
Speed of action	Slow	Fast
Duration of action	Long	Short
Examples	Thyroxine, insulin and growth hormone	Acetylcholine, norepinephrine and glutamate

'NEGATIVE FEEDBACK' MAINTAINS HOMOEOSTASIS

In the previous section, we discussed how chemical messengers called hormones are part of the endocrine regulatory system. But what happens if too much of a hormone is secreted? How does the body control the level of hormone so that there are no side effects? In order to understand this, let us take the example of a hormone thyroxine which is released from the thyroid gland. It is an important hormone which has actions on the heart and metabolism, among other actions which are described in Section 6. However, too much of a hormone can be a bad thing. When thyroxine levels are raised, it gives rise to a condition called hyperthyroidism. The patient begins to lose weight, feels irritable, has a rapid heart rate and experiences tremors (fine shaking of the hand). Thus, it is important to control the level of the hormone. The level of thyroxine is controlled within normal concentrations through a process called **negative feedback**.

Look at Fig. 1.3. You will see that while thyroxine is secreted by the thyroid gland, it is in fact controlled by another hormone called thyroid-stimulating hormone (TSH) which is released from the pituitary gland. TSH is itself controlled by the thyroid hormone–releasing hormone (TRH) released from the hypothalamus. Thus, TRH stimulates the release of TSH which in turn stimulates (increases) the release of thyroxine.

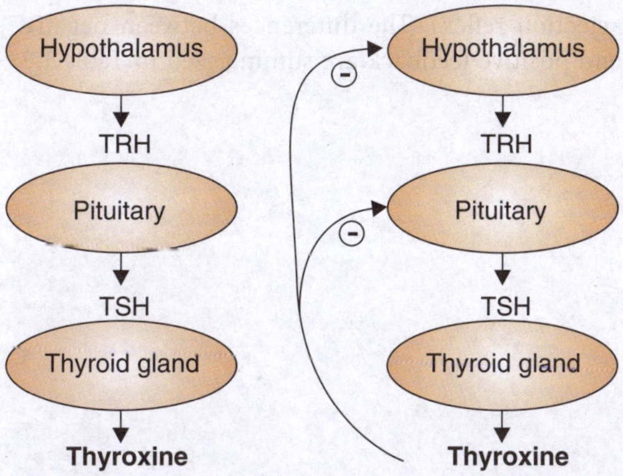

FIG. 1.3 Negative feedback illustrated using the example of thyroxine hormone levels.

In Fig. 1.3, you will see that the level of thyroxine is high (indicated in bold letters). The result of this is that the increased level of thyroxine acts 'backwards' to inhibit (decrease) the release of both TSH and TRH. When TSH and TRH levels are low, less thyroxine will be secreted. Thus, increased levels of thyroxine act to inhibit the further secretion of thyroxine and bring the concentration of thyroxine back to normal.

This backward regulation which inhibits the stimulus, which triggered (started) the regulation, is called negative feedback. Thus, the substance, which is in increased concentration, acts to decrease its own secretion and therefore its own concentration in negative feedback. Other examples of negative feedback include the control of blood pressure and body temperature, among others.

Negative feedback loops are sometimes classified based on how long these feedback loops are. These are as follows:

1. Long-loop feedback, that is, between the peripheral endocrine gland and the pituitary or hypothalamus
2. Short-loop feedback, that is, between the pituitary gland and the hypothalamus
3. Ultrashort-loop feedback, that is, when the secretion of the hypothalamus regulates its own secretion

'POSITIVE FEEDBACK' INCREASES RESPONSES AND MAKES THEM FASTER

Another type of feedback called positive feedback also occurs in the body.

Let us take an example. When we cut ourselves, we bleed. It would be best if bleeding stops fast. This happens through different ways, one of which is the formation of a clot. The formation of a clot is an example of positive feedback. Another example of positive feedback happens during the birth of the baby. When a woman goes into labour, her uterus continues to contract harder at shorter intervals until the baby is born (parturition reflex). A third example of positive feedback occurs when a baby sucks the breast. More and more milk is ejected from the breast when the baby continues to suck at the breast (milk ejection reflex). The differences between negative feedback and positive feedback are summarized in Table 1.3.

Table 1.3 A Comparison of Negative Feedback and Positive Feedback

	Negative Feedback	Positive Feedback
Definition	Stimulus acts to inhibit (reduce) its own activity	Stimulus acts to increase its own activity
Purpose	Maintains homoeostasis	Faster and bigger (amplified) response
Where seen?	Many, in multiple processes in the body	Fewer, seen in specific processes
Examples	Control of body temperature, pH, ionic concentrations, hormone levels and blood pressure	Clotting, child birth, shock and milk ejection

SUMMARY

- The cell is the basic unit of the human body. Many cells make a tissue. Many tissues make an organ.
- Body function is regulated by the endocrine system which acts through hormones and the nervous system which acts through neurotransmitters.
- The endocrine system acts slower and lasts longer than the nervous system.
- Chemical messengers may act far way from the site of their secretion (endocrine), on adjacent cells (paracrine) or on the cell which secretes the chemical (autocrine).
- Negative feedback is a process by which a stimulus regulates itself by reducing its own activity. The aim of negative feedback is homoeostasis.
- Positive feedback increases responses and makes them happen faster.

CHAPTER REVIEW QUESTIONS

1. Define homoeostasis. List three parameters which are controlled by homoeostasis.
2. Define negative feedback. What is its function? Give one example.
3. Define positive feedback. What is its function? Give one example.
4. List four features of a hormone.
5. Explain three differences between endocrine system and nervous system.

CHAPTER 2

The Cell Membrane and Transport Across the Cell Membrane

SPECIFIC LEARNING OBJECTIVES

At the end of this chapter, the student should be able to:

- Draw a diagram of the cell membrane and label its parts..
- List the functions of the proteins in the cell membrane.
- List the different types of transport across the cell membrane with examples.
- Distinguish between active and passive transport.
- Distinguish between simple and facilitated diffusion.

GLOSSARY OF TERMS

- **Passive transport:** transport of substances across the cell membrane along their concentration gradient, without the use of energy
- **Active transport:** transport of substances across a cell membrane against their concentration gradient, requiring the use of energy
- **Vesicular transport:** transport of substances into and out of the cell in the form of cell inclusions called vesicles (common examples are exocytosis and endocytosis)
- **Simple diffusion:** movement of molecules from an area of high concentration to an area of low concentration
- **Osmosis:** movement of water molecules from an area of low solute concentration to an area of high solute concentration

In this chapter, we focus on the cell membrane – the outer covering of the cell.

The cell membrane has several functions:

1. It gives the cell its shape.
2. It separates the constituents of the cell from the fluid outside the cell.
3. It helps transfer substances into and out of the cell.

The cell membrane also has other functions because of its components in different cells.

STRUCTURE OF THE CELL MEMBRANE

The cell membrane is a 'fluid mosaic model'. The cell membrane is made up of fats, proteins and carbohydrates.

Fats

The fats that make up the cell membrane are largely phospholipids and cholesterol. The fats in the membrane contribute to its 'fluid' nature. Fig. 2.1 depicts the structure of the cell membrane. It shows that the cell membrane is made up largely of a type of fat called phospholipid. A phospholipid has a head which is hydrophilic (liking water) and a tail which is hydrophobic (not liking water). Phospholipids naturally arrange themselves in a bilayer so that the heads face out and the tails in. This ensures that the tails do not come in contact with water. This is what happens in the cell membrane too. The phospholipid is arranged in two layers; thus, the cell membrane is described as having a lipid bilayer. The lipid bilayer ensures that small substances which are lipid soluble will be able to cross the cell membrane, while large substances and water-soluble substances will not be able to cross, unless there is some way to transfer them across the membrane.

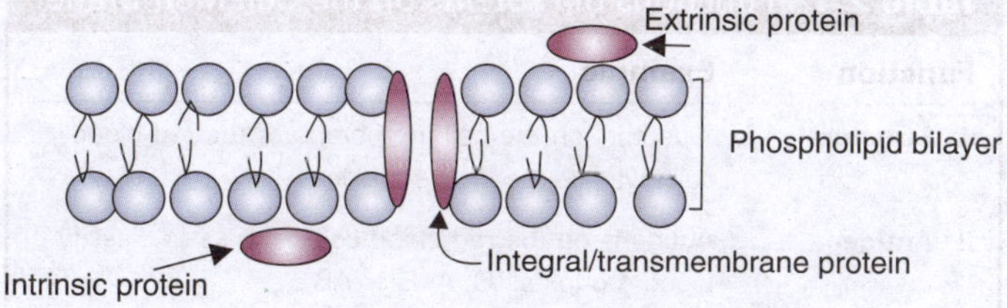

FIG. 2.1 Schematic representation of the cell membrane.

Proteins

Some of the proteins are on the outer surface of the cell membrane and are called extrinsic (outside) proteins. Some of the proteins are located on the inner surface of the cell membrane towards the cytoplasm of the cell. These are called intrinsic (inside) proteins. Intrinsic and extrinsic proteins are together called peripheral proteins. Other proteins cross the two lipid layers – these are called integral or transmembrane (trans = across) proteins. The proteins in the cell membrane have many functions. Some of these are summarized in Table 2.1.

Carbohydrates

Carbohydrates in the cell membrane are often combined with proteins (glycoproteins) and lipids (glycolipids).

TRANSPORT ACROSS THE CELL MEMBRANE

Substances are transported into and out of the cell by a variety of methods. Substances tend to move *along* their concentration gradient (i.e. from high to low concentration) and do not require energy to do this. This type of transport which does not require energy is called PASSIVE transport. If a substance has to be moved *against* a concentration gradient, it can be done only by using energy. This type of transport is called ACTIVE transport. This is summarized in Table 2.2.

Passive Transport

Passive transport includes diffusion and osmosis.

Diffusion is the passive movement of substances along their concentration gradient, that is from a higher to a lower concentration. Since sodium is present at a higher concentration outside the cell than inside, sodium diffuses from outside the cell to inside the cell if the cell membrane is permeable to sodium. Since sodium is normally present in the body as a hydrated ion (i.e. with water), it cannot cross the lipid bilayer. Therefore, sodium enters the cell through channels (pores) when these channels are open.

Table 2.1 Functions of Proteins on the Cell Membrane

Function	Example
1. **Structural**	'Spectrin' on the cell membrane of the red blood cell gives its biconcave shape
2. **Antigen**	Antigens on the red blood cell allow us to classify blood groups as O, A, B or AB
3. **Receptor**	Receptors for many hormones and neurotransmitters
4. **Channel**	Allow water-soluble substances to be transported across the cell membrane; e.g. channels for sodium or potassium
5. **Carrier proteins**	Carry large molecules across the cell membrane; one example is GLUT-4 for glucose
6. **'Pump'**	Substances that need to be moved against their concentrations need a 'pump' to move them across the membrane; e.g. Na^+–K^+-ATPase pump present in all cells
7. **Enzyme**	E.g. 'adenylate cyclase' on the inner surface of the membrane which results in cAMP formation; cAMP is an important intracellular messenger

Table 2.2 Differences Between Active and Passive Transport

	Active Transport	Passive Transport
Movement	Against the concentration gradient	Along the concentration gradient
Use of energy	Uses energy (directly or indirectly)	No use of energy
Examples	Primary active transport Secondary active transport Vesicular transport • Endocytosis • Exocytosis	Osmosis Diffusion • Simple • Facilitated

There are two types of diffusion across a cell membrane. The first is called simple diffusion. In **simple diffusion**, movement of a substance occurs without the help of any protein. In **facilitated diffusion**, the movement occurs along a concentration gradient with the help of a carrier protein.

The differences between simple and facilitated diffusion are described in Table 2.3.

Factors which affect simple diffusion are:

- Concentration gradient
- Size of the molecule
- Charge of the molecule
- Lipid solubility of the molecule (since the cell membrane is a bilipid layer)

Osmosis is the passive movement of water (solvent) from an area of low solute concentration to an area of high solute concentration. When osmosis occurs, it equalizes the solute concentrations in both areas.

Active Transport

Active transport includes primary active transport and secondary active transport.

Primary active transport directly utilizes energy to move a substance against its concentration gradient. The concentration of sodium (Na) is higher outside the cell, that is in the extracellular fluid, than inside the cell. In contrast, the concentration of potassium (K) is higher inside the cell (intracellular) than outside. Movement of sodium out of the cell and potassium into

CHAPTER 7

Applications and Implications of Cellular Physiology and Body Fluid Compartments for Nursing

SPECIFIC LEARNING OBJECTIVES

At the end of this chapter, the student should be able to:

- Describe a simple application of the use of cell membrane transport in relation to diffusion, osmosis and active transport.
- Describe the importance of input–output chart.
- List features of dehydration.
- List common intravenous fluids used in clinical medicine.
- Apply the learning in Section 1 to the understanding of simple clinical problems.

GLOSSARY OF TERMS

- **Input–output chart:** a recording of all the fluid intake (oral and intravenous) and fluid loss (urine, stools, fluid loss via drainage tubes) in a day
- **Intravenous:** via a vein
- **Enteral:** via the gastrointestinal tract

APPLICATIONS OF CELL TRANSPORT

Understanding cellular transport helps us to understand both physiology and the basis of treatments better. Although this cannot be covered in detail here, simple examples are discussed as follows:

Diffusion: A patient is given oxygen through a gas mask. How does this oxygen enter the cell? Gases like oxygen, carbon dioxide and nitrogen which are lipid soluble freely cross the cell membrane by simple diffusion. When oxygen is given to a patient, it is transported in blood mainly by haemoglobin contained within the red blood cells but also dissolved in plasma in a small quantity. When it reaches the cells, oxygen diffuses across the cell membranes again. Fig. 7.1 shows the process of diffusion of oxygen in the lungs and the tissues. You can understand that the lipid solubility of oxygen is important since it has to cross many cell membranes to reach the tissues.

Osmosis: In patients with severe end-stage kidney disease, the treatments available are haemodialysis and kidney transplant. Patients with end-stage kidney disease often have oliguria (reduced urine output) and therefore need a way to eliminate fluid from the body. A cheaper treatment is peritoneal dialysis. In peritoneal dialysis, a hyperosmolar solution (solution with a high osmolarity) is injected through a tube into the peritoneal cavity. Fluid then moves into the peritoneal cavity through a process of osmosis (from a lower solute concentration to a higher solute concentration) and this can then be drained. Peritoneal dialysis is shown in Fig. 7.2.

Secondary active transport: In patients who are severely dehydrated, we give oral rehydration solution (ORS). This contains glucose and salts including sodium in water. Glucose is transported in the intestine by secondary active transport along with sodium, using a carrier protein. Giving sodium along with the glucose ensures that a high concentration gradient for sodium is maintained (high in the intestinal lumen and low in the cell). Thus sodium moves from the gastrointestinal lumen into the intestinal cell and carries glucose with it. The concentration gradient for sodium is maintained by a sodium–potassium pump in the cell (an example of primary active transport) which helps to keep the concentration of sodium inside the cell low.

APPLICATIONS OF BODY FLUID COMPARTMENTS

Measuring fluid balance: Patients admitted into the hospital with conditions of fluid imbalance need to have an intake–output chart maintained. The nurse will be required to do this and fluid intake needs to be matched to fluid output. This is important because if too much fluid is given, it can cause fluid overload, and if too little fluid is given, the patient may get dehydrated.

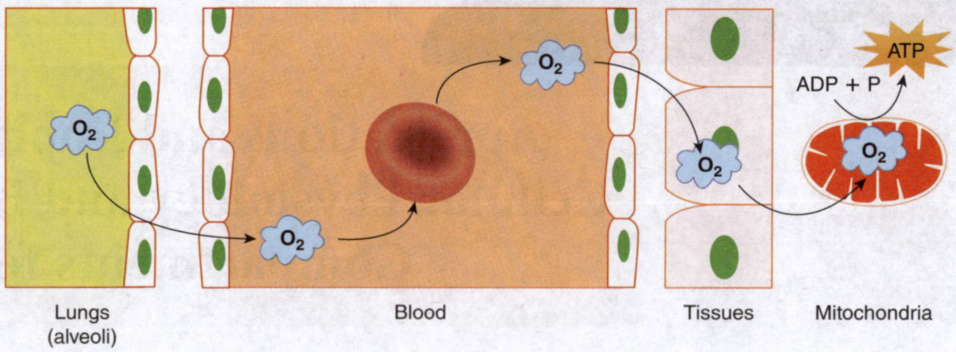

FIG. 7.1 Diffusion of oxygen in the lungs and tissues. Note the number of cell membranes that oxygen has to cross.

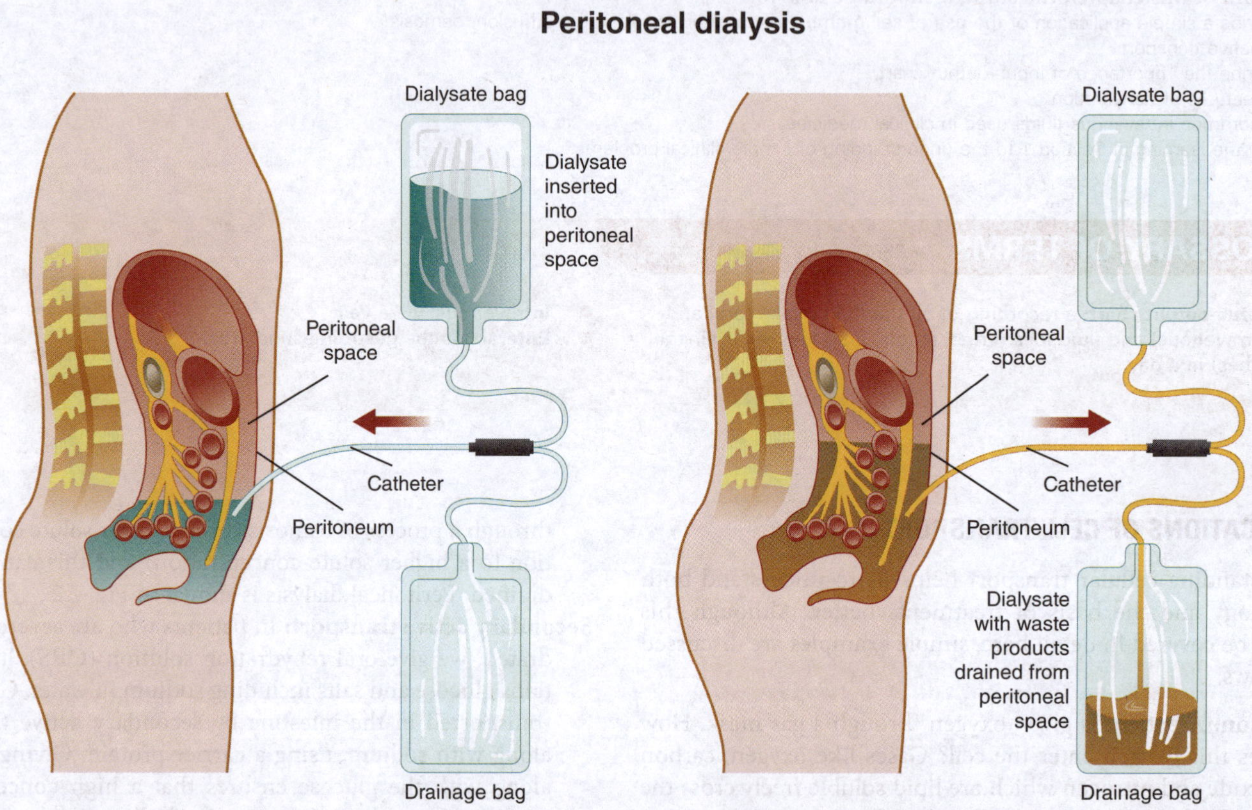

FIG. 7.2 Peritoneal dialysis using the principle of osmosis.

Fluid intake includes those ingested (in food and drink) and fluid administered intravenously. Fluid output is typically measured by adding collected urine volumes but could also include other losses including loss in faeces and loss through other tubes that may be inserted into the body (e.g. drainage tubes from the chest or abdomen). Fig. 7.3 depicts an example of an unfilled input–output chart. The nurse is required to make these entries as and when they occur.

Evaluating dehydration: Clinical history of the patient is important when there is dehydration. Questions that we ask include – does the patient have diarrhoea or persistent vomiting? What fluid has the patient consumed? Has the patient been able to retain the fluids?

Patients who are dehydrated may experience tiredness, headaches, a strong sense of thirst and muscle weakness, and may pass small quantities of high coloured urine.

Signs that need to be checked include the following:

- Dry skin and mucous membranes.
- Decreased skin turgor (when a fold of skin is pinched, it takes longer to go back to its original state).
- Feeble, rapid pulse.
- Fast and deep breathing.
- Sunken eyes.
- Low blood pressure.
- Depression of the fontanelle in infants (the skull is not completely fused in infants – there is a small depression

Input/Output chart

Name.............................

Date...............................

Input		Output	
Time	Volume and type of fluid	Time	Volume

FIG. 7.3 Input–output chart.

in the skull where the bones have not fused – this is the fontanelle).

- Decreased urine flow.

Recognizing dehydration at an early stage is important for early treatment.

NATURE OF REPLACEMENT FLUIDS USED IN CLINICAL MEDICINE

Fluids are given to patients orally and intravenously.

Oral fluids: These include water, ORS, clear soups and juices. While commercial preparations are available, ORS can also be prepared at home with little cost. In its simplest form, ORS is made by dissolving six teaspoons of sugar and half a teaspoon of salt in 1 L of clean drinking water. New formulations also exist.

Intravenous (i.v.) fluid preparations: These include a large number of fluids with varying composition. A few of the most commonly used i.v. preparations include the following:

Normal saline (0.9% NaCl): This is the most common i.v. fluid used to replace extracellular fluid and when starting i.v. drips for hydration. The volume of i.v. fluids needs to be monitored especially in patients who may have fluid retention (e.g. heart and kidney failure) as excess fluid can lead to fluid overload.

Ringer's lactate: This fluid most closely resembles plasma. It is for this reason that it is preferred for persons with burns and those who have suffered trauma. This fluid contains several solutes including sodium chloride, potassium chloride, calcium chloride and sodium lactate in sterile water.

Five per cent dextrose: Because of the dextrose, this fluid contains some calories but this is limited.

Half-normal saline (0.45%): It is a fluid that is used when there is hyperosmolarity or hypernatraemia. It may be used, for instance, in diabetic ketoacidosis.

PARENTERAL NUTRITION

Some patients may need to be maintained for long periods only on i.v. fluids. In these situations, the fluids listed earlier are not enough as they do not provide adequate nutrition. In this situation, the nutritional needs of the patient are provided in the form of glucose, amino acids, lipids, vitamins and minerals and salts. Parenteral nutrition is most often given as pre-prepared commercially available products, although these can be supplemented in various ways. Some patients may also be on prolonged enteral feeds, that is through tubes (Ryle's tube) which are placed in the stomach through the nasal cavity and oesophagus.

CLINICAL CASE PROBLEMS

(A) ***A young, 20-year-old male comes to the hospital with a history of feeling tired and weak for the last 3 months. He has also noticed that he feels puffy around the eyes and his face looks fuller in the mirror. He has also noticed some swelling of the feet.***

Some of the investigations that were done were the following:

Serum sodium: 123 mEq/L

Serum potassium: 6.2 mEq/L

1. Comment on his sodium and potassium levels. (What are these conditions called?)
2. What is the normal percentage of body water?
3. Do you think that body water in this patient will be reduced or increased?

At the hospital, the patient undergoes haemodialysis and since he comes from a small town far away, he is advised peritoneal dialysis. His wife is advised to maintain an input–output chart to ensure that he is in fluid balance.

4. What is the physiological basis of peritoneal dialysis?
5. As a nurse, what instructions will you give to the wife so that she can maintain an adequate input–output chart?

(B) ***A 2-year-old child is brought to a clinic in a rural health centre. The child has been suffering from many bouts of large-volume watery diarrhoea over the last 2 days. The child is listless but does appear very sick. You are the nurse at the clinic.***

1. Which features will alert you to dehydration in the child?
2. What instructions can you give to the mother to prepare ORS at home for any future episodes?
3. By what transport process is the glucose in ORS absorbed in the intestine?

(C) **A 35-year-old woman has been discharged from the hospital on enteral (oral) feeds via a Ryle's tube inserted through the nasal cavity. The patient's relatives have been carefully trained by the nurse in the hospital on how to prepare and administer the feeds. At home, the patient's attender feels that she is not recovering fast enough and doubles the nutrients in the feed. The patient develops diarrhoea.**

Why could this happen, assuming all hygienic measures have been taken? (Clue: Will a hyperosmolar feed cause diarrhoea – why?)

SELF-DIRECTED LEARNING

1. What is the alternative to giving fluids orally or intravenously to infants with severe dehydration?
2. What is a paladai? How and when is it used?
3. What are the most common causes of dehydration in infants?
4. We give many medications in hospital – some of which need to enter the cells. How do drugs cross the cell membrane?
5. What is a Ryle's tube? How is it inserted? What are the precautions to take while inserting a Ryle's tube?

WHAT YOU CAN LEARN FROM A HOSPITAL VISIT?

1. Visit the hospital and review an input–output charge with a nurse. Ask why the patient requires an input–output chart. Ask the nurses what practical difficulties they face while filling the chart and monitoring the patient.
2. Visit a nursing station – find out what the different types of i.v. fluids are stocked. Ask the nurse what the common reasons are for administering i.v. fluids in the ward you have visited.
3. Go to a ward where a patient is on enteral feeds via a Ryle's tube. Ask the nurses how they insert the Ryle's tube and the practical difficulties they face while inserting the Ryle's tube.

2

SECTION

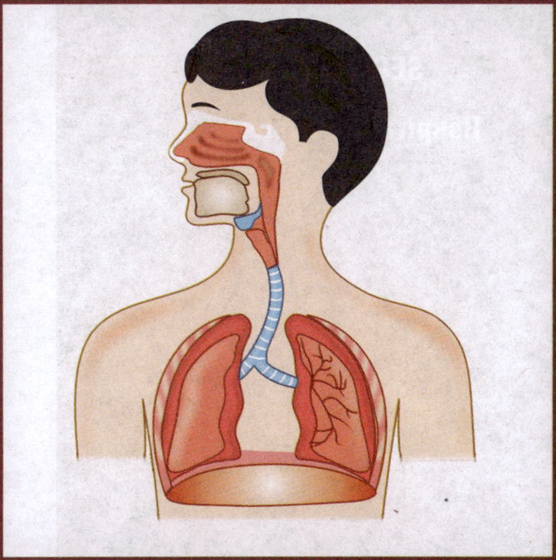

Respiratory System

Section Outline

Table 2.3 Comparison of Simple and Facilitated Diffusion

	Simple Diffusion	Facilitated Diffusion
Movement	Along the concentration gradient (high to low)	Along the concentration gradient
Type of substance	• Small • Lipid soluble	• Large • Water soluble
Need for a carrier protein	No	Yes
Expenditure of energy	No	No
Speed of transport	Slow	Fast
Characteristics of transport	As concentration gradient increases, diffusion increases	As concentration gradient increases, diffusion increases till all carrier molecules are filled – this is **saturation**
Examples	Movement of sodium from outside to inside of the cell through channels Movement of oxygen and carbon dioxide directly across the lipid bilayer	Movement of glucose into the cell by GLUT-4

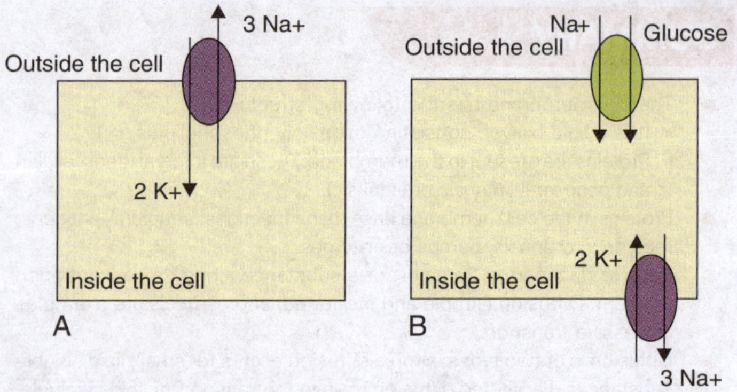

FIG. 2.2 **(A)** Primary active transport, for example the Na–K-ATPase pump. **(B)** Secondary active transport, for example Na–glucose transport.

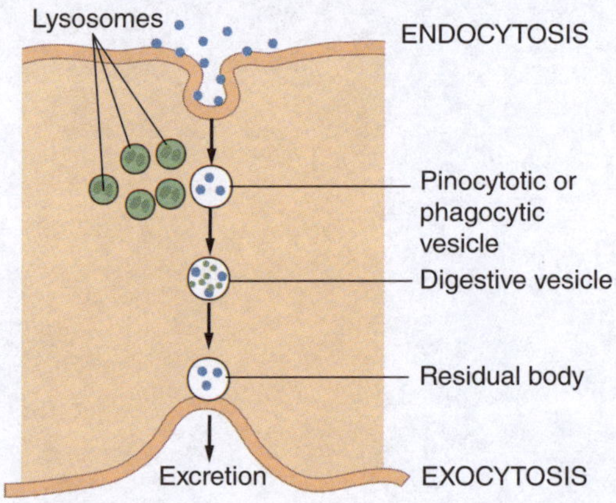

FIG. 2.3 Endocytosis and exocytosis as a part of phagocytosis.

the cell is against their concentration gradients and requires energy for transport. This is done by a 'pump' called the Na–K-ATPase pump, an example of primary active transport. The pump moves three sodium ions out of the cell (against the concentration gradient of sodium) for every two potassium ions that it moves in (against the concentration gradient of potassium) Fig. 2.2A.

Secondary active transport does not directly use energy in the form of adenosine triphosphate (ATP), but ATP is used during the transport process. An example of this is the transport of glucose in the intestine and the nephron (kidney). Fig. 2.2B illustrates this. You will see that glucose is transported into the cell along with sodium using a carrier protein. This movement is possible because the sodium concentration inside the cell is low. So, sodium moves along its concentration gradient (high outside, low inside) and carries glucose with it. The low concentration of sodium inside the cell is because of the Na–K-ATPase pump which keeps pumping sodium out of the cell. Thus, ATP is used to maintain the sodium gradient to transport glucose inside the cell along with sodium. ATP is thus used indirectly.

Vesicular transport is the transfer of substances into or out of the cell by vesicles which are cell organelles. The two major types of vesicular transport are endocytosis and exocytosis.

In **endocytosis**, the cell membrane engulfs some substance and then takes it into the cell. Phagocytosis is a process in which a white blood cell engulfs bacteria and takes inside the cell. Another form of endocytosis is pinocytosis. In pinocytosis, extracellular fluid is engulfed and taken into the cell as a vesicle. Pinocytosis helps to clear the extracellular fluid of large molecules in the fluid and also helps in 'immune surveillance'. Immune surveillance is the process by which the immune system monitors the body for infection or malignant cells.

In contrast, in **exocytosis**, a vesicle within the cell moves towards the cell membrane and 'throws out' its contents into the extracellular space. The secretion of hormones is an example of exocytosis. Release of neurotransmitters from the nerve ending into a synapse is another example of exocytosis. Phagocytosis includes both endocytosis and exocytosis and this is shown in Fig. 2.3.

SUMMARY

- The cell membrane has the following structure:
  - a. It is a lipid bilayer, consisting of mainly phospholipids.
  - b. Proteins are present in the membrane. These are integral (transcellular) and peripheral (intrinsic or extrinsic).
- Proteins in the cell membrane have many functions: structural, antigens, receptors, channels, pumps or enzymes.
- Passive transport is transport of a substance along its concentration gradient. Diffusion (simple and facilitated) and osmosis are examples of passive transport.
- Diffusion is of two types: simple diffusion occurs for small, lipid-soluble substances. Facilitated diffusion is used for transport of lipid-insoluble, large molecules and requires a carrier protein.
- Active transport is transport against a concentration gradient which utilizes energy. There are two types: primary active transport and secondary active transport.
- Vesicular transport is of two types: endocytosis and exocytosis.

CHAPTER REVIEW QUESTIONS

1. Describe the structure of the cell membrane with the help of a diagram.
2. List the functions of the proteins in the cell membrane.
3. Compare active and passive transport.
4. Compare simple and facilitated diffusion.

CHAPTER 3

Body Water Compartments

SPECIFIC LEARNING OBJECTIVES

At the end of this chapter, the student should be able to:

- List the factors which affect total body water.
- List the factors that contribute to the intake and output of water on a daily basis.
- Describe the components of total body water.
- Distinguish between intracellular fluid and extracellular fluid.

GLOSSARY OF TERMS

- **Intracellular fluid:** fluid present inside the cell
- **Extracellular fluid:** fluid present outside cells
- **Transcellular fluid:** fluid contained in spaces in the body; fluid includes cerebrospinal fluid (CSF), pleural fluid, peritoneal fluid, intraocular fluid and pericardial fluid
- **Insensible water loss:** water loss from the body without us being aware of it
- **Homeostasis:** constancy of the internal environment

Most of the body weight is water. In males, about 60% of the body weight is water. In females, 50% of body weight is water. One of the main reasons for this difference is that females have more body fat than males. Fat cells are almost completely filled up with a fat droplet. Therefore, fat cells have little water and since women have more fat than men, the percentage of body water in them is also lower. Other factors that affect body water include the body composition (the proportion of body fat to nonfat tissues). People who are obese have less body water. People who are very physically active may have relatively little fat and more muscle tissue. In these individuals, body water will be more. In comparison, people who are sedentary (physically inactive) will have more fat and less muscle and will have a lower percentage of body water. Body water also depends on age. In newborn infants, the percentage of body water can be as high as between 70% and 75%. Body water can also change if there is an imbalance between the intake of water and the output of water. This is discussed in a later part of this chapter. Body water can also change in various diseases; although we list some of these conditions in the subsequent text, a detailed understanding of these conditions is out of the scope of this chapter.

Total body water is dependent on a number of factors:

1. Gender (males > females)
2. Body composition (more fat, less water)
3. Age (infants > adults)
4. Imbalance between fluid intake and fluid output (e.g. dehydration)
5. Diseases (e.g. severe malnutrition, kidney diseases, liver failure and heart failure)

FLUID INTAKE AND OUTPUT

An 'imbalance' of fluid intake and output can alter total body water.

The greatest portion of our daily fluid intake comes from the fluid that we ingest or drink. A smaller proportion of our fluid intake comes from metabolism, particularly of carbohydrates.

The largest proportion of our fluid output is in the form of urine, and variable amounts are excreted in sweat. The amount we lose in sweat depends on the weather, whether we are exercising, etc. The water loss in addition to this is what we call 'insensible loss'. This is the loss of fluid which occurs without our being even

Table 3.1 Daily Intake and Output of Water by Various Methods

Intake		Output	
Methods	**Volume (mL)**	**Methods**	**Volume (mL)**
Ingested	2000	Urine	1400
Metabolism	200	Sweat	100
		Faeces	100
		Insensible – skin	300
		Insensible – breath	300
Total intake (mL)	**2200**	**Total output**	**2200**

aware of it and which is difficult to measure. It includes loss of fluid from the skin, in breath and in faeces. Table 3.1 outlines the different ways and amounts of water we take in and lose. The figures are average for an adult, but, these can vary. Under normal conditions, intake and output are equal, that is we do not lose or gain body water.

COMPONENTS OF BODY WATER

In the beginning of this chapter, we showed that 50%–60% of the body weight is water. This water is distributed in different parts of the body which are referred to as body water compartments.

Nearly, two-thirds of the body water is located inside cells (intra = inside). Because of this, this body water compartment is referred to as the intracellular water.

The remaining one-third of the body water is located outside cells (extracellular water) in the interstitial spaces (the spaces between the cells), in the fluid component of blood (plasma) and in various other spaces of the body such as the pleural cavity which surrounds the lungs, the joint spaces and the cerebrospinal fluid (CSF) which surrounds the brain. This last component of body water is called the transcellular compartment.

Fig. 3.1 outlines the distribution of water in the various compartments of the body. This figure shows that two-thirds of body water is intracellular and one-third is extracellular. Most (three-fourths) of the extracellular fluid is in the extravascular (outside the blood vessels) compartment, while one-fourth, approximately 3 L, is in the form of plasma within the blood vessels (intravascular). The extravascular fluid is further divided into the interstitial fluid (tissue fluid) and the transcellular fluid (fluid contained within cavities; peritoneal fluid, pleural fluid, pericardial fluid, synovial fluid, aqueous humour, vitreous humour, CSF).

MEASUREMENT OF BODY WATER AND ITS COMPARTMENTS

Body water and its compartments are measured using the 'indicator-dilution' principle. This is easy to understand with an example. Let us say we have an irregular container which we fill with water. We want to know the volume of water. We can take a dye which completely dissolves in the water and determine its concentration once it has completely dissolved and has mixed equally throughout the water. Let us say we used 5 g of the dye and after completely dissolving and mixing, the concentration of the dye in the water was 1 g/L. The volume of the water can then be calculated as follows: Volume = amount of indicator/concentration. In the example above, the volume of the irregular container is 5 g (amount of indicator)/1 g/L (concentration) = 5 L.

Total body water is measured using radioactive (tritiated) or stable (deuterated) isotopes of water as indicators. Stable isotopes are more expensive to measure but are safe to use in all people including children and pregnant women. Individual body water compartments can be measured using specific indicators which are retained in that particular compartment. The only large body water compartment that cannot be directly measured is the intracellular water – this is because any indicator would first need to enter the extracellular fluid before getting into the cell.

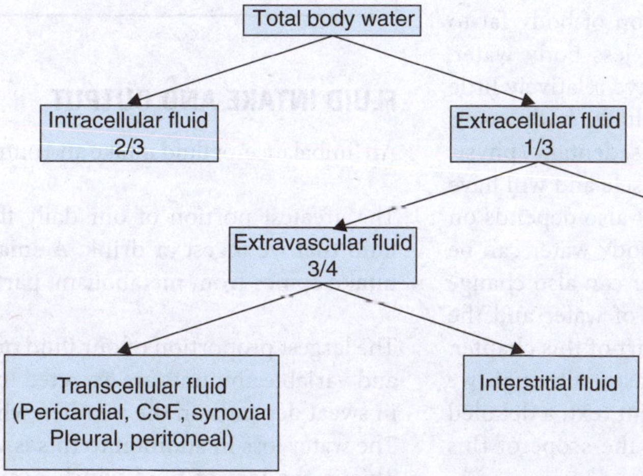

FIG. 3.1 Distribution of water across the different body water compartments.

The ideal indicator is one which:

- Is nontoxic
- Distributes freely and completely in the body water compartment of interest
- Is not metabolized or excreted before the measurement of its concentration
- Can be easily measured

The indicators that can be used for the measurement of different body water compartments are as follows:

- Total body water: ^2H_2O (deuterated water), ^3H_2O (tritiated water), antipyrine
- Extracellular fluid: ^{22}Na, thiosulphate, inulin
- Plasma volume: ^{125}I-albumin (retained in plasma because of its size)
- Blood volume: ^{51}Cr-labelled red blood cells

DIFFERENCES BETWEEN INTRACELLULAR FLUID AND EXTRACELLULAR FLUID

As mentioned earlier, intracellular fluid is the fluid contained inside the cell, while extracellular fluid is the fluid present outside cells in various compartments: interstitial, plasma and transcellular fluid.

Ions constitute 95% of the solutes present in body fluids. However, the concentration of ions in the intracellular and extracellular fluids is very different. Thus, Na^+ is the major cation in the extracellular fluid, while K^+ is the major cation in the intracellular fluid. The main extracellular anions are Cl^- and HCO_3^-, while the major intracellular anions are phosphates, proteins and organic ions. Most of these ions diffuse across the cell membrane, but some ions such as protein anions are large and do not diffuse across the cell membrane.

Table 3.2 provides the concentration in mEq/L of selected ions in the extracellular and intracellular fluids.

Implications of the different distribution of ions in the extracellular and intracellular fluids

1. Diffusible ions can move passively from an area of high concentration to an area of low concentration. Thus, provided channels are open on the cell membrane, sodium will normally move from outside the cell inwards (along its concentration gradient) while potassium will move from inside outwards.
2. If an ion needs to be moved against a concentration gradient, this can be achieved through an active process which utilizes energy. Thus, the sodium–potassium pump moves sodium against its concentration outwards, while at the same time moving potassium against its concentration gradient inwards.
3. Nondiffusible ions, such as the proteins inside the cell, because they result in an unequal distribution of ions on either side of the cell membrane, affect the movement of other diffusible ions across the cell membrane. This effect is called the **Gibbs–Donnan effect**.

Table 3.2 Comparison of the Composition of Extracellular and Intracellular Fluids

	Extracellular Fluid (mEq/L)	Intracellular Fluid (mEq/L)
Na^+	145	10
K^+	4	145
Cl^-	117	5
HCO_3^-	27	10
Phosphates	2	100
Protein	1	60

The nature of the movement of ions across the cell membrane has been discussed in Chapter 2.

Many years ago, a physiologist named Claude Bernard recognized the importance of keeping the ionic concentrations of the extracellular and intracellular fluids constant. After him, Walter Cannon coined the term 'homeostasis' to mean 'constancy of the internal environment'.

Importance of Understanding Body Water and its Distribution

Understanding body water compartments is important for the well-being of the patient. Nurses will need to:

- Record and monitor the fluid intake and output of patients in a variety of clinical conditions including the postoperative period (i.e. following surgery).
- Monitor the 'hydration' of patients suffering from dehydration due to severe diarrhoea or vomiting. Untreated diarrhoea is a major cause of infant mortality in India.
- Teach mothers and supervise the use of oral rehydration solution (ORS) for the treatment of children suffering from diarrhoea-induced dehydration.
- Start and monitor the use of intravenous (i.v.) fluids in patients.

SUMMARY

- Body water constitutes between 50% and 60% of body weight in a typical adult.
- Body water percentage depends on age, gender, body composition, fluid balance and the presence of specific diseases.
- Body water is distributed in different compartments. Two-thirds of body water is intracellular, while one-third is extracellular.
- Extracellular body water is further divided into extravascular and intravascular (plasma) fluid compartments.
- Extravascular body water is divided into interstitial (tissue) fluid and transcellular (cavity) fluid.
- The ionic concentrations in extracellular and intracellular fluid are different; Na^+, Cl^- and HCO_3^- are in higher concentration in the extracellular fluid, while K^+, phosphates and proteins are higher in the intracellular fluid.

CHAPTER REVIEW QUESTIONS

1. List the factors which affect total body water.
2. List the methods of water intake and water output.
3. What are the differences between intracellular and extracellular fluids?
4. What is the method used to measure body water compartments?
5. What are the features of an ideal indicator?

CHAPTER 4

Fluid and Electrolyte Balance

SPECIFIC LEARNING OBJECTIVES

At the end of this chapter, the student should be able to:

- Outline the composition of the fluid in the different body compartments.
- Describe the methods by which fluid intake occurs.
- Describe the ways in which fluid is lost from the body.
- List the key electrolytes in the body.
- Describe how fluid balance is maintained in the body.
- Describe how electrolyte concentrations are in the body regulated.

GLOSSARY OF TERMS

- **Dehydration:** the excessive loss of body water
- **Plasma osmolarity:** normal 280–300 mOsm/L, it is a reflection of the hydration of the body and is dependent on the concentration of substances in the plasma such as sodium, chloride, glucose and urea
- **Natriuresis:** process of sodium excretion in the urine

About 60% of our body weight is water. This means that a 70-kg person will have about 42 kg or litres of body water. This is variable across individuals. For instance, men tend to have a higher percentage of body water than women. This is because women, in general, have a higher percentage of body fat, and fat (adipose) cells contain large droplets of fat with very little water. It is for this reason that obese individuals have a lower percentage of body water than lean individuals.

DISTRIBUTION OF BODY WATER

The total body water is distributed in different compartments of the body. This has been described in Chapter 3. Two-thirds of body water is present inside the cells of the body and is called intracellular fluid (intra = inside). The remaining one-third of fluid is extracellular, that is outside the cells. Of this extracellular fluid, the major portion (about 75%) is present in between the cells in the interstitial fluid (interstices = spaces that are in between [cells]). The other large portion of the extracellular fluid is plasma. Blood is made up of about 60% plasma and 40% cells. There is 5 L of blood in the body, so about 3 L is plasma. Water is also present in lymph and in 'transcellular spaces'. Transcellular spaces are those spaces which are completely enclosed, for example cerebrospinal fluid in the brain and spinal cord, pericardial fluid within the pericardial cavity that covers the heart, pleural fluid in the pleural cavity that covers the lungs, synovial fluid in the joint spaces where the fluid lubricates the joints and intraocular fluid in the eye as aqueous and vitreous humour.

These basic fluid compartments are illustrated in Fig. 4.1.

COMPOSITION OF THE FLUIDS IN THE DIFFERENT BODY COMPARTMENTS

Intracellular and extracellular fluids are separated by the cell membrane. The intracellular fluid is rich in potassium and phosphate ions. In addition, the intracellular space is rich in proteins which are synthesized in the cell and which are largely trapped within the cell by the cell membrane. In contrast, the extracellular fluid resembles brine (salt water) and is rich in sodium and chloride ions as well as calcium ions.

The extracellular fluid is not uniform in composition. For instance, plasma has a greater concentration of proteins than the interstitial fluid. This is because the blood vessel walls are a barrier that do not allow free movement of protein from the plasma to the interstitial space. Lymph has a composition that is similar to plasma but is rich in white blood cells, especially lymphocytes. Lymph formed in the gastrointestinal tract is rich in lipids (fats) that have been absorbed in the digestive system.

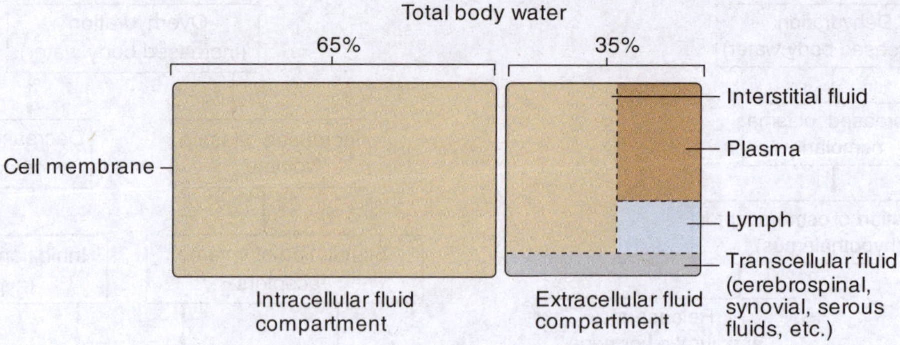

FIG. 4.1 The fluid compartments of the body.

FLUID INTAKE

1. **Fluids that are drunk:** The amount of fluids that we ingest depends on a number of factors including the weather, the extent to which we are physically active or exercise, whether we are ill (as with a fever) and, in the case of women, whether they are pregnant or are breastfeeding. On average, we consume about 2 L of fluids per day.
2. **Water as a by-product of metabolism:** Water is produced as a result of metabolism of carbohydrates and free fatty acids. For example, about 3 g of water is produced for every gram of glycogen that is broken down. The quantity of water produced as a result of metabolism is typically less than 10% of the total fluid intake.

LOSS OF FLUIDS

Fluids are lost from the body in many ways including:

1. **Loss in urine:** The amount of urine volume is variable (1–3 L/day) in a healthy individual but can be as low as 500 mL or as high as 15–20 L, depending on the amount of water that has been drunk, weather conditions, etc.
2. **Loss in faeces:** Under normal circumstances, the amount of fluid lost in the faeces is quite small – about 100 mL/day. This can, however, increase very much in severe diarrhoea. The extent of fluid loss can be life-threatening in some diarrhoeas like cholera.
3. **Insensible water loss:** This is the water loss that occurs through the respiratory system and the skin which cannot be controlled very well. When air is breathed in, it has the humidity (water content) of air. However, the expired air is much more humid. We can see this when we breathe out on a cold day in winter – our breath comes out as a 'mist'. Water is also lost in the form of sweat. The amount that we sweat clearly depends on the environmental temperature. Even on a day that is at a comfortable environmental temperature, we may lose about 0.5 L from insensible water loss per day.

ELECTROLYTES IN THE BODY

Electrolytes in the body are minerals that can be ionized (i.e. they can carry a charge). The major electrolytes that affect function in the body include sodium, potassium, calcium, chloride, phosphorus and magnesium. These minerals may take the form of acids, bases or salts.

MAINTENANCE OF FLUID BALANCE IN THE BODY

Under normal circumstances, fluid intake is roughly equal to fluid loss – this is called fluid balance. If we lose excess water from the body, we become dehydrated. The two major ways of regulating fluid balance are (1) to regulate the intake of water and (2) the excretion of water. The intake of water is regulated based on how thirsty we feel, while the major component of water excretion under normal circumstances is through the volume of urine that we excrete.

How does the body know that there is fluid imbalance?

When we lose or gain an excess amount of body water, many things can happen. First, if the loss of water is greater than the loss of electrolytes, the concentration of electrolytes in body fluids including plasma increases. This increased concentration can be measured as an increase in plasma osmolarity. Thus, receptors which sense plasma osmolarity are able to determine an abnormal loss of water from the body. These receptors are called osmoreceptors (because they detect changes in plasma osmolarity) and are present in the hypothalamus of the brain.

Second, if we gain water in large amounts, this results in an increase in blood volume. Thus, receptors that can sense blood volume can determine an abnormal gain in body water. These receptors called volume receptors are located in the right atrium of the heart.

So what happens if the body senses a fluid imbalance?

DEHYDRATION

Dehydration which is the excessive loss of body water can occur in severe diarrhoea, vomiting and excessive sweating if the fluid loss is not replaced. If water is lost to a greater extent than salts (electrolytes), there is an increase in the osmolarity of plasma. This increase in osmolarity is sensed by the osmoreceptors in the hypothalamus of the brain. Information is then

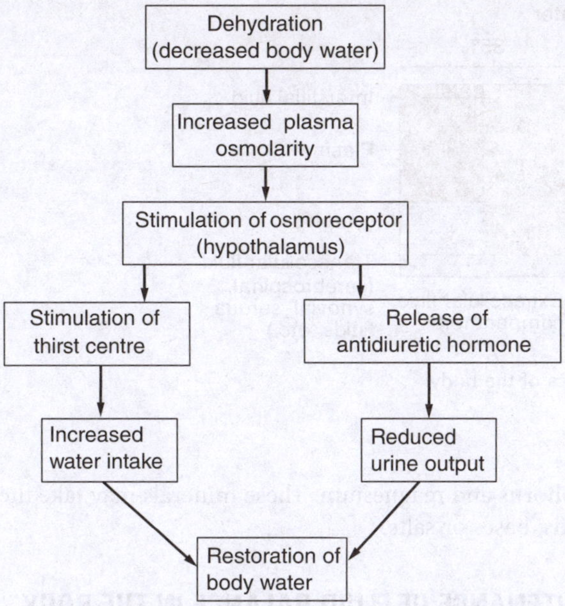

FIG. 4.2 Response of the body to dehydration.

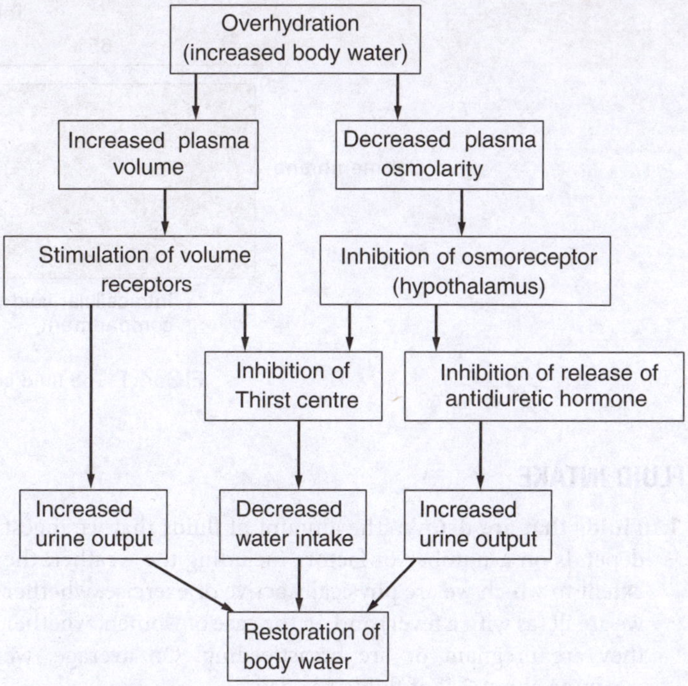

FIG. 4.3 Response of the body to overhydration.

carried from the osmoreceptors to the 'thirst centre' in the hypothalamus which increases our urge to drink water. Information from the osmoreceptors also acts on other parts of the hypothalamus which secrete antidiuretic hormone (ADH). This hormone acts on the kidney to reduce the excretion of water. Therefore, urine output reduces and helps to maintain body water. These two mechanisms of a decreased urine output and an increased water intake help to restore body water and are summarized in Fig. 4.2.

INCREASE IN BODY WATER

An excess of total body water occurs when people drink too much water or when less fluid is excreted.

When body water increases, there is an increase in the plasma volume which stimulates the volume receptors in the right atrium. This in turn increases urine output both by increasing glomerular filtration rate (see Section 9) and by releasing certain hormones, for example atrial natriuretic peptide (ANP), which act on the kidney. The increase in water content also reduces plasma osmolarity and this inhibits the 'thirst centre' as well as the release of ADH. Thus, reduced water intake and the increase in urine output help to restore fluid balance. This is summarized in Fig. 4.3.

REGULATION OF ELECTROLYTES

Although there are many electrolytes in the body, we focus this subsection to the regulation of sodium and potassium.

Sodium

Sodium is filtered in very large quantities in the kidney, but about 99% of this filtered sodium is reabsorbed and retained in the body. This is due to various hormones such as aldosterone, glucocorticoids and natriuretic hormones like ANP. Natriuresis is the process by which sodium is excreted in the urine. Natriuretic hormones, therefore, increase sodium excretion. An increased concentration of sodium in the plasma is called *hypernatraemia*, while a reduced concentration of sodium on plasma is called *hyponatraemia*. Table 4.1 outlines some common causes of hypernatraemia and hyponatraemia.

Hypernatraemia increases plasma osmolarity and, as described earlier, stimulates osmoreceptors which in turn increases water intake (by stimulating the thirst centre) and reduces urine output by stimulating the release of ADH. These two effects restore plasma osmolarity to its normal value.

Potassium

Plasma potassium levels are also maintained within a narrow range. An increase in the plasma concentration of potassium is called *hyperkalaemia*, while a decrease in the plasma concentration

Table 4.1 Causes of Hypernatraemia and Hyponatraemia

Hypernatraemia (>145 mEq/L)	Hyponatraemia (<135 mEq/L)
Excess fluid loss (sweating, burns, etc.)	Renal loss, e.g. patients on diuretics
Insufficient fluid intake	Extrarenal loss: vomiting, diarrhoea
Some kidney diseases	Syndrome of inappropriate secretion of ADH (SIADH)
	Low salt intake
	Heart failure, renal failure

Table 4.2 Common Causes of Hyperkalaemia and Hypokalaemia

Hyperkalaemia (>5.5 mEq/L)	Hypokalaemia (<3.5 mEq/L)
Increased intake	Reduced intake
Addison's disease (decreased aldosterone which normally retains sodium and excretes potassium)	Excess insulin dose (insulin normally moves potassium into cells)
Insulin deficiency	Some diuretics (medications that increase urine output; often used to treat hypertension)

of potassium is called *hypokalaemia*. Table 4.2 outlines some common causes for hyperkalaemia and hypokalaemia.

About 98% of the potassium in the body is located inside cells (i.e. intracellularly). One of the hormones which plays an important role in shifting potassium into the cells is insulin. Thus, after a standard meal, insulin levels in the blood increase and this helps to shift both glucose and potassium from the extracellular fluid into the cell.

In the long term, the potassium levels in the body are maintained constant by regulating the excretion of potassium by the kidneys, so that excretion of potassium in the urine matches potassium intake/levels in the blood. Potassium levels in the blood can increase with the consumption of potassium-rich foods, certain transfusions and decreased K^+ excretion from the kidneys due to medications or renal failure, or certain endocrine diseases such as Addison's disease. Under normal circumstances, potassium is freely filtered in the glomerulus of the nephron, but it is taken up and secreted at various points of the nephron, so that only about 15% of the potassium that is filtered is excreted. One of the hormones that secretes potassium into the lumen of the nephron and thereby increases potassium excretion, in conditions of potassium excess in the body, is aldosterone.

SUMMARY

- About 60% of body weight is water. Approximately two-thirds of body water is intracellular; the remaining is extracellular which is further divided into interstitial fluid, plasma and transcellular water.
- Fluid intake occurs through ingestion and the metabolism of food. Fluid output occurs through urine, sweat, faeces and other insensible water loss.
- Fluid balance occurs through the detection of imbalance by osmoreceptors and volume receptors. These in turn affect thirst and water intake, and through antidiuretic hormone, among other mechanisms, regulate urine output.
- Dehydration is associated with increased thirst and water intake and reduced urine output.
- The major electrolytes that affect function in the body include sodium, potassium, calcium, chloride, phosphorus and magnesium. These minerals may take the form of acids, bases or salts.
- Sodium and potassium are regulated within a narrow range of normal values. In the long term, this regulation occurs by matching urinary excretion of these electrolytes with intake/plasma levels.

CHAPTER REVIEW QUESTIONS

1. Explain the response of the body to dehydration.
2. Explain the response of the body to water excess.
3. What is fluid balance?
4. What do the following terms mean: (a) hypernatraemia, (b) hyponatraemia, (c) hyperkalaemia, (d) hypokalaemia?

CHAPTER 5

Cell Cycle

SPECIFIC LEARNING OBJECTIVES

At the end of this chapter, the student should be able to:

- List the functions of cell division.
- Describe the phases of mitosis.
- Describe the process of meiosis.
- Distinguish between mitosis and meiosis.
- Describe the phases of the cell cycle.

GLOSSARY OF TERMS

- **Cell cycle:** the period between one cell division and another cell division
- **Chromosome:** a long deoxyribonucleic acid (DNA) molecule that contains genetic information (in humans, chromosomes are in pairs, one from the father and one from the mother; this pairing is referred to as homologous chromosomes)
- **Chromatids:** the DNA replication of a chromosome forming an identical DNA molecule results in two 'sister chromatids' joined together by a 'centromere'
- **Mitosis:** a form of cell division in which the number of chromosomes in the two daughter cells is the same as in the parent cell
- **Meiosis:** a form of cell division in which the chromosomes in the four daughter cells are halved as compared to the parent cell
- **Diploid:** two copies of each chromosome (in humans, 23 *pairs* of chromosomes, i.e. 46 chromosomes)
- **Haploid:** a single copy of each chromosome (in humans, 23 chromosomes)

INTRODUCTION

The process of a single cell division is called the cell cycle. The cell cycle involves the actual process of cell division and the preparatory phase before cell division when the cell increases its size and undergoes several changes in the nucleus and cytoplasm.

Cell division serves many functions. These include:

- Wound healing
- Replacement of old or dead cells
- Formation of ova and sperm
- Embryogenesis and the development of the foetus

In some parts of the body, cells are continuously being replaced. These include the skin, gastrointestinal tract and the haemopoietic system (which gives rise to the blood cells).

In addition to normal cell division in healthy people, cell division also occurs in diseases. For example, uncontrolled, abnormal cell division occurs in cancers.

DIFFERENT TYPES OF CELL DIVISION

There are two types of cell division: mitosis and meiosis. During cell division, there is a transfer of nuclear and cytoplasmic material to the daughter cells (the cells formed by cell division).

Mitosis

Here each daughter cell has the same genetic make-up as the parent cell. This is possible because each chromosome in the parent cell replicates itself and each daughter cell therefore receives an identical copy of the chromosomes. Thus, in humans, each cell has 23 pairs of chromosomes, that is 46 chromosomes. Before mitosis, the parent cell after chromosome replication has 46 chromosomes but 46×2, that is 92, sister chromatids, which are divided equally in the daughter cells resulting in 46 chromosomes in each daughter cell.

Mitosis involves two stages: (1) nuclear division in the parent cell, called *karyokinesis*, and (2) separation of the cytoplasm resulting in two daughter cells, called *cytokinesis*.

Active mitosis occurs in five stages. The appearance and events of each of these stages are summarized in this chapter. After mitosis, the cycle enters a phase called 'interphase' before the next mitotic division occurs. Interphase is the longest phase of the cell cycle and is discussed in a later section.

Prophase This phase of mitosis has a duration that is more than half that of the total duration of mitosis. At the start of this phase, each chromosome has two identical copies because of replication during interphase (this is discussed later in the chapter). These two identical copies of chromosomes are held together by a 'centromere'. During this phase, several things happen:

1. The 'centrosome' is a structure which is associated with the nuclear membrane of the cell and is important for the formation of the mitotic spindle along which the chromosomes migrate during cell division. During prophase, the centrosome duplicates to form 'daughter centrosomes'.
2. The 'daughter centrosomes' migrate to two ends of the cell.
3. A 'mitotic spindle' forms between the two daughter centrosomes. The mitotic spindle is made up of microtubules. Microtubules are made up of a molecule called tubulin which has many functions within a cell – it contributes to the cytoskeleton of the cilia and helps form cilia. It is also involved in the movement of organelles within the cell and plays an important role in cell division.
4. There is the beginning of the breakdown of the nuclear membrane. The nuclear membrane is a cell membrane that keeps the nucleus separate from the other contents of the cell located in the cytoplasm.

Fig. 5.1 outlines the changes that occur during prophase.

Prometaphase During this phase:

1. The nuclear membrane breaks down into vesicles. The contents of the nucleus can now move into the cytoplasm.
2. The sister chromatids attached by the centromere (which were initially confined within the nuclear membrane) begin to migrate along the mitotic spindle towards the centre of the cell. This is depicted in Fig. 5.2.

Metaphase During this phase:

1. The sister chromatids align themselves in the centre of the mitotic spindle. The centre of the mitotic spindle is sometimes called the equator of the cell (also called the metaphase plate or equatorial plate). The sister chromatids at this stage are equally distant from two daughter centrosomes at the poles of the cell.
2. Only when all of the sister chromatids joined at the centromere are aligned in the centre can mitosis proceed to the next phase. This phase is important in cytogenetics because it allows the chromosomes to be viewed under a light microscope during a test called karyotyping. Metaphase is depicted in Fig. 5.3.

Anaphase During this phase:

1. The centromere which holds the two sister chromatids together divides.
2. The division of the centromere allows the two sister chromatids (now called 'daughter chromosomes') to move away from each along the mitotic spindle to the opposite ends of the cell. Anaphase is depicted in Fig. 5.4.

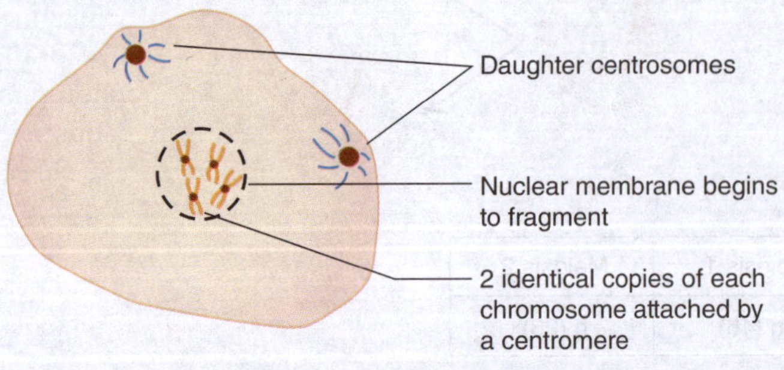

FIG. 5.1 Mitosis – prophase.

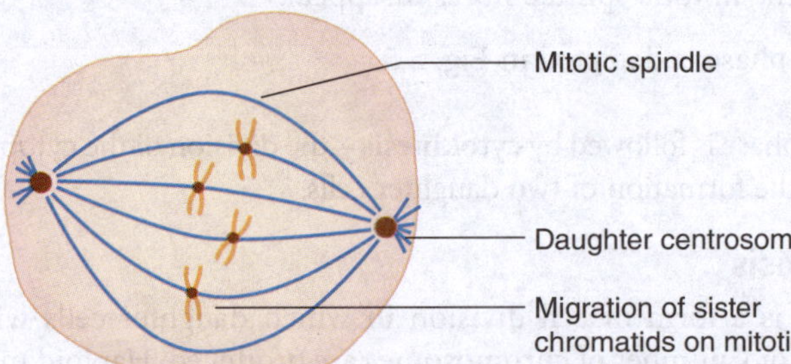

FIG. 5.2 Mitosis – prometaphase.

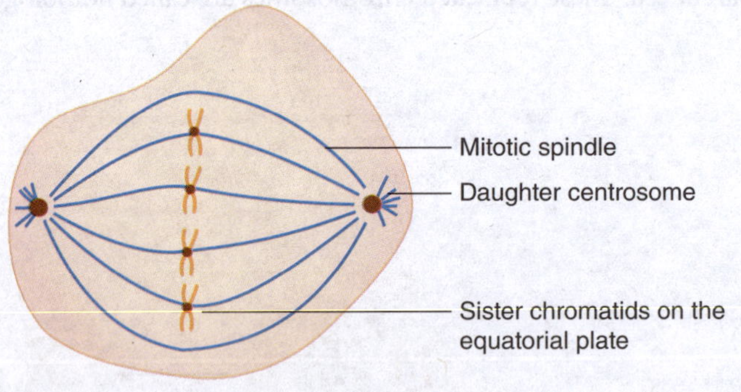

FIG. 5.3 Mitosis – metaphase.

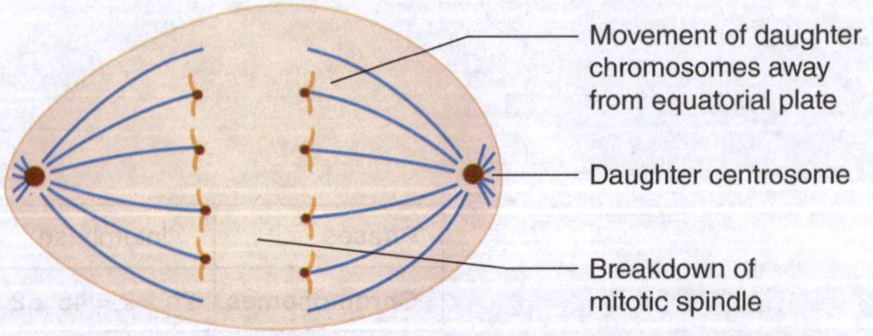

FIG. 5.4 Mitosis – anaphase.

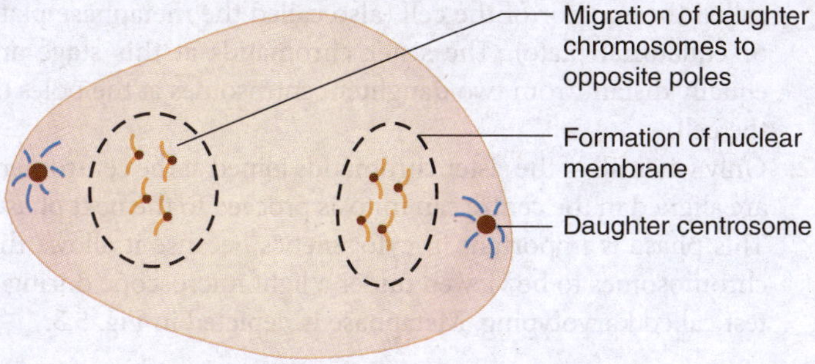

FIG. 5.5 Mitosis – telophase.

Telophase During this phase:

1. The daughter chromosomes have reached the opposite poles of the cell.
2. A nuclear membrane begins to form around each set of daughter chromosomes.
3. The mitotic spindle fibres disappear.

This phase is depicted in Fig. 5.5.

Telophase is followed by **cytokinesis** – the division of the cytoplasm and the formation of two daughter cells.

Meiosis

This is a form of cell division in which daughter cells with a 'haploid' number of chromosomes are produced. Haploid means that there is a single set of chromosomes as opposed to two pairs of a set of chromosomes (diploid).

Before meiosis takes place, the chromosomes are replicated in the parent cell. These replicated chromosomes are called homologous chromosomes. There are now two successive cell divisions. In the first cell division (meiosis 1), homologous chromosomes are separated and pulled to opposite ends of the cell which then divides. In the second cell division (meiosis 2), each of the two cells produced during meiosis 1 undergoes a cell division in which each half of every chromosome is pulled towards the opposite ends of the cell, which then divides. In the process of meiosis, four daughter cells are produced (by two successive cell divisions) and each of these four cells contains only one set of chromosomes (haploid) as opposed to pairs of chromosomes that are found in diploid cells. Both meiosis 1 and meiosis 2 go through successive phases of prophase, metaphase, anaphase and telophase.

The process of meiosis is depicted in Fig. 5.6.

EXAMPLES OF MITOSIS AND MEIOSIS IN THE HUMAN BODY

Fig. 5.7 outlines the process of spermatogenesis (formation of sperm) in the human body. While this topic is discussed in a separate chapter (Section 10), it is illustrated here because spermatogenesis includes both mitosis and meiosis.

In spermatogenesis, the cell division that occurs in the primordial germ cell (spermatogonium) is mitosis. This allows the chromosomal material to be preserved in its entirety (2n) in the daughter cells. Mitosis is followed by two cell divisions, that is meiosis 1 and meiosis 2 – the result of these divisions is the formation of four spermatids, each of which has a single set of chromosomes (1n). In meiosis, because there is a random segregation of homologous chromosomes into each of the four resultant cells, there is a greater chance of genetic recombination which results in genetic diversity.

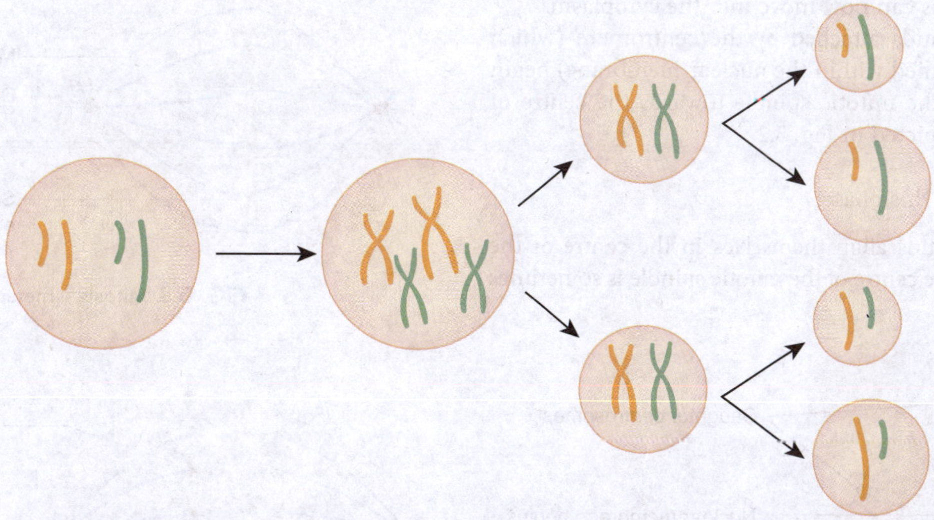

Phases	Interphase	Meiosis 1	Meiosis 2
Chromosomes	2n × 2 = 46 × 2	2n (46)	n (23)

FIG. 5.6 Process of meiosis.

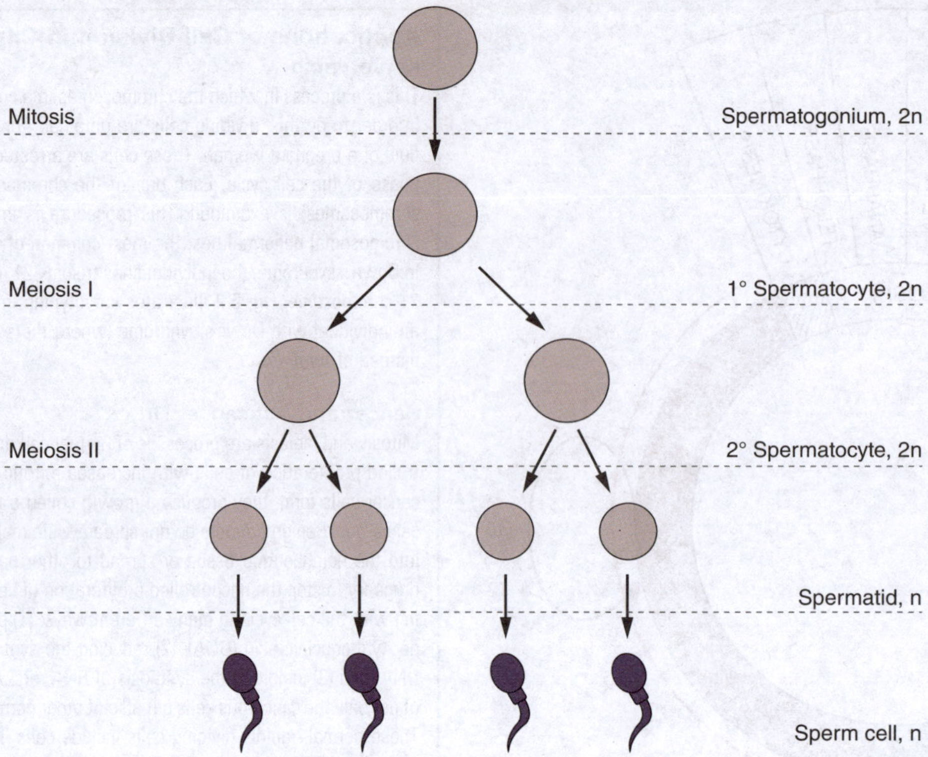

FIG. 5.7 Mitosis and meiosis during spermatogenesis.

In humans, the mature sperm and the ovum each has a single set of chromosome, that is 1n. When the ovum is fertilized by the sperm, the result is an inheritance of genes from both parents and the cell is restored to a diploid state (i.e. one pair of each chromosome, i.e. 2n).

> **Significance of Mitosis and Meiosis**
>
> **Mitosis** occurs in most but not all cells. Nerve cells are an example where mitosis does not occur. Mitosis is significant because:
> - It contributes to the healing and replacement of old/dead cells.
> - It contributes to the development of the foetus in utero.
> - It ensures genetic stability of cells because it results in genetically identical daughter cells.
>
> **Meiosis** is typically seen in gametes (i.e. sex cells). It is significant because:
> - It allows for an exchange of parental chromosomes.
> - It contributes to genetic diversity.

DIFFERENCES BETWEEN MITOSIS AND MEIOSIS

Table 5.1 summarizes the differences between mitosis and meiosis. Mitosis occurs in somatic cells except those which do not divide like nerve cells while meiosis is seen in the gametes. Mitosis is characterized by a single cell division while meiosis has two cell divisions, at the end of which two daughter cells are produced in mitosis and four daughter cells in meiosis. The number of chromosomes in the daughter cells in mitosis is diploid (in humans, this is 23 pairs of chromosomes, i.e. 46 chromosomes) while in meiosis the number of chromosomes is haploid (in humans, this is 23 chromosomes). Mitosis produces genetically similar daughter cells and therefore preserves genetic stability while meiosis is associated with more genetic diversity than meiosis.

Table 5.1 Differences Between Mitosis and Meiosis

	Mitosis	Meiosis
Cells involved	Somatic cells	Gametes
Number of cell divisions	1	2
Number of daughter cells produced	2	4
Number of chromosomes in daughter cells	Diploid	Haploid
Genetic recombination	No	Yes
Impact on genetic variation	Promotes genetic stability	Promotes genetic diversity

THE CELL CYCLE

Mitosis and meiosis are specific examples of cell division. However, between actual cell divisions, there is a long phase called the interphase. Interphase is further divided into smaller stages. This is depicted in Fig. 5.8 taking mitosis as an example.

The first thing that Fig. 5.8 shows is that the actual phase of cell division (mitosis) is only a small part of the cell cycle. The larger part of the cell cycle is interphase, amounting to about

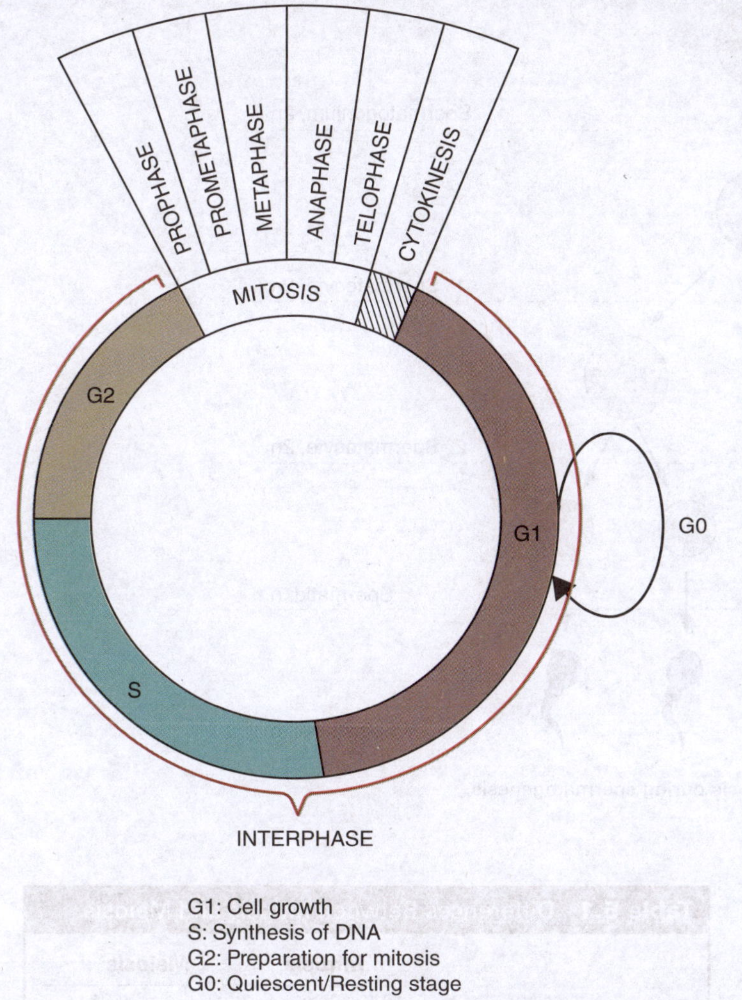

FIG. 5.8 Stages of the cell cycle.

95% of the cell cycle. Interphase is divided into the following stages:

- G1 stage (gap 1): During this phase, the cell begins to grow to almost double its size. Protein synthesis increases and organelles within the cell are produced.
- S stage: 'S' stands for synthesis. During this phase, the cell synthesizes DNA so that the DNA content of the cell doubles.
- G2 stage (gap 2): During this phase, the cell continues to grow and mitochondria divide. This phase precedes mitosis and is the final preparatory stage before actual cell division.

Not all cells divide. Cells which are not dividing move from the G1 stage to a G0 stage. Cells such as neurons which do not divide remain in the G0 stage. Other cells may shift from a resting (quiescent) stage to a stage of active cell division. Thus, the G0 stage may be reversible or irreversible.

Applications of Cell Division in Clinical Medicine

Karyotyping

This is a process in which the chromosomes in a cell are paired and examined. In order to do this, dividing cells are obtained, for example from the amniotic fluid of a pregnant woman. These cells are arrested in metaphase or prometaphase of the cell cycle. Each pair of the chromosomes (22 pairs + the sex chromosomes) is examined. This procedure is important to identify certain chromosomal abnormalities, the most common of which is Down's syndrome. In Down's syndrome, the individual has trisomy 21, that is an additional number 21 chromosome. Fig. 5.9 illustrates karyotyping in a normal individual and in an individual with Down's syndrome (where there are three chromosome 21s instead of two).

Cancer and Anticancer Drugs

Mitosis and meiosis are processes of normal cell division. Cancer is the uncontrolled proliferation of cells with increased mitotic activity. As more and more cancer cells form, they produce a growth called a tumour. Not all tumours are cancerous. Benign tumours do not spread while malignant tumours may extend into the neighbouring tissue or spread to other parts of the body. Anticancer drugs try to stop the uncontrolled proliferation of cells. They do this by interfering with the cell cycle in many different ways: (1) preventing the replication of deoxyribonucleic acid (DNA); (2) reducing the synthesis of components of the DNA; and (3) inhibiting the synthesis of RNA, etc. All this inhibits cell division of not only the cancerous cells but also of other normal but rapidly dividing cells. These normal, rapidly dividing cells include cells in the bone marrow and the gastrointestinal tract, among others. As a result, patients who receive these anticancer drugs may, for instance, experience a fall in red blood cells, white blood cells and platelets due to suppression of cell division in the bone marrow.

Susceptibility of Rapidly Dividing Cells to Environmental Toxins/Insults

There are many rapidly developing cells in the adults which include the cells in the bone marrow and the cells of the gastric mucosa which lines the gastrointestinal tract. In utero, the growing foetus has many rapidly dividing cells. There are many environmental toxins that can affect rapidly dividing cells causing damage to DNA and resulting in developmental defects in utero or in functional defects that may manifest later in life. Environmental toxins may also increase the likelihood of certain cancers. There are a large number of environmental toxins which include dioxins in plastics, DDT used to control malaria and pesticides such as endosulfan. Major disasters highlight the extent to which human health can be affected by environmental toxins particularly in relation to growth and development and cancers in which cell division is central to the processes. The Minamata disaster in Japan (the 1950s) occurred when mercury waste from an industrial plant contaminated the fish in the sea and entered the food chain causing neurological disease in adults and also affected foetuses. Children most heavily exposed to the radiation following the atomic bomb blasts in Hiroshima and Nagasaki experienced stunted growth; the children had lower heights, weight and head circumference. Children exposed to higher levels of radiation were also more likely to have functional problems like mental retardation. Adults exposed to high levels of radiation were more likely to develop cancers than people in other cities who had not been exposed to radiation. In India, in Bhopal in 1984, people living near the Union Carbide plant were exposed to 42 tons of a deadly gas called methyl isocyanate – many people died immediately and many more suffered the long-term consequences of exposure. There were also reports of increased numbers of children being born with developmental defects.

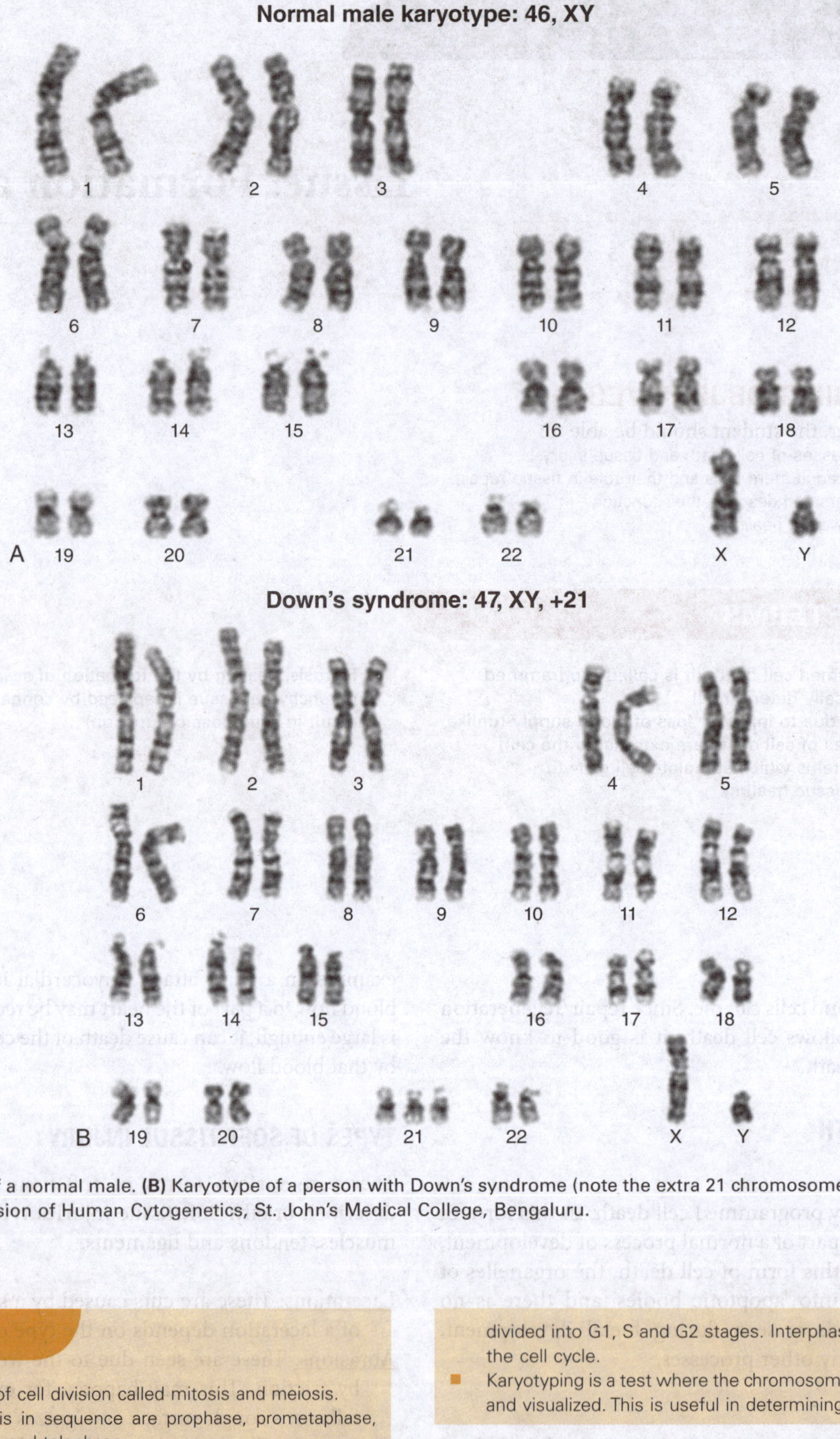

FIG. 5.9 **(A)** Karyotype of a normal male. **(B)** Karyotype of a person with Down's syndrome (note the extra 21 chromosome compared to the normal karyotype). Courtesy: Division of Human Cytogenetics, St. John's Medical College, Bengaluru.

SUMMARY

- There are two types of cell division called mitosis and meiosis.
- The phases of mitosis in sequence are prophase, prometaphase, metaphase, anaphase and telophase.
- Mitosis results in the formation of two daughter cells with identical chromosomes as the parent cell (2n; diploid) while meiosis results in the formation of four daughter cells, each with half the number of chromosomes as the parent cell (1n; haploid).
- The development of the sperm (spermatogenesis) and the ovum, both include mitosis and meiosis.
- The cell cycle includes the stage of cell division as well as interphase which is the preparatory stage before cell division. Interphase is divided into G1, S and G2 stages. Interphase is the longest stage of the cell cycle.
- Karyotyping is a test where the chromosomes are paired in sequence and visualized. This is useful in determining chromosomal disorders.

CHAPTER REVIEW QUESTIONS

1. List the phases of the cell cycle and explain the role of 'interphase'.
2. Compare and contrast mitosis and meiosis.
3. Describe the phases of mitosis in sequence.
4. What is karyotyping and what is its use?

CHAPTER 6

Tissue: Formation and Repair

SPECIFIC LEARNING OBJECTIVES

At the end of this chapter, the student should be able to:

- Outline the various processes of cell death and tissue injury.
- Describe the location of adult stem cells and their role in tissue repair.
- List various growth factors and describe their function.
- Describe the stages of wound healing.

GLOSSARY OF TERMS

- **Apoptosis:** programmed cell death (it is called programmed because it is genetically determined)
- **Necrosis:** cell death due to injury or loss of blood supply (unlike apoptosis, the causes of cell death are external to the cell)
- **Growth factors:** proteins which stimulate cell growth, differentiation and tissue healing
- **Fibrosis:** healing by the formation of scar tissue (normal parenchymal tissue is replaced by connective tissue – this may result in some loss of function)

INTRODUCTION

Tissues can get injured and cells can die. Since repair/regeneration of tissues sometimes follows cell death, it is good to know the different types of cell death.

TYPES OF CELL DEATH

Apoptosis

This refers to genetically programmed cell death. In this form of cell death, cells die as a part of a normal process of development, growth and ageing. In this form of cell death, the organelles of the cell are packaged into 'apoptotic bodies' and there is no inflammation. Apoptosis is seen during foetal development, normal ageing and many other processes.

Necrosis

It is a form of cell death that occurs due to injury or reduced blood supply to a tissue. In this form of cell death, there is inflammation. Nurses will encounter various forms of inflammation – a common form is that of a boil or an abscess. In this situation, the area that is affected appears red (rubor), it is warm to the touch (calor), it is painful (dolour) and it may be associated with some loss of function. Necrosis can also occur in organs inside the body. For example, in a heart attack (myocardial infarction; Fig. 6.1), the blood flow to a part of the heart may be reduced – if this reduction is large enough, it can cause death of the cells in the heart supplied by that blood flow.

TYPES OF SOFT-TISSUE INJURY

There are various forms of soft-tissue injury and these are described briefly. Soft-tissue injuries typically involve the skin, muscles, tendons and ligaments.

<u>Lacerations:</u> These are cuts caused by a sharp object. The depth of a laceration depends on the type of the injury.

<u>Abrasions:</u> These are seen due to the wearing away of the skin by friction. This may happen, for example when a person falls on a rough surface and 'grazes' the knee.

<u>Contusions:</u> These are bruises caused by a crush injury or a blunt object. There is typically bleeding under the skin (haematoma).

There are other specific soft-tissue injuries that affect the nerves, ligaments and tendons. These are not considered in this chapter.

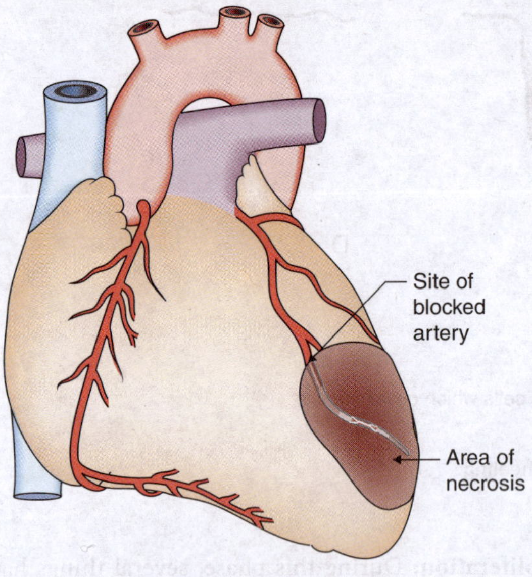

FIG. 6.1 Myocardial infarction following block to a coronary artery. Note the area of necrosis below the block.

RESPONSE TO CELL DEATH/INJURY

The body responds by two broad processes: (1) repair and (2) regeneration.

Repair is a form of healing that often results in scar tissue. The presence of scar tissue (fibrosis) means that the normal structure and function of the tissue or organ may be impaired.

Examples of repair by fibrosis: There are many examples of repair by fibrosis. In the **lungs**, delayed treatment of chronic infections such as tuberculosis can result in scarring or fibrosis of the lungs. The problem with this form of healing is that extensive scarring replaces the normal tissue. This can result in difficulty of breathing and patients may experience a shortness of breath (dyspnoea). The **liver** can also heal by scarring following chronic infections or chronic alcohol abuse. The scarred liver called cirrhosis of the liver can result in liver failure in which the liver is unable to function normally. Deep injuries to the **skin** as occur with serious burns also heal by scarring. Scarring is also seen with surgical incisions.

Regeneration involves the replacement of injured/dead cells with new cells from the tissue. In some situations, there is growth of an injured cell. In regeneration, healing may restore the former function of the tissue or organ.

Examples of healing by regeneration: There are some cells in our body which are being constantly replaced. The **cells of the blood** are an example. Red blood cells are replaced by a process called erythropoiesis and white blood cells by a process called leucopoiesis. The **endometrium of the uterus** is replaced once menstruation occurs. The **mucosal lining** of various organ systems such as the gastrointestinal system is continuously being shed and replaced. **Skin** also shows regeneration. While new nerve cells cannot be formed in the adult, when nerves are cut, new growth begins to appear from the cut end. Peripheral nerves regenerate much more than nerves of the central nervous system (brain and spinal cord).

Factors that Affect Tissue Repair/Healing

Not all individuals and not all tissues show the same degree of speed of tissue repair. Some of the factors which affect tissue repair are the following:

1. Age of the individual: Healing is slower in older individuals.
2. Extent of injury: More extensive injuries which distort the normal tissue structure are associated with slower healing.
3. Presence of infection: Infection of the site of injury delays healing and this needs to be addressed first.
4. Nutritional status: Individuals who are undernourished show delayed healing. This is because various nutrients are required for the healing process.
5. Other clinical comorbidities: Patients with other clinical conditions such as diabetes mellitus show delayed healing. In fact, individuals who report to the hospital with a history of delayed wound healing should be checked for diabetes.
6. Absence of rest for the injured area: If a wound is an area where there is considerable movement as, for instance, over a joint, healing will be delayed. In such a situation, the area may need to be immobilized to accelerate the rate of healing.
7. Presence of foreign bodies in a tissue can delay wound healing. These foreign bodies can include, for instance, glass and clothing fibres. The wound must therefore be cleaned thoroughly for healing to occur.
8. Behavioural factors: Smoking and chronic alcohol consumption can impair the healing process.

STEM CELLS

Stem cells are of two types: (1) embryonal stem cells and (2) adult (somatic) stem cells. Embryonal stem cells are important during foetal development in utero. Stem cells are special cells in the body which have two major characteristics:

1. They can self-replicate, that is they can produce more cells like themselves.
2. They can differentiate, that is they can be altered into other cells with more specialized functions.

Stem cells are important for the process of healing in many tissues and adult stem cells are present in many tissues. These include, among others, the following:

- Haemopoietic stem cells – found in the bone marrow and umbilical cord blood which can produce the cells of the blood.
- Breast stem cells – which are important for the growth of the breast during puberty and pregnancy.
- Intestinal lining of both the small and large intestine.
- Blood vessels – these stem cells can produce endothelial cells which line all blood vessels.

GROWTH FACTORS

While there are many hormones which are important for growth such as growth hormone, thyroxine and insulin, there are also growth factors that act locally. Growth factors are a class of

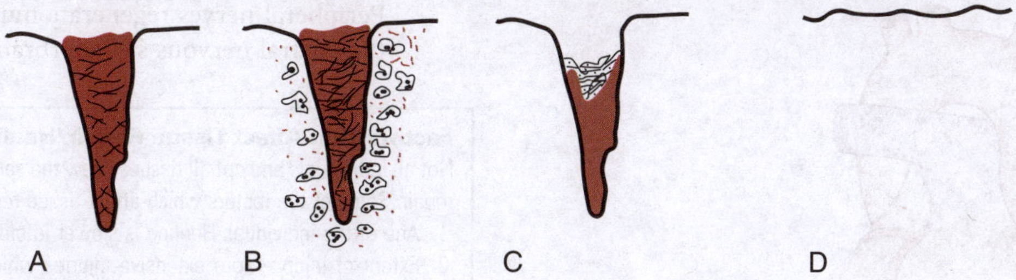

FIG. 6.2 Stages of wound healing.

substances that stimulate growth in living cells. There are several growth factors that have been described and a few of these include the following:

1. Nerve growth factor – first described by an Italian scientist, Rita Levi-Montalcini, who went on to win the Nobel Prize in 1986
2. Epidermal growth factor
3. Fibroblast growth factor
4. Platelet-derived growth factor
5. Vascular endothelial growth factor

These growth factors help to communicate between cells and help in cell differentiation and maturation.

STAGES OF WOUND REPAIR

Since nurses are often involved in the care of wounds, this section specifically addresses the issue of wound healing which may be accidental as in a road traffic accident or intentional as occurs following surgery.

There are four distinct stages of wound healing. These are depicted in Fig. 6.2.

1. **Haemostasis:** During this stage, the bleeding at the wound site is controlled. This happens because of a number of things:
   a. Vasoconstriction: The blood vessels at the wound site contract and bleeding is slowed down.
   b. Formation of a platelet plug: This is also called a temporary haemostatic plug. Platelets at the wound site adhere to the collagen of the damaged tissue, and then aggregate (come together) to block the loss of blood. A platelet plug can easily be dislodged, and bleeding can restart.
   c. Formation of a clot: Here, through the coagulation cascade, described in Section 5, fibrin threads are produced at the wound site and this helps to stabilize the platelet plug.
2. **Inflammation:** During this stage, immune cells such as neutrophils and macrophages arrive at the site of the wound. These cells have several functions:
   a. They help remove damaged cells and tissue debris.
   b. They help to control infection at the site of tissue injury.
3. **Proliferation:** During this phase, several things happen to reduce the size of the wound and repair the wound:
   a. New blood vessels are formed – this is called angiogenesis.
   b. Fibroblasts at the site lay down extracellular matrix on which new cells can be laid down. This process is called *granulation*. In healthy wound healing, granulation tissue is typically pink/red, granular and uneven and free of pus.
   c. Epithelial cells begin to cover the wound site.
   d. Myofibroblasts at the wound site contract and bring together the edges of the wound, reducing its size.
4. **Remodelling:** During this phase, the healed wound is stabilized, and excess cells are removed by apoptosis.

SUMMARY

- There are different types of cell death. Apoptosis is programmed cell death. Necrosis occurs following injury or ischaemia (reduced blood supply).
- There are two responses to injury: (1) repair which involves the formation of scar tissue and in which tissue function may be affected and (2) regeneration in which damaged cells are replaced by new cells.
- Factors that influence healing/repair include the age of the patient, the nature of the injury, the presence of comorbidities such as diabetes, the presence of infection, the nutritional status of the patient, the presence of foreign bodies, the absence of rest for the affected part and patient behaviours such as smoking and consumption of alcohol.
- Healing is facilitated by the local release of chemicals called growth factors; nerve growth factor and platelet-derived growth factors are examples.
- Healing takes place in four stages which include haemostasis (stoppage of bleeding), inflammation, proliferation and tissue remodelling.

CHAPTER REVIEW QUESTIONS

1. What is the difference between apoptosis and necrosis?
2. What is the difference between repair and regeneration?
3. List the factors that affect tissue healing.
4. List two characteristics of stem cells.
5. Describe the stages of wound repair.

SECTION 2

Respiratory System

CHAPTER 8

Functional Anatomy of the Respiratory System

SPECIFIC LEARNING OBJECTIVES

At the end of this chapter, the student should be able to:

- List the functions of the respiratory system.
- Describe the constituents and functions of the different zones of the respiratory system.
- Describe the tracheobronchial tree.
- Describe the characteristics of the pulmonary circulation.

GLOSSARY OF TERMS

- **Pulmonary oedema:** a condition in which there is excess fluid in the lung parenchyma and the air sacs
- **Pulmonary embolism:** blockage of a blood vessel in the pulmonary circulation, usually due to a clot
- **Dyspnoea:** uncomfortable breathing as experienced by the patient

The aim of respiration is to provide tissues with oxygen which they use to generate energy and to remove carbon dioxide, a by-product of metabolism, away from the tissues. The respiratory system also has other functions and these will be described later.

ZONES OF THE RESPIRATORY SYSTEM

The respiratory system can be divided into two broad zones:

1. **The conducting zone** which includes the upper airways starting from the nose, mouth, pharynx, trachea, bronchi and up to the terminal bronchioles. This part of the respiratory system **does not take part in gas exchange.**
   Important functions of the conducting zone include the following:
   a. Acting as a passage for air during inspiration (breathing in) and expiration (breathing out).
   b. Adjusting the incoming air to body temperature. Air is also humidified (water vapour is added) when breathing occurs through the nose. When we breathe through the mouth, dry air reaches the lungs – this can dry up secretions and produce a dry, irritating cough.
   c. Removal of particles in the air. Particles are prevented from reaching the lungs by the following:
      i. Nasal hair which filters some of these particles.
      ii. Sedimentation in the conducting zone of the respiratory system.
      iii. Some particles also dissolve in the mucus that lines the passages.
      iv. The cilia of the pseudostratified columnar epithelium that line the airways also help to trap particles and move them away from the lungs.
2. **The respiratory zone** consists of the respiratory bronchioles, alveolar ducts and alveoli. The function of this zone is gas exchange, and this is discussed in greater detail in Chapter 10.

THE TRACHEOBRONCHIAL TREE

Fig. 8.1 illustrates the tracheobronchial tree. The airway which starts with the trachea divides 23 times between the trachea and the alveoli. The result is a large number of alveoli; the tracheobronchial tree thus resembles an upside-down tree which keeps dividing. The first 16 divisions up to the terminal bronchi form the conducting zone of the respiratory system. The next seven divisions form the respiratory zone. The alveolus is the site where maximal gas exchange occurs. There are about 500 million alveoli in the adult human being. The actual number of alveoli is closely related to the total lung volume.

FUNCTIONS OF THE RESPIRATORY SYSTEM

1. **Gas exchange:** This is the main function of the respiratory tract. Oxygen diffuses from the alveoli into the capillaries, and this oxygenated blood is distributed to the various

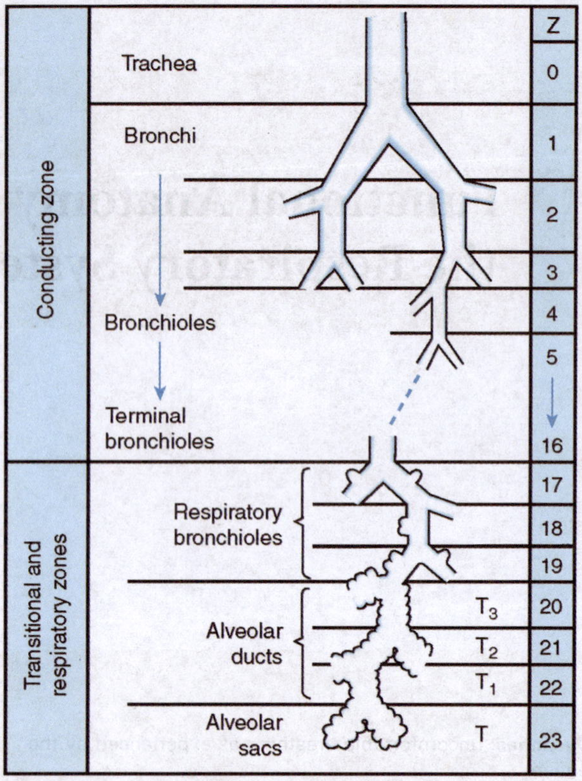

FIG. 8.1 Tracheobronchial tree.

tissues. In contrast, carbon dioxide diffuses from the capillaries into the alveoli from where it is eliminated during expiration.

2. **Speech:** Various parts of the respiratory tract are involved in speech. Articulation (the production of clear and distinct sounds) involves the nasal cavities and mouth while phonation (production of sound itself) is a function of the vocal cords in the larynx.
3. **Protection:** The respiratory tract helps to protect the body from particles, pathogens and harmful chemicals. This is done by the following:
   a. Trapping particles and limiting their movement towards the lungs
   b. Sneezing
   c. Coughing
   d. Resisting infection through the immune system (cells in the respiratory system such as alveolar macrophages help in phagocytosis; antibodies such as IgA [the secretory antibody] also help to resist infection)
4. **Endocrine and metabolic function:**
   a. Angiotensin-converting enzyme (ACE) converts angiotensin I to angiotensin II in the pulmonary circulation. Angiotensin II is a powerful vasoconstrictor and helps stimulate the release of the hormone aldosterone; thus, angiotensin II is important to maintain blood pressure. This is discussed in greater detail in Section 4.
   b. Type II alveolar cells produce a chemical called surfactant which reduces the surface tension in the alveoli, keeps them dry and decreases the work of breathing. This is discussed in Chapter 9.
   c. Several other substances such as histamine, bradykinin and serotonin, among others, are released by the lungs.

THE PULMONARY CIRCULATION

The pulmonary circulation is also known as the 'lesser circulation'.

- It receives the blood that is pumped out by the right ventricle.
- This circulation thus receives the entire cardiac output which is approximately 5 L/minute at rest.
- Deoxygenated blood is pumped out of the right ventricle into the pulmonary artery.
- The pulmonary capillaries are arranged in such a way that the blood flows in thin sheets between the alveoli maximizing the area for gas exchange.
- The pulmonary veins carry the oxygenated blood to the left atrium.

The pulmonary circulation has several characteristics:

1. The pulmonary and total systemic blood flow is normally equal, that is 5 L/minute at rest.
2. The average pulmonary artery pressure is much lower (25/8-10 mm Hg) than that of the systemic arterial pressure (120/80 mm Hg).
3. The blood flow is not the same in all parts of the lungs in the upright position (standing or sitting). The basal part of the lung receives greater blood flow while the apical parts of the lungs receive less blood flow. This is because in the upright individual, the intravascular pressures (pressures within the blood vessel) increase from apex to base and this increase in pressure gradient increases blood flow in the base of the lungs.
4. Hypoxia (reduced oxygen content) results in vasoconstriction in the pulmonary circulation. This is different from the systemic circulation where hypoxia causes vasodilation. Hypoxic vasoconstriction in the lungs means that the blood flow is reduced to those alveoli which receive less air.

CLINICAL DISORDERS OF THE PULMONARY CIRCULATION

Pulmonary embolism is a block in the main artery of the lung or in its branches. It is associated with chest pain, dyspnoea, rapid breathing, cough and haemoptysis (blood in the sputum). Pulmonary embolism is seen more often in people who are bedridden. These people may develop clots in the legs (deep vein thrombosis). These clots can travel in the bloodstream and enter the pulmonary circulation, where they cause embolism.

Pulmonary hypertension is an increase in the pressures in the pulmonary circulation. It may result from left heart failure (Section 4). This results in a backlog of blood in the pulmonary circulation due to the inefficient pumping of the left heart. It may also be seen in a variety of chronic lung diseases. Increased pulmonary intravascular pressure results in a shift of fluid from the intravascular compartment (blood vessel) to the lung parenchyma and alveoli, a condition called **pulmonary oedema**. A patient with pulmonary oedema will have difficulty in breathing (dyspnoea) and will cough up blood; this often appears pink and frothy.

APPLICATIONS IN NURSING

- The nurse will need to take care of a patient with pulmonary hypertension and pulmonary oedema. This will involve monitoring medication intake including morphine and diuretics, and oxygen administration. The nurse will also need to carefully monitor for any fluid overload as this will worsen symptoms. The patient will need to be maintained in Fowler's position (i.e. with a back rest), as this reduces symptoms and promotes oxygenation.
- Patients with pulmonary embolism are typically given medications called thrombolytics to dissolve (lyse) the clots; these medications can, however, trigger bleeding. Nurses will need to keep a close watch for any bleeding. In order to prevent pulmonary embolism in patients who are bedridden, the nurse will need to teach and supervise patient attendants to do passive exercises regularly. Nurses must ensure mobilization (movement) of patients as per doctor's instructions in those recovering from surgery, etc.

SUMMARY

- The respiratory system is primarily involved in gas exchange. In addition, it helps in speech and protection against pathogens, particulates and chemicals, and has endocrine and metabolic functions.
- The respiratory system consists of a conducting zone (up to 16 divisions of the tracheobronchial tree) which acts as the conduit for air and a respiratory zone (remaining seven divisions) which takes part in gas exchange.
- The conducting zone acts as a passage for air during respiration, humidifies air and makes it warmer, and removes particles in the air.
- The pulmonary circulation arises out of the right heart, blood flow is 5 L/minute at rest and has pressures which are one-fifth to one-sixth that of the systemic circulation.
- An important property of the pulmonary circulation is that hypoxia causes vasoconstriction unlike in the systemic circulation where hypoxia causes vasodilation.

CHAPTER REVIEW QUESTIONS

1. Describe the functions of the conducting zone of the respiratory system.
2. What are the functions of the respiratory system?
3. Write a short note on the pulmonary circulation.
4. What is (a) pulmonary embolism and (b) pulmonary hypertension?

CHAPTER 9

Mechanics of Ventilation

SPECIFIC LEARNING OBJECTIVES

At the end of this chapter, the student should be able to:

- List the muscles that are involved in inspiration and expiration.
- Define the following terms: respiratory minute volume, dead space, alveolar ventilation, maximal voluntary ventilation and breathing reserve.
- Describe the changes in pressures (intrapleural, alveolar, transpulmonary) that occur during inspiration and expiration.
- Describe the concept of compliance and list the factors that affect it.
- List the functions of surfactant.

GLOSSARY OF TERMS

- **Dead space:** that part of the respiratory system which does not take part in gas exchange
- **Vital capacity:** the volume of exhaled air during a maximal expiration following a maximal inspiration
- **Residual volume:** the volume of air left in the lungs after a maximal expiration
- **Dyspnoea:** a subjective experience of discomfort during breathing
- **Hyaline membrane disease:** difficulty in breathing in the newborn often due to a deficiency of surfactant related to prematurity
- **Hyperventilation:** an increase in the rate and depth of breathing

Ventilation is the flow of air into and out of the lungs during breathing. There are two phases of ventilation. These are (1) inspiration in which air enters the lungs and (2) expiration where air is expelled from the lungs.

During inspiration, the chest cavity expands. This occurs in the vertical plane, that is by the diaphragm moving downwards, as well as in the transverse and anteroposterior planes due to the actions of specific muscles.

An adult breathes between 12 and 20 times in a minute. This is called the respiratory rate and can be counted by carefully looking at the breathing pattern in 1 minute. In newborn babies, the respiratory rate is high – between 30 and 50 per minute. This decreases rapidly in the first year. As individuals age, the respiratory rate again begins to rise.

MUSCLE OF VENTILATION

Muscles of Inspiration

1. *Diaphragm*: Quiet inspiration is completely due to this muscle.
2. Those muscles which help to lift the rib cage upwards (increasing the vertical expansion), forwards (increasing the anteroposterior expansion) and outwards (increasing the transverse expansion), thereby increasing the volume of the chest cavity. These include the following muscle:
   a. *External intercostal muscles*: These cause the lower ribs to move upwards.
   b. *Sternocleidomastoid* and *scalene muscles* in the neck: These elevate the first rib and are often called 'accessory' muscles of inspiration since they can be seen contracting most clearly during forced breathing. For example, patients experiencing an acute asthma attack, have 'air hunger' and the neck muscles are prominent.

Muscles of Expiration

1. During quiet expiration, there is passive recoil of the lungs and the diaphragm relaxes (moving upwards). This compresses the air contained in the lungs and the air is expelled.
2. In forced expiration or during heavy breathing (such as coughing, or during heavy exercise), two more muscle groups act. These include:
   a. The *internal intercostals*: These muscles cause the ribs to move downwards and reduce the volume of the chest cavity.
   b. The *anterior abdominal muscles*: These act in two ways – (1) they pull the ribs down and like the internal

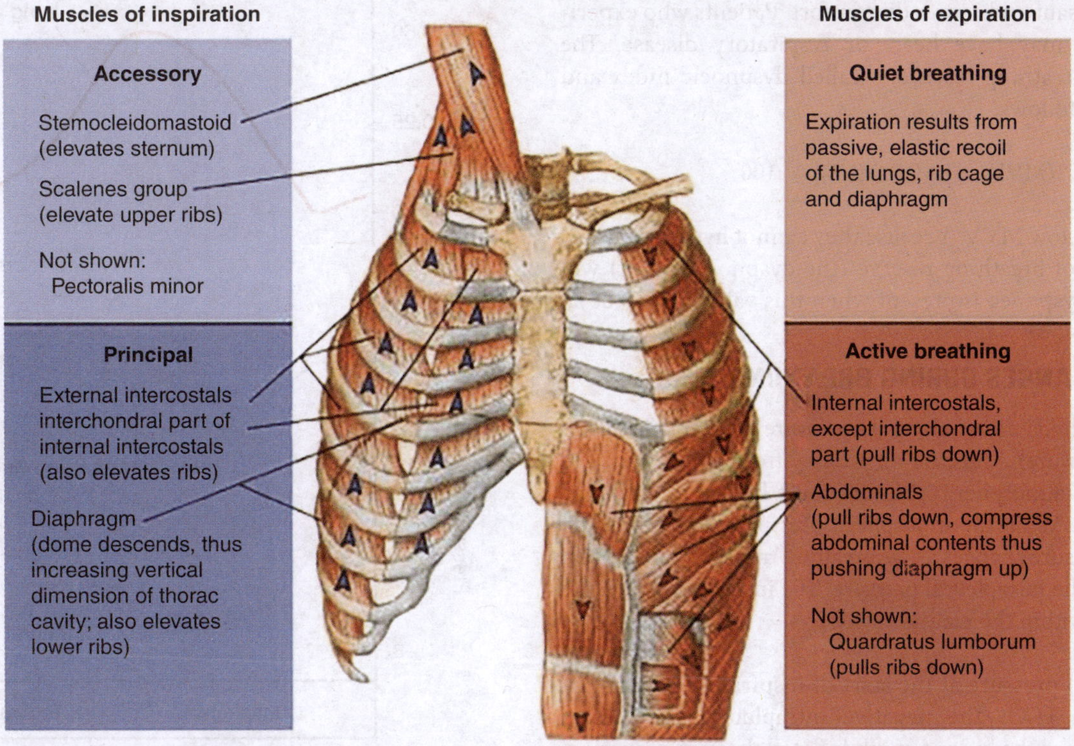

FIG. 9.1 Muscles involved in respiration.

intercostals help to reduce the chest volume; (2) they increase the intra-abdominal pressure when they contract and push the diaphragm upwards.

The muscles involved in respiration are summarized in Fig. 9.1.

VENTILATION AT REST AND DURING HYPERVENTILATION

The amount of air that is breathed in and out during quiet, resting ventilation is called the tidal volume. In an adult, this is about 500 mL.

If the respiratory rate is 12 per minute and the tidal volume is 500 mL, we can calculate the volume of air that is breathed in 1 minute. This volume is called the *respiratory minute volume* and is calculated as respiratory rate × tidal volume, that is 12 × 500 = 6000 mL or 6 L/minute.

Not all of this air that is breathed is available for gas exchange in the alveoli. This is because the respiratory system also has a conducting zone in which no gas exchange occurs (see Chapter 8). This conducting zone where no gas exchange takes place is called the *anatomical dead space*. The volume of the anatomical dead space in an adult is about 150 mL. This means that of the 500 mL that is breathed in with each breath, only 500–150 mL (350 mL) reaches the alveoli where gas exchange can take place. As an example, if the respiratory rate is 12 per minute, the tidal volume is 500 mL and the anatomical dead space is 150 mL, the amount of air that actually reaches the alveoli in 1 minute = (500-150) × 12 or 350 mL × 12= 4200 mL. This is called *alveolar ventilation.*

Dead space is not only in the conducting zone. For example, a part of the lung may receive enough air but the blood flow may be low leading to inefficient transfer of oxygen from the lung to the blood. There may also be parts of the lung where blood flow is adequate but ventilation is poor. In these areas, gas exchange is less and these areas comprise the *physiological dead space.*

Hyperventilation is an increase in the rate and depth of breathing. Hyperventilation occurs when we are physically and, sometimes, mentally stressed. A simple example of when hyperventilation occurs is during exercise. Maximal voluntary ventilation (MVV) refers to the volume of air that we could breathe if we hyperventilated maximally for 1 minute. The calculation is theoretical because we cannot hyperventilate for a whole minute. Sustained hyperventilation may be associated with a feeling of light-headedness, chest pain and fainting. So, we determine MVV by asking the person to breathe as deeply and rapidly as possible for a shorter period like 12 seconds. The volume that we get in 12 seconds is then multiplied by 5 to obtain the MVV for 1 minute (12 × 5 = 60 seconds). MVV in normal, healthy adult subjects is greater than 100 L. Breathing reserve refers to the volume of air that a person has in reserve and is calculated as MVV − respiratory minute volume (RMV).

The breathing reserve is important because it helps us understand the idea of **dyspnoea**. Dyspnoea is difficult breathing which is unpleasant and causes discomfort. Patients who experience dyspnoea may have heart or respiratory disease. The percentage of breathing reserve is called dyspnoeic index and is calculated as follows:

$$[(\text{MVV} - \text{RMV})/\text{MVV}] \times 100$$

If a person has a low MVV (because they cannot hyperventilate), the percentage of breathing reserve (the dyspnoeic index) will fall. Typically, dyspnoea is present when this value falls to 60%.

PRESSURE CHANGES DURING BREATHING

Air, like other fluids, flows along its pressure gradient (i.e. from high to low pressure). Thus, for air to flow from the atmosphere into the alveoli, atmospheric pressure must be greater than the alveolar pressure. While the atmospheric pressure is fairly constant, the alveolar pressure changes as we breathe. Another pressure that is important is the intrapleural pressure. The intrapleural pressure is the pressure within the pleural cavity.

The intrapleural pressure at the start of inspiration is approximately −5 cm H_2O. The negative intrapleural pressure is important because the lungs remain inflated through a 'suction' effect. During inspiration, due to the outward and upward movement of the chest wall, the intrapleural pressure falls further to about −7.5 cm H_2O. During expiration, the intrapleural pressure goes back to −5 cm H_2O.

If the atmospheric pressure and the alveolar pressure are the same, there will be no net movement of air into or out of the lungs. During inspiration, the alveolar pressure falls by just about 1 cm H_2O relative to the atmospheric pressure. This small decrease allows air to rush into the alveoli along the pressure gradient. During expiration, the alveolar pressure rises by about 1 cm above the atmospheric pressure; the pressure gradient is therefore reversed (alveoli > atmosphere) and the air is expelled from the lungs.

The difference between the alveolar pressure and the intrapleural pressure is referred to as the **transpulmonary pressure**. Since the alveolar pressure is normally always higher than the pleural pressure, the transpulmonary pressure is normally positive and this ensures that the lungs are inflated. In an injury to the chest wall, air may enter the pleural cavity (pneumothorax) resulting in a loss of the negative pleural pressure. When this happens, the transpulmonary pressure falls and the lung collapses.

Fig. 9.2 illustrates the changes in the various pressures during quiet breathing.

LUNG COMPLIANCE

Compliance (distensibility) is the change in volume of the lungs (i.e. the expansion of the lungs) per unit change in transpulmonary pressure. Transpulmonary pressure = alveolar pressure − intrapleural pressure. The unit of transpulmonary pressure is cm H_2O. The average lung compliance in an adult is about 200 mL/cm. The compliance in simple language refers to the expansibility or distensibility of the lungs. Thus, a high compliance means that the lungs expand more easily.

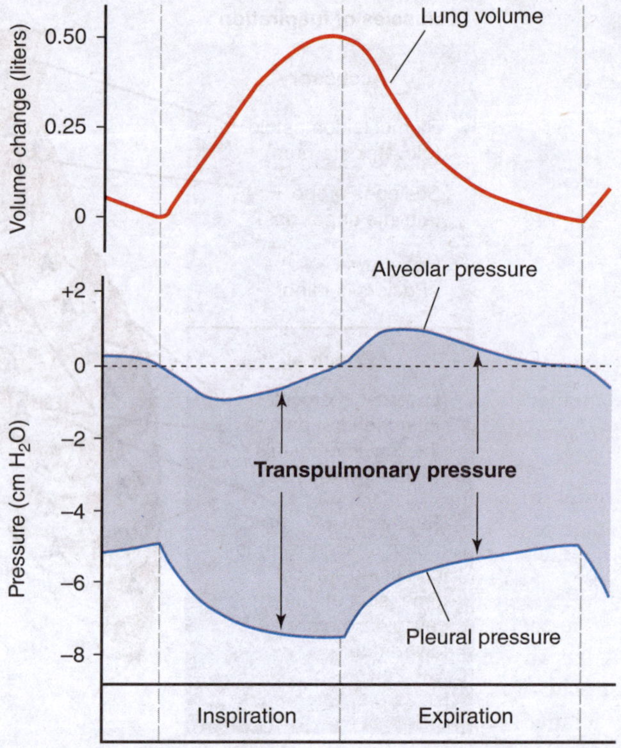

FIG. 9.2 Changes in lung volume and pressures during breathing.

Compliance can be altered by many factors:

1. Ageing is associated with reduced lung compliance.
2. Diseases in which there is increased fibrotic tissue (scarring) in the lungs reduce compliance.
3. Fluid in the lungs, for example in pulmonary oedema, reduces lung compliance.
4. Reduced surfactant (discussed in the subsequent text).

SURFACTANT

The lungs are made up of close to 500 million alveoli. These alveoli or air sacs are lined by a thin fluid coating. The high surface tension of this fluid layer would cause the alveoli to collapse because water molecules tend to be attracted to each other. In order to overcome this high surface tension, more work would need to be done to keep the lungs inflated. In addition, alveoli differ in size. In Fig. 9.3, we see two alveoli of different sizes connected to each other.

In the first image of Fig. 9.3, we see that the pressure within an alveolus is given by Laplace's law, that is pressure = $2T/r$, where T is the tension and r is the radius of the alveolus. In other words, the larger the radius, the smaller would be the pressure assuming that T is constant. This means that the pressure in the smaller alveolus would be greater than the pressure in the large alveolus.

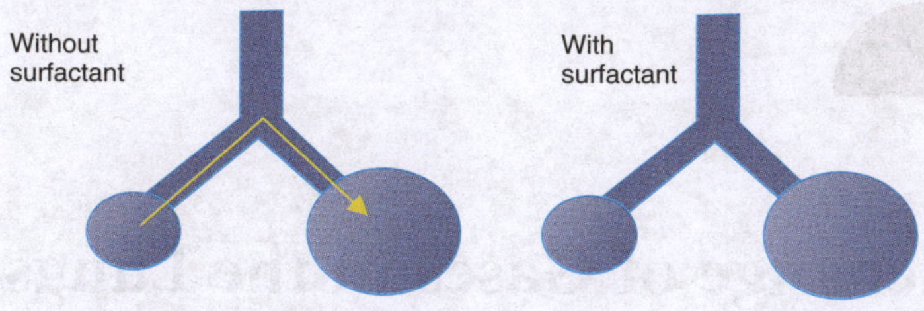

FIG. 9.3 Role of surfactant in stabilizing alveoli.

This would cause air to move along the pressure gradient from the smaller alveolus to the larger alveolus, leading to a collapse of the smaller alveoli.

In order to reduce the surface tension in the alveoli, type II alveolar cells secrete a substance called *surfactant*. Surfactant is a complex substance, the main component of which is dipalmitoylphosphatidylcholine (DPPC). It forms a thin layer on the inner surface of the alveoli and reduces the surface tension. The lung has alveoli of different sizes. In small alveoli, the surfactant is spread over a smaller area; therefore, the concentration of surfactant is high and surface tension is reduced to a greater extent. In larger alveoli, surfactant is spread over a larger area, the concentration of surfactant is thus less and surface tension is reduced to a lower extent. Let us go back to Laplace's law ($P = 2T/r$). If the tension (T) is reduced to a larger extent in smaller alveoli compared to in larger alveoli, this helps to equalize the pressures between the alveoli and prevents small alveoli from collapsing into large alveoli.

Surfactant has many functions:

1. Reduces the surface tension in the alveoli
2. Prevents alveoli from collapsing
3. Reduces the work of breathing
4. Improves lung compliance
5. Keeps the lungs dry
6. Helps in the immune responses of the lungs

Neonatal Respiratory Distress Syndrome

The duration of normal pregnancy is 40 weeks. Babies that are born before 37 weeks are called premature babies. It is estimated that about 15 million babies are born prematurely each year throughout the world. In premature infants who are born before 35 weeks, surfactant is not produced in sufficient quantities in the lungs. When these babies are born, they have difficulty in breathing because the work of breathing is much greater without surfactant. When surfactant deficiency is severe, it can even lead to death. Nearly half of all babies born at 26–28 weeks suffer from this condition called *neonatal respiratory distress syndrome* or *hyaline membrane disease*. The problem becomes less as the gestational age of the newborn increases. Babies with the condition may need to be ventilated and given oxygen. Artificial surfactant may also have to be given through the breathing tube directly into the lungs.

APPLICATIONS IN NURSING

- The recording of respiratory rate and depth of breathing are among the vital signs routinely monitored by the nurse in patients who are admitted in hospital.
- The nurse is an integral part of the team for the care of patient requiring assisted ventilation. Assisted ventilation can take different forms:
- In acute situations, ventilation can be provided by mouth-to-mouth breathing.
- In the absence of a mechanical ventilator, ventilation can be sustained using a mask and compression bag and a one-way valve. The compression bag is the size of a small football and is compressed by the hand at a fixed rate. This 'Ambu' bag (Ambu – for ambulance) was originally used to provide mechanical ventilation for people in transport.
- Mechanical ventilators: In patients who require ventilation for prolonged periods of time, a tube is inserted into the trachea (endotracheal tube) and connected to a programmable ventilator in which the rate, depth and pressure of ventilation can be controlled.

SUMMARY

- During quiet respiration, the diaphragm is the main muscle of inspiration and expiration occurs by passive recoil of the lungs.
- More forceful inspiration uses the external intercostals, the sternocleidomastoid and the scalene.
- Forced expiration uses the internal intercostals and the anterior abdominal muscles.
- During respiration, changes in intrapleural pressures and alveolar pressures allow for the movement of air into and out of the lungs. Intrapleural pressures range from −5 cm H_2O during expiration to −7.5 cm H_2O during inspiration. Alveolar pressures fall by about 1 cm H_2O in relation to atmospheric pressure during quiet inspiration and increase 1 cm H_2O above the atmospheric pressure during expiration.
- Respiratory minute volume is the amount of ventilation in one minute (tidal volume × respiratory rate).
- Alveolar ventilation is the amount of air that reaches the alveoli for gas exchange ((tidal volume – anatomical dead space) × respiratory rate).
- Compliance refers to the expansibility of the lungs and is the change in lung volume per unit change in transpulmonary pressure.
- Surfactant is produced by type II alveolar cells. It helps reduce surface tension in the alveoli, increase compliance, reduce the work of breathing, prevent collapse of alveoli and keep alveoli dry.
- Premature babies may suffer from neonatal respiratory distress syndrome due to a deficiency of surfactant.

CHAPTER REVIEW QUESTIONS

1. What are the muscles used in quiet and forced inspiration?
2. What is the mechanism of quiet expiration? What are the muscles used in forced expiration?
3. Describe the alveolar and intra-pleural pressure changes in quiet inspiration and expiration.
4. What is lung compliance? List the factors that affect lung compliance.
5. What is the composition and functions of surfactant?

CHAPTER 10

Exchange of Gases in the Lungs

SPECIFIC LEARNING OBJECTIVES

At the end of this chapter, the student should be able to:

- Describe the basic gas laws as applied to the respiratory system.
- Describe the composition of atmospheric, alveolar and expired air.
- Describe the process by which gas diffuses across the respiratory membrane.
- Describe the concept of ventilation–perfusion ratio.
- Describe the regional distribution of air and blood flow in the lungs.

GLOSSARY OF TERMS

- **Perfusion:** delivery of blood to a capillary bed
- **Ventilation–perfusion ratio:** applied either to the whole lung or to a part of the lung (in the case of the latter, it is the ratio of alveolar ventilation in that part of the lung to the capillary blood flow in the same part)
- **Partial pressure of a gas:** in a mixture of gases, each gas is described in terms of its own partial pressure which is the hypothetical pressure of that gas if it alone occupied the volume of the mixture

In this chapter, we review some basic gas laws in chemistry and discuss how gases are exchanged in the lungs.

GAS LAWS

Air is a mixture of gases. The major constituents of air are nitrogen, oxygen, carbon dioxide and water vapour. Some of these gases like nitrogen (78.8%) and oxygen (20.95%) have relatively constant concentrations, while others like carbon dioxide (average 0.04%) and water vapour (0%–7%) have concentrations that vary.

Dalton's Law of Partial Pressures

The amount of each gas that is in air in absolute terms is given by **Dalton's law of partial pressures** which states that (1) each gas in a mixture of gases exerts a pressure, known as its partial pressure, that is equal to the pressure that the gas would exert if it were the only gas present; (2) the total pressure of the mixture is the sum of the partial pressures of all the gases present.

As an example, we can look at oxygen availability at different altitudes. Atmospheric pressure falls as altitude increases. Thus, atmospheric pressure at sea level is 760 mm Hg, while it is only 523 mm Hg at an altitude of 10,000 feet. Assuming that the oxygen concentration is 20.95%, the partical pressure of oxygen at sea level would be $20.95/100 \times 760 = 159.2$ mm Hg. At an atmospheric pressure of 523 mmHg (10,000 feet), the partial pressure of oxygen would be $20.95/100 \times 523 = 109.6$ mm Hg.

Boyle's Law

Boyle's law states that at constant temperature, the volume of a gas is inversely proportional to the pressure on it. This law is given by the equation $P_1V_1 = P_2V_2$. There are many applications of this law. Travellers in an aeroplane notice that their ears pop when they ascend in an aeroplane and then pop again on the way down. Aeroplanes are pressurized (i.e. the pressure is kept constant inside the aeroplane). They are typically pressurized for an altitude of between 6000 and 8000 feet above sea level. Thus, even when the aeroplane is flying at 35,000 feet above sea level, the pressure in the aeroplane is at about 7000 feet. So, when the aeroplane ascends, the air contained in the middle ear is now subjected to less pressure than at sea level and the air inside the middle ear expands pushing the tympanic membrane outwards – this is an uncomfortable sensation – air can escape through the Eustachian tubes and the pressure in the middle ear is normalized with a 'pop'. When the aeroplane descends, the atmospheric pressure now increases and the tympanic membrane is pushed inwards – in order to equalize pressure, air must enter the middle ear through the Eustachian tube. This can be facilitated by chewing or swallowing – as the air rushes in,

Table 10.1 Composition of Atmospheric and Alveolar Air

Constituent	Atmospheric Air		Alveolar Air		Reason for Difference Between Atmospheric and Alveolar Air
	mm Hg	%	mm Hg	%	
N_2	597.36	78.6	570	75	Contribution of other gases – H_2O/CO_2
O_2	158.08	20.8	102.6	13.5	O_2 constantly diffusing into pulmonary circulation
CO_2	0.30	0.04	41.8	5.5	CO_2 constantly diffusing into alveoli from blood
H_2O	4.26	0.56	45.6	6	Air is humidified during its passage into the lungs
Total	760	100	760	100	

it 'pops'. These changes in volume with changing pressure occur not only in the ear but also in every place where air is in a confined space such as the stomach and sinuses.

Henry's Law

Henry's law states that the amount of gas dissolved in a solution is directly proportional to the partial pressure of the gas over the solution. We will discuss more about the application of this law in a later chapter, when we discuss decompression sickness.

ATMOSPHERIC, ALVEOLAR AND EXPIRED AIR

Although atmospheric air enters the alveoli with each breath, atmospheric air and alveolar air have a different composition from each other. These compositions are represented in Table 10.1.

Table 10.1 shows that the concentration of N_2 in the alveoli is lower than in the atmosphere as is oxygen. However, carbon dioxide and water vapour concentrations are higher in the alveoli than in the atmosphere. This may seem surprising. For instance, if we are breathing in oxygen at a higher concentration (20.8%), why is it lower in the alveoli (13.5%)? This is mainly because oxygen in the alveoli is constantly diffusing from the alveoli into the bloodstream and oxygenating the blood. Thus oxygen in the alveoli falls. Similarly, carbon dioxide is constantly diffusing from the blood into the alveoli from where it can be expelled. Thus, carbon dioxide content is higher in the alveoli. In Chapter 8, we learned that air is humidified in the conducting system especially when we breathe through the nose. This is why water vapour in the alveoli has a higher concentration. The higher concentration of water vapour in the alveoli also reduces the concentrations of the other gases, including nitrogen (as compared to if water vapour was not present).

Table 10.2 shows the composition of expired air.

Table 10.2 Composition of Expired Air

Constituent	Expired Air	
	mm Hg	%
N_2	570	75
O_2	117.8	15.5
CO_2	26.6	3.5
H_2O	45.6	6
Total	760	100

A comparison of the expired air and the alveolar air (Table 10.1) shows that concentration of oxygen is higher in expired air than that of alveolar air, while carbon dioxide is at a lower concentration in expired air than alveolar air. This is because the alveolar air mixes with the air in the dead space (which has the composition of atmospheric air since it does not take part in gas exchange). Thus, carbon dioxide is diluted by the air in the dead space which has a lower concentration of carbon dioxide, while oxygen is concentrated by the air in the dead space since the concentration of oxygen in the dead space is higher than alveolar air. In Chapter 8, we learned that the conducting zone of the respiratory system does not take part in gas exchange and constitutes the anatomical dead space. Thus, in the anatomical dead space, the concentration of oxygen is high and of carbon dioxide is low (like atmospheric air).

THE RESPIRATORY MEMBRANE

Oxygen diffuses from the alveoli into the bloodstream and carbon dioxide diffuses in the opposite direction, from the bloodstream into the alveoli. Between the alveolus and the bloodstream is the respiratory membrane. This is depicted in Fig. 10.1.

You will observe that oxygen needs to pass through six distinct layers before it reaches the bloodstream. These include (1) the fluid and surfactant layer that lines the alveolus, (2) the alveolar epithelium, (3) the epithelial basement membrane, (4) the interstitial space, (5) the capillary basement membrane and (6) the capillary endothelium. Carbon dioxide needs to pass through these same layers but in the opposite direction.

The rate of diffusion of a gas depends on several factors and is summarized in **Fick's law of diffusion**. This is given by the following equation:

$$\text{Rate of diffusion} = (\text{Area/thickness}) \times \text{diffusion constant} \times \text{pressure gradient}$$

where the diffusion constant = solubility of the gas/molecular weight.

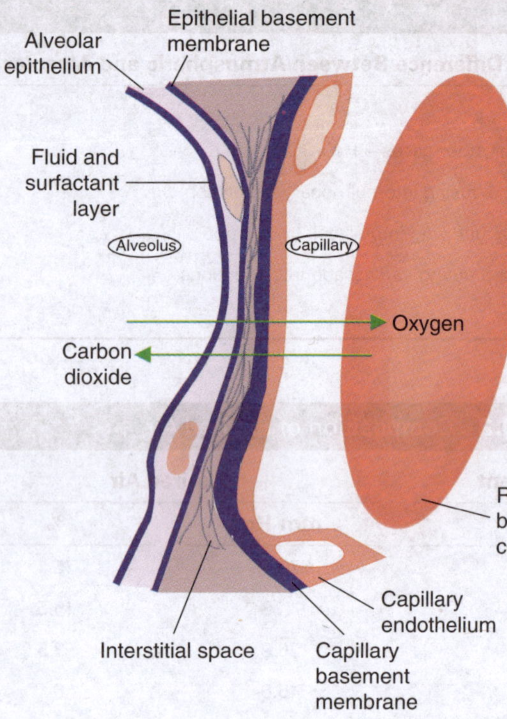

FIG. 10.1 The structure of the respiratory membrane.

The area and thickness are the same for diffusion of oxygen and carbon dioxide since both have to cross the same respiratory membrane. However, the pressure gradient for oxygen and carbon dioxide is different. The oxygen content in the alveolus is 102.6 mm Hg and in the pulmonary capillary is about 40 mm Hg. Thus, the gradient for oxygen is alveolar content − capillary content, that is $102.6 - 40 = 62.6$ mm Hg. In contrast, the pulmonary capillary CO_2 content is 46 mm Hg and the alveolar content is 41.8 mm Hg. The pressure gradient for CO_2 is therefore pulmonary capillary content − alveolar CO_2 content, that is $46 - 41.8 = 4.2$ mm Hg. Based on this, it might seem that CO_2 diffuses very poorly, while oxygen diffuses very well. However, CO_2 has a greater solubility compared to oxygen and although the molecular weight of CO_2 is higher than that of O_2, the diffusion constant of CO_2 is about 20 times higher than that of O_2.

Any factor that increases the thickness of the respiratory membrane reduces diffusion. This is what happens when fluid collects in the interstitial space as in pulmonary oedema or when the lung is 'scarred' as in fibrosis or interstitial lung disease.

VENTILATION–PERFUSION RATIO

For the effective diffusion of gases to take place, the lungs must not only be aerated (filled with air) but also be adequately perfused (with a good blood flow). This ensures that oxygen and carbon dioxide is transferred effectively across the respiratory membrane (between the alveolus and the pulmonary capillary).

At rest, with quiet breathing, the ventilation of the lungs and the amount of blood flow in the pulmonary circulation are roughly equal, about 5 L/minute. This gives a ventilation–perfusion ratio of around 1 (5/5). However, because about one-quarter of the tidal volume (125 mL) is in the conducting zone (where no gas exchange occurs), less air reaches the alveoli. Alveolar ventilation is thus about 4 L/minute and the corrected ventilation–perfusion ratio is, therefore, about 0.8 (4 divided by 5).

However, not all parts of the lung are equally ventilated and equally perfused as indicated in Fig. 10.2.

Regional Differences in Ventilation–Perfusion Ratio

In the erect posture, the alveoli at the apex (top) of the lung are larger than the alveoli at the base (bottom) of the lung. This is because the weight of the lung compresses the alveoli at the base. However, larger alveoli do not necessarily mean that gas transfer in those alveoli is better. This is because gas transfer by diffusion also depends on the perfusion (blood flow) of the alveoli. The blood flow of the lungs is also dependent on the posture. Thus, in the erect posture, due to gravity, the base of the lungs is better perfused than the apex. This means that gas transfer is better in the base of the lungs than at the apex.

The better gas transfer in the base compared to the apex is seen in the alveolar gas composition in the apex as compared to in the base. Earlier in this chapter, we discussed the composition of alveolar air as compared to that of atmospheric air. We showed

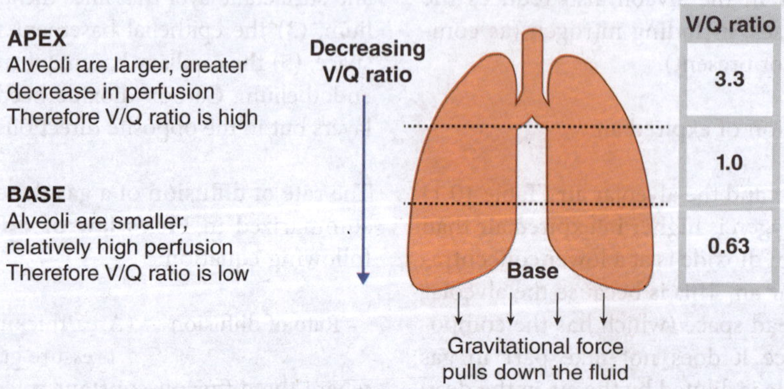

FIG. 10.2 Regional differences in ventilation and perfusion in the upright lung. V = ventilation; Q = perfusion.

that the alveoli have a lower oxygen concentration and a higher carbon dioxide concentration than atmospheric air because oxygen is being continuously removed from the alveolus and carbon dioxide is constantly being added to the alveolus. In alveoli in the apex of the lung where the perfusion is lower, less gas exchange occurs. Because of less removal of oxygen from the alveoli in the apex, these alveoli have a higher oxygen concentration than the alveoli at the base of the lung. Similarly, the carbon dioxide concentration in the apical alveoli is lower than that of alveoli at the base. The higher oxygen concentrations in the apical alveoli make the apex of the lung more likely to develop certain aerobic infectious diseases (organisms that require oxygen) like tuberculosis. A reduced blood flow and lymphatic drainage in the apex may also result in increased infections.

Because of the regional differences in both ventilation and perfusion in different parts of the lungs during the erect posture, it is clear that the ventilation–perfusion ratio also differs in different regions of the lung. Thus, in the apex of the lung, during the erect posture, while both ventilation and perfusion are reduced, the alveoli are better ventilated than perfused. In the apex, in the erect posture, therefore, the ventilation–perfusion ratio is high. In the base of the lungs which is better perfused than ventilated, the ventilation–perfusion ratio is lower.

APPLICATIONS IN NURSING

- The position of the patient is important during mechanical ventilation (ventilator) in intensive care settings. Appropriate position not only reduces the likelihood of pneumonia but also reduces the risk of gastric aspiration. The details of this are beyond the scope of this book.
- When oxygen is being administered to a patient at high flow, the oxygen needs to be humidified; otherwise, secretions of the respiratory tract become thick and are difficult to clear. In patients with asthma, delivery of dry air can worsen the problem
- In some patients, a tracheostomy is done – this involves opening the trachea and placing a tube in it through which the patient breathes. Because a tracheostomy bypasses the nasal cavity, the air entering the lungs is dry and the air needs to be humidified. This is done by various methods.

SUMMARY

- Alveolar air is different in composition from the atmospheric air: oxygen concentration is lower, carbon dioxide concentration is higher and the air is more humidified in alveolar air.
- Oxygen and carbon dioxide are transferred across the respiratory membrane from alveoli to blood and blood to alveoli, respectively. The respiratory membrane consists of (1) the fluid and surfactant layer that lines the alveolus, (2) the alveolar epithelium, (3) the epithelial basement membrane, (4) the interstitial space, (5) the capillary basement membrane and (6) the capillary endothelium.
- Expired air has a lower carbon dioxide concentration and higher oxygen concentration than alveolar air due to the mixing of alveolar air with the air in the anatomical dead space.
- The ventilation and perfusion ratio is not equal in all parts of the lung. In the erect posture, the base of the lung is better perfused than the apex. The apex thus has a higher ventilation–perfusion ratio than the base.

CHAPTER REVIEW QUESTIONS

1. State the following laws: (a) Dalton's law of partial pressures, (b) Boyle's law and (c) Henry's law.
2. Explain the differences between (a) atmospheric and alveolar air and (b) alveolar and expired air.
3. What are the layers of the respiratory membrane?
4. List the factors that affect the simple diffusion of oxygen and carbon dioxide across the cell membrane.
5. What is ventilation–perfusion ratio? How does it differ in the erect person from apex to base of the lungs?

CHAPTER 11

Gas Transport and Exchange

SPECIFIC LEARNING OBJECTIVES

At the end of this chapter, the student should be able to:

- Describe the ways in which oxygen is transported in the blood.
- Draw and explain the oxygen–haemoglobin dissociation curve.
- Describe the ways in which carbon dioxide is transported in the blood.

GLOSSARY OF TERMS

- **Bohr's effect:** haemoglobin's oxygen binding affinity is inversely related to the concentration of carbon dioxide; thus, as carbon dioxide concentration increases, the oxygen affinity decreases
- **Haldane's effect:** oxygenation of blood in the lungs displaces carbon dioxide from haemoglobin

TRANSPORT OF OXYGEN IN THE BLOOD

Once oxygen is transferred from the alveoli into the bloodstream, it is carried to the tissues where it is required for metabolism.

A small portion (about 2%) of the oxygen is carried dissolved in plasma. The amount of a gas that dissolves in a fluid is given by *Henry's law* which states that the solubility of a gas in a liquid is directly proportional to the partial pressure of the gas above the liquid.

A total of 97%–98% of the oxygen is transported in blood bound to a molecule called haemoglobin. Haemoglobin is contained within the red blood cells (RBCs). There is a reason why haemoglobin is inside the RBC and not in plasma. The reason is that while haemoglobin carries oxygen very well, it is also toxic to cells in its free form. This is why when a RBC is destroyed, haemoglobin gets bound to other molecules such as haptoglobin and gets rapidly broken down.

When fully saturated, each gram of haemoglobin can carry 1.34 mL of oxygen. If the haemoglobin concentration of blood is 15 g/dL, this means that 100 mL (1 dL) of blood contains 15×1.34 mL of oxygen, that is ~20 mL. The combination of haemoglobin and oxygen is called *oxyhaemoglobin*.

Thus, oxygen is carried in two ways:

1. Two per cent as dissolved oxygen
2. Ninety-eight per cent bound to haemoglobin (oxyhaemoglobin)

THE OXYGEN–HAEMOGLOBIN DISSOCIATION CURVE

Oxygen binds to haemoglobin so that it can be carried to the tissues. Oxygen then dissociates from haemoglobin in the tissues so that it is available for cellular metabolism.

Fig. 11.1 illustrates the association between the partial pressure of arterial oxygen (*x*-axis) and the per cent saturation of haemoglobin (*y*-axis).

Features of the Curve

There are several things that Fig. 11.1 illustrates:

1. The shape of the curve is described as 'sigmoid'.
2. From an arterial oxygen partial pressure (PO_2) of 60 mm Hg up to 100 mm Hg, the saturation of haemoglobin is almost 100%. The normal arterial PO_2 at sea level is about 100 mm Hg. At about 10,000 feet above sea level, due to the fall in barometric pressure and alveolar PO_2 concentrations, the

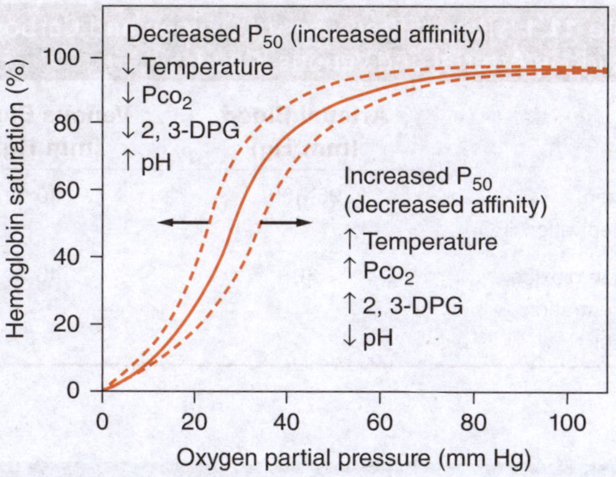

FIG. 11.1 The oxygen–haemoglobin dissociation curve.

arterial PO_2 of oxygen is about 60 mm Hg. Despite this big fall in arterial PO_2, however, haemoglobin continues to be close to 90% saturated with haemoglobin.

3. There is a rapid decline in saturation of haemoglobin between arterial PO_2 of 60 and 20 mm Hg.

Shifts in the Curve

Fig. 11.1 also illustrates that the oxygen–haemoglobin dissociation curve is not fixed but can shift to the left or right. Let us for a moment consider the arterial partial pressure of oxygen of about 27 mm Hg which corresponds to a haemoglobin saturation of 50% (sometimes called P50). When the curve shifts to the right (dashed line to the right of the main line), you will notice that the saturation of haemoglobin falls. Thus, when the curve shifts to the right, haemoglobin has less affinity for oxygen and oxygen dissociates from haemoglobin more easily. This is what happens in tissues which are metabolically active and which require more oxygen. The factors that shift the curve to the right and make oxygen more available, like increased temperature, increased PCO_2 and reduced pH, are all factors associated with metabolically active tissues. A shift of the oxygen–haemoglobin dissociation curve to the right because of an increase in PCO_2 is called the *Bohr's effect*. 2-3 DPG (BPG) is a compound which is produced more in conditions of hypoxia (like high altitude). This also shifts the curve to the right making more oxygen available to the tissues.

There are some factors which tend to shift the oxygen–haemoglobin dissociation curve to the left. These include a fall in PCO_2 and temperature and a rise in pH. These are features of metabolically inactive tissues where the requirement of oxygen is less. In this situation, a shift to the left means a higher affinity of haemoglobin for oxygen and a reduced dissociation of oxygen from haemoglobin. In a pregnant woman, the foetus has a different type of haemoglobin called foetal haemoglobin (HbF). This haemoglobin has a high affinity for oxygen and this high affinity which is greater than that of the adult haemoglobin allows for the better transfer of oxygen from the mother to the foetus. Thus, if we were to draw the oxygen–haemoglobin dissociation curve for HbF, we would find that it is shifted to the left (i.e. greater affinity, less dissociation).

How can we determine whether the oxygen–haemoglobin dissociation curve has shifted to the left or right? We use the parameter called P50. The P50 for the oxygen–haemoglobin dissociation curve is the arterial partial pressure of oxygen at which the haemoglobin is 50% saturated with oxygen. In Fig. 11.1, this is at the point where the horizontal arrows are. If you drop a line to the *x*-axis (oxygen partial pressure), you will observe that the normal P50 is around 27 mm Hg. If the P50 value is less than this, there is a shift to the left and if the P50 value is more than this, there is a shift to the right.

TRANSPORT OF CARBON DIOXIDE IN BLOOD

Carbon dioxide is transported from the tissues to the lungs in the blood in three forms:

1. **Dissolved:** About 7% of all carbon dioxide transported from the tissues is in the dissolved form. Carbon dioxide is 20 times more soluble than oxygen.
2. **As bicarbonate:** About 70% of carbon dioxide is carried this way. When carbon dioxide enters the RBC in the tissues, it combines with the water in the cell in the presence of an enzyme called *carbonic anhydrase* to form carbonic acid. Carbonic acid rapidly breaks down to form bicarbonate (HCO_3^-) and hydrogen (H^+) ions. The H^+ ion binds to haemoglobin which is a powerful acid–base buffer. The HCO_3^- ions diffuse into plasma while chloride (Cl^-) ions diffuse from plasma into the RBC to take their place. This exchange of bicarbonate and chloride between the RBC and the plasma is referred to as the **chloride shift**. Thus, in this method, CO_2 is transported in the form of bicarbonate in the plasma. This is summarized in Fig. 11.2.
3. **Combined with haemoglobin:** About 23% of carbon dioxide is carried this way. In the tissues, the haemoglobin molecule gives up the oxygen that it is carrying. Carbon dioxide released from the tissues binds to the haemoglobin molecule to form *carbaminohaemoglobin*.

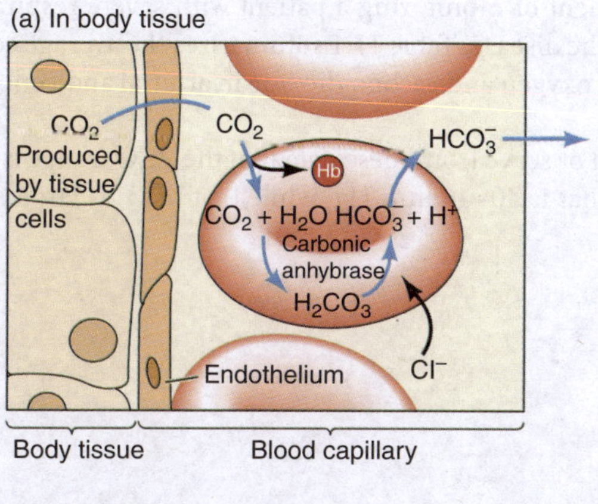

FIG. 11.2 The chloride shift.

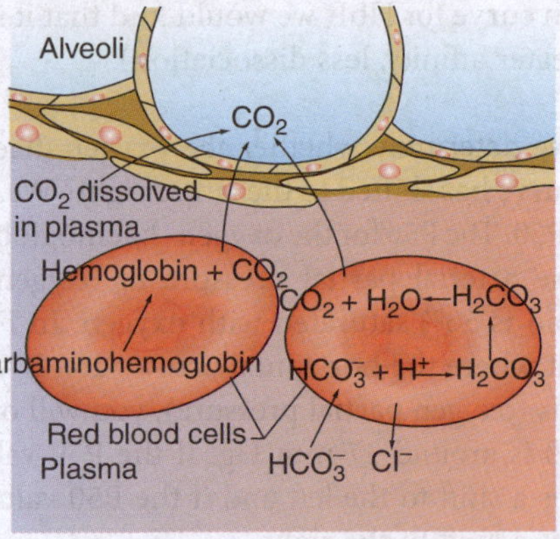

FIG. 11.3 The reverse chloride shift in the lungs.

Once carbon dioxide reaches the lung, several events occur to ensure that carbon dioxide is transferred to the alveoli from where it can be expelled:

1. In the lungs, when oxygen binds with haemoglobin, carbon dioxide is released from the haemoglobin. This effect is called the *Haldane's effect*.
2. The bicarbonate ion moves back into the RBC and chloride ion moves out of the red cell into plasma. This is called the *reverse chloride shift* (Fig. 11.3).
3. Hydrogen ions dissociate from haemoglobin and again combine with the bicarbonate ions to form carbonic acid. This dissociates to form carbon dioxide and water – the carbon dioxide diffuses into the alveoli and is then expelled in the expired air.

A common mistake that students make is to refer to the combination of carbon dioxide and haemoglobin as *carboxyhaemoglobin*. Carboxyhaemoglobin is, in fact, the combination of carbon monoxide and haemoglobin. Carbon monoxide is a pollutant, as, for example, of vehicle exhausts. Carbon monoxide has about 200 times greater affinity for haemoglobin than for oxygen, so when carbon monoxide binds to haemoglobin, it reduces the binding and transport of oxygen.

BLOOD GASES

An analysis of the blood gases in arterial blood is an important component of monitoring a patient with severe respiratory and metabolic disease. Table 11.1 summarizes the average concentrations of oxygen and carbon dioxide in arterial and venous blood.

You will observe from these data that the PCO_2 range is relatively small, that is 40–46 mm Hg, while that of O_2 is larger.

Table 11.1 Partial Pressures of Oxygen and Carbon Dioxide in Arterial and Venous Blood

	Arterial Blood (mm Hg)	Venous Blood (mm Hg)
Oxygen concentration (PO_2)	95–100	40
Carbon dioxide concentration (PCO_2)	40	46

APPLICATIONS IN NURSING

The nurse will be required to monitor blood gases of patients who are in critical care units. Arterial blood gases can be altered in patients with respiratory, cardiac, renal and metabolic disorders. These blood gas concentrations can help guide treatment with oxygenation, acid–base correction or ventilation, among other things.

SUMMARY

- Oxygen is transported in two ways in blood: (1) 2% is dissolved and (2) 98% is bound to haemoglobin as oxyhaemoglobin.
- Carbon dioxide is transported in three forms in blood: (1) 7% is dissolved, (2) 70% is transported as bicarbonate and (3) 23% is bound to haemoglobin as carbaminohaemoglobin.
- The oxygen–haemoglobin dissociation curve describes the saturation of haemoglobin with oxygen over a range of arterial PO_2. The curve is shifted to the right with an increase in PCO_2, 2–3 DBG, and temperature and a decrease in pH.
- Bohr's effect is the shift of the oxygen–haemoglobin dissociation curve due to an increase in PCO_2.
- Haldane's effect is the reduced affinity of carbon dioxide for haemoglobin when oxygen binds to haemoglobin.

CHAPTER REVIEW QUESTIONS

1. Describe the ways in which oxygen is carried in blood.
2. Describe the ways in which carbon dioxide is carried in blood.
3. Draw an oxygen–haemoglobin saturation curve and explain its features.
4. List the factors which cause a shift in the oxygen–haemoglobin dissociation curve to the (a) right and (b) left.
5. What is Haldane's effect? What is its importance?

CHAPTER 12

Regulation of Respiration

SPECIFIC LEARNING OBJECTIVES

At the end of this chapter, the student should be able to:

- Describe the chemical control of respiration in terms of the following:
  - Anatomical sites involved
  - Stimuli that trigger chemical control of respiration
  - Effects of simple manoeuvres on the chemical control of respiration
- Describe the neural control of respiration in terms of the following:
  - Anatomical sites involved
  - Function of each of the anatomical sites
  - Reflexes concerning respiration
  - Describe the cough reflex.

GLOSSARY OF TERMS

- **Apnoea:** temporary stoppage of breathing
- **Tachypnoea:** increased rate of respiration
- **Hyperpnoea:** increase in the depth of breathing
- **Hypoxaemia:** decreased levels of oxygen in the blood
- **Hypercapnia:** increased levels of carbon dioxide in the blood

We do not breathe the same way all the time. For example, during exercise, breathing becomes faster and deeper. If we hold our breath for a while, the rate and depth of breathing increase once we have stopped holding our breath. In this chapter, we will discuss how we control our respiration.

There are two types of regulation of respiration. One is chemical where the rate and depth of respiration vary depending on the increase or decrease in the bloodstream of certain chemical stimuli. The other type of regulation is neural regulation, where respiration is controlled from centres in the brain.

CHEMICAL REGULATION OF RESPIRATION

In order to regulate respiration chemically, the body has sensors or receptors that detect chemicals that are linked to breathing. These receptors are called chemoreceptors because they respond to chemical stimuli.

Location of Chemoreceptors (Fig. 12.1)

Chemoreceptors regulating respiration are located in two areas:

1. *Peripheral chemoreceptors* are located in the vessel wall at the bifurcation of the common carotid artery and in the arch of the aorta. These are called *carotid bodies* and aortic bodies.
2. *Central chemoreceptors* are located on the ventral surface of the medulla oblongata in the brain.

Stimuli for the Chemoreceptors

Peripheral chemoreceptors:

Since the primary role of respiration is to acquire oxygen and to expel carbon dioxide, chemoreceptors respond to these two signals. In fact, the peripheral chemoreceptors (i.e. the carotid and aortic bodies) are primarily stimulated by a high PCO_2 and a low PO_2 in the arterial blood. A fall in pH can also stimulate the chemoreceptors.

Central chemoreceptors:

Carbon dioxide crosses the blood–brain barrier easily and sp: diffuses from the blood into the cerebrospinal fluid which bathes the brain. Here, CO_2 reacts with the water to generate H^+ ions. These H^+ ions then stimulate the central chemoreceptors. Note that H^+ ions from the blood cannot cross the blood–brain barrier. So, a low pH in the blood due to an increase in H^+ ions cannot directly stimulate the central chemoreceptors.

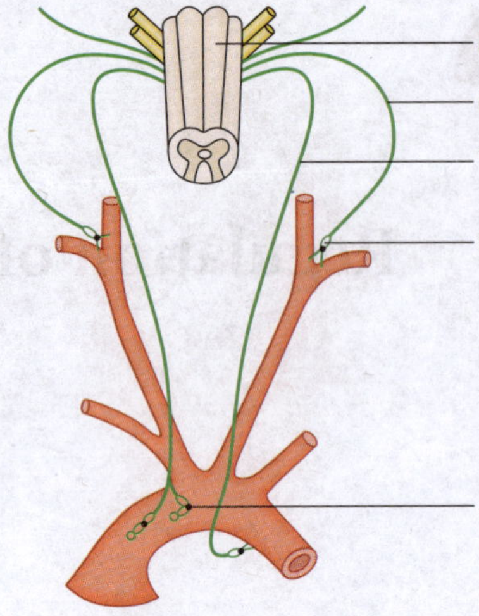

FIG. 12.1 Location of the chemoreceptors regulating respiration.

RESPONSE TO STIMULATION OF CHEMORECEPTORS

A reduced PO_2, a reduced pH and an increased PCO_2 all increase the rate and depth of breathing. This increased rate and depth of breathing allows the body to get a greater amount of oxygen. It also allows the body to expel a greater amount of CO_2 – this is referred to as *carbon dioxide washout*. When we hyperventilate (increase the rate and depth of breathing), PO_2 increases, the PCO_2 decreases (because of CO_2 washout) and the pH rises.

Two manoeuvres help to demonstrate the process of chemo-regulation of respiration:

Breath holding: When we hold our breath for as long as we can, we reach a point when we cannot hold our breath – this is called the *breakpoint*. We then observe that our rate and depth of breathing increases soon after we start breathing again. Why does this occur? This is because when we hold our breath, there is a build-up of CO_2 in the body as a result of which the PCO_2 of arterial blood increases (*hypercapnia*). This stimulates the chemoreceptors to increase the rate and depth of respiration after the breakpoint.

Hyperventilation: This is the increase in rate and depth of breathing. If an individual voluntarily hyperventilates for some time, there is a short period which follows when the breathing is inhibited – this is called *apnoea* (a temporary cessation of breathing). This is followed by slower and shallower breathing till the breathing returns to its original rate and depth. Why does this occur? During hyperventilation, there is carbon dioxide washout; there is thus a decrease in the PCO_2 (*hypocapnia*). This inhibits breathing resulting in a short period of apnoea when breathing stops and then by the more shallow and slower breathing. It is important to know that hyperventilation for longer periods of time can result in light-headedness, dizziness and even fainting, so these manoeuvres should be done under supervision.

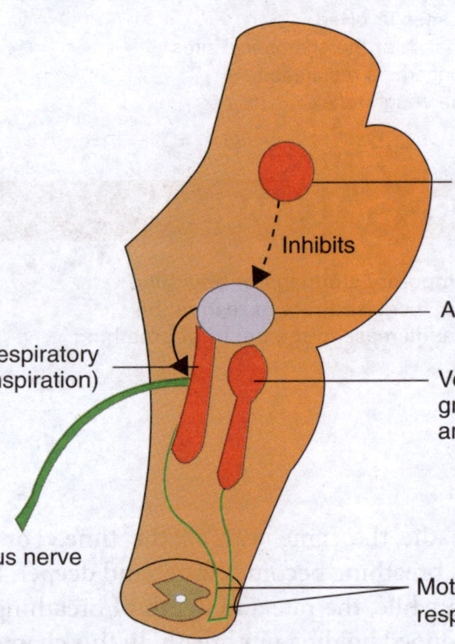

FIG. 12.2 The central neural areas involved in the nervous regulation of respiration.

NEURAL REGULATION OF RESPIRATION

There are several areas of the brain which control respiration (Fig. 12.2).

Medullary Centres

The two main groups of neurons involved in the control of respiration in the medulla are the *dorsal respiratory group* and the *ventral respiratory group* of neurons. The dorsal respiratory group of neurons are involved primarily in inspiration, while the ventral respiratory group is involved primarily in expiration, although it also influences inspiration. You can remember this quite easily if you remember the word DIVE (**d**orsal-**i**nspiratory; **v**entral-**e**xpiratory). The medullary centres also help to generate the respiratory rhythm.

The medulla also contains the respiratory control pattern generator which is responsible for rhythmic and automatic respiration. The major cells which contribute to this rhythmicity are the pacemaker cells of the pre-Bötzinger complex. Pacemaker cells are able to generate their own electrical rhythm independent of nerves or hormones, although these can influence them. Pacemaker cells are also found in other parts of the body such as the heart.

Pontine Centres

The pons is situated above the medulla in the brain. There are two important centres in the pons which regulate respiration:

Apneustic centre: This is located in the lower pons. The apneustic centre stimulates the inspiratory neurons which are located in the medulla (mainly in the dorsal group neurons). When the lungs expand, the apneustic centre receives signals from the lung which inhibit it – thus limiting the inflation of the lungs. Apneusis refers to a type of breathing characterized by prolonged and deep inspiration followed by insufficient expiration. This can be seen when there is damage to the pons, for example, in some strokes.

Pneumotaxic centre: This is also located in the pons. The pneumotaxic centre acts to inhibit the apneustic centre. Since the apneustic centre acts to increase inspiration, the pneumotaxic centre by inhibiting the apneustic centre decreases inspiration.

THE ROLE OF THE CEREBRAL CORTEX

We can voluntarily control our breathing. This tells us that there is higher cortical control of respiration. Emotions can affect cerebral cortical activity and we know that emotion can affect breathing patterns. The cerebral cortex acts by altering the function of the respiratory centres located in the pons and medulla. There are, however, limits to cortical control. For instance, voluntarily overcoming the effect of very high PCO_2 levels is difficult – this is seen with breath holding as described earlier.

Ondine's curse is a severe respiratory disorder which can be congenital and can also occur later in life due to severe brain trauma, stroke, etc. In this life-threatening disorder, people most often suffer from respiratory arrest during sleep and need to be on a mechanical ventilator.

RESPIRATORY REFLEXES

Respiratory reflexes regulate the rate and depth of respiration based on the condition of the lung.

Located within the bronchial wall are stretch receptors which are activated when the lungs expand. When the lungs are inflated beyond their resting state by between 800 mL and 1.5 L, expiration is started. This reflex is called the **Hering–Breuer inflation reflex** and helps to limit inspiration.

When the lungs deflate (i.e. decrease in size), there is reflex hyperpnoea (i.e. an increased depth of breathing). This reflex is called the **Hering–Breuer deflation reflex** and helps to limit deflation and open up alveoli that have collapsed.

Fig. 12.3 is a diagram which summarizes the chemical and neural control of respiration. The chemical control of respiration is indicated in orange. You can see that the central chemoreceptors located in the medullary chemosensitive zone are stimulated by an increase in PCO_2 in the blood. H^+ ions are unable to enter the brain because of the blood–brain barrier. The peripheral chemoreceptors located in the carotid and aortic bodies are stimulated by a decrease in PO_2 and an increase in H^+ ions and PCO_2 in the blood. The chemoreceptors act by stimulating the neural centres in the brain (depicted in purple) and increasing the rate and depth of respiration.

THE COUGH REFLEX

Definition

Cough is a common symptom. It is defined as a sudden and rapid expulsion of air which is aimed at removing foreign particles, irritants, germs, mucus or fluids. Since the air is expelled through open vocal cords, it gives rise to a sharp sound.

Causes

There are many causes of cough, and the following list includes only some of them:

1. Postnasal drip (when you have a cold, the mucus from the nose drips back into the throat causing an irritation)
2. Asthma
3. Allergies
4. Pneumonia (an infection of the lung parenchyma)
5. Inhalation of irritants (smoke, chemicals, etc.)
6. Upper respiratory infections involving the throat, larynx, etc.

Causes of Cough Outside the Respiratory System Not all causes of cough are due to conditions of the respiratory system. For instance, cough is also a feature of the following:

1. **Heart failure:** In this situation, fluid leaks into the alveoli and this can trigger a cough and the production of pink frothy sputum. Heart failure is discussed in Chapter 33.
2. **Gastro-oesophageal reflux:** In this situation, acid that is normally produced in the stomach may be regurgitated into the oesophagus due to a weak sphincter at the junction of the oesophagus and the stomach. This acid can reach as far as the throat or the larynx and can cause cough because of the irritation. Gastric acid secretion is discussed in Chapter 19.

Phases of the Cough Reflex

The cough reflex goes through three distinct phases:

1. **Inspiratory phase:** During this phase, the person takes a deep breath (typically greater than 2 L; remember normal tidal volume is 500 mL).
2. **Compressive phase:** The expiratory muscles contract against a closed glottis (the vocal cords are closed) resulting in a build of pressure inside the lungs.
3. **Expulsive (expiratory) phase:** The glottis opens and the air is expelled with a sound at a high velocity.

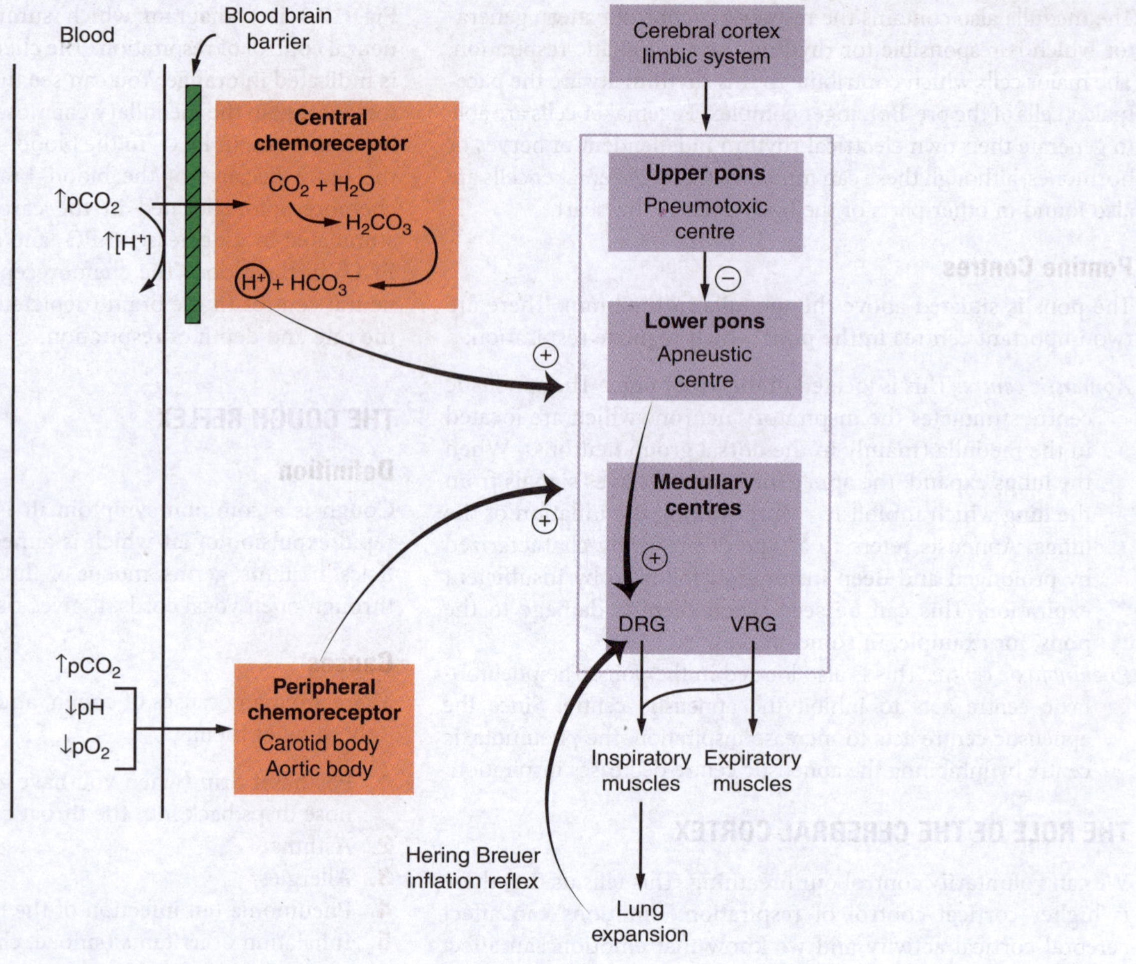

FIG. 12.3 Regulation of respiration – chemical and nervous interactions.

APPLICATIONS FOR NURSING

In patients who are acutely ill and in intensive care, the nurse will be required to monitor respiration and identify respiratory distress. Adults with respiratory distress will be breathing rapidly, their lips may turn blue and they may be disoriented. Patients will often have a pulse oximeter placed on a finger. This device measures the extent to which haemoglobin is saturated with oxygen as a percentage. In patients with a lot of secretions in the lungs, the nurse may be required to help with chest physiotherapy so that the patient can easily cough out the secretions.

SUMMARY

- There are two types of regulation of respiration: chemical and neural.
- Chemoregulation of respiration involves peripheral chemoreceptors (carotid and aortic bodies) and central chemoreceptors (in the medulla).
- Peripheral chemoreceptors respond to a decrease in pH and PO_2 and an increase in PCO_2. Central chemoreceptors respond to an increase in arterial PCO_2.
- The neural centres involved in the regulation of respiration include the dorsal and ventral respiratory groups in the medulla and the apneustic and pneumotaxic centres in the pons. Voluntary control of breathing also indicates control by the cortex.
- The dorsal respiratory group in the medulla consists mainly of inspiratory neurons. The apneustic centre stimulates inspiration. The pneumotaxic centre inhibits the apneustic centre.
- The cough reflex is a protective reflex triggered by microbes, irritants, fluid and foreign particles in the airways or in the lungs. Cough may have pulmonary but also cardiac causes. There are three phases of cough: inspiratory, compressive and expulsive.

CHAPTER REVIEW QUESTIONS

1. Where are the chemoreceptors for regulation of respiration located? What stimuli do they respond to?
2. What is the role of the (a) pontine and (b) medullary respiratory neural centres?
3. What is cough? What are the phases of cough?

CHAPTER 13

Hypoxia, Cyanosis, Dyspnoea and Periodic Breathing

SPECIFIC LEARNING OBJECTIVES

At the end of this chapter, the student should be able to:

- List the causes of different types of hypoxia.
- Differentiate between the different types of hypoxia.
- Distinguish between central and peripheral cyanosis.
- Describe the different types of dyspnoea.
- Describe the different types of periodic breathing.

GLOSSARY OF TERMS

- **Hypoxia:** a reduction in oxygen at the tissue level
- **Cyanosis:** a bluish discolouration of the skin and mucous membranes due to an elevation in deoxyhaemoglobin
- **Dyspnoea:** a subjective feeling of difficulty of breathing
- **Periodic breathing:** abnormal pattern of breathing in which normal or increased depth of breathing alternates with periods of reduced breathing or apnoea

HYPOXIA

Hypoxia is defined as a reduction in oxygen supply at the level of the tissues.

This can happen because of problems at various levels. For example, if breathing is shallow or respiratory function is depressed, inadequate oxygen may be transferred to the blood. Even if adequate oxygen is transferred to the blood, this oxygen must be carried effectively to the tissues. Finally, even if oxygen is carried to the tissues, the cells need to be able to utilize this oxygen appropriately. Problems can occur at all these levels and can result in different types of hypoxia.

Types of Hypoxia

1. **Hypoxic hypoxia:** This form of hypoxia occurs if the air that is breathed in is deficient in oxygen or if the respiratory system is depressed. If breathing is shallow, inadequate transfer of oxygen can occur even in the presence of adequate oxygen in the air.
   Causes:
   a. High altitude, because the barometric pressure falls, there is a reduction in oxygen content.
   b. Lung diseases in which lung function is reduced as, for example, in severe pneumonia and pulmonary oedema.
2. **Anaemic hypoxia:** This form of hypoxia occurs when the oxygen that is transferred in the lungs cannot be transported adequately in the blood because of anaemia. Anaemia is a condition where there is reduced oxygen-carrying capacity of the blood and is associated with low haemoglobin levels or abnormal haemoglobins. Since most of the oxygen is carried by haemoglobin, a low haemoglobin level results in reduced transport of oxygen.
   Causes:
   Seen in all forms of severe anaemia.
3. **Stagnant hypoxia:** It occurs when there is inadequate blood flow to the tissues. Thus, even if the lungs are functioning adequately and if the blood is carrying oxygen well, the reduction in blood flow means that the tissues get a reduced supply of oxygen.
   Causes:
   In conditions which affect the circulatory system such as severe heart failure or shock.
4. **Histotoxic (cytotoxic) hypoxia:** It occurs when the tissues are poisoned and cannot utilize the oxygen that is supplied to them.
   Causes:
   For example, cyanide poisoning and alcohol intoxication.

Fig. 13.1 diagrammatically represents the different types of hypoxia.

DIFFERENCES BETWEEN THE TYPES OF HYPOXIA

Table 13.1 summarizes the differences between the types of hypoxia based on the description provided in the earlier section of this chapter. In hypoxic hypoxia, arterial PO_2 is low. This is due to low dissolved oxygen content in the blood because enough oxygen is not transferred from the lungs to the blood.

It is important to recognize that all forms of hypoxia do not respond to oxygen therapy. For instance, histotoxic hypoxia cannot respond to oxygen therapy because the tissues which are poisoned are unable to use the oxygen that is present. However, hypoxic hypoxia responds best to oxygen therapy since increased oxygen concentration in the alveoli will allow more oxygen to diffuse into the blood.

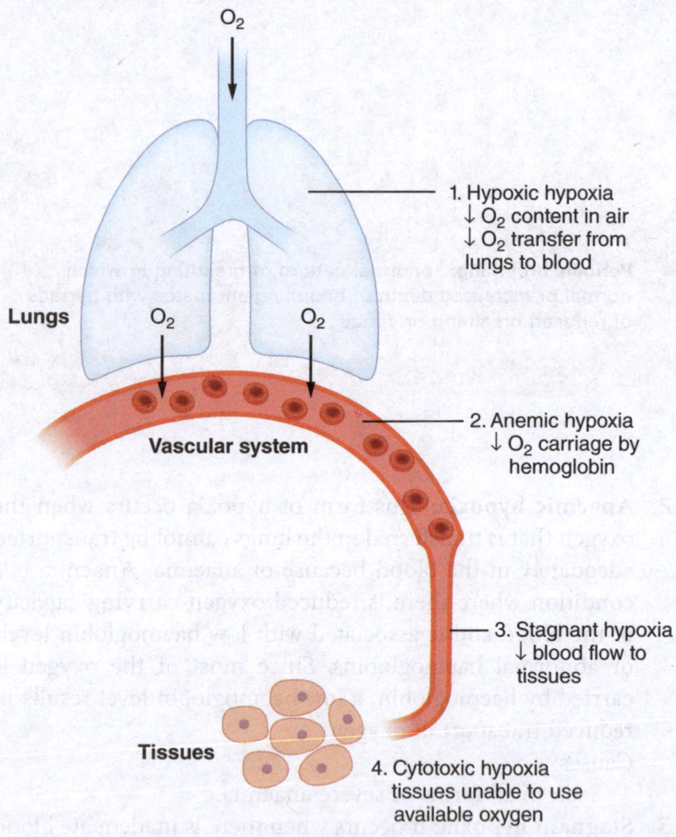

FIG. 13.1 Different types of hypoxia.

CYANOSIS

Cyanosis is a bluish colouration of the skin and mucous membranes because of low oxygen saturation. It is typically seen when deoxyhaemoglobin concentration is in excess of 5 g/dL. Since a minimum of 5 g/dL of deoxyhaemoglobin needs to be present for cyanosis to be seen, cyanosis cannot be seen in severe anaemia if the total haemoglobin concentration is <5 g/dL. There are two kinds of cyanosis:

1. **Peripheral cyanosis:** It is typically seen in the fingertips and the extremities. This is because the blood that reaches these areas is poor in oxygen content. It is seen in people who have peripheral vascular disease in which the peripheral arteries are involved. In these people, the peripheral arteries may be chronically constricted resulting in a reduced blood supply to the extremities. Some people also experience this on exposure to even mild or moderate cold.
2. **Central cyanosis:** It occurs in a variety of cardiac and respiratory disorders in adults and children. In adults, central cyanosis may be seen when blood is inadequately oxygenated in the lungs. This can occur in extensive lung disease in which ventilation is reduced and in situations in which the oxygen is unable to diffuse effectively into the blood. In newborn babies, this may be seen if there is a right-to-left shunt in the heart. In this situation, of which Fallot's tetralogy is an example, there is a 'hole' in the heart between the right and the left ventricle. As a result, blood flows directly from the right ventricle into the left ventricle without going to the lungs to be oxygenated. Thus, arterial blood is deoxygenated and the lips and tongue appear bluish in colour.

DYSPNOEA

Dyspnoea is defined as a subjective feeling of difficulty of breathing. The person may experience shortness of breath or laboured breathing. It is important to recognize that dyspnoea is not just due to primary problems in the lung but may also be seen in clinical conditions involving the heart.

Table 13.1 A Comparison of the Different Types of Hypoxia

	Hypoxic Hypoxia	Anaemic Hypoxia	Stagnant Hypoxia	Histotoxic Hypoxia
Atmospheric oxygen content	Low or normal	Normal	Normal	Normal
Arterial PO_2	Low	Normal	Normal	Normal
Percentage saturation of haemoglobin with O_2	Low or normal	Low or normal	Normal	Normal
Tissue PO_2	Low	Low	Low	Normal
Response to oxygen therapy	+++	+	No response	No response

Causes of Dyspnoea

Some pulmonary conditions:

- Pulmonary oedema
- Pneumonia
- Asthma
- Interstitial lung disease (this refers to a group of diseases in which the lungs are fibrosed [scarred]; this may be due to exposure to harmful compounds such as asbestos [resulting in asbestosis], or certain autoimmune disorders [see Chapter 39])

Some cardiac causes:

- Myocardial infarction (heart attack)
- Heart failure (see Chapter 33)

Severity of Dyspnoea

The severity of dyspnoea can be assessed based on whether patients are dyspnoeic at rest or during exercise. If their symptoms are related to exercise, it is important to know whether the problems occur during mild, moderate or severe exercise.

Types of Dyspnoea

Exertional dyspnoea: It occurs when there is increased activity or physical exertion. Among the many conditions that are associated with exertional dyspnoea are asthma and chronic obstructive pulmonary disease (COPD; which can occur with chronic asthma or smoking).

Orthopnoea: It is dyspnoea which occurs at rest in the recumbent (lying-down) position. This can be seen in heart failure, pulmonary oedema, heart attacks, etc.

Paroxysmal nocturnal dyspnoea: It typically occurs 1–2 hours after the person goes to sleep (nocturnal = night) and is relieved when the person sits upright. This is typically seen in congestive heart failure.

ABNORMAL BREATHING PATTERNS

There are some situations when the breathing pattern becomes irregular and the breathing is characterized by pauses, or when the person stops breathing or has very shallow breathing. This is called periodic breathing.

Cheyne–Stokes breathing: It is characterized by slowly waxing (increasing depth) and waning (decreasing depth) respiration. This type of breathing is seen in various clinical conditions including severe heart failure and brain damage and is illustrated in Fig. 13.2.

Biot's breathing: It is another form of periodic breathing in which periods of breathing are interspersed with periods of apnoea (Fig. 13.3) and can be seen in some situations of brain damage.

Another abnormal type of breathing is called Kussmaul's breathing (Fig. 13.4). This is seen when the pH of arterial blood reduces in acidosis. One example of acidosis is diabetic ketoacidosis, which occurs in uncontrolled type II diabetes mellitus. Because

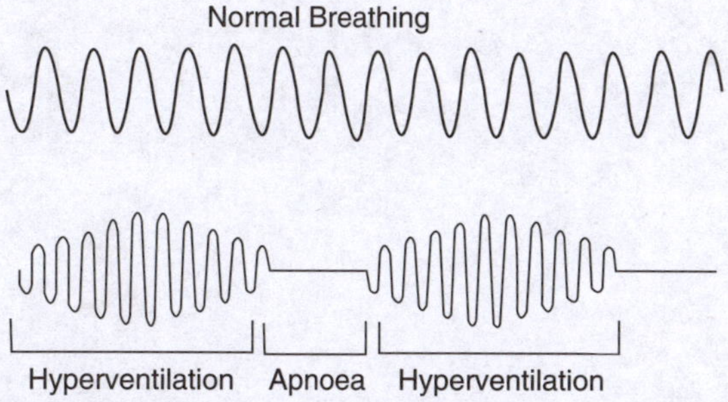

FIG. 13.2 Cheyne–Stokes breathing.

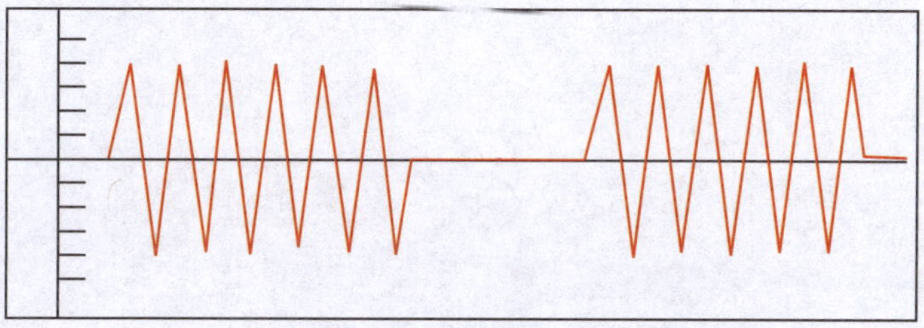

FIG. 13.3 Biot's breathing.

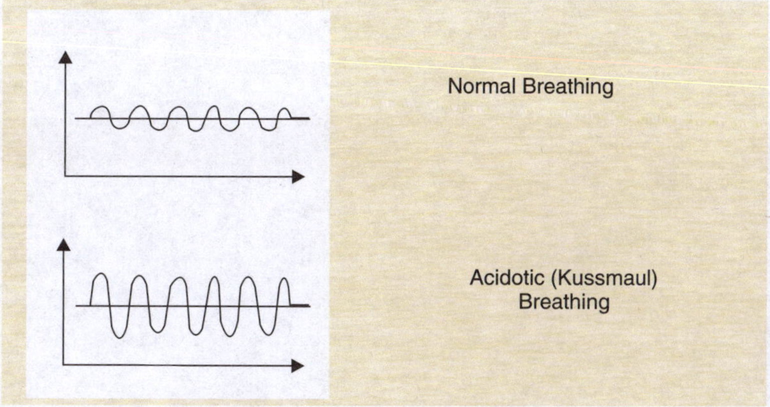

FIG. 13.4 Acidotic (Kussmaul) breathing.

of the increased acidity of the blood (reduced pH), the peripheral chemoreceptors are stimulated and breathing becomes deep and laboured; the patient appears to be gasping.

SUMMARY

- Hypoxia is a lack of oxygen at the level of the tissues. There are four types: hypoxic, anaemic, stagnant and histotoxic. Hypoxic hypoxia is most responsive to oxygen therapy.
- Cyanosis is a bluish discolouration of the skin and mucous membranes because of an increased concentration of deoxyhaemoglobin. The two types of cyanosis are central and peripheral.
- Dyspnoea is an uncomfortable awareness of one's own breathing. It can occur at rest or with exertion. Dyspnoea can occur due to pulmonary and cardiovascular causes.
- There are several types of abnormal breathing patterns. Cheyne–Stokes breathing and Biot's breathing are examples of periodic breathing.
- Kussmaul's breathing pattern is seen in acidosis, most commonly diabetic ketoacidosis. Here, breathing is deep and laboured.

CHAPTER REVIEW QUESTIONS

1. What is hypoxia? What are the causes of the different types of hypoxia?
2. Distinguish between the different types of hypoxia? Why types of hypoxia respond to oxygen therapy?
3. What is cyanosis? What are the types of cyanosis?
4. What is dyspnoea? What are its causes?

CHAPTER 14

Pulmonary Function Tests

SPECIFIC LEARNING OBJECTIVES

At the end of this chapter, the student should be able to:

- Draw a normal spirogram and label the various volumes and capacities.
- Describe the timed vital capacity with the help of a diagram.
- Describe the use of peak expiratory flow rate.
- Differentiate between restrictive and obstructive lung diseases.
- Describe the use of spirometry in clinical practice and list the criteria for an acceptable test.

GLOSSARY OF TERMS

- **FEV_1:** the amount of air forcefully expired in 1 second after a maximal inspiration
- **FVC:** the amount of air that can be completely expired after a maximal inspiration
- **PEFR:** the maximal expiratory flow that is achieved when expiring maximally and as rapidly as possible following a maximal inspiration

SPIROGRAM

The volumes that are breathed in and out during quiet, forced and maximal respiration can be recorded on a spirogram. The instrument used is a spirometer. A patient has to breathe in and out through a mouthpiece while the nose is clamped. The volumes of air inspired and expired are detected using transducers (sensors) and a recording is obtained on paper or as a soft copy on a computer. In some spirometers, the spirogram itself is not visible but the various volumes are displayed digitally on a small screen. Fig. 14.1 shows a patient performing spirometry.

Fig. 14.2 is a graphical representation of a typical spirogram.

The first three breathing cycles in Fig. 14.2 show quiet breathing. The volume that is breathed in and out during quiet respiration is called the *tidal volume (TV)*. TV is about 500 mL in an adult male.

After the first three quiet breaths in Fig. 14.2, the individual takes a maximum inspiration; the volume of air that a person can inspire over and above TV is called the *inspiratory reserve volume (IRV)*. IRV is about 3000 mL in an adult male.

After a single quiet breath, the person then expires maximally. The volume that a person can expire after a normal expiration is called the *expiratory reserve volume* (ERV; 1100 mL). Note from Fig. 14.2 that even after a maximal expiration, some air remains in the lungs. The volume of air that remains in the lungs after a maximal expiration is called the *residual volume (RV)*. This is about 1200 mL in an adult male. RV cannot be measured by a spirometer.

In addition to the volumes described above, the combination of two or more volumes gives a 'capacity'.

Vital capacity is the total volume expired from the lungs following a maximal inspiration and a maximal expiration. Thus, vital capacity is equal to IRV + TV + ERV = 3000 + 500 + 1100 = 4600 mL.

Functional residual capacity is equal to ERV + RV, that is 1100 + 1200 = 2300 mL.

Inspiratory capacity is equal to IRV + TV, that is 3000 + 500 = 3500 mL.

Total lung capacity = Vital capacity + RV = 4600 + 1200 = 5800 mL.

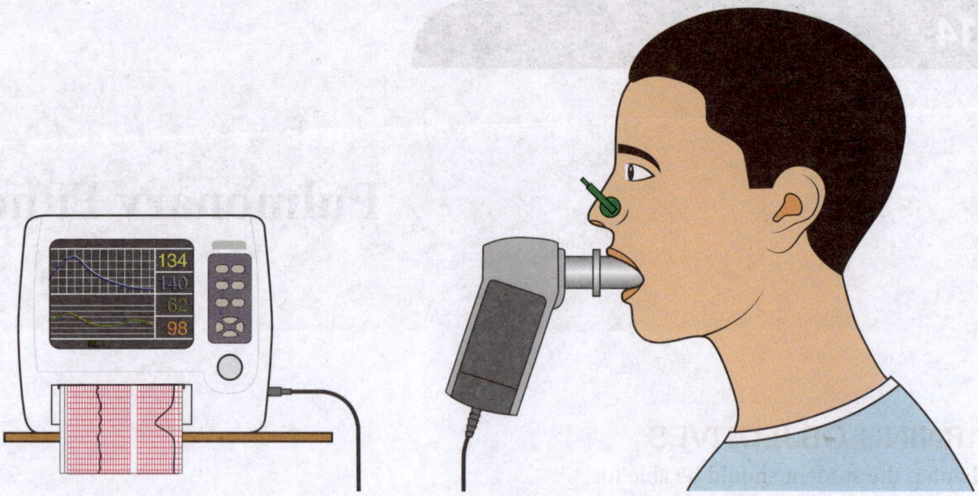

FIG. 14.1 Patient undergoing spirometry.

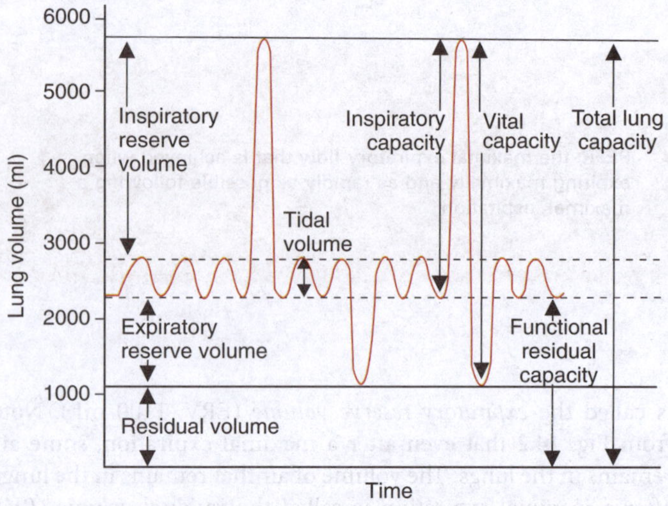

FIG. 14.2 A typical spirogram.

The values given above are an average for a healthy adult male. However, these values can vary depending on the following:

1. Body size: Smaller individuals have smaller volumes.
2. Gender: Females have smaller volumes.
3. Age: Smaller volumes in old age.
4. Fitness: Higher volumes in trained athletes.
5. Posture: Higher volumes while standing or sitting than while lying down.
6. The presence of illness.

TIMED VITAL CAPACITY

In order to measure vital capacity, an individual is asked to breathe in maximally and then breathe out as rapidly, as forcefully and as completely as possible while exhaling for at least 6 seconds. This is sometimes called forced vital capacity (FVC). During such a manoeuvre, automated spirometers allow us to calculate the volume of air that is expired after 1, 2 and 3 seconds of forced expiration.

At the end of 1 second of forced expiration, the volume of air expired (forced expiratory volume in 1 second; FEV_1) is approximately 80% of the vital capacity, that is $FEV_1/FVC \times 100 = 80\%$. In 2 seconds, about 95% of the air is expired and in 3 seconds, 97%.

FEV_1/FVC helps us to distinguish between different types of lung diseases. There are a group of respiratory diseases called *obstructive lung diseases*, in which the person is unable to exhale (expire) comfortably because of the narrowing of the airways. These individuals complain of being 'short of breath'. Examples of obstructive lung disease include bronchial asthma and chronic obstructive pulmonary disease (COPD) which is often seen with chronic smokers. In contrast, there are some respiratory diseases called *restrictive lung diseases*, in which the person is unable to inhale fully, that is fill his or her lungs fully with air. Examples of these diseases include people with chest wall abnormalities like kyphosis (severe 'hunchback') or scoliosis (lateral curvature of the spine), in which the skeletal abnormality does not allow the lungs to expand fully. Other examples are severe obesity and muscular disorders involving the respiratory muscles.

In obstructive lung disease, the person is unable to expire adequately; therefore, FEV_1/FVC decreases to less than 80%. If the person is treated with a bronchodilator (which widens the airways), FEV_1/FVC can increase to more than 80% in acute obstructive lung disease.

In contrast, people with restrictive lung disease cannot inhale adequately and in these individuals, FVC itself is reduced. This is not hard to understand, given that the inspiratory capacity accounts for the bulk of the vital capacity, that is 3500/4600 = 76%. In patients with restrictive lung disease, FEV_1 may be

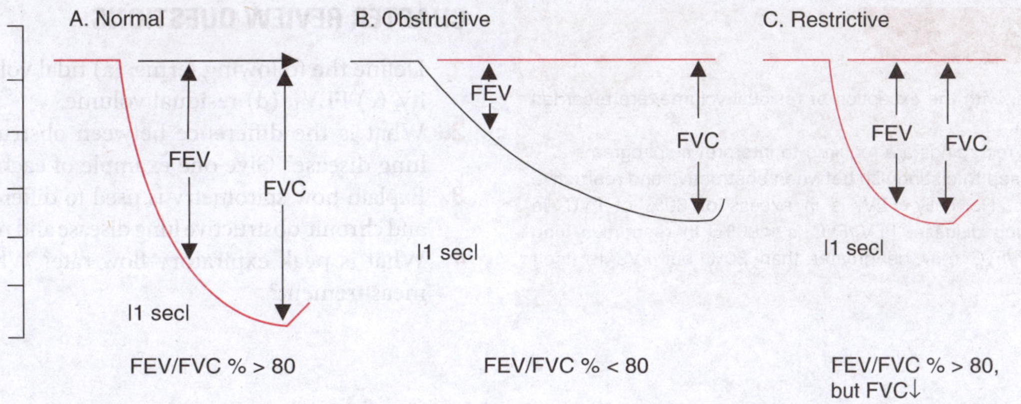

FIG. 14.3 Lung function findings in obstructive and restrictive lung diseases.

Table 14.1 Comparison of Spirometry Results in Acute and Chronic Obstructive Lung Disease and Restrictive Lung Disease

	Acute Obstructive Lung Disease	Chronic Obstructive Lung Disease	Restrictive Lung Disease
Example	Acute bronchial asthma	Chronic bronchitis	Lung fibrosis, chest wall abnormalities
FVC	Normal	Decreased	Decreased
FEV_1	Decreased	Decreased	Decreased
FEV_1/FVC (%)	<80	<80	≥80
PEFR	Decreased	Decreased	Decreased

lower because of the decrease in FVC but FEV_1/FVC as a percentage is normal. These concepts are illustrated in Fig. 14.3 and summarized in Table 14.1.

PEAK EXPIRATORY FLOW RATE

This is the maximal flow rate that is generated during a forceful expiration. This can be measured using computerized spirometers or with small hand-held devices. The normal peak expiratory flow rate (PEFR) is dependent on gender, the age of the person and the height (size) of the person.

Prediction equations allow people to compare their values with what is predicted. An average healthy adult male in his early 20s would have PEFR values greater than 600 L/minute, while a corresponding female would have values in excess of 400 L/minute.

The most common use of this device is in the home monitoring of asthma, as it can be used to check response to treatment and to predict worsening of asthma and as a guide to changing treatment. If a person is monitoring his or her PEFR on a regular basis, values greater than 80% of usual, healthy values would be considered normal. Values between 50% and 80% indicate bronchial constriction and medication will need to be started or increased. Values less than 50% are usually associated with severe bronchial constriction requiring a hospital visit.

APPLICATION IN NURSING: SPIROMETRY IN A CLINICAL SETTING

Spirometry as described earlier is performed routinely in hospitals. The reasons for conducting spirometry include the following, among other reasons:

- To help in diagnosis (distinguish obstructive from restrictive lung disease)
- To monitor a patient's response to treatment
- To assess risk before surgery

To obtain a spirogram that can be interpreted correctly, the patient needs to perform the test adequately. Since patients in hospitals are often ill, the recorded volumes may be lower than for healthy people. But low values can also be obtained if the patient does not perform the test adequately.

A nurse assigned to the lung function laboratory will need to do the following:

- Ensure that (1) the spirometer is in working order, ancillary equipment like computers are put on and made ready for measurement and (2) sterilized or disposable mouthpieces are available on and made ready for the measurement.
- Explain to the patient the procedures – demonstrating if necessary. The patient is typically asked to take a maximal breath (inspiration) and then blow out as rapidly and as hard as possible and to sustain this until asked to stop.
- Conduct the measurements – doing repeats as is required. Repetitions are required to ensure that the patients achieve their maximal levels since it takes time to get used to the mouthpiece and nose clip and follow the instructions. As a result, the first measurement may not be the best effort of the patient. A minimum of three measurements is recommended for adults.
- Determine whether the measurements have been done adequately and can be accepted.

SUMMARY

- Lung volumes, with the exception of residual volume, are recorded in a spirogram.
- At least three recordings are required to interpret a spirogram.
- FEV_1/FVC is used to distinguish between obstructive and restrictive lung diseases. Normally, FEV_1 is in excess of 80% of FVC. In obstructive lung disease, FEV_1/FVC is <80%. In restrictive lung disease, FEV_1/FVC may be greater than 80% but FVC is itself decreased.

CHAPTER REVIEW QUESTIONS

1. Define the following terms: (a) tidal volume, (b) vital capacity, (c) FEV_1, (d) residual volume.
2. What is the difference between obstructive and restrictive lung disease? Give one example of each.
3. Explain how spirometry is used to differentiate between acute and chronic obstructive lung disease and restrictive lung disease.
4. What is peak expiratory flow rate? What is the use of this measurement?

CHAPTER 15

Respiratory Changes During Exercise

SPECIFIC LEARNING OBJECTIVES

At the end of this chapter, the student should be able to:

- Describe the pulmonary responses to acute exercise.
- Explain the regulation of respiration during acute exercise.
- Describe the effect of chronic exercise on lung function.
- Describe the pulmonary changes with exercise in:
  - High altitude
  - Cold environment
  - Hot environment

GLOSSARY OF TERMS

- **Physical activity:** any bodily movement produced by the contraction of skeletal muscle that increases energy expenditure above a basal level
- **Exercise:** structured physical activity aimed at achieving some end point, for example, increased fitness
- **Oxygen debt:** the extra oxygen consumed following strenuous activity to break down accumulated lactic acid and replenish energy stores
- **VO_2 max:** the maximum amount of oxygen that the body can use during intense exercise – typically determined by increasing the intensity of exercise until this is achieved
- **Tachypnoea:** rapid breathing
- **Hyperpnoea:** abnormal rapid or deep breathing

When a person exercises, the muscles, the lungs and the heart work harder. The muscles consume more oxygen and release more carbon dioxide during exercise.

Respiration during exercise has many functions:

1. Adequate oxygen is supplied to the exercising muscles.
2. Increased carbon dioxide that is produced during exercise is eliminated.
3. During intense exercise, there is an increase in acid production from muscle, in the form of lactic acid. This lactic acid enters the bloodstream and needs to be buffered.

CHANGES IN RESPIRATION DURING ACUTE EXERCISE

In Chapter 9, we discussed the mechanics of ventilation during normal breathing. During acute exercise, ventilation increases. Ventilation is the amount of air that we breathe. Thus, the increase in ventilation during exercise can happen in two ways – the respiratory rate (the number of times we breathe in and out in 1 minute) can increase and the depth of breathing, that is the tidal volume (the amount of air breathed in one breath), can increase.

Table 15.1 shows the changes in respiration that occur during maximal whole-body exercise (e.g. running and cycling). These values are average. Actual values depend on a number of factors including age, gender, level of training and environmental factors. The table shows that the increase in ventilation that occurs with maximal acute exercise is duc to both an increase in the respiratory rate and in the tidal volume. However, the change in tidal volume appears to be greater than the change in respiratory rate. The increase in tidal volume is better than an increase in respiratory rate during exercise for two reasons:

1. A slower respiratory rate allows for a greater time for the exchange of gases in the lungs.
2. The energy used is less for an increase in tidal volume as compared to for an increase in respiratory rate.

Table 15.1 Respiratory Changes with Acute Maximal Exercise in an Untrained Person

	Respiratory Rate (Breaths/min)	Tidal Volume (L/min)	Total Ventilation (Respiratory Rate × Tidal Volume) (L/min)
Rest	12	0.5	6
Maximal exercise	40	2.5	100
Increase	3.3 times	5 times	16.6 times

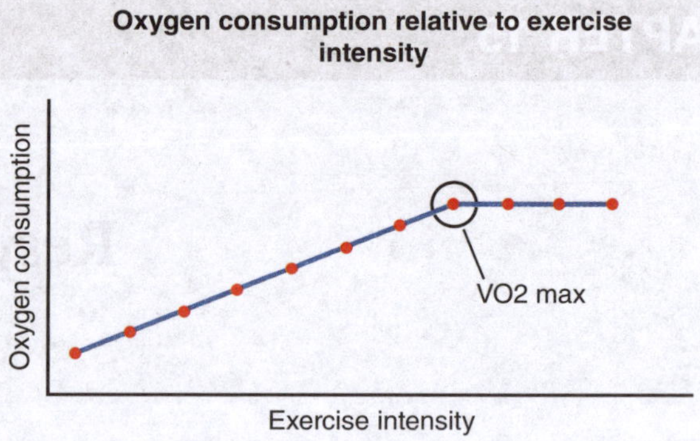

FIG. 15.1 Intensity of exercise and VO_2 max.

The increase in ventilation during exercise has all the major roles of respiration outlined earlier, that is greater oxygen uptake, greater carbon dioxide removal or washout and buffering for acid production during exercise.

MAXIMAL OXYGEN UPTAKE (VO_2 MAX)

The ventilatory response to exercise depends on the intensity of exercise. As the intensity of exercise increases, the ventilatory response and the oxygen uptake also increases. The increased oxygen uptake is required for exercising muscles to produce the energy required for contraction. Metabolism that uses oxygen to provide energy is called aerobic metabolism. At some point with increasing intensity of exercise, the body achieves its maximal oxygen uptake – this is referred to as VO_2 max (Fig. 15.1).

Thus, VO_2 max represents the maximum amount of oxygen that the body can consume per minute. Sometimes, the index is represented as mL/kg body weight to explain differences based on the size of the individual. VO_2 max reflects the aerobic capacity of the individual and is a measure of cardiorespiratory fitness. Thus, VO_2 max is increased with endurance training and is higher in athletes compared to untrained adults. VO_2 max is also dependent on gender with higher levels in males compared to in females for the same level of training. It is also dependent on the age of the individual – values decline slowly from the age of 30 years, but the rate of decline depends on how physically active the person is and whether they exercise or train.

OXYGEN DEBT

Sometimes if the intensity of exercise is high, the amount of oxygen that is consumed is unable to meet the needs of the exercising muscles. When this happens, the muscles need to produce energy without using oxygen. This is referred to as anaerobic metabolism. Anaerobic metabolism is less efficient than aerobic metabolism but is the only way muscles can produce energy if they are not receiving enough oxygen. A by-product of anaerobic metabolism is lactic acid. When lactic acid accumulates in the muscle, it causes a burning or painful sensation. In order to get rid of this lactic acid, the body needs lactic acid to combine with oxygen. However, since oxygen is already insufficient, this breakdown continues only after a person stops exercising when oxygen consumption levels continue to be high. Because oxygen consumption levels continue to be high even after the exercise has stopped, it is as though oxygen is repaying a debt and for this reason, this phenomenon is called 'oxygen debt' and is depicted in Fig. 15.2.

REGULATION OF RESPIRATION DURING EXERCISE

In Chapter 12, we discussed the nervous and chemical regulation of respiration. During an acute bout of exercise, regulation of respiration depends on the phases of exercise. As soon as a less than maximal (submaximal) exercise starts, there is an immediate rise in ventilation (Phase I). As exercise proceeds, ventilation continues to rise (Phase II) and achieves a near-steady state (Phase III) before declining when the exercise is stopped.

In Phase I, the immediate increase in ventilation is largely neurally mediated. This is, in part, due to what we call 'central command' in which the brain sends motor signals to the exercising muscle and respiratory muscles. Since this initial phase also depends on the number of muscles involved and the intensity of contraction, it is also believed that afferent impulses (sensory) from the joints, limbs and muscles send signals to the brain to increase respiration.

Regulation during Phases II and III is not easy to explain. While we might think that the increase in CO_2 and lactic acid production from exercising muscles might stimulate ventilation, the increased ventilation results in CO_2 washout so that the fluctuations in PCO_2 in arterial blood are extremely small.

LONG-TERM EFFECTS OF PHYSICAL ACTIVITY/EXERCISE/TRAINING ON THE RESPIRATORY SYSTEM

- Increased physical activity in growing children shows that it has positive benefits in terms of lung volumes and expiratory flow rates. This shows that it is important to promote physical activity in children.
- In adults who are lung-healthy, that is without any lung disease, higher levels of daily moderate to vigorous physical

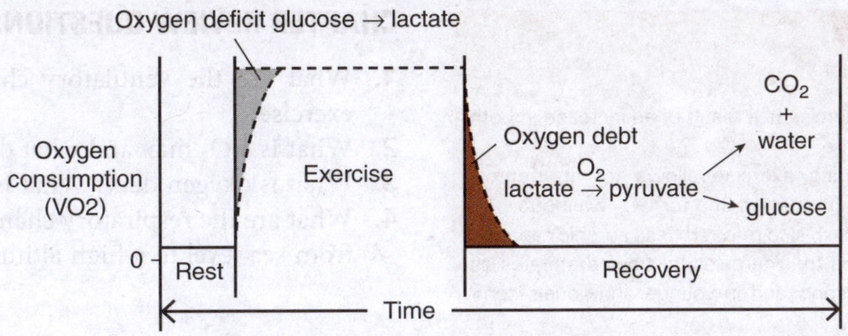

FIG. 15.2 Oxygen debt during high-intensity exercise.

activity are associated with better lung volumes and spirometric values; these include an increased vital capacity and a FEV_1/FVC ratio.

- Regular moderate to vigorous exercise/physical activity can increase the maximal oxygen uptake (VO_2 max; also called maximal aerobic capacity). This is important because a low VO_2 max predicts a higher risk of death from all causes and specifically, from heart disease.

PULMONARY FUNCTION DURING EXERCISE IN DIFFERENT ENVIRONMENTAL CONDITIONS

In this section, we address the pulmonary response to exercise in three environmental conditions, that is high altitude, cold and hot conditions.

High Altitude

When a person who normally lives at a low altitude, for example, sea level, moves to a higher altitude (say around 10,000 feet above sea level), several changes occur to allow the person to function at this higher altitude:

- The person begins to hyperventilate – this increase in the rate and depth of ventilation allows a person to acquire enough oxygen in spite of the lower barometric pressure which reduces the total amount of oxygen available in the air.
- The red blood cell count begins to rise – this is a result of the stimulation of erythropoiesis by hypoxia through the release of hormone from the kidney, called erythropoietin.
- The oxygen–haemoglobin dissociation curve shifts to the right – this allows the oxygen contained in the RBCs bound to haemoglobin to dissociate more easily and be available in the tissues.

Despite all these changes, ascent to high altitudes may be associated with a reduced endurance until acclimatization occurs. This is because maximal oxygen uptake reduces by about 10% for every 3000 feet ascent above an altitude of about 5000 feet above sea level. It is important that individuals do not ascend to high altitudes above 10,000–12,000 feet rapidly as this can sometimes be associated with acute mountain sickness which can sometimes be fatal. Endurance athletes sometimes train under supervision at higher altitudes. This is because when they return to sea level, the changes that occur at high altitude are sustained for some time and this improves their performance. However, over time after returning to sea level, the benefits of training at high altitude slowly decrease.

Cold Environment

Exercising in a cold environment may be associated with air at a low humidity. Both these conditions can increase the chances of exercise-induced bronchoconstriction or asthma. In addition, because of the increased bulk of clothing worn in cold climates, the energy needed to perform a given intensity of exercise is higher – this increases the ventilation and the work of breathing.

Hot Environment

Exercising in conditions with a high environmental (ambient temperature) is associated with a reduction in maximal aerobic capacity which reduces endurance during sustained exercise. This is further affected by dehydration (due to the increased sweating) and reduced muscle function at high environmental temperatures.

APPLICATIONS IN NURSING

Nurses should be aware of the following issues related to exercise:

1. People who have been physically inactive should embark on an exercise training programme or increased physical activity that involves moderate- or high-intensity activity only after a full clinical evaluation. This clinical evaluation includes screening for cardiovascular, metabolic and kidney diseases. Also important is an understanding of the current levels of physical activity of the person and whether there are any symptoms developed during physical activity.
2. Some individuals may experience exercise-induced asthma. Between 5% and 20% of the population may experience this. While close to 80% of people with asthma experience bronchoconstriction (narrowing of the bronchial tree) during exercise, some people without asthma may also have this problem. Young children who have exercise-induced asthma have an increased risk of developing asthma as adults. Exercising in the cold and dry conditions at high intensities of exercise can precipitate exercise-induced asthma. Nurses need to be aware of the medications that are used to treat asthma. Since children and adults can improve their lung function with exercise and increased physical activity, it is important that these individuals are encouraged to be physically active. However, it is also important that they are made aware of the need to take their medications regularly, have regular follow-ups and recognize the symptoms and signs of severe bronchoconstriction.

SUMMARY

- Increased ventilation during exercise is a result of an increase in both respiratory rate and tidal volume.
- The increased ventilation during exercise allows for an optimal delivery of oxygen to exercising muscles and for CO_2 washout.
- Maximal oxygen uptake (VO_2 max), also referred to as aerobic capacity, is higher in males as compared to in females, in trained athletes as compared to in sedentary persons, and in younger individuals compared to in older individuals.
- Oxygen debt is the continued oxygen utilization that occurs after an exercise has stopped. This oxygen is required to react with lactic acid which is the product of anaerobic metabolism in exercising skeletal muscle.
- Elevation to high altitudes is associated with hyperventilation, an increase in red blood cell count and a shift in the oxygen–haemoglobin dissociation curve to the right. These changes aim to ensure that oxygen is adequately transferred to the tissues.
- Exercising can trigger exercise-induced bronchoconstriction and the risk of this is increased if it is cold and the humidity is low.
- Exercising in hot environments is associated with decreased endurance and is also affected by dehydration.

CHAPTER REVIEW QUESTIONS

1. What are the ventilatory changes that are seen in heavy exercise?
2. What is VO_2 max and what does it represent?
3. What is oxygen debt? What is the mechanism?
4. What are the respiratory changes seen when a person moves from sea level to a high altitude (>10,000 feet)?

CHAPTER 16

Respiratory Changes Across the Life Cycle

SPECIFIC LEARNING OBJECTIVES

At the end of this chapter, the student should be able to:

- Describe the changes that occur in the foetal respiratory system in utero.
- Describe the changes that occur in the respiratory system during infancy.
- Describe the changes that occur in the respiratory system in ageing.

GLOSSARY OF TERMS

- **Surfactant:** a surface tension–reducing agent produced by the alveolar type II cells in the lung (surfactant reduces the work of breathing and ensures that alveoli are kept dry and open)
- **Dendritic cell:** an immune cell found in tissues that is capable of phagocytosis and also helps in presenting antigens to other immune cells
- **Senescence:** a state in which cells age and are unable to divide
- **Natural killer cells:** a lymphocyte that binds to tumour cells and viruses and helps to destroy them

So far, we have described the physiology of the respiratory system in a young healthy adult. However, respiratory function changes across the entire life cycle. In India, approximately 24 million babies are born in a single year. Respiratory infections are a major cause of death in infants and children who are under 5 years of age. The Government of India 'National Policy on Older Persons' (1999) defines 'senior citizen' or 'elderly' as a person who is of age 60 years or more. The number of people older than 60 years in India is expected to rise from about 8% to 20% of the whole population by 2050. The elderly are more prone to respiratory infections and this can contribute significantly to mortality.

In this chapter, we will review respiratory function at the extremes of the life cycle.

CHANGES IN THE RESPIRATORY SYSTEM IN UTERO (FOETUS)

The development of the lung in utero occurs in two phases:

- Structural development during which the respiratory system develops anatomically.
- Functional development during which the foetal lungs acquire properties that allow them to function following the first breath after birth.

The anatomical development of the respiratory system in utero occurs in the following phases:

1. **Embryonic and pseudoglandular phase** extends from about 3 to 16 weeks of gestation. During this phase, the foregut is split into the oesophagus and the trachea with the lung buds. The lung buds continue to divide to form the bronchopulmonary segments and by the end of this phase, the terminal bronchioles have formed but not the respiratory bronchioles or the alveoli.
2. **Canalicular phase** extends from 16 weeks to about 26 weeks. During this phase, the respiratory bronchioles are formed and also the alveolar ducts. Type I pneumocytes also appear. These are the major cells that forms the alveoli.
3. **Terminal sac phase** extends from about 26 weeks to birth. During this phase, the primitive alveoli are formed. During this phase, the capillaries of the pulmonary circulation also become closely aligned with the alveoli. This is important because after birth, gas transfer occurs between the alveoli and the blood vessels.
4. **Alveolar phase** is from the eighth month of gestation onwards and is characterized by a maturation of the alveoli.

The development of the pulmonary circulation closely mirrors the anatomical development of the lungs.

The respiratory system also undergoes certain functional changes in utero. These include the following:

- The epithelial cells of the foetal airways secrete a chloride-rich fluid into the foetal respiratory system. Thus, the foetal lungs are filled with fluid. This fluid compresses the blood vessels that are in close proximity to the developing alveoli.
- Although the pulmonary circulation develops with the foetal respiratory system, blood flow through the respiratory system in the foetus is low for several reasons:
  - The fluid-filled respiratory tract compresses the blood vessels, increasing the resistance in them.
  - The pulmonary vessels show hypoxic vasoconstriction – since the foetal environment is relatively hypoxic, this results in increased pulmonary vascular resistance (remember that pulmonary vessels constrict during hypoxia unlike systemic blood vessels which vasodilate when there is hypoxia).
  - Blood which reaches the foetal right atrium is shunted into the left atrium via the foramen ovale. Thus, less blood goes into the right ventricle and into the pulmonary artery. Blood that does reach the pulmonary artery is directed into the aorta via the ductus arteriosus. These are shown in Fig. 16.1.
- Surfactant begins to be secreted by the type II alveolar cells by about 20 weeks of gestation. However, these amounts of surfactant are insufficient for the lungs to function adequately and most of the surfactant secretion occurs in the third trimester reaching a peak by about 35 weeks. Surfactant secretion is increased by cortisol and by thyroid hormones. Surfactant is important because it lowers the alveolar surface tension and this has been described in greater detail in Chapter 9.
- Foetal breathing movements start appearing at about 10 weeks of gestation. These are not important for gas transfer but serve two other important functions:
  - They are important for lung growth. Reduced foetal breathing movements have been associated with pulmonary hypoplasia, a condition in which there is inadequate development of the foetal lungs in utero.
  - They ensure that the respiratory muscles have enough strength to sustain breathing after birth.

CHANGES THAT OCCUR IN THE RESPIRATORY SYSTEM AT BIRTH

- As labour proceeds and the foetus is squeezed through the birth canal, much of the fluid that is contained within the foetal respiratory system is also squeezed out. This reduces the external pressure on the pulmonary blood vessels.
- When the baby takes the first cry, because of the huge inspiratory effort, the lungs fill with air.
- The filling of the lungs with air increases the oxygen availability as a result of which the pulmonary blood vessels are no longer hypoxic and they vasodilate. This increase in pulmonary blood flow also occurs due to the closure of the foramen ovale so that blood no longer flows from the right atrium to the left atrium but goes into the right ventricle and the pulmonary artery. The ductus arteriosus connecting the pulmonary artery and the aorta also closes. These

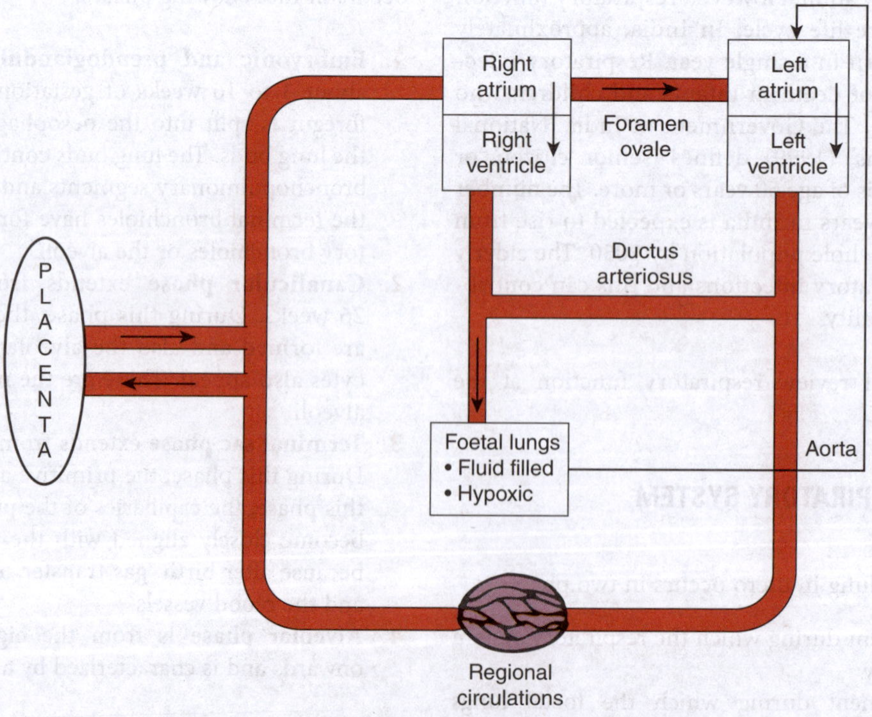

FIG. 16.1 The foetal pulmonary circulation.

changes allow gas exchange to occur in well-ventilated and well-perfused alveoli.

CHANGES IN THE RESPIRATORY SYSTEM WITH INFANCY

The newborn baby does not emerge with fully developed lungs. Many changes occur during the first year of life and beyond:

- Alveoli continue to develop and mature. It is believed that the adult number of alveoli is not reached until the age of about 8 years.
- Alongside the development and maturation of alveoli, the pulmonary microvasculature, that is, the capillaries that supply the alveoli, also develops to ensure adequate perfusion (blood flow) for the new alveoli.
- Although new airways do not develop after birth, the size of the existing airways increases as the child grows.

CHANGES IN THE RESPIRATORY SYSTEM WITH AGEING

Multiple changes occur in the respiratory system with ageing. Some of these are outlined as follows:

- There is a reduction in the lung volumes and capacities. One of the things that contributes to this is a reduction in the intervertebral disc space in the vertebral column. This results in a gradual kyphosis (a hunchback) which is more pronounced in women as compared to in men. Because of this, both forced expiratory volume in 1 second (FEV_1) and forced vital capacity are reduced with ageing (see Chapter 14 for a more detailed account of spirometry).
- Respiratory muscles also show a decline with ageing. The overall muscle decline with ageing is referred to as sarcopaenia. Not only the muscle mass but also the function is reduced. Thus, in the case of respiratory muscles, the maximal inspiratory and expiratory pressures are reduced with ageing. This reduction in muscle strength has two important results:
  - The ageing person may be unable to ventilate adequately in high-demand situations (i.e. when ventilation needs to be increased, e.g. heavy exercise).
  - The person may be unable to cough adequately and this may increase the risk of the person for respiratory infections.
- The ageing lung is characterized by 'inflammaging'. Normally a person generates inflammatory cytokines (molecules from immune cells) in response to an infection. In 'inflammaging', the ageing lung produces these cytokines even in the absence of an infection. This can result in the destruction of the lungs and loss of its normal elasticity.
- Ageing lungs are characterized by mucociliary dysfunction. Normally the ciliated columnar epithelium helps to get rid of particles that are breathed in. This occurs by the movement of the cilia of the epithelial lining of the airways. In ageing, there is reduced cilia beating and an inability to remove foreign particles that are breathed in. There is also a decreased mucus production by the bronchial epithelium.
- Aged people have reduced pulmonary immunity. Therefore older people develop infections more often. This is due to a number of factors other than those listed earlier. At a cellular level:
  - The alveolar macrophages, dendritic cells and neutrophils which are all important phagocytic cells show reduced function.
  - The natural killer cells also show decreased function and maturation and there are reduced antiviral responses.
  - The T lymphocyte numbers reduce. T lymphocytes are important for cell-mediated immunity.
  - The alveolar epithelial cells show increased senescence and apoptosis. As a result of this, surfactant production and composition are altered.

APPLICATION FOR NURSING

1. At birth, the nurse helps to suction and clear the airways of the child to allow for effective breathing. The nurse also assesses the child using the APGAR score at 1 and 5 minutes. The APGAR score requires an assessment of five parameters: A, appearance (skin colour); P, pulse; G, grimace (reflex irritability); A, activity (muscle tone); and R, respiration. Each of these parameters is graded with a score of 0, 1 or 2. With regard to respiration, the baby is graded 0 if it is apnoeic (i.e. not breathing), 1 if the breathing is slow and irregular, and 2 if it cried vigorously. The APGAR score is depicted in Fig. 16.2.
2. Nurses working in paediatric and neonatal units will need to recognize respiratory distress, that is, when the child is finding it difficult to breathe. This is addressed in Chapter 17.
3. Because of the difficulty that aged people have in coughing effectively and also because of poor mucus clearance, nurses may require to help such patients to cough with chest physiotherapy. Chest therapy has broader aims. By helping the patient to get rid of secretions in the chest, the work of breathing is improved, patients feel more comfortable and gas exchange in the lungs improves. In order to provide effective chest physiotherapy, the patient is rhythmically struck over the thorax with a cupped hand to allow the affected lung segment(s) to drain.

SUMMARY

- The development of the lungs in utero is of two types: anatomical and physiological. In utero, the alveoli develop and mature but the final numbers of alveoli are not achieved until 8 years of age. Surfactant production is an important part of the functional development of the lungs. The development of the pulmonary circulation closely mirrors the development of the foetal lung. Foetal breathing occurs from 10 weeks of gestation and is aimed at ensuring normal lung development and respiratory muscle strength.
- At birth, the fluid in the respiratory tract is squeezed out during labour. The first cry results in oxygenation of the lungs and the pulmonary circulation is opened. The foramen ovale and the ductus arteriosus close.
- During infancy, alveoli continue to develop and mature along with the pulmonary microvasculature and the airways widen.
- Ageing is associated with a reduction in lung volumes, respiratory muscle strength, mucociliary clearance and immune function. These changes make coughing and high-demand ventilation less effective and the individual becomes more prone to infections.

CHAPTER REVIEW QUESTIONS

1. What are the phases of the anatomic development of the lung in utero?
2. What are the physiological changes seen in the lung in utero?
3. Describe the changes that occur in the respiratory system at birth.
4. Describe the changes that occur in the respiratory system with ageing.

Apgar scoring system

	0 Points	1 Point	2 Points	Points totaled
Activity (muscle tone)	Absent	Arms and legs flexed	Active movement	
Pulse	Absent	Below 100 bpm	Over 100 bpm	
Grimace (reflex irritability)	Flaccid	Some flexion of extremities	Active motion (sneeze, cough pull away)	
Appearance (skin color)	Blue, pale	Body pink, extremities blue	Completely pink	
Respiration	Absent	Slow, irregular	Vigorous cry	

Severely depressed	0–3
Moderately depressed	4–6
Excellent condition	7–10

FIG. 16.2 The APGAR score to assess a newborn baby.

CHAPTER 17

Applications of Respiratory Physiology

SPECIFIC LEARNING OBJECTIVES

At the end of this chapter, the student should be able to:

- Describe the respiratory changes in high altitude in native highlanders and those who ascend to high altitudes.
- List the clinical features of respiratory distress in children and adults.
- Describe the modalities and principles of oxygen therapy.
- Describe the physiological principles of ventilatory support.
- List the aims and describe the process of nebulization.
- Describe the role of tracheostomy in clinical medicine.

GLOSSARY OF TERMS

- **Aspiration:** accidental inhalation of fluid or food into the trachea and lungs which may result in pneumonia
- **Mechanical ventilation:** process by which a person breathes with the help of an external device called a ventilator
- **Nebulization:** the conversion of a liquid medication into a fine spray which can then be inhaled directly into the lungs
- **Tracheostomy:** a surgical procedure which involves the insertion of a tube directly into the trachea and which is then used for spontaneous breathing or mechanical ventilation

In this chapter, we describe what happens to healthy adults who are native inhabitants at high altitudes and also to those who ascend rapidly to high altitude. We also describe the physiological basis of various clinical interventions including oxygen therapy, mechanical ventilation, nebulization and tracheostomy and the role of the nurse in evaluating respiratory distress.

PHYSIOLOGICAL CHANGES IN RESPIRATION TO HIGH ALTITUDE

When we ascend to high altitudes, several things happen:

1. The barometric pressure falls and the absolute oxygen content in the air reduces (Table 17.1).
2. The air becomes less humid (i.e. more dry).
3. The temperature falls.

Both the fall in temperature and the humidity with increasing altitude vary during the day (diurnal variation) and across seasons.

It is clear from Table 17.1 that in order to respond to the reducing oxygen content of air at higher altitudes, the body would need to transport oxygen from the lungs to the tissues more efficiently.

CHANGES IN NATIVE HIGHLANDERS

In different parts of the world, people live all their lives at high altitude. In Asia, this is seen in Tibetan highlanders who inhabit the Tibetan plateau. In Africa, natives live all their lives in the Ethiopian highlands, and in South America, natives inhabit the mountains of the Andes. These highland groups have lived for many generations and have inhabited the highlands for long periods of time (Fig. 17.1).

The responses of each of these groups to high altitudes are slightly different and are beyond the scope of this book. Here, we will describe some of the things that are seen in Tibetan highlanders:

- They have a bigger chest circumference and various lung volumes such as the vital capacity, total lung capacity and residual volume are all increased.
- They also have higher peak expiratory flow rates and higher FEV_1/FVC ratios compared with people who live at sea level.

Table 17.1 Changes in Barometric Pressure, Oxygen Content and Inspired Oxygen at Different Altitudes

Altitude (Feet)	Barometric Pressure (mm Hg)	Oxygen Content (mm Hg)	Inspired Oxygen (mm Hg)
0–sea level	760	159	149
3000	675	141	132
6000	600	125	117
10,000	535	110	102
20,000	365	78	65
29,000 (Mount Everest)	252	53	43

Values have been rounded off for simplicity.

- Hypoxia (insufficient oxygen) in the lungs normally causes the pulmonary blood vessels to constrict. This is the response that is seen when lowlanders ascend to high altitudes. However, in Tibetan highlanders, this response is reduced allowing blood to flow in the pulmonary circulation and this allows oxygen to be transported from the lungs into the bloodstream.
- Normally hypoxia causes an increase in the production of red blood cells (RBCs) and of haemoglobin. This increases the transport of oxygen to the tissues. However, an increase in the RBCs also increases the viscosity of blood and the heart has to pump harder to move the blood in the circulation. This can cause problems. Tibetans have lower haemoglobin and RBC increases with increasing altitude and this favours long-term survival and the absence of chronic mountain sickness.
- Once the oxygen reaches the tissues, it needs to be transferred effectively to the cells. Tibetans show higher capillary densities in muscle which allows for better oxygen transfer.
- Tibetans have other genetic traits which favour survival at high altitudes.

CHANGES ON ASCENT FROM SEA LEVEL TO HIGH ALTITUDES (ABOVE 10,000 FEET)

In contrast to what is seen in native highlanders, this section describes the changes which occur in people who do not normally live at high altitudes. People ascend to high altitude for a variety of reasons including trekking, tourism and defence (army personnel), among others.

Changes that are seen include the following:

- Hyperventilation: The increase in ventilation increases the transfer of oxygen from the lungs to the blood.
- Increased RBC production and increased haemoglobin: Since the major form of oxygen transport (~98%) is via attachment to haemoglobin (oxyhaemoglobin) in RBCs, the increased RBC count and haemoglobin content is an attempt to effectively transfer the oxygen to the tissues. This is under the influence of a hormone called erythropoietin which is released from the kidneys.
- Heart rate and cardiac output (the amount of blood pumped out of each ventricle per minute) is increased.

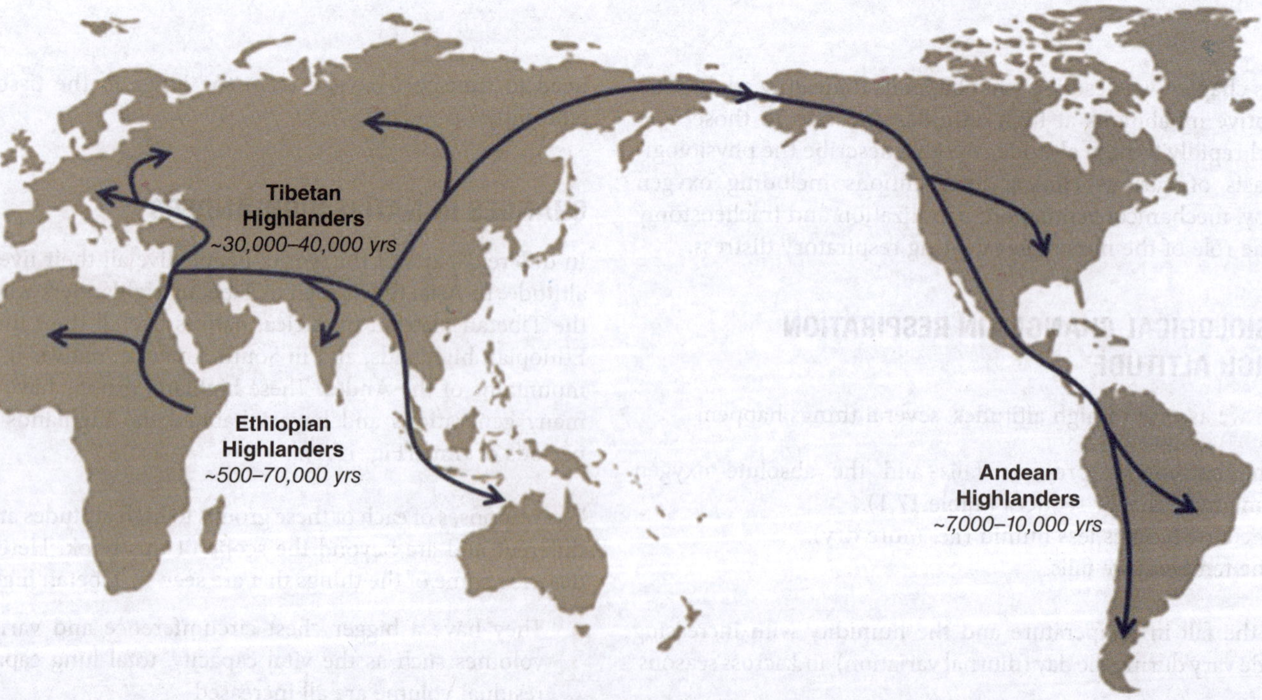

FIG. 17.1 The migration and residence of natives at high altitude. (From: Michael M. Tymko, Joshua C. Tremblay, Damian M. Bailey, Daniel J. Green, Philip N. Ainslie. The Journal of Physiology 2019;597:5759–5776; First Published: 02 November 2019.)

DISEASES SEEN WITH RAPID ASCENT TO HIGH ALTITUDE

This is seen typically when people ascend rapidly to elevations of 2500 m (a little more than 8000 feet) or more; most often above 10,000 feet.

Three different conditions are described:

- **Acute mountain sickness (AMS):** This occurs within 4–12 hours of arrival at a high altitude. Major symptoms include headache, loss of appetite or nausea, dizziness, tiredness and insomnia (inability to get sufficient sleep).
- **High-altitude cerebral oedema (HACE):** Here, there is altered consciousness which can rapidly progress to coma and even death if inadequately treated.
- **High-altitude pulmonary oedema (HAPE):** This may occur within 1–5 days of arrival at the high altitude. Initial symptoms may include an exertional dyspnoea (difficulty in breathing), cough and tightness in the chest. In later stages, the dyspnoea worsens and the patient may have cough with pink frothy sputum characteristic of pulmonary oedema.

CHRONIC MOUNTAIN SICKNESS

This problem affects people who live at high altitude above 2500 m for the greater part of their lives. It is estimated that between 5% and 10% of these people may suffer from chronic mountain sickness. In this situation, the affected individuals have pronounced erythrocytosis (increased RBCs); this results in increased viscosity of blood as a result of which the heart needs to pump harder. In the later stages, the heart shows hypertrophy (an increase in size) and the person goes into heart failure in which the heart is unable to pump blood effectively.

ACUTE RESPIRATORY DISTRESS

Acute respiratory distress defined as a sudden widespread inflammation of the lungs resulting in a build-up of fluid in the lungs is seen in both children and adults.

In children, it is most often associated with an infection of the lungs but may also be seen following inhalation injuries, aspiration and from other causes. As this is a condition which requires immediate attention, a nurse needs to be able to identify the features of acute respiratory distress. These include the following:

- Shortness of breath
- Cough
- Flared nostrils
- Rapid breathing
- Noisy breathing
- Retractions, that is the pulling in of the muscles between the ribs and around the collar bone

The nurse should check whether the lips show any bluish discolouration suggestive of cyanosis. Oxygenation of the blood can be rapidly checked using a pulse oximeter on the finger tip.

In adults, the patients have rapid and laboured breathing and cough, and may be mentally confused. The patient has a rapid pulse rate and blood pressure may be low. Fever may be present if there is an infection.

OXYGEN THERAPY

Oxygen is widely used in hospitals and also in the home care of certain patients. Among the conditions that it is used for are the following:

- Cardiac and respiratory arrest
- Hypoxia
- Hypotension (a low blood pressure may result in inadequate perfusion of blood to the tissues)
- Low cardiac output as in heart failure
- Respiratory distress

Oxygen can be delivered using various means including the following:

- **Nasal cannulae (prongs):** These are twin tubes which are inserted into the nostrils. This is a simple and safe way of delivering oxygen at low flow rates (up to 6 L/min) and allows the patient to eat and talk.
- **Face mask:** This covers the nose and mouth and comes in different designs to allow for low or high flow of air. It is particularly useful when there is nasal obstruction. Some patients may find it hot and claustrophobic (confining) and it interferes with eating and talking.
- **Endotracheal tube:** Here a flexible tube is placed through the mouth and between the vocal cords into the trachea. This tube can be connected to a mechanical ventilator. The introduction of the endotracheal tube requires skilled personnel and – since air is normally humidified in the nasopharynx and oropharynx and this is bypassed with an endotracheal tube – oxygen that is supplied needs to be humidified.
- **Via a tracheostomy:** This is described in a later section.

A nurse taking care of a patient who is receiving oxygen must:

- Ensure that the oxygen delivery system is properly placed (nose prongs, masks, etc.).
- Monitor the flow rate at which oxygen is delivered.
- Monitor the patient for clinical signs of improvement or worsening.

MECHANICAL VENTILATION

This is needed in different pulmonary and neuromuscular conditions, among others, when natural ventilation cannot be sustained at levels that are required. This occurs in many conditions associated with respiratory failure. It includes extensive infections of the lungs, brain trauma, neuromuscular disorders, which affect the functioning of the respiratory muscles, and cardiogenic or septic shock, among others.

The mechanical ventilator is a machine (Fig. 17.2) that ventilates the patient through the control of the following parameters:

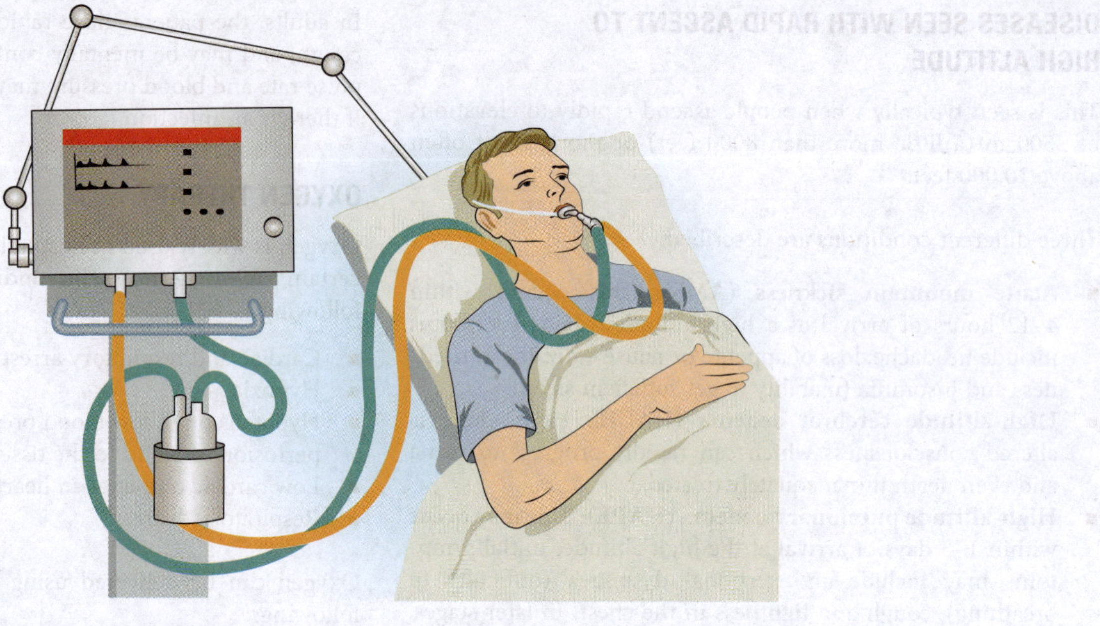

FIG. 17.2 Mechanical ventilation in a patient with endotracheal intubation.

- Volume of each breath
- Pressure of air delivery
- Flow rate of air delivered
- Timing of each breath – in effect the respiratory frequency

Noninvasive ventilation is a form of ventilation that does not use an artificial airway like an endotracheal tube or air delivery via a tracheostomy. Instead, air is delivered through a tight-fitting mask or with nasal prongs.

Once a patient has been placed on a mechanical ventilator and is recovering, the medical team 'weans' the patient off the ventilator, that is getting the patient back to spontaneous ventilation without any mechanical assistance. Successful weaning of the patient depends on a number of factors including recovery from the clinical condition, the overall state of the patient and the duration for which mechanical ventilation was used.

NEBULIZATION

This process uses a mechanical device called a nebulizer which converts a liquid medication into a mist which can then be inhaled through a mask and delivered directly to the lungs.

The most common use for nebulizers is to treat and prevent asthma. You may be aware that people with asthma often use a pocket-held device called an inhaler. However, this requires a coordination between the release of the medication from the inhaler and inhalation by the patient and often the full dose does not reach the lungs. For this reason, nebulization may be preferred in small children, the elderly and patients with severe asthma in whom coordination between inhalation and the drug release from the inhaler device becomes difficult.

Although the costs of nebulizers have come down, they may not be affordable by everyone. In such situations, it is possible to use another simpler and more cost-effective device called a 'spacer'. A 'spacer' has an opening which snugly fits an inhaler while at the other end is a mouthpiece with a valve. The 'spacer' typically has a volume of 500 mL or less, that is close to the tidal volume of a person. The inhaler is pressed and the drug is released into the inhaler which the patient then breathes in through the mouthpiece (Fig. 17.3).

A nurse needs to inform the patient on the following:

- How to correctly use the spacer
- How to clean the spacer appropriately

TRACHEOSTOMY

This is a surgical procedure in which an incision is made in the neck to allow for a tube called a tracheostomy tube to be inserted into the trachea. This is done below the vocal cords (Fig. 17.4).

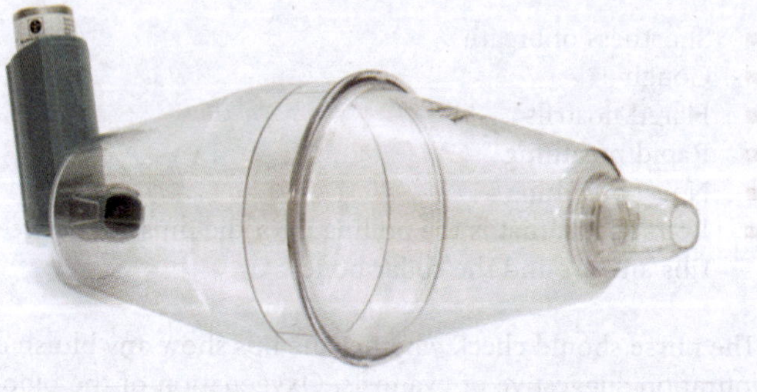

FIG. 17.3 Delivery of a drug as an aerosol using an inhaler and spacer.

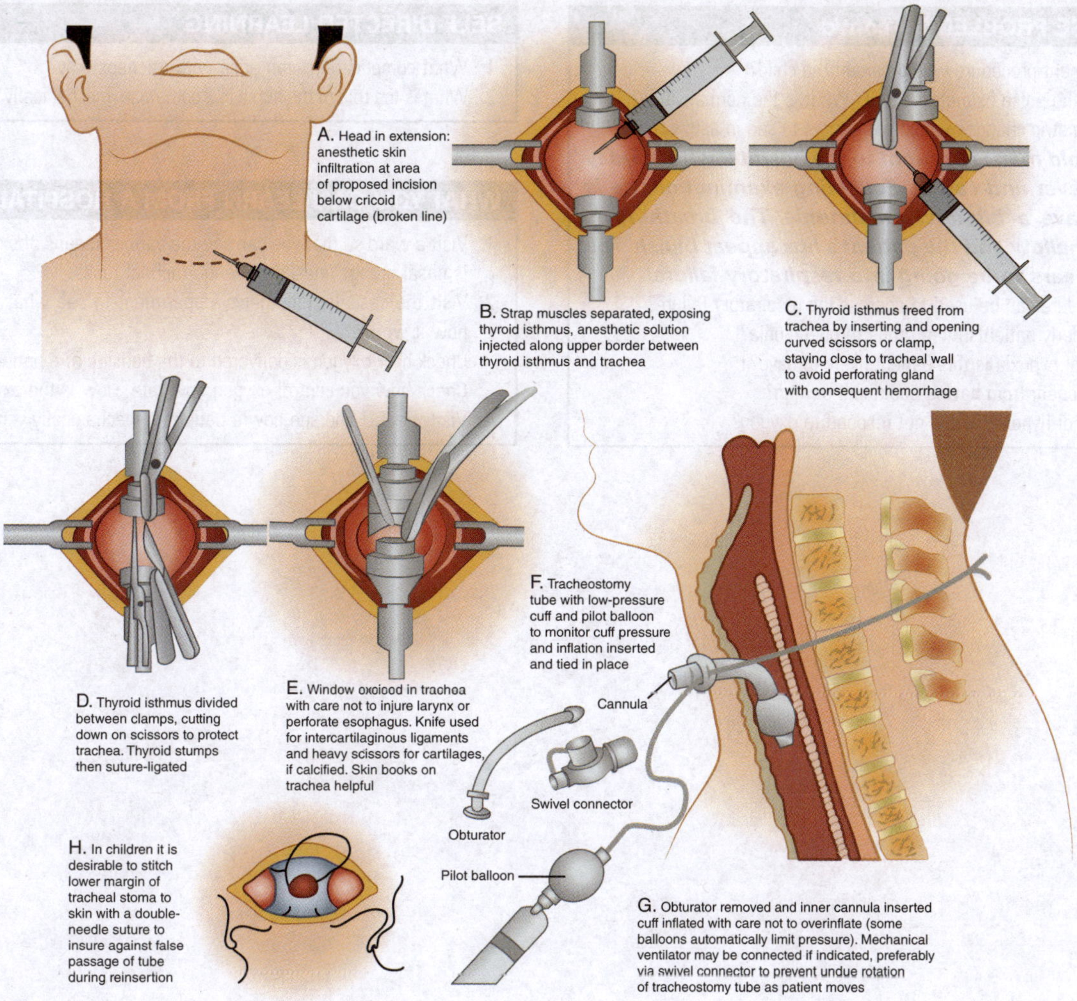

FIG. 17.4 Procedure and position of a tracheostomy tube.

After a tracheostomy, a patient can breathe normally or in specific conditions may be connected to mechanical ventilator. The indications for a tracheostomy include:

- Blockage to the upper airways, for example in cancers in which the growth does not allow for normal breathing.
- Need for mechanical ventilation for a prolonged period of time.
- During extensive surgery to the head and neck.
- Following certain forms of head and neck injury.

A tracheostomy has some problems:

- Speaking becomes difficult because for sound to be produced, air needs to flow past the vocal cords. In a tracheostomy, air directly flows into the trachea without passing the vocal cords.
- The air inspired through the tracheostomy is dry since humidification normally occurs in the nasopharynx and oropharynx. This can be associated with increased irritation, cough and more mucus production.

Apart from the care of tracheostomy sites in the hospital, nurses also need to educate patients who are at home with a tracheostomy on how to take care of the tracheostomy site and the tracheostomy tubes. This involves, among others, to:

- Maintain the site clean to ensure no possibility of infection.
- Maintain the patency of the tube by removing mucus and secretions.
- Check for the position of the tracheostomy tube and ensure that it has not been displaced.

CLINICAL CASE PROBLEMS

(A) ***A young child with a history of asthma is brought to the emergency department. The child is breathless, unable to speak, and gasping for air – clearly short of breath. The nurse observes that breathing is rapid, the nostrils are flared and the child shows retractions as he struggles to breathe. The nurse applies a pulse oximeter to the finger of the child and reads off a value of 75%.***

a. Underline the words in the case history above which suggest that the child has acute respiratory distress.
b. What type of condition is asthma (obstructive or restrictive)?

Continued

CLINICAL CASE PROBLEMS—cont'd

c. What treatment procedure would benefit the child?
d. What does the pulse oximeter record? What is the normal value?
e. What spirometric changes would you expect to see in asthma?

(B) ***An 85-year-old man is brought to the hospital with a 5-day history of fever and cough. Following examination, he is found to have a bilateral pneumonia. The breathing is rapid and shallow and the patient's lips appear bluish. The patient appears to be going into respiratory failure.***

a. What procedure can be used to address the respiratory failure?
b. Why are elderly patients more prone to pneumonia?
c. What type of hypoxia is this patient likely to have?
d. Would he benefit from having additional oxygen?
e. Which type of hypoxia would not respond to oxygen?

SELF-DIRECTED LEARNING

1. What complications can arise with tracheostomy?
2. What is the role of the nurse in a comatose, mechanically ventilated patient?

WHAT YOU CAN LEARN FROM A HOSPITAL VISIT

1. Visit a ward so that you can see the various means of oxygen delivery, that is nasal prongs, masks and endotracheal tubes.
2. Visit the casualty/emergency department to see what a nebulizer is and how it works.
3. Check how oxygen is delivered to the bedside of a patient in your hospital. Check how you control oxygen flow rate. How is the oxygen humidified?
4. Visit the ICU and see how a patient is mechanically ventilated.

3
SECTION

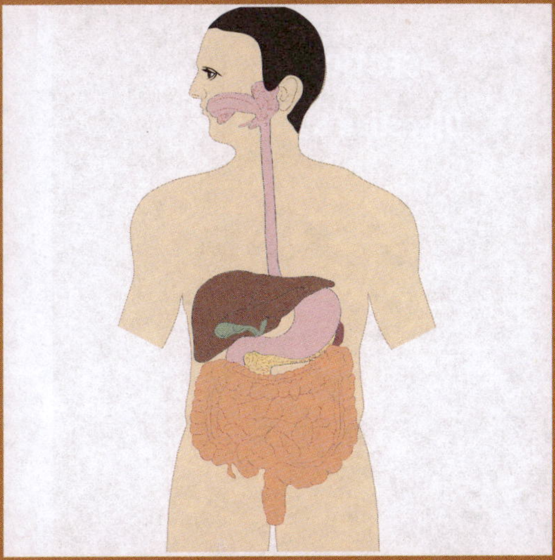

Digestive System

Section Outline

CHAPTER 18

Functions of the Organs of the Digestive System

SPECIFIC LEARNING OBJECTIVES

At the end of this chapter, the student should be able to:

- Describe with the help of a diagram the parts of the gastrointestinal (GI) system.
- List the broad functions of the GI system.
- Describe the cross-section of the gut.
- Describe the neural control of GI function.
- Describe the circulation of digestive system.

GLOSSARY OF TERMS

- **Digestion:** the process by which the food that we eat is converted into simpler substances that can be used by the body
- **Absorption:** the process by which the products of digestion are taken up from the lumen of the gut into the blood vessels and lymphatics so that they can be used by the body
- **Motility:** the movement of the gut resulting in the passage of the contents of the gut
- **Portal circulation:** two capillary beds in series

THE FUNCTIONS OF THE GASTROINTESTINAL SYSTEM

The gastrointestinal (GI) system has many functions in the body:

1. It moves food down the alimentary tract (*motility*) where it is broken down into smaller particles and thoroughly mixed.
2. It secretes various enzymes that break down the foods into diffusible substances (*digestion*).
3. It ensures the movement of the digested diffusible substances into the body (*absorption*).
4. The faeces is a major excretory route for the body.
5. The local nervous system of the digestive system (enteric nervous system) regulates all the processes listed previously, that is motility, secretion of enzymes, digestion and absorption, by nerves, hormones and local factors.
6. The gut–brain axis has been described. This is a communication between the enteric nervous system and the central nervous system. Through this system the function of the gut, especially the gut microflora (bacteria; called the gut microbiome), can affect the emotional state and well-being of the individual.
7. The bacteria of the gut also produce important molecules for the body. Included among these are vitamin B and vitamin K.
8. The digestive system through its mucosal barrier, the acid secretion of the stomach and secretory antibodies forms a part of the immune defence system of the body.

THE BASIC ORGANIZATION OF THE GASTROINTESTINAL SYSTEM

Fig. 18.1 shows the anatomical arrangement of the GI system.

We can trace the movement of the food along the alimentary tract:

- Food that is eaten is broken into smaller pieces in the oral cavity and then goes via the pharynx and the oesophagus into the stomach.
- In the stomach, gastric juices are added and the food is thoroughly mixed so that it exits the stomach as semiliquid acidic chyme.
- It then enters the duodenum which is the first part of the small intestine where it receives the secretions of the pancreas and the bile from the liver (via the gallbladder).
- The bile and pancreatic juice converts the acidic chyme into alkaline chyme and this then moves down the small intestine, first through the jejunum and then the ileum. Pancreatic enzymes continue the process of digestion.

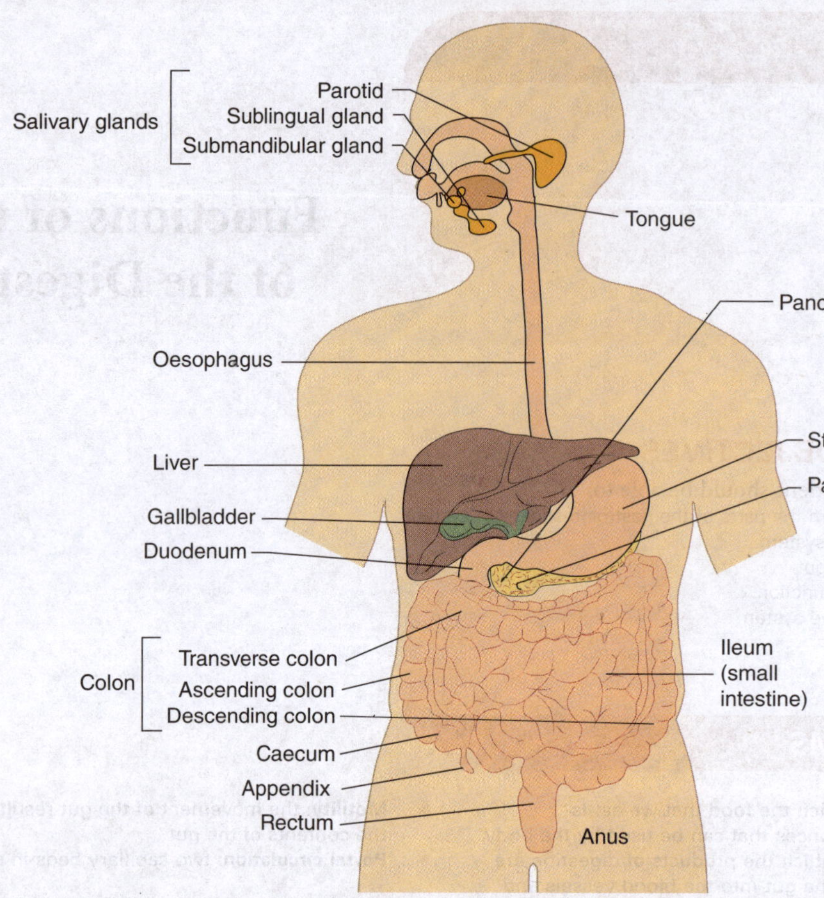

FIG. 18.1 A schematic diagram showing the parts of the gastrointestinal system.

- In the small intestine, further digestive juices are added and absorption of many nutrients takes place.
- The contents of the small intestine then enter the large intestine (caecum – ascending colon – transverse colon and descending colon) where water and salts are absorbed.
- Faeces are stored in the rectum and expelled through the anus in an act called defaecation. We will be describing the functions of the GI system in greater detail in subsequent chapters.

CROSS-SECTIONAL STRUCTURE OF THE GUT

In order to understand the functional anatomy of the gut, it is useful to describe the cross-sectional structure of the gut. This is the microscopic structure of the cut section of the gut. The gut is not uniform throughout, but this section gives a general understanding. Fig. 18.2 shows the cross-sectional structure of the gut.

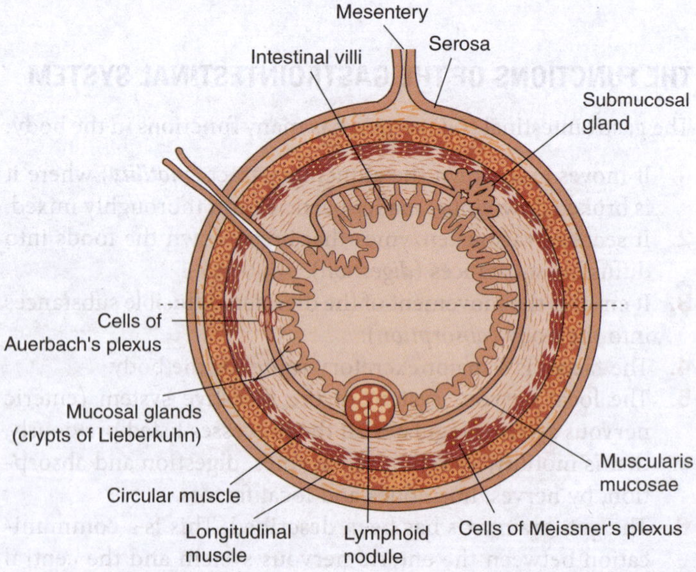

FIG. 18.2 A cross-section of the intestinal wall.

There are several things that are shown in Fig. 18.2:

1. The epithelium which lines the lumen of the gut is thrown into a series of small finger-like projections called villi.
   a. Villi are the sites through which the end products of digestion (glucose and other simple sugars for carbohydrate, amino acids for proteins and fatty acids and glycerol for fats) are absorbed.
   b. They increase the surface area of the intestines and therefore increase the efficiency with which absorption occurs.

2. There are two types of smooth muscle in the gut: (1) an inner circular muscle and (2) an outer longitudinal muscle.
   a. Circular muscle, as the name suggests, encircles the gut, while longitudinal muscle extends lengthwise down the gut. These muscles are responsible for peristalsis, that is the wave of contraction of the gut which helps to move food downwards.
   b. In addition, circular muscle is also important for the function of sphincters in the gut. These sphincters regulate the rate at which the contents of the gut are moved forward. Among the various sphincters in the gut, three deserve mention here:
      (i) The lower oesophageal sphincter is at the junction of the oesophagus and the stomach. This serves two purposes: it controls the entry of food into the stomach and also prevents the contents of the stomach from moving back into the oesophagus. When the lower oesophageal sphincter is weak, the acidic chyme can move backwards into the oesophagus and irritate the lower end of the oesophagus, a condition called oesophageal reflux. During vomiting, there is antiperistalsis, and the contents of the stomach are regurgitated, due to the movement of food in the opposite direction.
      (ii) The pyloric sphincter controls the movement of acidic chyme from the stomach to the duodenum.
      (iii) The anal sphincter is important during the act of defaecation.
3. There are two types of local nerve networks in the gut which form the enteric nervous system. These are the Auerbach's plexus and Meissner's plexus.
   a. Auerbach's plexus of nerves is also called the myenteric plexus because it is located between the longitudinal and circular muscle layers of the gut. Because of its location, Auerbach's plexus acts to regulate the 'tone' of the gut and its motility.
   b. Meissner's plexus lies in the submucosa layer and acts to control intestinal secretions and absorption.
4. In addition to the enteric nervous system, the gut is also innervated by the autonomic nervous system.
   a. As a rule of thumb, the sympathetic nervous system inhibits the motility of the gut while causing an increased contraction of the sphincters. This can be easily understood since the sympathetic nervous system is activated as part of the fight-or-flight response.
   b. The parasympathetic nervous system, in contrast, increases gut secretions and gut motility (rest and digest).

CIRCULATION OF THE GUT

The circulation of the gut is called the splanchnic circulation or hepatomesenteric circulation.

- This circulation is important because it is through this circulation that absorbed nutrients are distributed to different sites in the body.
- The splanchnic circulation is an example of a portal circulation. A portal circulation is characterized by two capillary beds in series. Normally, a terminal artery supplies a capillary bed with blood which then empties into venules and then through the venous system is returned to the heart.
- In a portal system, the blood in the first capillary bed empties into venules but then circulates through a second capillary bed before being returned to the heart. In the splanchnic circulation, the first capillary bed is around the alimentary tract which empties into the portal vein. The portal vein then supplies the liver in which there is a second capillary bed. The liver also receives arterial blood through the hepatic artery. The splanchnic circulation is depicted in Fig. 18.3.

INTESTINAL CIRCULATION

1. The gastrointestinal tract (GIT) receives its blood via the coeliac, superior and inferior mesenteric arteries.
2. The mesenteric circulation is controlled by the sympathetic nervous system which constricts the blood vessels. Thus, during the flight-or-fight response, sympathetic activation reduces blood flow to the intestine and allows this blood to be used by tissues that require more blood at that time such as skeletal muscle and the heart.
3. Intestinal blood flow increases with food ingestion. This is referred to as functional hyperaemia. This increase in blood flow is due to several GI hormones which are secreted as a response to the ingestion of food and also due to the absorption of nutrients.

HEPATIC BLOOD FLOW

1. The liver normally receives around 20%–25% of cardiac output, that is about 1000–1250 mL/min.
2. The blood supply to the liver is through two sources: three-fourths of the blood that the liver receives is from the portal vein and one-fourth from the hepatic artery. The portal vein drains the intestinal tract and is thus partly

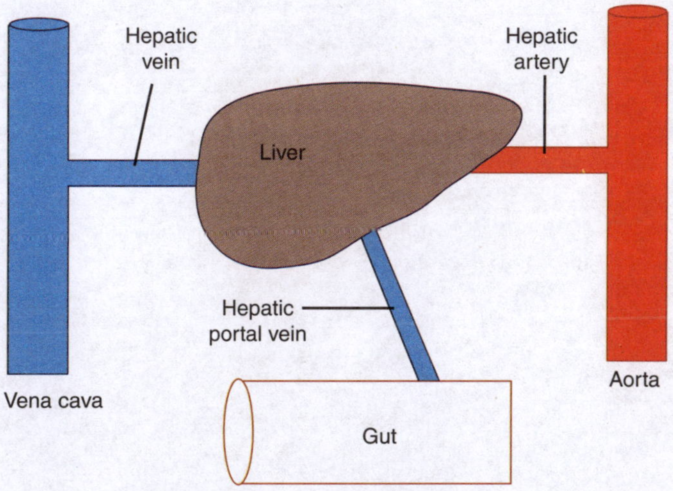

FIG. 18.3 The splanchnic circulation.

deoxygenated, while the hepatic arterial blood is fully oxygenated. The GI capillary bed together with the hepatic capillary network constitutes a portal circulation, that is two capillary beds in series, in this case with the portal vein in between.

3. The liver contains about 15% of the total blood volume.

APPLICATIONS IN NURSING

Nurses need to know the functional anatomy of the gut. One of the procedures that the nurse may need to perform is the insertion of a Ryles tube for feeding (nasogastric intubation). This involves passing down a tube through the nose into the stomach of the individual so that the person can be fed through the tube. This may be needed when the patient has difficulty in swallowing. The insertion of the tube may also be required for diagnostic purposes as, for instance, when a sample of gastric juice is required.

SUMMARY

- The GI system has multiple functions including motility which ensures the passage of food down the gut, digestion through the secretion of enzymes and absorption, among others.
- The GI system has two types of smooth muscle in its wall – longitudinal and circular. These muscles help in peristalsis. Circular muscle also forms sphincters at various locations.
- The nervous supply of the gut consists of an intrinsic (enteric) system made up of the Auerbach's plexus and Meissner's plexus, and an extrinsic nervous system which consists of the sympathetic and parasympathetic nerve supply to the gut.
- The circulation of the GI system is a portal system with two capillary beds in series: the first is the capillary bed around the alimentary tract and the second is in the liver.
- Three-fourths of the blood supply to the liver is from the portal vein and one-fourth from the hepatic artery.

CHAPTER REVIEW QUESTIONS

1. What are the layers of the intestinal wall?
2. What are the types of smooth muscle seen in the intestinal wall and what are their functions?
3. Describe the splanchnic circulation.

CHAPTER 19

Secretions of the Gastrointestinal Tract

SPECIFIC LEARNING OBJECTIVES

At the end of this chapter, the student should be able to:

- Describe the source, composition, functions and regulation of salivary secretion.
- Describe the source, composition, functions and regulation of gastric juice secretion.
- Describe the source, composition, functions and regulation of pancreatic juice secretion.
- Describe the source, composition, functions and regulation of biliary secretion.
- Describe the source, composition and functions of small intestinal secretions.

GLOSSARY OF TERMS

- **Digestion:** the mechanical, enzymatic and chemical breakdown of food such that it can be absorbed into the body
- **Absorption:** the process by which the end products of digestion pass from the lumen of the intestine into the bloodstream or the lymphatic vessels in the intestinal wall

The total daily secretion into the gastrointestinal (GI) tract is greater than 6500 mL in an adult. In this chapter, we consider five of these secretions.

SALIVARY SECRETION

Source

About 1000 mL of saliva is secreted in a day. This comes largely from three salivary glands that are located around the oral cavity, namely the parotid glands, the submandibular glands and the sublingual gland. The location of these glands is indicated in Fig. 19.1.

Composition

Saliva consists mainly of water. The inorganic components of saliva include different ions of which the most important are potassium and bicarbonate ions. Organic components include an enzyme called salivary amylase (ptyalin), mucin (which is largely responsible for the mucus in saliva) and lysozymes, among others.

Functions

Saliva has many functions:

1. It keeps the mouth moist and helps in lubrication. This is important for the following:
   a. Formation of the bolus (ball of chewed food) and swallowing
   b. Speech
2. It helps in digestion through the action of salivary amylase. This enzyme starts the process of digestion of starch, which is completed later in the small intestine. A small quantity of lingual lipase is also present.
3. Saliva is protective – it destroys viruses, bacteria and fungi. People who do not secrete enough saliva develop small ulcers in the mouth and may also suffer from dental caries, a condition in which there is tooth decay due to the action of certain bacteria.
4. Because of its high bicarbonate ion content, saliva also acts as a buffer.

Regulation of Salivary Secretion

The smell, thought and taste of food can all increase salivary secretion. The texture of food is also important. Salivary secretion is controlled by the sympathetic and parasympathetic nervous system. Parasympathetic activation results in salivary secretion that is copious and watery, while sympathetic activation results in much smaller increases in salivary secretion.

GASTRIC JUICE SECRETION

Food that has been broken down into smaller pieces in the oral cavity and formed into a bolus moves down the oesophagus and reaches the stomach. The food is acted on by gastric juices released in the stomach and thoroughly mixed before entering the small intestine.

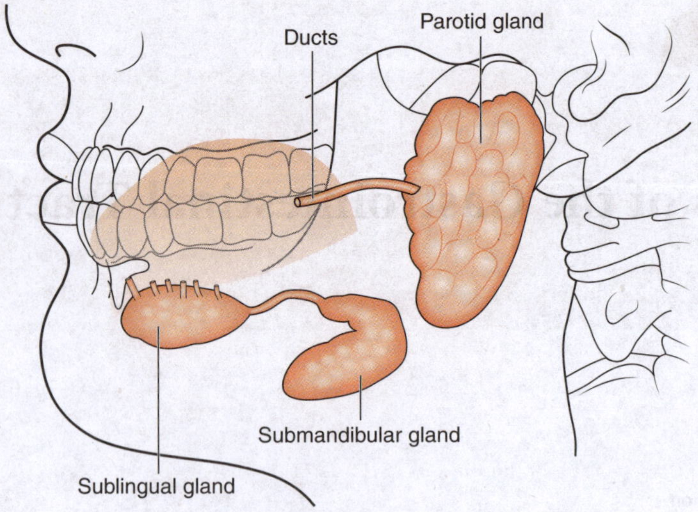

FIG. 19.1 The salivary glands.

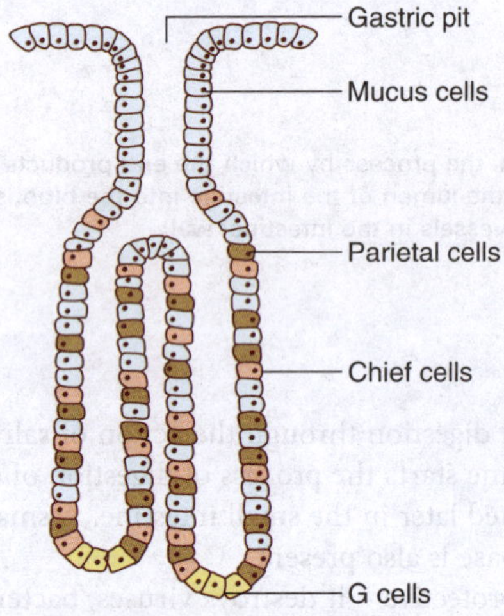

FIG. 19.2 Cells of the gastric mucosa.

Source

The stomach secretes about 1.5–2 L of gastric juice in a day. This gastric juice is secreted from the gastric glands which consist mainly of three different types of cells. These are (1) mucous cells, (2) peptic or chief cells and (3) parietal or oxyntic cells. There are, in addition, other cells. Fig. 19.2 illustrates a typical gastric gland with its cells.

Components of the Gastric Juice

Apart from water, the gastric juice is composed of various ions and some substances which are important for digestion. These substances include hydrochloric acid (HCl) which is produced by the parietal cell, pepsinogen which is produced by the peptic cells, and mucus produced by the mucous cells. Other substances include 'intrinsic factor' and gastric lipase. The importance of these components of gastric juice is described later. Table 19.1 summarizes the contribution of each type of cell to the gastric juice.

Table 19.1 Source and Composition of Gastric Juice

Type of Cell	Component of Gastric Juice	Functions
Mucous cell	Mucus	Lines the stomach – protects it from acid
Peptic (chief) cell	Pepsinogen Gastric lipase	Partial digestion of protein and fat
Parietal (oxyntic) cell	HCl Intrinsic factor	Kills bacteria, converts pepsinogen to pepsin, provides pH for pepsin to act Absorption of vitamin B12

In addition, the cells of the gastric glands also secrete hormones. For example, the G cells secrete a hormone called gastrin which increases the acid secretion of the parietal cell. We will discuss the role of hormones and of nerves in the section that deals with the regulation of gastric juice.

Functions of Gastric Juice

The large volume of gastric juice allows the food to be mixed in the stomach. As a result, the food gets converted into a semifluid consistency which is acidic in nature; this is called acid chyme. The specific functions of gastric juice are as follows:

1. **HCl:** The acid that is secreted by the parietal cells of the gastric glands has several functions:
   a. It helps kill bacteria and other microorganisms.
   b. It converts pepsinogen to its active form, pepsin.
   c. It provides the acidic pH at which pepsin can act.
2. **Pepsinogen:** Once converted to pepsin, the enzyme pepsin exerts its proteolytic action – it digests proteins partly into peptides.
3. **Gastric lipase:** It is another enzyme that is secreted in the stomach. It is an 'acidic' enzyme which means that it acts in an acidic environment. Its function is to break down lipids – the main site of digestion of lipids, however, is in the small intestine.
4. **Mucus:** This provides a protective barrier against the action of HCl on the gastric cells. In people who secrete excessive amounts of HCl, the mucus barrier may be insufficient to prevent the action of HCl on the lining of the stomach and the person develops acid peptic disease (APD) which may later result in an ulcer.
5. **Intrinsic factor:** This is important for the absorption of vitamin B_{12}. Although vitamin B_{12} is absorbed only in the terminal ileum, the receptor involved in the absorption of vitamin B_{12} binds to the intrinsic factor component of the vitamin B_{12}–intrinsic factor complex.

Regulation of Gastric Juice Secretion

Gastric juice starts being secreted even before the food reaches the stomach and continues after the acid chyme starts entering the duodenum. The secretion of gastric juice occurs in three phases.

Phases of Gastric Juice Secretion

1. *Cephalic phase:* The thought, sight, smell and taste of food can trigger the secretion of gastric juice. This phase accounts for 30% of gastric juice secretion. One of the experiments that demonstrated this phase of gastric secretion is 'sham feeding'. In this experiment, an experimental animal had the lower end of the oesophagus exteriorized (brought out to the exterior of the animal), so that the food that the animal ate never reached the stomach. In this situation, the animal continued to increase its gastric secretions whenever it was fed.
2. *Gastric phase*: This phase of secretion starts once the food enters the stomach. It accounts for the bulk (60%) of gastric secretion.
3. *Intestinal phase*: This phase refers to the continued secretion of gastric juice even after acid chyme has entered the duodenum. It accounts for about 10% of gastric secretion.

Nervous and Hormonal Control of Gastric Secretion

The three phases of gastric secretion are under nervous and hormonal regulation, but to different degrees. The cephalic phase of gastric secretion is largely under nervous control with the signals reaching the stomach via the vagus nerves. In contrast, the gastric phase is under both nervous and hormonal control. One of the hormones that act to increase HCl secretion via the parietal cell is gastrin which is secreted by the G cells in the gastric glands. The intestinal phase is again controlled by both nerves and hormones.

Regulation of Acid Secretion by the Parietal Cell

Fig. 19.3 represents the parietal cell which secretes HCl. There are three receptors which are linked to an increase in HCl secretion. Acetylcholine (ACh) muscarinic receptors are acted upon by ACh which is released from the branches of the vagus nerve. Gastrin released from the G cells of the gastric glands acts on the gastrin receptors, while histamine is released from enterochromaffin-like cells in the GI system and binds to H_2 (histamine) receptors on the parietal cell. HCl secretion into the stomach lumen occurs via the H^+/K^+ pump. Thus, if any of these receptors or the H^+/K^+ pump is blocked, acid secretion decreases. This is, in fact, what is used to control acid secretion in patients with APD.

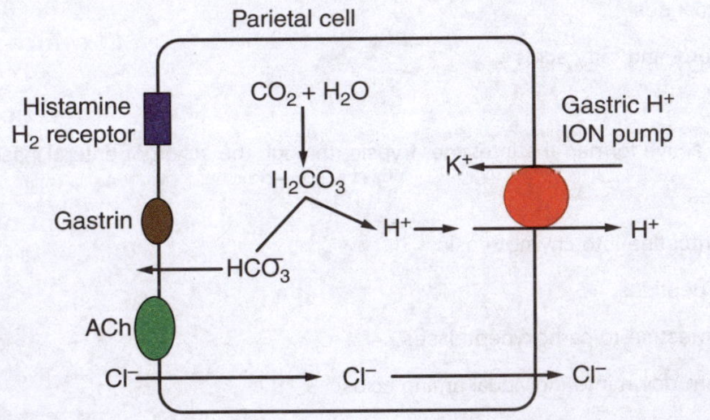

FIG. 19.3 The parietal cell: receptors and mechanism of secretion of H^+ ions.

Protection of the Gastric Mucosa from Its Own Secretions

You might wonder why the gastric acid that is produced by the parietal cell does not damage the lining of the stomach and why the pepsin which breaks down proteins does not act on the proteins present in the cell membranes of the cells lining the stomach. This does happen sometimes when the gastric acid secretion is increased or when the protective mechanisms in place fail. In this situation, a gastric ulcer might form. Normally, the stomach lining is protected through the following mechanisms:

1. Mucus and bicarbonate produced by the mucous cells that line the stomach form a barrier at the cell surface and prevent the acid from directly acting on the cell.
2. The cells of the stomach lining have a high turnover. This means that the cells are rapidly replaced. Thus, cells that are damaged are replaced by new undamaged cells.
3. Chemicals called prostaglandins are produced in the stomach and these protect the stomach lining.
4. The relatively high blood flow of the stomach flushes irritants that might otherwise damage the stomach lining.

PANCREATIC SECRETION

The pancreas is a complex organ which has an exocrine part that secretes a variety of enzymes that act on the foods that we eat, as well as an endocrine part which secretes hormones (Chapter 44). In this chapter, we will discuss the secretions of the exocrine component. The exocrine secretion of the pancreas is about 1200–1500 mL/day.

Source

Pancreatic enzymes are derived from the cells of the pancreatic acini (Fig. 19.4).

The acinar cells of the pancreas produce digestive enzymes which are stored in 'zymogen' granules and are then secreted when appropriate into small ductules. The contents of these ductules flow into the pancreatic duct which joins the hepatic duct (carrying bile) before it empties into the duodenum through the ampulla of Vater. Flow at this point is controlled by a

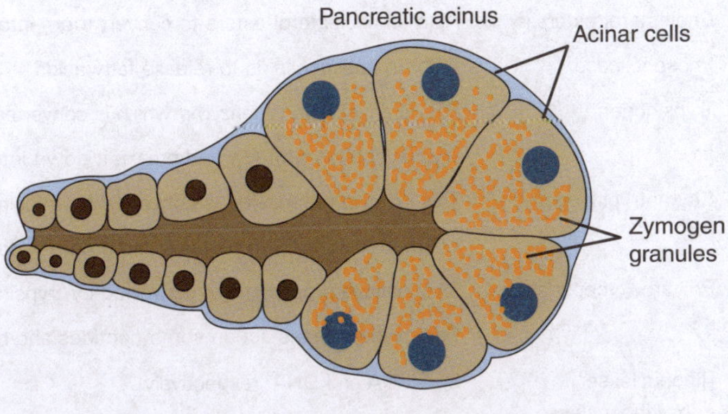

FIG. 19.4 The structure of the pancreatic acinus.

sphincter (the sphincter of Oddi). The anatomical arrangement of the pancreatic duct is depicted in Fig. 19.5.

Components of the Pancreatic Secretion

Pancreatic secretion is clear, colourless and alkaline with a pH of between 7.6 and 8.2. It is rich in bicarbonate ions (HCO_3). The bicarbonate ions have two functions:

- it neutralizes the acid chyme and convert it into alkaline chyme
- it provides the optimal pH for pancreatic enzymes to act. The enzymes of the pancreas act on all three of the major macronutrients in food, that is carbohydrate, protein and fat.

Table 19.2 summarizes the enzymatic components of the pancreas and their individual actions.

Functions of the Pancreatic Secretions

Based on the components of the pancreatic secretion, the functions can be summarized as follows:

1. Conversion of acid chyme to alkaline chyme
2. Digestion of all major food groups (details in Table 19.2)

Control of Pancreatic Secretions

Like the gastric juice secretions, pancreatic secretion occurs in three phases.

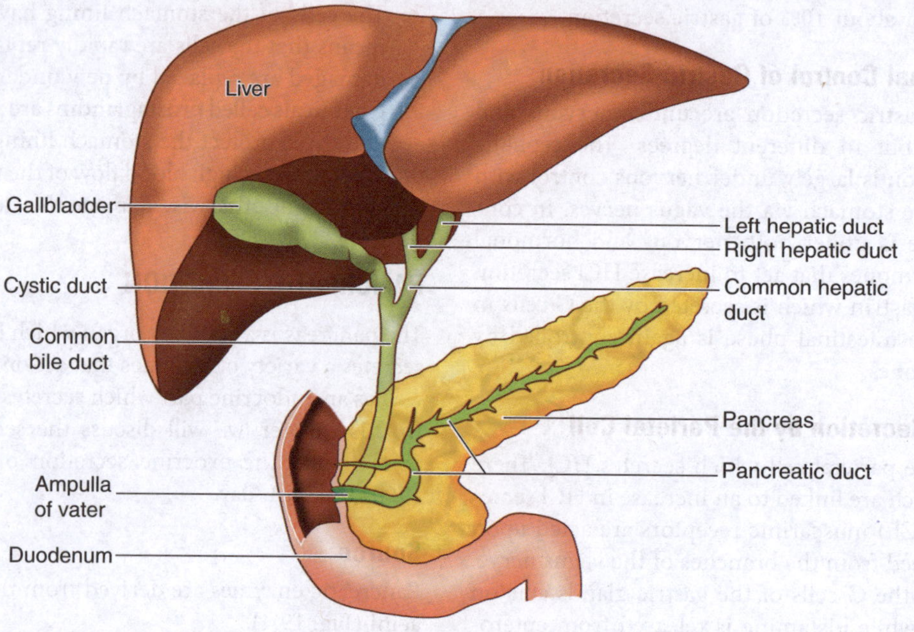

FIG. 19.5 The hepatobiliary system.

Table 19.2 Pancreatic Enzymes and Their Functions

Name of Enzyme	Function of Enzyme
Amylase	Acts on starch, glycogen and other complex carbohydrates and converts them into disaccharides
Lipase	Acts on fat and converts it into fatty acids and monoglycerides
Cholesterol esterase	Acts on cholesterol esters to convert them into cholesterol and fatty acids
Phospholipase	Acts on phospholipids to release fatty acids
Trypsinogen	This is an inactive proenzyme which is converted into its active form in the intestine, trypsin, through the action of enterokinase
	Trypsin acts on proteins and breaks it down into peptides
Chymotrypsinogen	This inactive proenzyme is converted by trypsin in the intestine into chymotrypsin
	Chymotrypsin acts on proteins and breaks it down into peptides
Procarboxypeptidases	This inactive proenzyme is converted by trypsin in the intestine to carboxypeptidases
	Carboxypeptidases act on some peptides and break them down into individual amino acids
Ribonuclease/ deoxyribonuclease	Spilt RNA and DNA, respectively

Cephalic phase (20% of pancreatic secretion) occurs when food is being eaten, or when the person is exposed to the sight, smell and taste of food. This is due to signals which are carried by the vagus nerve.

Gastric phase (10% of pancreatic secretion) occurs while the food is in the stomach.

Intestinal phase (70% of pancreatic secretion) occurs when the acid chyme enters the small intestine. Here, a hormone called *secretin* is produced by the S cells of the duodenum which causes a large amount of watery pancreatic secretion rich in bicarbonate to occur. Secretin was the first hormone to be discovered by two scientists named Bayliss and Starling. Another hormone which is released by the intestine is *cholecystokinin* (CCK) which also increases pancreatic secretion, but, unlike secretin, it increases the secretion predominantly of pancreatic enzymes.

BILIARY SECRETION

The liver secretes between about 500 and 1000 mL of bile every day. Bile is produced by the hepatocytes of the liver and is then secreted into small bile canaliculi which lie between the hepatocytes. It then flows into bile ducts which get progressively larger, finally reaching the hepatic duct. This enters the common bile duct and may be directly emptied into the intestine or the bile may be diverted into the gallbladder for some duration of time (minutes to several hours) where it gets concentrated before being released into the intestine.

Composition of Bile

Bile is largely water (97%–98%). It contains no enzymes. However, it is important for digestion because it contains bile salts. In addition to bile salts, bile also contains bile pigments (bilirubin and biliverdin) which are responsible for the yellow-green colour of bile. The bile contains a large number of salts and ions which are similar to those in plasma.

As you will see in the next section, the bile salts play an important role in the digestion of fats. In order to ensure a ready supply of bile salts, about 95% of the bile salts that are secreted into the bile are reabsorbed in the terminal ileum and are transported back to the liver by the portal system. The liver then extracts the bile salts from the blood and secretes them once again in the bile. The recirculation of bile back to the liver is referred to as the *enterohepatic circulation* (Fig. 19.6).

Functions of Biliary Secretion

1. The major function of bile is that the bile salts help to *emulsify* the large fat particles. Emulsification is the breaking up of fat globules into much smaller emulsion droplets. This increases the surface area of the fats and allows the pancreatic lipase to act more effectively. Once acted upon by lipase, the products of fat digestion can then be absorbed into the intestinal wall (Fig. 19.7).
2. Several substances are excreted in bile. These include cholesterol, drugs, steroid hormones and bilirubin.

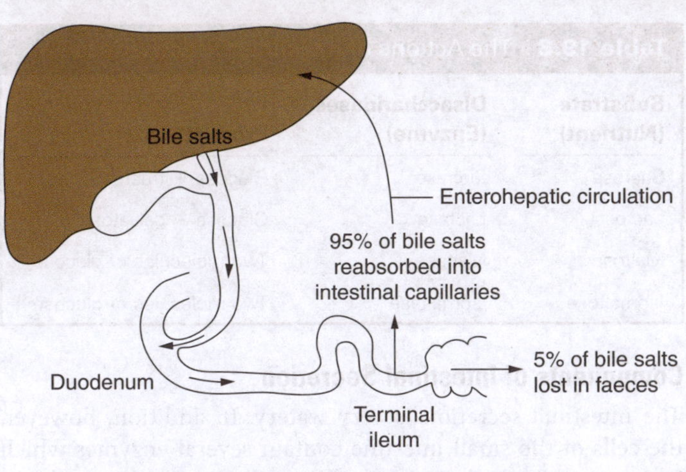

FIG. 19.6 The enterohepatic circulation.

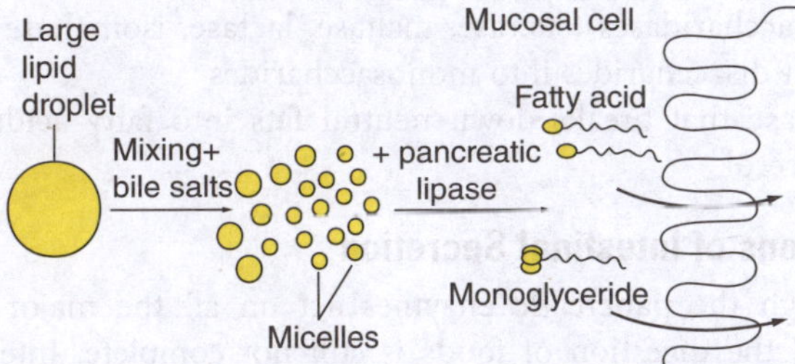

FIG. 19.7 Mechanism of fat digestion.

Regulation of Biliary Secretion

The parasympathetic nervous system via the vagus nerve increases bile secretion. Secretin, the hormone secreted from the intestinal wall, increases bile secretion. Similarly, bile salts that have been recirculated to the liver via the enterohepatic circulation also increase bile secretion. Substances which increase the secretion of bile are called *choleretics*.

Bile stored in the gallbladder is released into the intestine when the gallbladder contracts. The major stimulus for the contraction of the gallbladder is CCK, a hormone that is released when the acid chyme enters the small intestine from the stomach. Substances which increase the contractility of the gallbladder are called *cholagogues*.

INTESTINAL SECRETION

Source

The small intestinal secretions amount to about 1.5–2 L/day. The major source of the intestinal juice, previously called *succus entericus*, is from the intestinal glands (the *crypts of Lieberkuhn*). In addition, other glands which are present only in a part of the duodenum called *Brunner's glands* secrete mucus. Further secretion of mucus along the entire length of the intestine occurs by the *goblet cells* in the intestinal epithelium.

Table 19.3 The Actions of Intestinal Disaccharidases

Substrate (Nutrient)	Disaccharidases (Enzyme)	Product
Sucrose	Sucrase	Glucose + fructose
Lactose	Lactase	Glucose + galactose
Maltose	Maltase	Two molecules of glucose
Isomaltose	Isomaltase	Two molecules of glucose

Components of Intestinal Secretion

The intestinal secretion is very watery. In addition, however, the cells of the small intestine contain several enzymes which ensure that the final products of digestion can be absorbed into the bloodstream. The enzymes include the following:

1. Peptidases that spilt peptides into amino acids
2. Disaccharidases (sucrase, maltase, lactase, isomaltase) that spilt disaccharides into monosaccharides
3. Lipase that breaks down neutral fats into fatty acids and glycerol

Functions of Intestinal Secretion

Although the pancreatic enzymes act on all the major food groups, the digestion of foods is still not complete. Intestinal enzyme breaks down foods into their final end products which are easily absorbed through the intestinal epithelium. The specific actions of the disaccharidases are depicted in Table 19.3.

Regulation of Intestinal Secretion

Small intestinal secretion is largely regulated by the enteric nervous system contained with the intestinal wall.

APPLICATIONS FOR NURSING

Nurses will be required to educate patients on lifestyle changes needed for patients with acid peptic disease. These will include advice on diet, regularity of meals, stress reduction methods, stopping smoking and reduction of alcohol intake, among others. Nurses will also need to be able to ensure patient understanding and compliance to medication that may have been prescribed for acid peptic disease.

SUMMARY

- Saliva is secreted from the submandibular, parotid and sublingual glands. It lubricates the mouth and helps to form the bolus, aids in swallowing and speaking, is antiviral and bacterial, and contains the enzyme amylase.
- The stomach secretes HCl, pepsinogen, gastric lipase, mucus and intrinsic factor. Gastric secretion occurs in three phases: cephalic (30%), gastric (60%) and intestinal (10%). Nerves and hormones (gastrin) affect gastric secretion. HCl secretion from the parietal cell is controlled by at least three receptors to which gastrin, histamine and acetylcholine bind.
- The pancreas secretes enzymes and proenzymes that act on all major food groups: amylase, lipase, trypsinogen, chymotrypsinogen, procarboxypeptidases and RNA and DNases. Pancreatic secretion is secreted in cephalic (20%), gastric (10%) and intestinal (70%) phases. It is regulated by nervous and hormonal (secretin and CCK) mechanisms.
- Bile is secreted in the liver, stored and concentrated in the gallbladder, and released into the duodenum. It contains bile salts which emulsify fats.
- Intestinal secretions and enzymes complete the process of digestion to end products that can be absorbed. Important enzymes of the small intestine include peptidases, disaccharidases and intestinal lipase.

CHAPTER REVIEW QUESTIONS

1. List the functions of saliva.
2. In a table, list the cells of the gastric mucosa, indicate their secretion and function.
3. How is gastric secretion regulated?
4. What are the enzymes secreted in pancreatic juice?
5. What are the intestinal disaccharidases and what are their functions?

CHAPTER 20

Functions of the Liver and Gallbladder

SPECIFIC LEARNING OBJECTIVES

At the end of this chapter, the student should be able to:

- Describe the functional anatomy of the hepatobiliary system.
- Describe the functions of the liver.
- List the factors which regulate the secretion of bile.
- List the tests that can be used to evaluate liver function.

GLOSSARY OF TERMS

- **Hepatitis:** an inflammation of the liver (the most common types are hepatitis A, B and C)
- **Cholecystitis:** an inflammation of the gallbladder
- **Cholestasis:** decrease in bile flow due to either decreased secretion or blockage of flow

The hepatobiliary system consists of the liver, the gallbladder and the ducts through which the secretion of the liver reaches the intestine.

FUNCTIONAL ANATOMY OF THE HEPATOBILIARY SYSTEM

The liver in the average adult male weighs approximately 1.5 kg. The liver is, thus, the largest organ in the body. It is situated just below the diaphragm on the right side of the abdomen. It receives its blood supply from two sources: (1) the hepatic artery contributes only 25% of the blood supply and (2) the portal vein which drains the gastrointestinal (GI) tract supplies 75% of the blood supply of the liver. The venous drainage of the liver is into the central vein located within the liver lobule. The central vein empties into the hepatic veins and then into the inferior vena cava.

Cells of the Liver

Hepatocytes: The cells of the liver are called *hepatocytes* and these are arranged in a unit called a 'lobule' with a central vein at its centre (Fig. 20.1). By the side of the hepatocytes are the *biliary canaliculi* which transport the bile produced by the hepatocytes into the bile duct. Around the rows of hepatocytes are tissue spaces called the spaces of Disse. These spaces separate the hepatocytes from small reservoirs of blood called hepatic sinusoids and are connected to lymphatic vessels. The hepatic sinusoids are lined by endothelial cells which are fenestrated (with large pores) and are, thus, sites where large molecules can leak from the sinusoids into the lymphatic vessels. Molecules as large as albumin can leak out of the blood vessels in this way.

Kupfer Cells: These cells help to phagocytose bacteria and other foreign material that may have reached the liver.

Gallbladder

The gallbladder is situated on the underside (inferior aspect) of the liver. It serves two main purposes:

1. It acts as a storage reservoir for bile.
2. It alters the composition of bile and through its absorption of water and other salts concentrates the bile. Thus, the concentration of bile salts and bile pigments in gallbladder bile is much higher than the bile that is secreted from the liver. The extent of concentration of bile in the gallbladder can be from 5 times to as high as 20 times.

Hepatobiliary System

So how does the bile from the liver reach the intestine? The two main bile ducts from the liver are the left and right hepatic ducts which drain the left and right sides of the liver. These two ducts join together to form the common hepatic duct which joins with the cystic duct of the gallbladder and then forms the common bile duct. The common bile duct enters the duodenum through

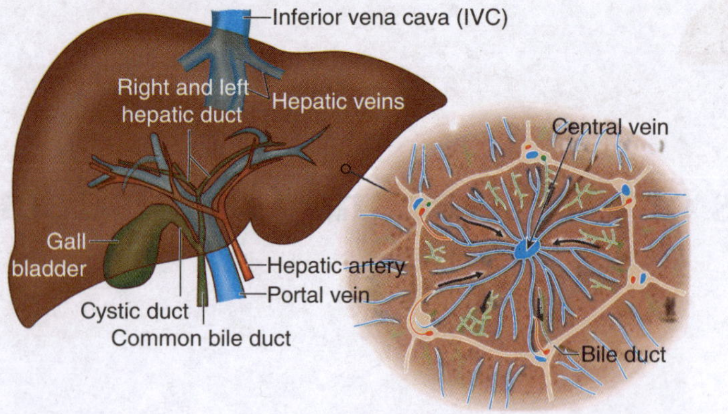

FIG. 20.1 The hepatobiliary system and the cellular architecture of the liver.

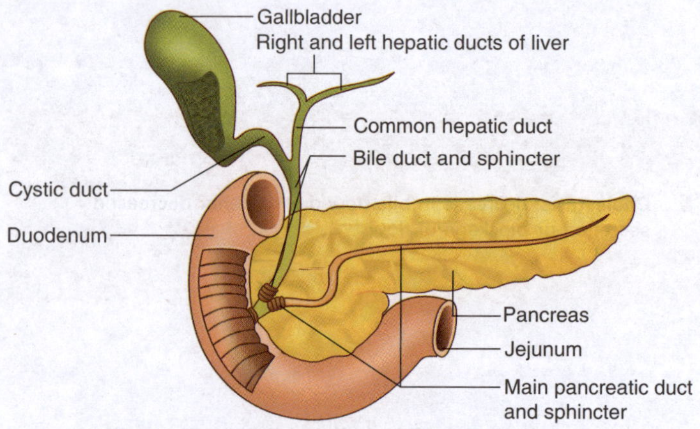

FIG. 20.2 The anatomy of the bile duct system.

a small opening called the Ampulla of Vater guarded by the sphincter of Oddi. Before reaching this opening, it is usually joined by the pancreatic duct which carries the exocrine secretions of the pancreas (including the pancreatic enzymes). This drainage system is depicted in Fig. 20.2.

The flow of bile can be obstructed by many factors. For example, some people (usually older, overweight women) develop stones in the gallbladder. These can travel down the cystic duct and may sometimes block the common bile duct. Sometimes, growths (tumours) from neighbouring structures can compress the common bile duct. This is what sometimes happens in cancer of the pancreas. When the flow of bile is obstructed, fat emulsification and absorption are affected and as a result the person may pass fatty, foul-smelling stools (steatorrhoea). Bilirubin excretion is also affected, resulting in a yellowish colouration of the skin and mucous membranes called jaundice. This type of jaundice is described as 'obstructive' or posthepatic and is discussed in Chapter 40.

FACTORS AFFECTING THE SECRETION OF BILE

Bile starts being secreted into the intestine as early as when food is ingested. Thus, the sphincter of Oddi (the opening of the common bile duct into the duodenum) relaxes when food is in the mouth due to the action of vagal nerve efferents.

Once the acid chyme from the stomach begins entering the duodenum, the fatty acids and the amino acids in the chyme stimulate the release of the hormone cholecystokinin (CCK). This causes contraction of the gallbladder and the release of bile into the cystic and common bile duct. Substances which cause the gallbladder to contract are called *cholagogues*.

Secretin which was the first hormone to be discovered and which is secreted in response to acid chyme entering the duodenum also increases bile secretion; in this case, the bile secretion is watery and rich in bicarbonate. Substances which cause the increased secretion of bile are called *choleretics*.

FUNCTIONS OF THE LIVER

The liver has functions that are related to digestion, absorption and metabolism but other functions as well.

1. **Metabolic functions:** The metabolic functions of the liver are best discussed under the three heads of carbohydrate, protein and fat metabolism.

   Carbohydrate metabolism: The liver is a major site of glycogen storage. Since glycogen is synthesized from glucose, this means that the liver can help remove excess glucose from the circulation. The liver can also make glucose through the process of *gluconeogenesis* and from galactose and fructose. The liver thus maintains normal levels of glucose in the blood.

   Fat metabolism: The liver is important for fat oxidation, that is the breakdown of fatty acids to release energy. This energy can then be utilized for many body functions. The liver is also an important site of synthesis of various fats such as cholesterol and phospholipids (which apart from other functions make up the cell membrane). This is important to understand – cholesterol not only comes from food but is also synthesized in the body, the major site of which is the liver. The liver can also synthesize and release triglycerides.

   Protein metabolism: The liver is an important site of protein synthesis especially of those proteins which are found in plasma (plasma proteins) and include the following:

   - Albumin: It is important for maintaining the osmotic pressure of blood. When albumin levels are low, fluid moves out of the blood vessels into the tissue spaces, resulting in oedema. This is why children who are malnourished may sometimes look 'fat'.
   - Clotting factors: The majority of the clotting factors which are responsible for the formation of a clot and which help to stop bleeding are made in the liver. This includes all the factors through which vitamin K acts (i.e. factors II, VII, IX and X).
   - Acute phase proteins: When the body is injured or when there is inflammation, the body responds by producing a number of proteins called acute phase proteins whose function is to limit inflammation,

destroy microbes and increase vascular permeability so that immune cells can reach the site of the inflammation. The liver is the source of many of these acute phase proteins.

2. **Synthesis and secretion of bile:** Bile is composed largely of water in addition to bile salts, bilirubin, cholesterol, fatty acids and various ions. It is important because:
   - It helps to emulsify fats, converting them into smaller particles that can be acted on by the appropriate enzymes (lipase). Since in this way, bile increases the absorption of fats, it follows that absorption of substances which are soluble in fat will also be increased. This is true of the fat-soluble vitamins (A, D, E, K).
   - It helps to excrete bilirubin, cholesterol, certain metals and bacterial toxins.
3. **An organ of storage:** The liver stores not only substances like glycogen which can be metabolized for energy but also a range of other substances including iron in the form of ferritin and vitamins (especially vitamin A, but also D and B_{12}).
4. **Detoxification:** The liver removes harmful toxins from the body. The liver does this in many ways:
   - Chemical alteration of the substance into less harmful substances
   - Excretion of the substance into the bile and subsequent elimination from the body
   - Physical trapping of bacteria and other harmful particles by the Kupffer's cells in the liver
5. **Immune function:** The liver is a part of the defence system against microbes and other injury to the body in the following ways:
   - Generation of acute phase proteins (described earlier)
   - Phagocytosis by the Kupffer's cells (it is estimated that close to 99% of bacteria which enter the liver from the portal circulation [i.e. the GI tract] are destroyed)
6. **As a reservoir for blood:** The liver has a high blood flow from both the portal vein and the hepatic artery. About 1500 mL of blood passes through the liver in 1 minute accounting for more than 25% of the cardiac output. In the adult male, within the liver, the sinusoids can accommodate close to 500 mL of blood and this amount can be even more in certain situations. For instance, when the right heart (i.e. the right ventricle) is not functioning well, there is a back pressure which extends to the liver. In this situation, the sinusoids get filled with even more blood, and the liver enlarges and can be felt on palpation of the abdomen.

APPLICATIONS IN NURSING: LIVER ENLARGEMENT

The liver is not normally felt in healthy individuals. It can, however, be palpated when the liver is enlarged in the upper right quadrant of the abdomen when the patient takes a breath and the liver is pushed into the abdomen beyond the rib margin. Enlargement of the liver can occur due to a variety of reasons including heart failure when the liver is congested and tumours of the liver.

CLINICAL BOX

Pathology of the Liver

The liver may be affected in a number of diseases. Some of these are enumerated as follows:

- **Viral hepatitis:** This is one the most common conditions that a nurse will encounter. There are different types of viral hepatitis. Viral hepatitis A is typically caused by consuming contaminated food or beverages. This type of hepatitis is usually self-limiting. Viral hepatitis B and C are, in contrast, typically transmitted by contamination through blood (shared needles, transfusion of unscreened blood products) and by unprotected sex (hepatitis B).
- **Alcoholic hepatitis:** In late stages, this can result in extensive scarring of the liver (cirrhosis) and liver failure.
- **Tumours of the liver:** This can be either a primary tumour within the liver or the result of malignant tumours (cancers) that have spread from other parts of the body to the liver.
- **Drug overdoses:** There are many medications which if taken in excessive doses can result in liver damage and liver failure. Some of these may be available as over-the-counter drugs and it is therefore important to instruct patients on the correct dose of all medications.

DISEASES OF THE GALLBLADDER

The two most common diseases of the gallbladder are inflammation (cholecystitis) and gallstones. Once the primary problem is treated, the nurse will be required to create a plan for the patients regarding weight reduction and dietary change to a low-fat diet since both these are risk factors for gallbladder disease (in addition to other problems such as cardiovascular disease).

SUMMARY

- The liver is arranged into functional lobules each of which drains into a central vein. The endothelial lining of the sinusoids is fenestrated and allows the leak of large molecules such as albumin into the lymphatic vessels.
- The liver has many functions. These include an important role in the metabolism of carbohydrates, protein and fat, in the synthesis and secretion of bile, as an organ of storage and detoxification, in the synthesis of multiple plasma proteins and in immunity.
- Biliary secretion starts when food is ingested and is in the mouth – this phase of biliary secretion is controlled by the vagus nerve. As food moves down the GI tract and acid chyme enters the duodenum, release of secretin and CCK increases biliary secretion and causes the gallbladder to contract.
- Liver function can be assessed by the concentrations of liver enzymes released into circulation, bilirubin levels and the concentration of various proteins formed in the liver.

CHAPTER REVIEW QUESTIONS

1. What are the metabolic functions of the liver?
2. What substances are synthesized in the liver?
3. What are the functions of the gallbladder?
4. How is the secretion of bile regulated?

CHAPTER 21

Movements of the Alimentary Tract

SPECIFIC LEARNING OBJECTIVES

At the end of this chapter, the student should be able to:

- Describe the phases and process of deglutition.
- List the factors which affect gastric emptying.
- Describe the movements of the small and large intestine.
- Describe the defaecation reflex.

GLOSSARY OF TERMS

- **Peristalsis:** contraction and relaxation of the gastrointestinal wall which propels food forwards
- **Law of the gut:** the direction of peristalsis is from oral (mouth) to aboral (anal) end

The movements of the gastrointestinal tract have two main functions:

1. They move the contents of the tract from the mouth where the food is ingested to the anus where it is expelled. The movements are regulated to maximize digestion and absorption of nutrients.
2. They help to churn (mix) and break down the contents of the tract into smaller particles so that digestive enzymes can act better.

DEGLUTITION

Deglutition is the process of the swallowing of food. Before swallowing can occur, however, the food must first be chewed, a process called *mastication*. Mastication tears food into smaller pieces and then grinds it so that saliva converts it into a ball of food (bolus) which can be transported to the stomach.

Deglutition occurs in three phases:

1. **Oral phase:** In this voluntary phase, the ball of food is pushed back into the pharynx by the tongue.
2. **Pharyngeal phase:** This phase is involuntary (i.e. not under our control). During this phase, the food passes from the pharynx into the oesophagus (Fig. 21.1). Within the pharynx, the bolus of food is prevented:
   a. From going back into mouth by the tongue
   b. From entering the nose by the soft palate which is pulled up
   c. From entering the trachea by:
      i. The epiglottis
      ii. Closure of the vocal cords

   The closure of the vocal cords means that for this brief period, the person stops breathing, a condition called *deglutition apnoea*.
3. **Oesophageal phase:** This phase of deglutition is also involuntary.
   a. If you look at the neck of a person swallowing, you will observe that the larynx (voice box) is pulled upwards. This enlarges the opening between the pharynx and the oesophagus.
   b. In addition, the muscles in the upper part of the oesophagus relax and the food can thus move easily from the pharynx to the oesophagus.
   c. The rest of the passage of the food down the oesophagus to the stomach is mediated by *peristalsis*. Peristalsis in the oesophagus is a wave of contraction of the muscles which starts in the pharynx and moves down.
   d. At the junction of the oesophagus and the stomach is a band of circular muscle which forms the lower oesophageal sphincter. This sphincter is normally contracted so that the acid contents of the stomach do not enter the oesophagus. When food needs to be transferred from the oesophagus to the stomach, however, the sphincter needs to relax.

The normal function of the lower oesophageal sphincter is very important.

a. In some people, the lower oesophageal sphincter may be too relaxed. As a result, the acid contents of the stomach may enter the lower part of the oesophagus, leading to a condition called *gastro-oesophageal reflux disease*. Patients with this

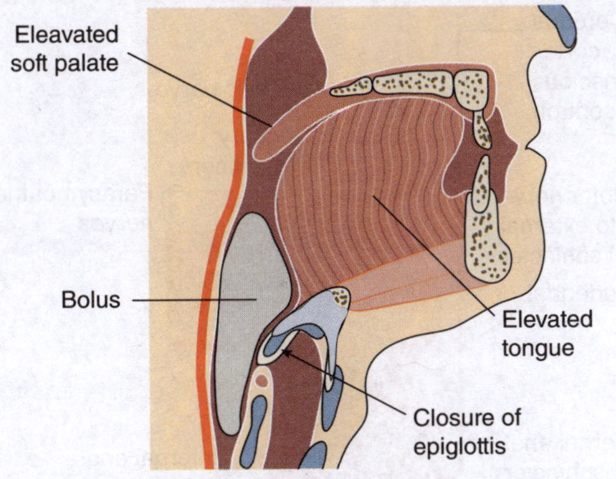

FIG. 21.1 The pharyngeal phase of deglutition.

condition may experience burning in the upper abdomen or chest pain and a bitter taste in the mouth, among other symptoms. If this condition is untreated, it can lead to ulcers and bleeding into the oesophagus, and is also associated with a higher risk of oesophageal cancer.

b. In a smaller number of patients, the lower oesophageal sphincter may not be able to relax completely. As a result, food is unable to enter the stomach easily – the food tends to build up in the oesophagus and the oesophagus becomes distended over a period of time. This condition is called *achalasia cardia*.

GASTRIC EMPTYING

During the oesophageal phase of deglutition, a part of the stomach (fundus) begins to relax to accommodate the food that it is about to receive – this is called *receptive relaxation*. The stomach is a storage organ for the food. It also mixes the food along with the gastric secretions to form a semifluid paste called *chyme*. Since this chyme is acidic in nature, it is called acid chyme.

Apart from gastric mixing of food, the muscles of the stomach make sure that there is a slow emptying of the contents of the stomach into the small intestine. The time taken for a fixed proportion of a standardized meal to be emptied from the stomach into the intestine is called *gastric emptying time*. The time for gastric emptying is not fixed but depends on a large number of factors.

Factors that are associated with faster gastric emptying times are:
1. Increased food volume
2. Liquids
3. Carbohydrate-rich meals

Factors that are associated with slower gastric emptying times are:
1. Solids
2. Fat-rich meals
3. Anxiety
4. Old age

INTESTINAL MOTILITY

The movements of the intestine can be divided into those of the small intestine and those of the large intestine. The small intestine movements include those which are essentially mixing in nature and those that help to propel food forwards.

Small Intestinal Motility (Fig. 21.2)

Segmentation contractions: Mixing contractions, otherwise called segmentation contractions ensure thorough mixing of the chyme with the secretions of the small intestine. This is essential to ensure that digestion of chyme is complete. In segmentation contractions, segments of the intestine contract so that it has a 'chain of sausages' appearance. The frequency of segmentation contraction varies from 12/min in the duodenum to about 8–9/min in the ileum.

Peristalsis: The aim of peristalsis is to propel the chyme along the intestine. This movement always occurs towards the anus (i.e. from oral [mouth] to aboral [anal] end), and comprises the **'law of the gut'**. There are many aims of this propulsion: (1) to transport waste or undigested food for excretion, (2) to ensure that the chyme is subjected to the various digestive enzymes present in the intestine and (3) to ensure that chyme is carried to the various sites of absorption of nutrients.

Peristalsis can be regulated. It is increased by:
1. Activation of the enteric nervous system by stretch (when the chyme enters the small intestine).
2. Distension of the stomach, which induces a reflex increase in small intestine peristalsis through reflex called the gastroenteric reflex.
3. Activity of the parasympathetic nervous system.
4. Various hormones such as gastrin, cholecystokinin, insulin and motilin.

Peristalsis is decreased by:
1. Activity of the sympathetic nervous system.
2. Hormones such as secretin and somatostatin.

Smaller movements: In addition to the above-mentioned movements, smaller movements such as 'villi movements' occur. These movements of the villi help to promote lymph flow in the lacteals of the villi. As mentioned in Chapter 22, fatty acids and glycerol are absorbed into the lacteals of villi.

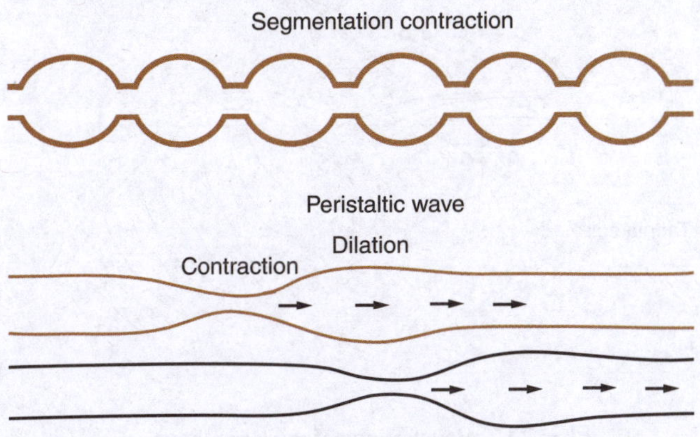

FIG. 21.2 Nature of small intestinal movements.

Large Intestinal Motility

Once the major part of the absorption of nutrients has taken place in the small intestine, the contents of the intestine now move to the large intestine. It is here that the water and electrolytes are absorbed and the faeces stored before it is finally excreted.

There are two major types of intestinal movements that are seen in the large intestine and, like the small intestine, these are concerned with 'mixing' and with 'propulsion'.

Haustrations: These are mixing movements of the large intestine which are similar to the segmentation contractions of the small intestine (Fig. 21.3). They cause the noncontracting segments of the large intestine to bulge out like little sacks called haustrations. Within each haustration, the faecal matter is thoroughly mixed and the electrolytes and water absorbed.

Mass movements: These contractions are modifications of peristalsis in which a fairly large segment of the large intestine (about two-thirds of 1 foot, i.e. 20 cm) contracts together and in the process pushes the entire contents of the contracting segment forward into the more distal part of the colon and into the rectum.

GASTROINTESTINAL REFLEXES

Defaecation reflex: This reflex is associated with the evacuation of the bowels and the excretion of faeces. The anus has two sphincters – the internal anal sphincter and the external anal sphincter. The external sphincter is under voluntary control.

- The stimulus for defaecation is the distension of the rectal wall. This occurs when the rectum has been filled with faeces as a result of the mass movements of the large intestine.
- The stretch of the rectal wall stimulates afferent (sensory) parasympathetic nerves within the wall. Signals from these nerves are transmitted to the spinal cord.
- The efferent (motor) nerves are the parasympathetic pelvic nerves. These initiate smooth muscle contraction and also relax the internal anal sphincter which is made up of smooth muscle. Simultaneous relaxation of the external anal sphincter (which is composed of skeletal muscle and therefore under voluntary control) results in defaecation. These events are summarized in Fig. 21.4.

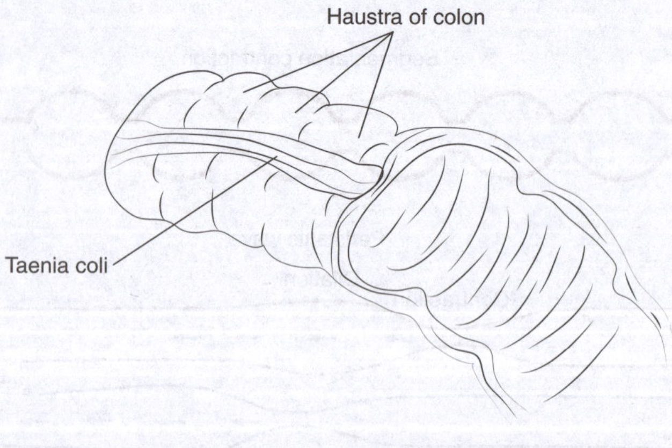

FIG. 21.3 Haustrations of the large intestine.

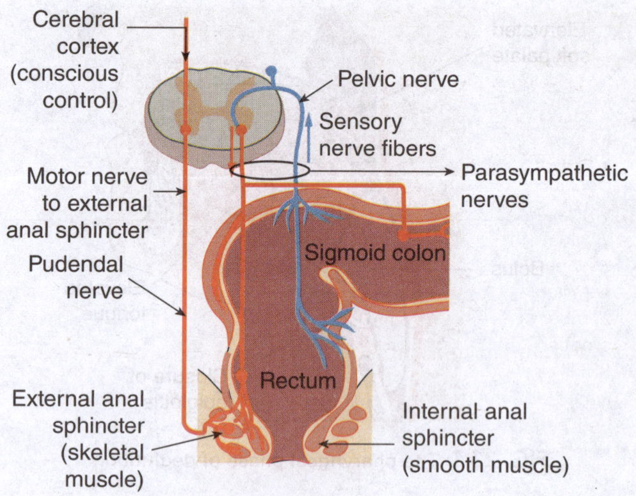

FIG. 21.4 The defaecation reflex.

Gastrocolic and duodenocolic reflexes: These are reflexes which, as the names suggest, result in increased colonic motility when the stomach or duodenum is stretched. These reflexes are responsible for the increased urge to defaecate after a meal which is exaggerated in patients who suffer from a condition called irritable bowel syndrome and is also seen in infants.

APPLICATIONS FOR NURSING

- Nursing care in gastro-oesophageal reflux disease in which gastric acid enters the oesophagus includes counselling the patient on better lifestyles and dietary habits. Patients are required to reduce tea and coffee intake, stop smoking and restrict alcohol intake since all these can aggravate the condition. Patients may also benefit from eating smaller meals and ensuring that the night meal is eaten at least 3 hours before going to sleep.
- Peristalsis in the gut can be determined by auscultating the abdomen. The presence of 'gurgling sounds' and the passage of flatus (gas) indicate intestinal motility. This is important to determine following abdominal surgery where the intestinal sounds initially often disappear because of the handling of the intestinal loops during surgery.
- Constipation is a condition in which there is difficulty in defaecation and is associated with a reduced frequency of passing faeces and the passage of hardened faeces. There are many causes of defaecation and treatment varies depending on the cause. On occasion, the nurse may be required to give an enema to the patient with constipation. This involves the introduction of liquid into the rectum to help evacuate its contents. Nurses will also be required to advise patients with constipation due to poor dietary habits to increase their intake of high-fibre foods and fluids.
- Irritable bowel syndrome is a condition in which people suffer from abdominal pain, bloating and discomfort along with altered bowel habits. Along with medication, the patient requires to make lifestyle changes including changes in the diet which include increasing fluid and dietary fibre intake and reducing some foods which can increase symptoms such as milk and cheese. Patients may also need to eat smaller, more frequent meals in order to get relief from symptoms – nurses are an integral part of the clinical team and have an important role in educating patients about lifestyle change.

SUMMARY

- Motility in the gastrointestinal tract (GIT) serves two key functions: (1) to move food down the tract and (2) to mix food thoroughly with the secretions of the GIT to ensure optimal digestion and absorption.
- Deglutition (swallowing) occurs in three phases. The oral phase is voluntary, while the pharyngeal and oesophageal phases are involuntary.
- While the stomach initially relaxes to receive the food from the oesophagus, subsequent contractions help to churn the food into a semiliquid paste called chyme. Gastric emptying depends on a large number of factors including the size and composition of the meal and emotional factors.
- Small intestinal contractions include segmentation contractions aimed at mixing the food thoroughly with the intestinal secretions and peristalsis which propels the chyme forward. Villi movements help to milk the lymph vessels inside the villi.
- Haustrations in the large intestine are the equivalent of segmentation contractions in the small intestine. Mass movements which involve the contraction of a fairly large segment of the large intestine help propel the faeces into the rectum.
- GI reflexes include the defaecation reflex and the gastrocolic and duodenocolic reflexes.

CHAPTER REVIEW QUESTIONS

1. What are the phases of deglutition? Describe the events in the pharyngeal phase.
2. What are movements of the small intestine? Indicate the function of each type of movement.
3. What are the movements of the large intestine? Indicate the function of each type of movement.
4. Describe the defaecation reflex.

CHAPTER 22

Digestion in Mouth, Stomach, Small Intestine, Large Intestine and Absorption of Food

SPECIFIC LEARNING OBJECTIVES

At the end of this chapter, the student should be able to:

- List the end products of digestion for the major food groups.
- List the features of the gastrointestinal tract that favour the absorption of nutrients.
- List the nutrients that are absorbed in each segment of the alimentary tract.
- Describe the role of the large intestine.
- Describe the basis of malabsorption syndromes.

GLOSSARY OF TERMS

- **Macronutrient:** a substance required in large amounts in the diet (e.g. fat, protein and carbohydrate)
- **Micronutrient:** a substance required by the body in small amounts (e.g. minerals and vitamins) which is required for growth and development
- **Villi:** folding of the small intestine into finger-like processes which are critical for the absorption of nutrients
- **Fermentation:** the digestion of nonstarch polysaccharides by anaerobic bacteria

The secretions of the gastrointestinal system have been described in Chapter 19. These secretions break down food into smaller components for absorption. In this chapter, we describe the process of digestion and absorption of different macronutrients and micronutrients.

DIGESTION OF CARBOHYDRATES

Sources of Carbohydrates in the Diet

Carbohydrates are consumed in many foods. These include cereals such as rice, wheat and millet in which the main form of carbohydrate is starch. Disaccharides such as lactose and sucrose are present in milk and cane sugar, respectively. Other nonstarch carbohydrates (called dietary fibre) are present in fruits and vegetables. Cellulose is also present in a variety of vegetables and fruits, typically as the covering of the food, but cannot be digested in the human gastrointestinal tract (GIT).

Digestion of Carbohydrate

- Carbohydrate digestion starts in the mouth. Saliva contains an enzyme called salivary amylase (ptyalin) which breaks down starch into maltose and glucose. Because the food spends a limited time in the mouth, the digestion of starch in the mouth is relatively small. Salivary amylase continues to act when the food passes down the oesophagus into the stomach.
- Starch continues to be only partly digested when it leaves the stomach and requires pancreatic amylase to complete digestion.
- Smaller sugars such as lactose, sucrose, maltose and glucose polymers are broken down by several specific enzymes (disaccharidases) that are secreted from the small intestinal wall.
- Carbohydrates which remain undigested in the small intestine pass into the large intestine. These undigested carbohydrates together with the dietary fibre (nonstarch polysaccharides) are acted upon by bacteria which normally reside in the large intestine through a process called *fermentation*. The end products of fermentation are short-chain fatty acids and gas (predominantly hydrogen and carbon dioxide).

End Products of Digestion of Carbohydrates

The main end product of carbohydrate digestion is glucose. However, fructose and galactose are also formed following the digestion of sucrose and lactose, respectively. Nonstarch polysaccharides (dietary fibre) result in the formation of short-chain fatty acids and gas.

Table 22.1 outlines the sites and fate of carbohydrate digestion in different parts of the GIT.

Table 22.1 Digestion of Carbohydrates: Sites, Enzymes and End Products

Site	Substrate	Enzyme	End Products
Mouth (saliva)	Starch	Salivary amylase	Maltose + glucose
Pancreas	Starch	Pancreatic amylase	Maltose + glucose
Small intestine	Lactose	Lactase	Galactose + glucose
	Sucrose	Sucrase	Fructose + glucose
	Maltose	Maltase	Glucose + glucose
	Glucose polymers	Isomaltase	Glucose
Large intestine	Nonstarch polysaccharides (dietary fibre)	Bacterial enzymes	Short-chain fatty acids + rectal gases

DIGESTION OF PROTEINS

Sources of Proteins in the Diet

The dietary requirement of proteins for adults in India is about 0.8 g/kg body weight/day. For nonvegetarians, meat, poultry and seafood are important sources of protein. Milk and other dairy products, cereals (because of the large amount eaten) and pulses and legumes are other sources of proteins.

Digestion of Proteins

- Once food reaches the stomach, the proteins in food are acted upon by the enzyme pepsin which breaks down the proteins into smaller peptides. You will recall from Chapter 19 that pepsinogen is secreted in the stomach and is converted into pepsin through the action of hydrochloric acid.
- Subsequent digestion of peptides occurs through the action of specific proteolytic enzymes which are released from the pancreas and from the small intestinal wall.

End Products of Protein Digestion

The final end products of protein digestion are amino acids.

Table 22.2 summarizes the sites and process of protein digestion in different parts of the GIT.

Table 22.2 Digestion of Proteins: Sites, Enzymes and End Products

Site	Substrate	Enzyme	End Products
Stomach, about 10%–20% of digestion	Protein	Pepsin	Peptones, polypeptides
Pancreas	Polypeptides, peptones	Trypsin Chymotrypsin	Polypeptides, amino acids
Small intestine	Polypeptides, dipeptides	Various peptidases	Amino acids

DIGESTION OF FATS

Sources of Fat in the Diet

Dietary fat is consumed in many foods and vegetable oils. A certain type of fat called saturated fat is present in higher concentrations in animal foods. Cholesterol is consumed in higher quantities in animal foods and eggs but is also made within our bodies in the liver. Some fish contain high quantities of omega-3 fatty acids which have many health benefits.

Digestion of Fats

- An important part of the digestion of fats is the breakdown of fats into smaller particles called *micelles* by bile salts contained within the bile, a process called *emulsification*. These smaller particles can be acted upon by enzymes more effectively.
- Fat digestion is achieved by three lipases:
  1. Gastric lipase, which is secreted from the stomach, accounts for no more than 10% of fat digestion.
  2. Pancreatic lipase secreted by the pancreas. It can act on the fats only in the GIT in the presence of another enzyme called colipase which is also secreted by the pancreas.
  3. Enteric lipase secreted by the small intestine.

End Products of Fat Digestion

The end products of fat digestion are fatty acids and glycerol. The complete digestion of one triglyceride molecule gives rise to one molecule of glycerol and three molecules of fatty acid.

FEATURES WHICH MAXIMIZE ABSORPTION

In addition to the absorption of the end products of carbohydrates, fats and proteins, a large amount of fluid also needs to be absorbed. This is because the total amount of fluid in the GIT is over 7 L. This includes the fluids that are ingested and those which are secreted at various sites of the GIT.

Since the small intestine is the site where the final end products of digestion are formed, the small intestine is also the site which needs to be specially adapted for absorption.

There are two features which increase absorption in the small intestine:

1. An increase in the surface area of the small intestine:
   This happens in three ways, so that the surface area for absorption of the small intestine is increased about 20 times:
   a. The small intestine is thrown into folds which increase the surface area of the intestine.
   b. On the surface of the small intestine are millions of finger-like projections called villi. These further increase the surface area over which absorption can take place.
   c. Each epithelial cell on a villus has a 'brush border' made up of microvilli which further increases the surface area.
2. There are various specialized proteins (carrier proteins) which ensure transport of the end products of digestion from the lumen into the intestinal epithelial cell.

Fig. 22.1 depicts a typical villus. The diagram helps you understand how the surface area is increased by the villi and the microvilli. Within the villus is a dense capillary network. This capillary network allows end products of digestion to be transferred from the intestinal lumen into the bloodstream where they can be distributed to various parts of the body. Glucose and amino acids are absorbed into these capillary networks. The villus also has a central lacteal which empties into larger lymphatic vessels and ducts. Most of the fatty acids and glycerol are absorbed into the lacteals.

ABSORPTION OF NUTRIENTS IN THE GIT

Stomach: The stomach does not have any villi and also has tight junctions between the lining epithelial cells. For these reasons, the stomach is not a major site of absorption. Alcohol and some highly lipid-soluble drugs are absorbed in the stomach.

Small intestine: The small intestine is especially suited for absorption of the end products of digestion. In addition, however, the small intestine also absorbs a large amount of water and electrolytes. These include sodium, chloride and bicarbonate ions. Minerals such as calcium and iron are also absorbed in the small intestine.

- ***Absorption of glucose:*** Glucose is transported into the apical surface of the epithelial cell by a protein which also transports sodium (secondary active transport). This is why oral rehydration solution contains not only glucose but also salt (sodium). This type of transport is called cotransport because two substances are carried into a cell together. At the basolateral surface of the epithelial cell, glucose is transported by a carrier protein (facilitated diffusion) into the blood stream. Fig. 22.2 shows the absorption of different end products of carbohydrate digestion across the intestinal epithelial cell.
- ***Absorption of amino acids:*** Most amino acids are transported like glucose along with sodium, that is cotransport (secondary active transport). However, some amino acids do not need sodium and are transported into the lining epithelial cell alone by a carrier protein. Because this second type of transport occurs along a concentration gradient without any energy being expended, it is called diffusion. Since it requires a *carrier* protein, however, it is called *facilitated diffusion*.
- ***Absorption of fatty acids and glycerol:*** These end products diffuse into the epithelial cell. There is some evidence that carriers are involved in their absorption. Within the cell, they form new triglycerides and are released as chylomicrons into the lacteals present in the villi. From here, they go into larger lymph vessels and finally enter the bloodstream.
- The role of the terminal ileum: There are many diseases which affect the terminal ileum – the last part of the small intestine. This can disrupt the absorption of substances which are specifically absorbed here such as vitamin B_{12} and bile salts.
- ***Absorption of micronutrients:*** Vitamin A, the deficiency of which is associated with night blindness, is absorbed in the jejunum and ileum. Vitamin D, which is important for healthy bones but which also affects many other processes including immune function, is most rapidly absorbed in the duodenum, but the largest amount is absorbed in the terminal ileum. Calcium is absorbed all along the small intestine and also in the colon. Iron is absorbed most in the duodenum, while zinc is absorbed in the jejunum.

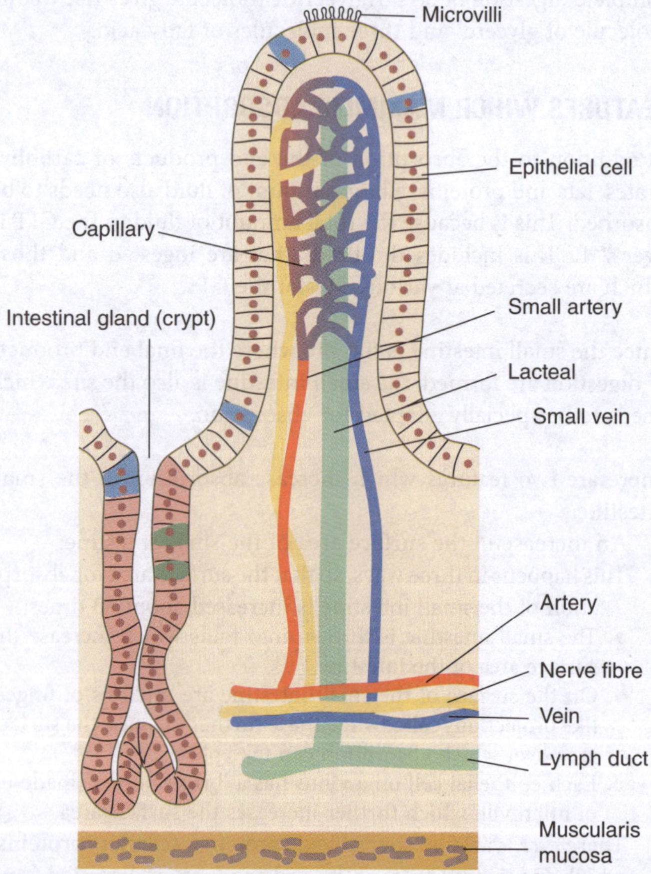

FIG. 22.1 The structure of the intestinal villus.

While many nutrients are absorbed over a large length of the GIT, Fig. 22.3 outlines the site of absorption of some selected nutrients.

ROLE OF THE LARGE INTESTINE

The large intestine has many functions in relation to absorption.

1. It is a major site for the absorption of water and electrolytes. The large intestine has a capacity to absorb between 5 and 8 L of fluid and electrolytes each day.
2. It is a site of 'fermentation'. The large intestine contains anaerobic (not requiring oxygen) bacteria which are part of its normal contents. These bacteria act on undigested food as well as dietary fibre. The end products of this fermentation are short-chain fatty acids and rectal gas (flatus). The colon absorbs vitamins that are created by the colonic bacteria, such as vitamin K (especially important as the daily ingestion of vitamin K is not normally enough to maintain adequate blood coagulation), vitamin B_{12}, thiamine and riboflavin. The short-chain acids are used by the epithelial lining of the colon for nourishment and also have anticancer effects.

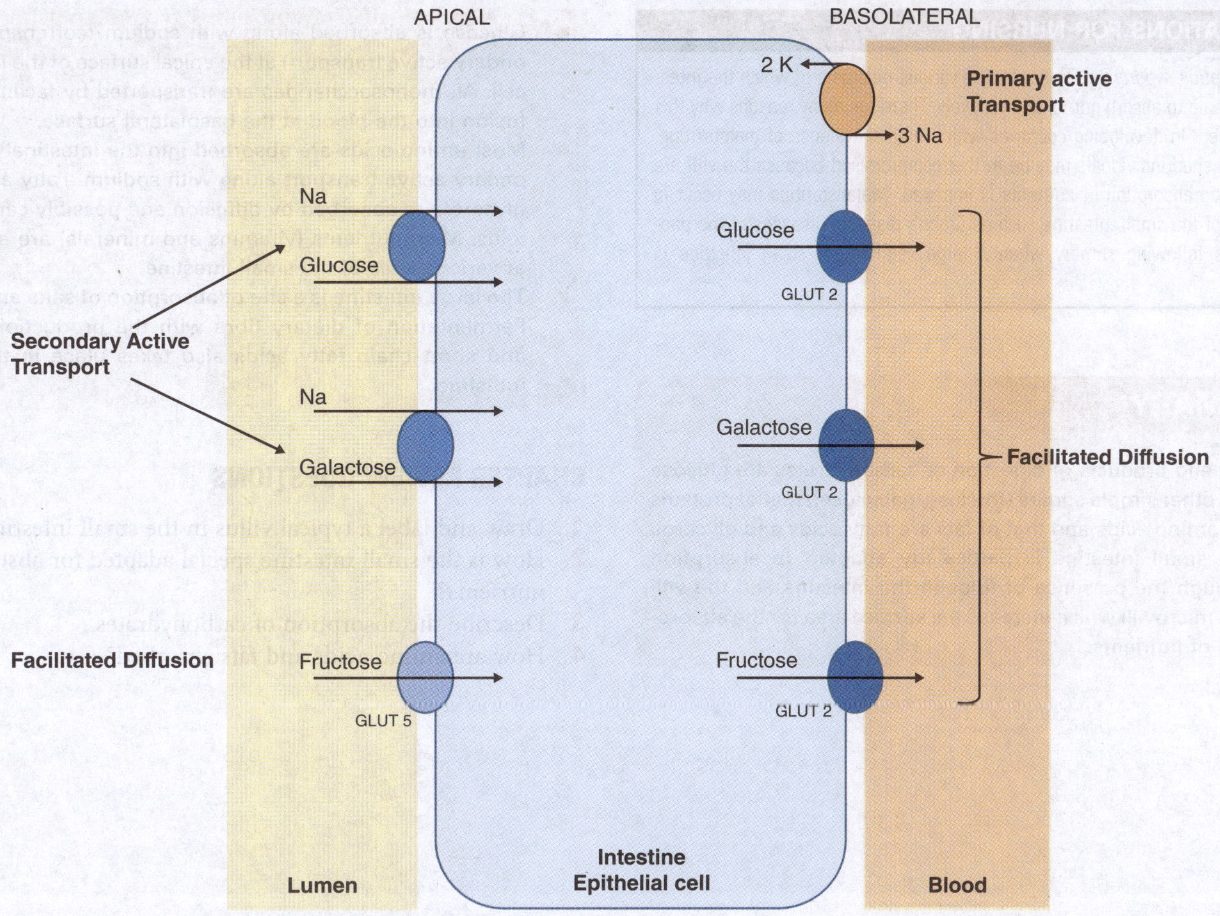

FIG. 22.2 Absorption of monosaccharides in the small intestine.

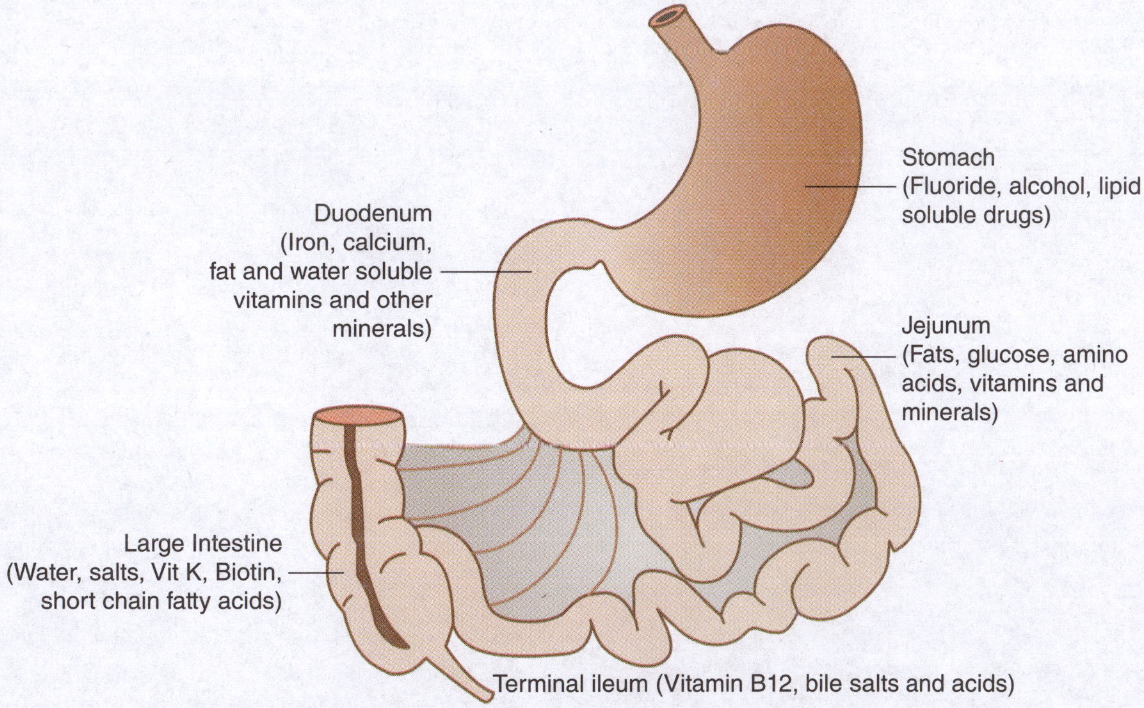

FIG. 22.3 Site of absorption of selected nutrients.

APPLICATIONS FOR NURSING

Malabsorption syndromes: This refers to various disorders in which the intestine is unable to absorb nutrients effectively. There are many reasons why this may happen. In developing countries with a high prevalence of malnutrition, undernourished individuals may be further compromised because the villi are blunted and absorption of nutrients is impaired. Malabsorption may occur in diseases of the small intestine such as Crohn's disease, diseases of the pancreas and following surgery when a large segment of small intestine is removed.

SUMMARY

- The end products of digestion of carbohydrates are glucose and other simple sugars (fructose, galactose), that of proteins are amino acids and that of fats are fatty acids and glycerol.
- The small intestine is particularly adapted to absorption through the presence of folds in the intestine and the villi and microvilli which increase the surface area for the absorption of nutrients.
- Glucose is absorbed along with sodium (cotransport; secondary active transport) at the apical surface of the intestinal cell. All monosaccharides are transported by facilitated diffusion into the blood at the basolateral surface.
- Most amino acids are absorbed into the intestinal cell secondary active transport along with sodium. Fatty acids and glycerol are absorbed by diffusion and possibly carrier proteins. Micronutrients (vitamins and minerals) are absorbed at various sites of the small intestine.
- The large intestine is a site of absorption of salts and water. Fermentation of dietary fibre with the production of gas and short chain fatty acids also takes place in the large intestine.

CHAPTER REVIEW QUESTIONS

1. Draw and label a typical villus in the small intestine.
2. How is the small intestine special adapted for absorption of nutrients?
3. Describe the absorption of carbohydrates.
4. How are amino acids and fats absorbed?

CHAPTER 23

Metabolism of Carbohydrates, Fats and Proteins

SPECIFIC LEARNING OBJECTIVES

At the end of this chapter, the student should be able to:

- Describe the pathways by which glucose is utilized in the cells.
- Describe how glucose is stored and how it can be mobilized for use.
- Describe how amino acids are utilized.
- Describe how fatty acids are metabolized and how fat is stored.

GLOSSARY OF TERMS

- **Glycolysis:** the breakdown of glucose by specific enzymes resulting in pyruvate or lactate and energy (ATP)
- **Glycogenesis:** the formation of glycogen from glucose
- **Glycogenolysis:** the breakdown of glycogen to glucose
- **Gluconeogenesis:** the formation of glucose from noncarbohydrate sources
- **Lipogenesis:** the formation of fat
- **Lipolysis:** the breakdown of fats into fatty acids and glycerol
- **Ketogenesis:** the formation of ketones following breakdown of fats

Once glucose, fatty acids and glycerol and amino acids are absorbed into the body, they take part in different reactions. These reactions generate energy, produce important substances within the body or store nutrients for future use. You will learn about these reactions in greater detail in your biochemistry classes. The aim of this chapter is to provide a brief overview.

UTILIZATION OF GLUCOSE

Entry of Glucose into the Cell

Once glucose is absorbed in the intestine, it can enter cells where it can be used. Glucose enters cells by 'facilitated diffusion' using special carrier proteins in the cell membrane called 'transporters'. Since these transporters carry glucose, they are referred to as GLUT (or **glu**cose **t**ransporter). There are many different types of GLUTs, but the most common one that helps glucose to be taken up in muscle and adipose (fat) tissue is GLUT-4. Entry of glucose into a cell using GLUT usually needs the hormone insulin, although there are exceptions.

Fate of Glucose in the Cell

Once glucose has entered a cell, it is rapidly phosphorylated and is converted into glucose 6-phosphate. This conversion is important because if glucose was not converted, there would be a build-up of glucose in the cell and this would reduce the concentration gradient of glucose so that less and less glucose would then enter the cell. Remember that facilitated diffusion occurs along a concentration gradient (i.e. from high to low concentration).

Once glucose 6-phosphate is formed, it can undergo three reactions:

1. ***glycolysis***: the ultimate aim of which is to produce ATP.
2. ***glycogenesis***: in which glycogen which is the storage form of glucose is produced.
3. ***pentose phosphate pathway:*** during which no ATP is produced, but important chemicals are produced. Some of these chemicals are reducing agents and help to reduce oxidant damage in cells.

Glycolysis

Glycolysis can occur under aerobic (oxygen-rich) or anaerobic (oxygen-depleted) conditions. The aim of glycolysis is to break down glucose and release energy – in this process, pyruvate is formed.

Under aerobic conditions, pyruvate enters the Krebs (citric acid) cycle. Within this cycle, energy-rich molecules (NADH and $FADH_2$) are produced. These molecules enter the electron transport chain in the mitochondria and help produce energy through *oxidative phosphorylation.* Since the mitochondria are the sites of major energy production, they are called the 'power houses' of the cell.

Under anaerobic conditions, pyruvate is converted to lactic acid. Anaerobic glycolysis produces less energy than what is produced under aerobic conditions. When lactic acid is produced in skeletal muscle, it can contribute to muscle fatigue. Table 23.1 compares aerobic and anaerobic glycolysis.

Storage Form of Glucose

The storage form of glucose is glycogen. Glucose is converted to glycogen through a process called ***glycogenesis***, while glucose is produced from glycogen by ***glycogenolysis***. Thus, glycogenesis is the process of formation of glycogen, while glycogenolysis is the process by which glycogen is broken down.

Glycogen is stored in two major sites in the body:

Liver glycogen: The concentration of glycogen in the liver is about five times higher than that in muscle. However, the total amount stored in the liver is only about 100 g of glycogen. The glycogen that is stored in the liver is used mainly to maintain glucose levels in between meals and during prolonged fasting. Thus, after 24 hours of a fast, the liver glycogen reduces to about 35% (i.e. 35 g) of its original value.

Muscle glycogen: Because skeletal muscle is present in much greater quantity in the body (40% of body weight or 25 kg in a 60-kg man vs 1.5 kg liver weight), the total quantity of glycogen stored in the body is greater in skeletal muscle, although its concentration is lower than in the liver. Thus, skeletal muscle stores approximately 500 g of glycogen. The glycogen stored in muscle is used during exercise.

As a storage form of glucose, glycogen provides a ready source of glucose in between meals and during exercise. It is important to have glucose readily available since the brain normally uses glucose as its only fuel for energy.

While glycogen is the primary storage form of glucose, glucose can also be converted to fat, which is another energy storage form in the body. This happens when a person eats a meal rich in carbohydrates (sugars) and glucose levels are then raised to a high level. Under normal circumstances, glucose is converted to pyruvate by glycolysis and then to acetyl-CoA which then enters the citric acid cycle to produce energy in the form of ATP. If the person is inactive, however, there is no need to produce energy and under these circumstances, insulin levels are raised (remember that insulin helps to bring down glucose levels) and the excess glucose is converted into fat. The process of manufacturing fat is called ***lipogenesis*** and in the long term, excess fat storage results in an increased risk of diabetes and cardiovascular disease. Now you know why eating high-carbohydrate, sugary food and physical inactivity work together to increase the risk of diabetes.

Table 23.1 Differences Between Aerobic and Anaerobic Glycolysis

	Aerobic Glycolysis	Anaerobic Glycolysis
Starting reactants	Glucose and oxygen	Glucose
Site of the reaction	Cytoplasm and mitochondria (mitochondria for oxidative phosphorylation)	Cytoplasm
End products	Carbon dioxide, water	Lactic acid
Energy produced	More (38 ATP)	Less (2 ATP)

Gluconeogenesis

While glycogenolysis provides glucose in between meals, another process which helps to maintain circulating glucose levels is gluconeogenesis. Gluconeogenesis is the production of glucose from noncarbohydrate sources such as amino acids and fat. The major site of gluconeogenesis is the liver. Gluconeogenesis occurs when the glucose levels are low and the process is stimulated by various hormones including glucagon (released from the pancreas) and glucocorticoids (released from the adrenal cortex).

UTILIZATION OF AMINO ACIDS

There are three broad categories of amino acids:

1. **Essential amino acids:** These amino acids cannot be synthesized in the body and must therefore be obtained in the diet. These include histidine, isoleucine, leucine, lysine, methionine, phenylalanine, threonine, tryptophan and valine.
2. **Nonessential amino acids:** These can be synthesized in the body, even if they are not consumed in food. These are alanine, arginine, asparagine, aspartic acid, cysteine, glutamic acid, glutamine, glycine, proline, serine and tyrosine.
3. **Conditional amino acids:** These are typically nonessential but become essential during specific conditions such as stress and illness. These are arginine, cysteine, glutamine, tyrosine, glycine, ornithine, proline and serine.

There are basically two ways in which amino acids can be utilized.

1. For protein synthesis in the body, since amino acids are the building blocks of proteins. Proteins that are synthesized may be structural or functional.
2. Amino acid breakdown: Here, amino acids are broken down but can have various fates.
   a. After amino acid breakdown, a part of the amino acid (containing the amino group) can enter a biochemical pathway called the urea cycle and can then be eliminated from the body in the form of urea.
   b. The amino group can be used for nucleotide synthesis (i.e. DNA and RNA).
   c. The carbon-containing portion can be used to form either glucose (through gluconeogenesis) or ketone bodies (ketogenesis). Most amino acids go on to form glucose, whereas only two (leucine and lysine) are purely ketogenic.

UTILIZATION OF FATS

Fatty acids and glycerol which are absorbed from the intestine can have several fates. There is general tendency to think of fats as unhealthy. This is true if excess fat or the unhealthy type is consumed in our diets. But we also need to know that fat is also useful in the body; it provides a layer of insulation when we are exposed to the cold, it provides a source of energy, it is structurally important especially since it is an integral part of our cell membranes and it is also needed to produce a lot of useful chemicals in our body.

1. **Storage in adipose tissue:** Fat is the largest storage form of energy in our body. In its typical form, fat is stored as triglyceride (i.e. three fatty acids + glycerol). This fat storage is part of the subcutaneous fat that is seen just below our skin as well as visceral fat (e.g. in the abdomen). Accumulation of fat within the abdomen is especially unhealthy. Much of the fat in our body is 'white' fat. There is also something called 'brown' fat – this fat not only looks different but also behaves differently. It can produce a lot of heat (thermogenesis) and is therefore very useful during exposure to cold. Newborns have a relatively large amount of brown fat which protects them from hypothermia (cold). However, brown fat continues to persist but in smaller quantities into adulthood. The process by which fat is formed and stored in the body is called *lipogenesis*. When fat is needed for energy, the fat in storage can be released and then broken down – this process is called *lipolysis*.
2. **Oxidation of fatty acids:** Fat is a good source of energy, and energy is released by a process called *beta oxidation*. This process occurs in all tissues except the brain and kidney. During beta oxidation, fatty acids are broken down to acetyl-CoA which then enters the citric acid cycle and produces energy.
3. **Ketogenesis:** When there is excessive beta oxidation as when glucose levels are very low, for instance, during starvation, or when glucose cannot be utilized efficiently as in type 1 diabetes mellitus, acetyl-CoA builds up to concentrations that the citric acid cycle cannot process. Under these circumstances, acetyl-CoA is then converted into ketones. The three main ketones are acetoacetate, acetone and β-hydroxybutyrate. Excess production of ketones is called ketoacidosis.

The various metabolic processes and their interactions are summarized in Fig. 23.1.

APPLICATIONS FOR NURSING

- Fatty acids are carried in the bloodstream either in combination with albumin or as lipoproteins (complexes of fatty acids, triglyceride and cholesterol). When patients are assessed for their 'lipid profile', serum cholesterol is measured along with lipoprotein concentrations and the concentration of triglycerides. Some of the lipoproteins may be 'healthy', such as high-density lipoprotein (HDL), while others are unhealthy. Unhealthy lipid profiles can be addressed through dietary advice, increasing physical activity (which has been shown to increase HDL) and medications which lower lipid concentrations.
- In type 1 diabetes, the excess production of ketones in the body because of excessive oxidation of fats results in ketoacidosis and this may progress to coma and even death. Nurses need to recognize this condition. The symptoms include excess thirst and urination, difficulty in breathing and a fruity odour in the breath, among others. The difficulty in breathing is characterized by deep and laboured breaths and is called Kussmaul's breathing.

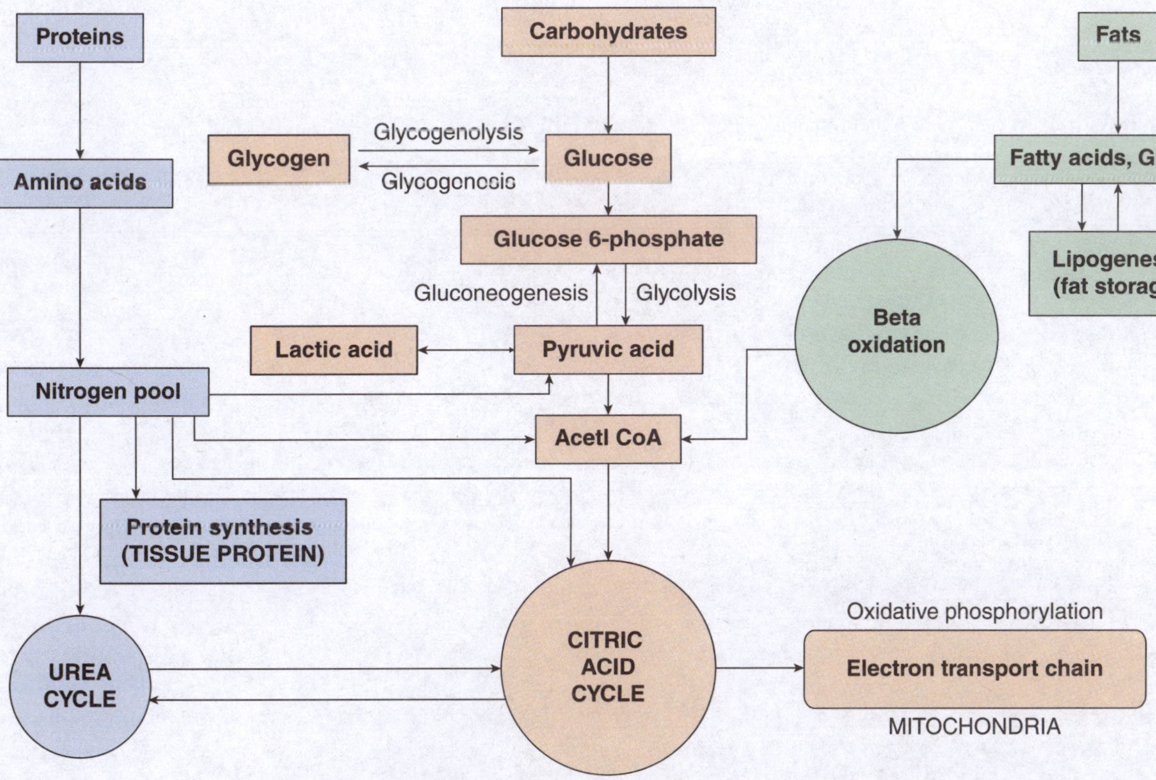

FIG. 23.1 Interactions of metabolic pathways in the human body.

SUMMARY

- Glucose is taken up into cells primarily via GLUT proteins located on the cell membrane. Once glucose enters the cell, it can undergo glycolysis and the generation of energy, glycogenesis, that is conversion into the storage forms of glucose (glycogen), or enter the pentose phosphate pathway.
- Between meals and during fasting, glucose is made available by glycogenolysis and gluconeogenesis.
- Pyruvic acid via acetyl CoA can enter the citric acid cycle. ATP can additionally be produced through oxidative phosphorylation in the mitochondria.
- Amino acids that are absorbed are primarily used for protein synthesis and for the manufacture of other chemical substances in the body.
- Fatty acids once absorbed may be stored as fat or oxidized to provide energy. Excess fat oxidation can result in ketosis.

CHAPTER REVIEW QUESTIONS

1. Explain the following terms: (a) glycolysis, (b) gluconeogenesis, (c) glycogenolysis, (d) glycogenesis, (e) lipogenesis, (f) ketogenesis.
2. What is the storage form of glucose? What is its importance in the body?

CHAPTER 24

Applications and Implications of Gastrointestinal Physiology in Nursing

SPECIFIC LEARNING OBJECTIVES

At the end of this chapter, the student should be able to:

- Describe the pathophysiology of gastro-oesophageal reflux disease (GERD).
- List the mechanism of action of drugs used for acid peptic disease based on the physiology of gastric acid secretion.
- Enumerate and interpret liver function tests.
- Describe the causes and consequences of malabsorption syndrome.
- Describe the pathophysiology and broad causes of constipation.
- Describe the pathophysiology of diarrhoea.
- Describe the pathophysiology of irritable bowel disease.

GLOSSARY OF TERMS

- **Gastro-oesophageal reflux disease (GERD):** a condition in which acid enters the oesophagus through the lower oesophageal sphincter resulting in various symptoms and, if chronic, oesophageal injury
- **Ulcer:** in the context of the digestive tract, a discontinuity of the mucosa
- **Malabsorption:** diseases in which there is an inability to absorb nutrients, minerals and vitamins from the digestive tract
- **Steatorrhoea:** increased excretion of fat in the stools (stools are typically bulky, fatty and foul smelling)
- **Constipation:** infrequent stools (<3 per week), difficult stool passage or both
- **Diarrhoea:** the passage of three or more loose/watery stools per day

In this chapter, we discuss the problems of the digestive system that a nurse commonly faces. The focus of this chapter is the altered physiology (pathophysiology) that occurs in these diseases.

GASTRO-OESOPHAGEAL REFLUX DISEASE

Gastro-oesophageal reflux disease (GERD) is a disease which affects millions of people throughout the world. In GERD, there is a weak lower oesophageal sphincter (between the oesophagus and the stomach). As a result, the acid and other stomach contents move from the stomach to the lower oesophagus (Fig. 24.1). Patients with this problem may experience 'heartburn' (a burning sensation in the lower chest), chest pain or a sour taste in the mouth associated with a sudden reflux of acid. Acid can move far up the oesophagus and also affect the throat and larynx. In this situation, patients may experience cough, a persistent sensation of a lump in the throat which requires constant clearing and, in susceptible individuals, asthma.

GERD is more common in those who smoke, consume alcohol and are obese or under severe stress. It may be triggered by the consumption of a large meal. Patients who suffer from night-time reflux may find that it interferes with their sleep.

Long-standing GERD can result in inflammation of the oesophagus, a condition called oesophagitis. This in turn can be a risk factor for oesophageal cancer in susceptible individuals.

How Nurses Can Help Patients with GERD

Nurses may need to provide health education about lifestyle and diet to patients with GERD. This includes the following:

- Consumption of small, frequent meals rather than few large meals.
- Night meal to be consumed 3 hours before sleeping.
- Avoiding greasy and spicy foods and this will promote sustained and higher acid secretion in the stomach.
- Avoiding smoking and alcohol consumption.
- Sleeping in the left lateral position with the head end of the bed elevated (in this position, the oesophagus is above the stomach and acid flow into the oesophagus tends to reduce; sleeping on the back and in the right lateral position places the stomach above the oesophagus, making acid reflux easier).

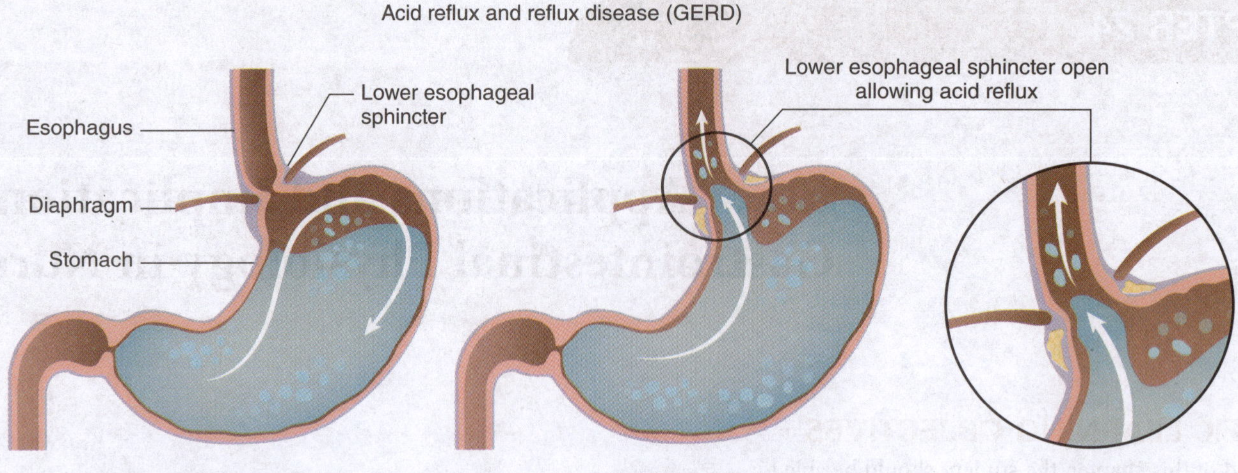

FIG. 24.1 The nature of gastro-oesophageal reflux disease (GERD).

- Increasing regular physical activity but restricting vigorous activity soon after a meal

ACID PEPTIC DISEASE

This refers to disease due to excessive secretion of acid in the stomach. It may range from a temporary gastritis to the development of peptic ulcers. An ulcer is a discontinuation of the mucosa. Peptic ulcers may be located in the stomach or in the upper duodenum.

The causes of acid peptic disease include the following:

- *Helicobacter pylori* infection (this bacillus causes an inflammation of the gastric mucosa and ultimately, if untreated, ulceration)
- Chronic consumption of nonsteroidal anti-inflammatory drugs (NSAIDs)
- Chronic stress
- Radiation/chemotherapy
- Chronic alcohol consumption and smoking

Since acid peptic disease is relatively common, it is important for nurses to understand the basic mechanism of the drugs that are used to treat acid peptic disease. It is good at this stage to quickly revise the regulation of gastric acid secretion in Chapter 19. As shown in Fig. 24.2, the parietal cell which secretes H^+ ions into the gastric lumen has three major receptors. These include the H2 histamine receptor, the gastrin receptor and the muscarinic receptor. H^+ ions are secreted into the gastric lumen using the proton pump which exchanges H^+ ion for K^+ ion.

Medications that are used to treat acid peptic disease are indicated in Fig. 24.2 in red. Antacids work by neutralizing the H^+ ions in the gastric lumen. The advantage is that they are easily available, act rapidly and provide immediate relief. H2 receptor antagonists such as ranitidine and cimetidine act by blocking the H2 receptor and reducing the formation of H^+ ion in the cell. Proton pump inhibitors like omeprazole act by reducing the action of the proton pump and reducing the secretion of H^+ ions into the gastric lumen. If *H. pylori* infection is suspected to be a cause of the symptoms, then specific antibiotics have to be used.

LIVER FUNCTION TESTS

There are many tests that can be performed to evaluate liver function.

1. Enzymes that are normally present within the liver cells escape into circulation when the liver cells are damaged. Two enzymes which are commonly present in liver cells and are used as an indicator of liver damage are serum aspartate aminotransferase (AST) and serum alanine aminotransferase (ALT).
2. Serum bilirubin levels will be elevated when the liver cells are inflamed and block the flow of bile within the liver (cholestasis). Bilirubin exists in two forms:
   a. Unconjugated bilirubin is the water-insoluble form that is present in plasma following the breakdown of the haem component of haemoglobin.
   b. Conjugated bilirubin is formed when unconjugated bilirubin is taken up into the liver cells and combined with glucuronic acid, making it water soluble.

   In liver disease, bilirubin levels will be increased and will be a mix of unconjugated and conjugated bilirubin.
3. Estimation of proteins normally produced in the liver: The production of proteins in the liver will be reduced in liver disease. The proteins normally assessed include albumin and clotting factors. Impaired production of clotting factors can also be assessed using a test of clotting such as the clotting time and prothrombin time.
4. Imaging of the liver: While earlier imaging of the liver was relatively limited using X-rays, current methods such as ultrasound, CT and MRI have allowed tumours within the liver to be seen more clearly.

MALABSORPTION SYNDROMES

In these diseases, there is an inability to absorb nutrients, minerals and vitamins from the digestive tract. Adequate absorption

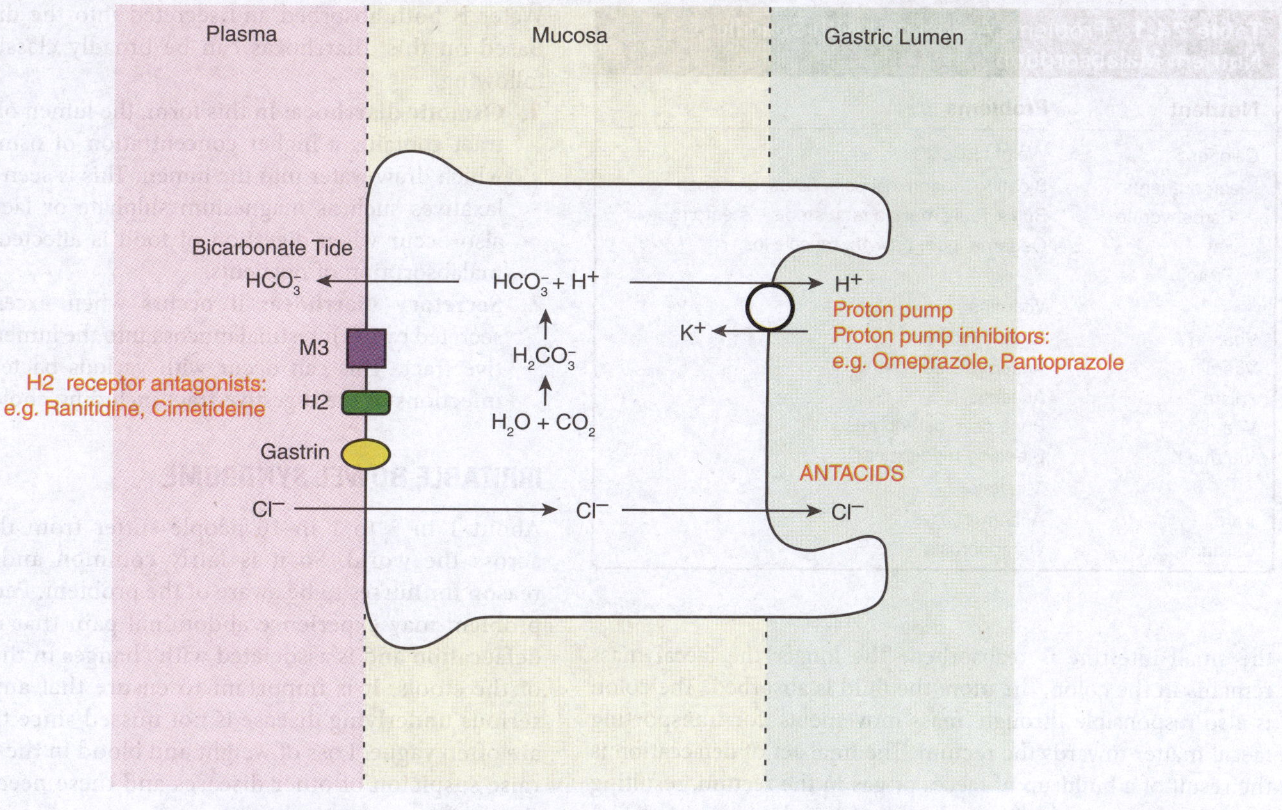

FIG. 24.2 Drugs acting to control acid secretion from the parietal cell of the stomach.

requires complete digestion. Nutrients are then moved along the digestive tract at a speed that allows for maximum absorption. The intestinal lining must be intact and functioning appropriately to allow nutrients to be absorbed. Even if nutrients are adequately absorbed, an individual may suffer from nutrient deficiencies if there are problems with the lymphatics or blood vessels that carry nutrients to the sites where they are utilized. Disruption of any of these processes can result in malabsorption. Malabsorption syndromes may be divided into three categories:

1. **Premucosal:** This refers to malabsorption in which the problem is incomplete digestion, most often due to enzyme or bile acid/salt deficiencies. Bacterial overgrowth and a large parasite load in the gut can also interfere with the absorption of nutrients.
2. **Mucosal:** This includes all causes that interfere with absorption across the mucosa. This may be due to defects in the structure and function of the intestinal wall but may also occur following surgery if a large part of the intestine is removed. In some situations, the absorption of multiple nutrients will be affected, and in others a single nutrient.
3. **Postmucosal:** This refers to obstruction in vascular (blood vessel) or lymphatic drainage of the gut.

The problems of malabsorption depend on the cause, the part of the digestive tract that is affected and the duration of the problem.

1. If carbohydrates are not digested and absorbed in the small intestine, they are transported into the large intestine. Here the carbohydrates undergo fermentation in the presence of anaerobic bacteria and this produces gas as a by-product. The patient may experience bloating and severe abdominal pain.
2. If bile salts are not secreted, emulsification of fats is reduced. This process is required for fats to be broken down into smaller particles which can be acted upon by lipases. In this situation, fat is not absorbed and the patient may excrete foul-smelling, fatty stools – a condition called steatorrhoea.
3. The inadequate absorption of nutrients can result in specific nutrient deficiencies. The patient may experience weight loss and anaemia due to the inadequate absorption of iron, vitamin B_{12} or folate. Growth may be impaired and bones may be inadequately mineralized, among many other problems. The major problem with malabsorption is malnutrition. Table 24.1 outlines the problems associated with the deficiency of specific nutrients.

CONSTIPATION

Constipation is characterized by infrequent passage of stools (i.e. less than three per week), straining while passing stools, passage of hard, lumpy stools and a sense of incomplete evacuation.

The colon plays an important part in defaecation. It is here that the majority of the fluid (approximately 1.5 L) that enters from

Table 24.1 Problems Associated with Specific Nutrient Malabsorption

Nutrient	Problems
Calories	Weight loss
Macronutrients:	Bloating, abdominal pain, flatus, diarrhoea
Carbohydrate	Bulky, foul-smelling fatty stools – steatorrhoea
Fat	Oedema, poor growth, muscle loss
Protein	
	Vitamins:
Vitamin A	Night blindness
Vitamin B_{12}	Anaemia, neuropathy
Folate	Anaemia
Vitamin D	Bone pain, osteoporosis
Vitamin K	Bleeding tendencies
	Minerals:
Iron	Anaemia
Calcium	Osteoporosis

the small intestine is reabsorbed. The longer the faecal mass remains in the colon, the more the fluid is absorbed. The colon is also responsible through 'mass movements' for transporting faecal matter towards the rectum. The final act of defaecation is the result of a build-up of faeces or gas in the rectum, resulting in an inhibition of the internal sphincter and an urge to defaecate. The external anal sphincter is under voluntary control.

Constipation may occur due to a variety of causes:

- Poor bowel habits.
- Low dietary fibre intake (some of the types of dietary fibre increase the retention of water – this results in the formation of larger, softer stools which are easier to evacuate).
- Various neurological and chronic diseases such as diabetes, Parkinson's disease and cancers of the colon.
- Various medications as a side effect.

Some treatments:

Large bowel enema:

This procedure is the injection of fluid via a nozzle into the lower bowel with the aim of relieving constipation and inducing defaecation, and as a means of bowel cleansing prior to lower abdominal surgery. Nurses in surgical wards will be familiar with this procedure as a method of preparing patients for surgery.

Laxatives:

These are medications that are used to induce defaecation. There are two broad categories of laxatives: (1) osmotic laxatives draw water into the gut lumen and result in bulkier and softer stools; and (2) stimulant laxatives increase gastrointestinal motility.

DIARRHOEA

The increased frequency of loose or watery stools is called diarrhoea. By convention, increased frequency is defined as three or more stools per day.

Water is both absorbed and secreted into the digestive tract. Based on this, diarrhoeas can be broadly classified into the following:

1. **Osmotic diarrhoea:** In this form, the lumen of the digestive tract contains a higher concentration of osmotic particles which draw water into the lumen. This is seen with osmotic laxatives such as magnesium sulphate or lactulose. It can also occur when digestion of food is affected, resulting in malabsorption of nutrients.
2. **Secretory diarrhoea:** It occurs when excessive fluid is secreted by the intestinal mucosa into the lumen of the digestive tract. This can occur with various bacterial and viral infections of the digestive tract including cholera.

IRRITABLE BOWEL SYNDROME

About 1 in 5 to 1 in 10 people suffer from this condition across the world. So it is fairly common and this a good reason for nurses to be aware of the problem. People with this problem may experience abdominal pain that is relieved by defaecation and is associated with changes in the consistency of the stools. It is important to ensure that any other more serious underlying disease is not missed since the symptoms are often vague. Loss of weight and blood in the stools should raise suspicion of other diseases and these need to be investigated for.

Some individuals with irritable bowel syndrome (IBS) present with diarrhoea, others with constipation, some have alternating diarrhoea and constipation, some have abdominal pain as the predominant symptoms and in some individuals the symptoms occur following an infection.

Although the pathophysiology of IBS is complex, it may be viewed simply as having two predominant features:

1. Visceral hypersensitivity which is associated with abdominal discomfort or pain.
2. Gastrointestinal motor disturbances which lead to diarrhoea or constipation.

The treatment of IBS is continuously improving but in the context of nursing, some nonpharmacological approaches include the following:

- **The promotion of physical activity/exercise/yoga:** These have been shown to reduce stress and abdominal pain and discomfort.
- **Dietary modification:** This is done through elimination diets where foods which are known to trigger allergies are stopped in the diet one by one to determine any improvement in symptoms.
- **Dietary fibre:** While some fermentable carbohydrates might increase the sense of bloating, 'gas' and abdominal pain, fibre from fruits and vegetables generally reduces symptoms. There are some dietary fibre supplements which are commercially available.

CLINICAL CASE PROBLEMS

(A) ***A 3-year-old boy presents with diarrhoea described as large volume, watery, and with bowel movements occurring eight times a day. His eyeballs are sunken and he appears lethargic. He does not have any fever on examination. A stool test is suggestive of cholera.***

a. Why are his eyeballs sunken? What other clinical features will you look for?

b. What is the pathophysiology of diarrhoea with cholera?

(B) ***A 24-year-old woman has undergone extensive small bowel (including terminal ileum) removal during surgery.***

a. What nutrients are absorbed in the terminal ileum?

b. What are the types of movements that are seen in the small intestine?

c. What problem is this woman likely to face if no action is taken?

(C) ***A 35-year-old business executive who is also a smoker comes to the hospital with the complaint that he experiences burning in his upper abdomen before he gets up in the morning and about 2–3 hours after every meal.***

a. What is the reason for the patient's complaints?

b. With the help of a diagram, indicate the formation and regulation of acid secretion in the parietal cell.

c. What medications can be used to relieve the symptoms and what are the mechanisms of action?

d. What advice will you give the patient as a nurse?

SELF-DIRECTED LEARNING

1. What is the mechanism of water absorption in the digestive tract?
2. What are the most common causes of diarrhoea in children younger than 5 years in India?
3. What is endoscopy and what are its uses?

WHAT YOU CAN LEARN FROM A HOSPITAL VISIT

1. Visit a nursing station in the surgical ward and talk to the nurse about the procedure used for the preparation of the digestive system prior to abdominal surgery.
2. Obtain a laboratory investigation form from the hospital. List the tests that are done to assess:
   a. Liver function
   b. Malabsorption

4 SECTION

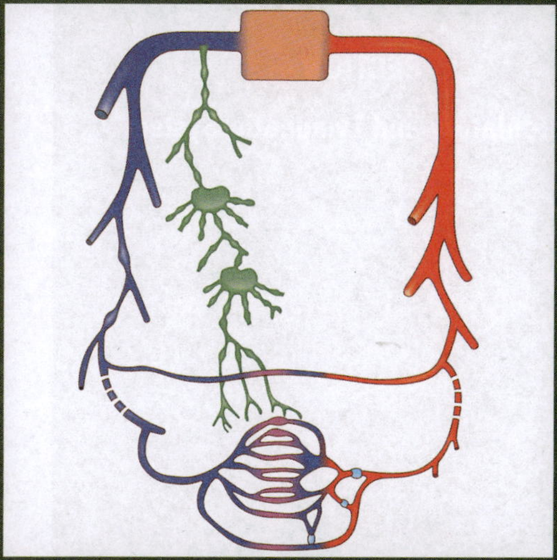

Circulatory and Lymphatic System

Section Outline

SECTION 4

Circulatory and Lymphatic System

CHAPTER 25

Organization of the Circulatory System and Functional Anatomy of the Heart

SPECIFIC LEARNING OBJECTIVES

At the end of this chapter, the student should be able to:

- Describe the organization of the circulatory system and differentiate between the pulmonary and systemic circulations.
- Describe the different blood vessels that make up the circulatory system.
- Describe the functional organization of the heart.
- Describe the cells in the heart.
- List the special features of cardiac muscle.

GLOSSARY OF TERMS

- **Autorhythmicity:** the ability to generate its own rhythm
- **Fatigue:** the inability to sustain a given amplitude of contraction (therefore, nonfatigability refers to the absence of fatigue)
- **Excitability:** the ability of a cell to respond to a stimulus
- **Syncytium:** many cells functioning as a single unit
- **Refractory period:** that time period when a cell does not respond to a stimulus

In this chapter, we discuss the anatomical and functional features of the circulatory system, especially the heart. The heart is a remarkable organ – it weighs only 300 g, is the size of a fist, and contracts at least once a second, on average, for our entire lives without tiring.

FUNCTIONAL ORGANIZATION OF THE HEART

While the heart is often thought of as a single muscular pump, the heart is actually made of two parts – the left heart comprising the left atrium and the left ventricle and the right heart comprising the right atrium and the right ventricle. These two parts of the heart function as two pumps in series. Thus, the left ventricle pumps out oxygenated blood into the aorta from where through multiple arteries it is distributed to different organs of the body. The deoxygenated blood returns to the right atrium via the superior and inferior vena cava. The right ventricle then pumps this blood through the lungs (the pulmonary circulation) where it gets oxygenated before entering the left atrium. This is shown in Fig. 25.1. The left ventricle pumps blood through a larger circulation, the systemic circulation. For this reason, the left ventricle is about three times the thickness of the right ventricle.

THE PULMONARY AND SYSTEMIC CIRCULATIONS

The left ventricle and the right ventricle pump equal amounts of blood into the systemic and the pulmonary circulation, respectively. However, since the systemic circulation is a larger circulation, the pressure required to drive the flow of blood through this circulation is higher than the pressure in the pulmonary circulation, which is much smaller. Thus, the pressure (which is pulsatile) in the systemic circulation is approximately five to six times higher than the pressure in the pulmonary circulation (120/80 mm Hg vs 25/8 mm Hg). The pulmonary circulation's main function is the oxygenation of blood and the transfer of carbon dioxide from the blood to the lungs. In contrast, the systemic circulation distributes oxygenated blood to the organs of the body and collects waste metabolites and carbon dioxide from metabolically active tissues.

The differences between the systemic and pulmonary circulations are summarized in Table 25.1.

BLOOD VESSELS OF THE CIRCULATORY SYSTEM

The blood vessels of the circulatory system vary in structure and function. Large arteries like the aorta have high elastin content in their walls and are called *elastic arteries*. Thus, when large arteries are stretched, they show elastic recoil and this helps to propel blood along the blood vessels. As arteries become smaller and smaller in diameter, they have more smooth muscle and less elastin content in their walls. Because of their higher muscle content, they are able to contract more strongly. Contraction of these smaller arteries and 'arterioles' results in a reduction in the

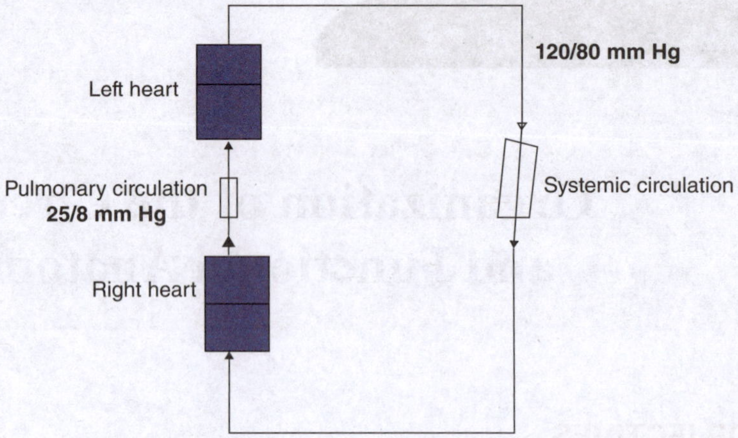

FIG. 25.1 A schematic representation of the organization of the circulatory system.

Table 25.1 A Comparison of the Systemic and Pulmonary Circulations

	Systemic Circulation	Pulmonary Circulation
Main purpose	Distribution of oxygenated blood to various tissues	Oxygenation of blood and removal of carbon dioxide
Pressures	120/80 mm Hg	25/8–10 mm Hg
Cardiac blood flow into the circulation at rest (cardiac output)	5 L/min	5 L/min
Main artery and type of blood	Aorta: oxygenated blood	Pulmonary artery: deoxygenated blood
Main veins and type of blood	Inferior and superior vena cava: deoxygenated blood	Pulmonary veins: oxygenated blood
Response of blood vessels to hypoxia	Vasodilation	Vasoconstriction

Table 25.2 Characteristics of Different Blood Vessels of the Circulatory System

Blood Vessel	Type of Vessel	Importance
Large arteries	Elastic vessels	Show elastic recoil which helps propel blood
Small arteries/ arterioles	Resistance vessels	Capable of strong muscle contraction – offer resistance to the flow of blood
Capillaries	Exchange vessels	Exchange of nutrients and waste products in the tissues
Veins	Capacitance vessels	Carry blood back to the heart; contain a large quantity of the blood in circulation

diameter of the blood vessel. When this happens, there is increased resistance to the flow of blood; these vessels are, therefore, called *resistance vessels.* In tissues, the smallest vessels are the capillaries which are nothing but a vessel lined by a single layer of endothelial cells. There are many capillaries and the blood flow through them is slow. This allows for an exchange of nutrients and waste products between the capillary and the tissue cells. Because the function of these blood vessels is mainly the exchange of substances between the blood and the tissues in both directions (nutrients from blood to tissues; waste products from tissues to blood), they are referred to as *exchange vessels.* Capillaries carry the waste products from tissues into venules which then empty into larger veins. Veins are more thin walled than arteries and have less smooth muscle. The pressure in veins is also low. Thus, they collapse when they are empty of blood. You can observe this by raising your hand above your head – the veins on the dorsum (back) of the hand appear to disappear when the hand is raised. A large amount of blood is contained in the veins and it is for this reason that they are referred to as *capacitance vessels.*

Table 25.2 summarizes the importance of different blood vessels that make up the circulatory system.

CELLS OF THE HEART

The heart has other cells apart from the cardiac muscle cells. The cells of the heart include:

1. **Cardiomyocytes:** These are the cardiac muscle cells. They have different properties from skeletal muscle and smooth muscle. They are striated, branched and involuntary. *Intercalated discs* connect adjacent cardiomyocytes. These are low-resistance pathways which allow an electrical impulse to pass

from one cell to another. Cardiomyocytes make up most of the heart.

2. **Conducting cells:** These cells form part of a specialized system in the heart called the conducting system (Chapter 26). One of the purposes of the conducting system is to conduct impulses even faster than they would be transmitted between cells through the intercalated discs.
3. **Pacemaker cells:** These cells are specialized cells that are capable of generating their own electrical rhythm even in the absence of nerves and hormones. The heart rate is determined by the pacemaker region of the heart called the sinoatrial (SA) node.
4. **Endocrine cells:** These cells secrete hormones which act on the cardiovascular system. An example of these is the endocrine cells in the right atrium which secrete a hormone called atrial natriuretic peptide: this hormone regulates excretion of urine and helps to maintain blood volume.

FUNCTIONAL FEATURES OF CARDIOMYOCYTES (CARDIAC MUSCLE CELLS)

This section deals with how cardiac muscle cells function and focuses on some special features of cardiac muscle cells.

1. **Excitability:** All living cells, including cardiomyocytes, respond to a stimulus – this property is called excitability. The stimulus for cardiomyocytes is variable and includes activation (which promotes contraction) or inhibition (which reduces contraction) through the autonomic nervous system, hormones, ions, drugs, etc.
2. **Contractility:** Cardiac muscle shares with smooth and skeletal muscles the property of contractility or muscle shortening. The contractility of the cardiac muscle cells allows the heart to function as a pump, propelling blood along the blood vessels.
3. **Autorhythmicity:** Cardiac muscle cells are capable of contracting independently in a rhythmic fashion. However, nerves and hormones help to regulate the rate and amplitude (strength) of contraction. This is why a completely denervated (without nerves) transplanted heart can contract rhythmically. In the heart, the rate at which the heart contracts is determined by the pacemaker of the heart; this is the SA node. The generation of the cardiac impulse from the SA node is discussed in Chapter 26.
4. **Conductivity:** Cardiac muscle can conduct impulses from one cell to another cell. This is because there are intercalated discs between the cardiac muscle fibres. These structures function as low-resistance pathways, allowing an electrical impulse to travel from one cell to another cell.
5. **Syncytium:** Cardiac muscle functions as a syncytium (i.e. a single functional unit). Thus, if a stimulus is directly applied to the heart, the entire cardiac muscle syncytium will contract. This is because the impulse will travel through the intercalated discs and stimulate other cardiac muscle fibres.
6. **Long refractory period:** Refractory period is that period during which a second stimulus applied to the cell elicits no response. While the primary function of the cardiomyocyte is to contract, this happens only when an electrical response called an action potential is generated in the cell. Skeletal muscle cells also contract and contraction like the cardiac muscle also requires an action potential. However, the duration and shape of the action potential in cardiac and skeletal muscles are different.

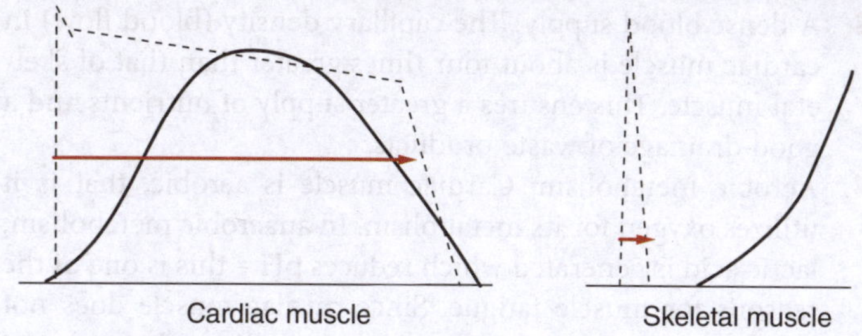

FIG. 25.2 A comparison of the action potential and refractory period of skeletal and cardiac muscles.

In Fig. 25.2, the dotted line represents the action potential and the solid line the contractile response. The red arrow represents the refractory period. There are several points which are shown in Fig. 25.2:

1. The action potential in skeletal muscle happens before the contraction, while it is simultaneous (occurs together) with the contraction in cardiac muscle.
2. The action potential is short in skeletal muscle and is long in cardiac muscle.
3. The refractory period is long in cardiac muscle and is relatively short in skeletal muscle.

In skeletal muscle, the short refractory period before the onset of contractions means that the skeletal muscle can be repeatedly stimulated during a contraction. While this results in a greater amplitude of contraction, there is also increased fatigability of skeletal muscle, where the skeletal muscle is unable to sustain a given amplitude of contraction. In contrast, cardiac muscle is nonfatigable and one of the reasons for this is the long refractory period. This is discussed further, in the subsequent text.

Nonfatigability of Cardiac Muscle Cells

One of the most fascinating things about cardiac muscle fibres is that they contract rhythmically without rest for the duration of our lives. Fatigue is the inability to sustain a given amplitude of contraction. Cardiac muscles do not demonstrate fatigue. This is because of a number of reasons:

1. Long refractory period.
2. Large amount of mitochondria: A cardiac muscle cell is about one-third mitochondria by weight. This means that the cardiac muscle can make large amounts of energy (ATP) for muscle contraction.

3. A dense blood supply: The capillary density (blood flow) in cardiac muscle is about four times greater than that of skeletal muscle. This ensures a greater supply of nutrients and a good drainage of waste products.
4. Aerobic metabolism: Cardiac muscle is aerobic, that is it utilizes oxygen for its metabolism. In anaerobic metabolism, lactic acid is generated which reduces pH – this is one of the reasons for muscle fatigue. Since cardiac muscle does not generate ATP through anaerobic metabolism, this cause of fatigue does not apply to cardiac muscle.

APPLICATIONS FOR NURSING

Although cardiac muscle in a healthy individual is nonfatigable, in clinical situations such as, for instance, following a myocardial infarction (heart attack), the nurse may need to assist or perform cardiopulmonary resuscitation (CPR).

While the detailed procedure of CPR is discussed in Chapter 33, there are a few basic principles:

- Act quickly.
- Check for pulse and for breathing.
- Ensure that the airway is open – this is done by head-tilt and chin-up position.
- Apply chest compressions – this compresses the heart externally and helps to sustain circulation.
- Support breathing – mouth to mouth/mouth to mask, etc.

SUMMARY

- The cardiovascular system is made up of two circulations: the systemic circulation and the pulmonary circulation. The pressures in the systemic circulation are about five to six times the pressures in the pulmonary circulation.
- The circulatory systems are made up of a variety of blood vessels which differ in structure and function. These include elastic vessels (large arteries), resistance vessels (small arteries and arterioles), exchange vessels (capillaries) and capacitance vessels (veins).
- The heart is largely made up of contractile cells called cardiomyocytes. Other cells include conducting cells, pacemaker cells and endocrine cells.
- Cardiac muscle is characterized by several features which include excitability, contractility, conductivity and autorhythmicity. It has a long refractory period and is nonfatigable. Because of the presence of intercalated discs between cells, cardiac muscle functions as a single unit called a syncytium.

CHAPTER REVIEW QUESTIONS

1. What are the differences in the pulmonary and systemic circulations?
2. What are the functions of the large arteries, arterioles, capillaries and veins?
3. Describe four special properties of cardiac muscle cells.
4. What are the reasons why cardiac muscle does not fatigue?

CHAPTER 26

Conduction of the Cardiac Impulse and Electrocardiogram

SPECIFIC LEARNING OBJECTIVES

At the end of this chapter, the student should be able to:

- List the pacemaker areas of the heart.
- Draw a diagram of the conducting system of the heart and describe the sequence of events.
- Explain the functions of the conducting system of the heart.
- List the leads of a 12-lead ECG.
- Draw a typical ECG and label its parts.
- List the uses of ECG with specific focus on (1) arrhythmias and (2) myocardial ischaemia and infarction.

GLOSSARY OF TERMS

- **Pacemaker (P) cells:** cells which generate their own electrical rhythm (seen in the SA and AV nodes in the heart)
- **Nodal delay:** delay in transmission of the cardiac impulse that occurs at the AV node
- **Chronotropy:** relating to heart rate
- **Tachycardia:** increase (tachy = fast) in heart rate above 100 beats per minute
- **Bradycardia:** decrease (brady = slow) in heart rate below 60 beats/min

INTRODUCTION

Excitability is the ability of a cell to respond to a stimulus. A stimulus is any change in the environment that induces a reaction.

At rest, living cells have a membrane potential because there are more negative charges inside of the cell membrane than on the outside. This is called the 'resting membrane potential'. When cells respond to a stimulus, they do so first with an electrical response (in which the cell changes its membrane potential) and then with a biological response. The electrical response to an adequate stimulus is **depolarization** where the inside of the cell membrane becomes positively charged. This is followed by a return of the cell to its resting state – a process called **repolarization** (Fig. 26.1). The biological response that follows the electrical response depends on the type of cell. Thus, muscle cells such as cardiomyocytes contract, endocrine cells secrete hormones, etc.

The heart is made up mainly of muscle cells called cardiomyocytes, or, simply, cardiac muscle cells. There are, however, also cells that have a special property of 'autorhythmicity'. These are called P cells. In this chapter, we will discuss where the P cells are and how the cardiac electrical impulse spreads throughout the heart. We will also discuss how the electrical activity of the heart can be recorded in an electrocardiogram (ECG).

THE PACEMAKER OF THE HEART

The heart contracts about 70 times/min at rest. This is the resting heart rate. When we are stressed or when we exercise hard, the heart rate goes up. The maximum heart rate depends on our age and is given by the following formula: 220 − age in years. So, if you are 20 years old, your maximum heart rate is 200 times/min (220 − 20), whereas the maximal heart rate for a 50-year-old is only 170 beats/min (220 − 50). What determines the rate at which the heart contracts?

Look at Fig. 26.2. In the upper corner of the right atrium is an area called the sinoatrial (SA) node. The lower part of the interatrial septum has an area called the atrioventricular (AV) node. Both these areas are special because they contain P cells or 'pacemaker' cells. They are called pacemaker cells because they have their own independent electrical activity. That is, they generate their own electrical activity even in the absence of nerves or hormones. The SA node pacemaker cells fire at about 70–80 times/min, while the AV node pacemaker cells fire at about 30–40 times/min. The rate at which the heart beats is determined by the higher firing rate, that is the SA node. So, the pacemaker of the heart is the SA node.

While the P cells have their own electrical activity even in the absence of hormones and nerves, the rate at which they fire can be regulated or controlled by nerves and hormones. Thus, when

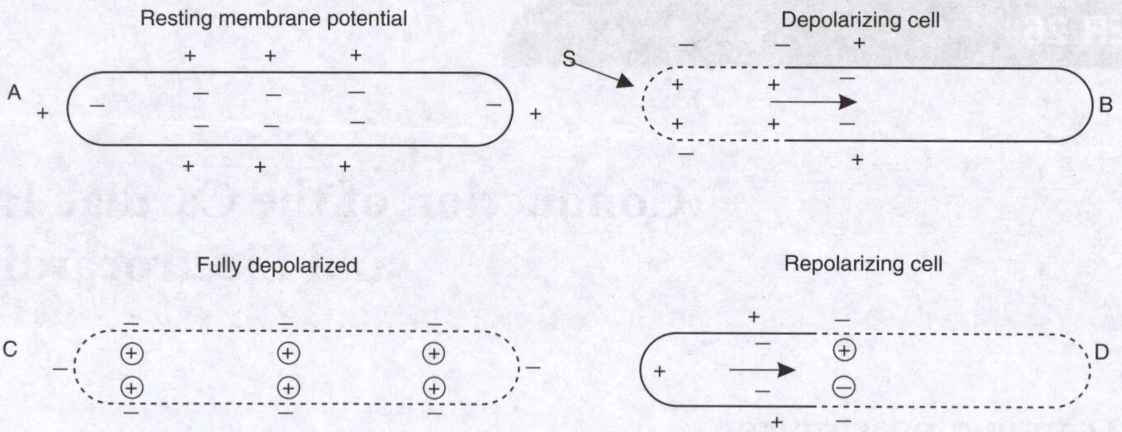

FIG. 26.1 The membrane potential at rest and with depolarization and repolarization.

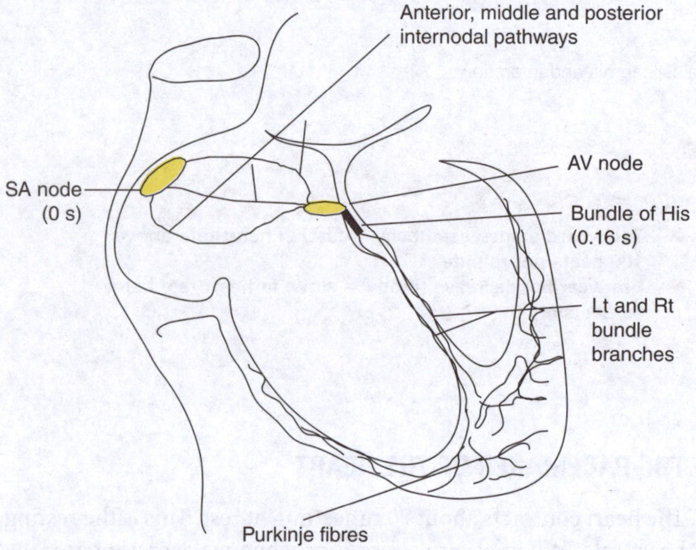

FIG. 26.2 The conducting system of the heart.

the sympathetic nervous system is stimulated (during 'fight' or 'flight'), the P cells of the SA node fire faster and the heart rate increases. Substances that increase the heart rate are said to be **positively chronotropic**, while substances that decrease the heart rate are said to be **negatively chronotropic**.

THE CONDUCTING SYSTEM OF THE HEART

The electrical activity generated by the P cells of the **SA node** travels to all parts of the heart so that contraction of the heart takes place properly. This occurs through specialized cells which form the conducting system of the heart. In order to understand the sequence of events, look once again at Fig. 26.2. The cardiac impulse generated in the SA node first travels throughout the atria through three pathways called the internodal pathways. By the time the impulse reaches the **AV node**, 0.03 second has passed.

The transmission of the cardiac impulse in the AV node now slows down. This happens because (1) the fibres in the AV node are thin and this reduces the speed of the cardiac impulse and (2) there are relatively few gap junctions in the AV node which normally helps the cardiac impulse to spread from one cell to another. The delay in the transmission of the cardiac impulse in the AV node is called **nodal delay**. Nodal delay is important because it ensures that there is a delay in the electrical activation of the ventricles. The delay in the electrical activation in the ventricles means that the contraction of the ventricle is also delayed. Thus, the atria will contract fully and the ventricles are filled with blood, before the ventricles begin to contract.

The cardiac impulse then travels through the **bundle of His** which divides into the **left and right bundle branches** in the interventricular septum before forming the **Purkinje's fibres** which go throughout the right and left ventricular myocardium. Although the right ventricle is one-third of the thickness of the left ventricle, the cardiac impulse reaches the outer surface of both ventricles at roughly the same time (0.21–0.22 second). This means that the cardiac impulse allows cardiomyocytes in the ventricles to be activated at roughly the same time.

Why Do We Need a Conducting System?

In Chapter 25, one of the properties of the cardiac muscle cells that was discussed was 'conductivity'. In other words, cardiac muscle can conduct electrical impulses through the intercalated discs, which are low-resistance pathways for conduction. We also discussed that because of this, cardiac muscle also behaves like a syncytium, that is cardiac muscle cells act together as a group. If that is so, you might wonder why we need a conducting system at all. There are several reasons:

1. Although the cardiac muscle cells can conduct an electrical impulse, the conducting system does this three to four times faster. This allows the heart to beat at a faster rate when this is required. Transmission of the cardiac impulse can also be regulated. Thus, the sympathetic nervous system increases the speed of conduction, while the parasympathetic nervous system decreases the speed of conduction – this allows for a greater regulation of the heart.

2. The nodal delay in the AV node ensures that atrial contraction and emptying of blood occurs before ventricular contraction starts. Thus, there is a sequential contraction of atria and ventricles.
3. Because the cardiac impulse reaches the outer parts of both ventricles at about the same time, it ensures that the ventricles contract together or synchronously, making the heart a more effective pump.

THE ELECTROCARDIOGRAM

The electrical activity of the heart can be recorded on an ECG. Although different cells in the heart are electrically active at different times, ECG records the electrical activity not of a single cell but of the whole heart at any point in time.

Recording of ECG

We record the electrical activity of the heart using electrodes or leads. The heart is a three-dimensional organ and the electrical activity is best recorded in more than one plane.

The 12-Lead ECG The standard ECG is recorded using 12 leads. Of these, six leads (I, II, III, avR, aVL and aVF) record the electrical activity in the frontal plane (i.e. vertically) and six leads (V1, V2, V3, V4, V5 and V6) are placed on the chest and record the electrical activity of the heart in the transverse (horizontal) plane.

Leads I, II and III are called **bipolar limb leads** since they are placed on the limbs and have both a positive and a negative lead.

Leads aVR, aVF and aVL are called the **augmented limb leads**.

Leads V1–V6 are called the chest or **precordial leads**.

Figs 26.3 and 26.4 show the placement of the electrodes for these 12 leads. While all leads record the electrical activity of the heart, there are some differences in the magnitude and direction of the different waves and this is because the leads are placed differently.

Einthoven's law states that the potential in lead II is the sum of the potentials in lead I and lead III. It is for this reason that lead II is often used to monitor arrhythmias on monitors in the hospital.

The actual procedure for the placement of the leads of an ECG is beyond the scope of this book. However, the placement of the bipolar limb leads can be easily remembered using Einthoven's triangle (Fig. 26.5). You will observe from this figure that the polarity of the right arm is always negative and that of the left leg is always positive.

ECG can be viewed on a monitor or can be recorded on a chart paper. The chart paper is run at a constant speed of 25 mm/s. Before recording ECG, calibration signals of 1 mV are typically recorded. This constant speed and amplitude calibration are important because in disease states, the various waves can change in both duration and amplitude.

The Waves of ECG

Fig. 26.6 is a detailed diagram of the waves and parts of ECG. Each of the small squares of the ECG chart paper is 1 mm wide. The chart paper also has larger squares with thicker lines which are 5 × 5 mm. Since the chart paper is run at a constant speed of 25 mm/s, it follows that each small square of 1 mm represents 1/25 second = 0.04 second. Similarly, 5 mm of a larger square will represent 5/25 of 1 second = 0.2 second. Thus, if we look at the RR interval, that is the interval between two consecutive R waves, we can compute the heart rate. For instance, if the RR interval is 25 mm, that is 1 second, the heart rate will be 60 beats/min because each RR interval is 1 second (25 mm) apart. In contrast, if the RR interval is 10 mm, the heart rate will be 25 × 60/10 = 150 beats/min. Since 25 × 60, that is 1500, is constant

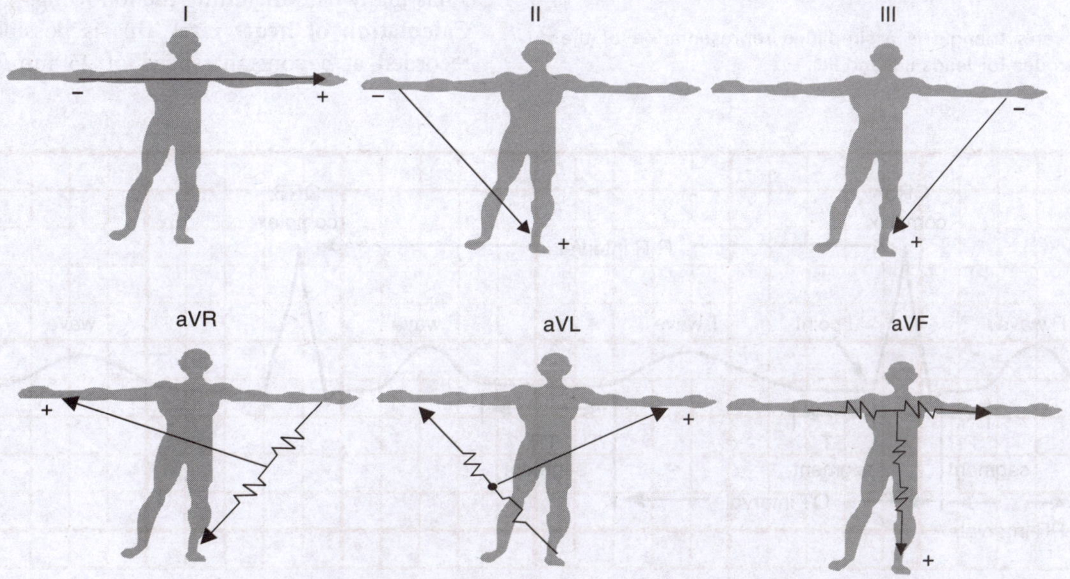

FIG. 26.3 The placement of leads I, II, III, aVR, aVL and aVF.

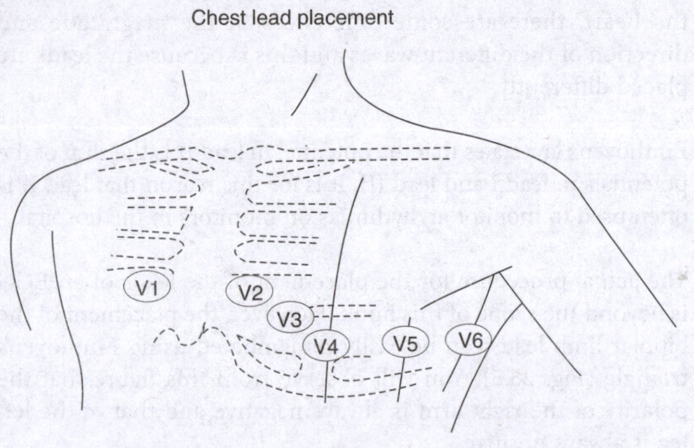

FIG. 26.4 Placement of chest leads V1, V2, V3, V4, V5 and V6.

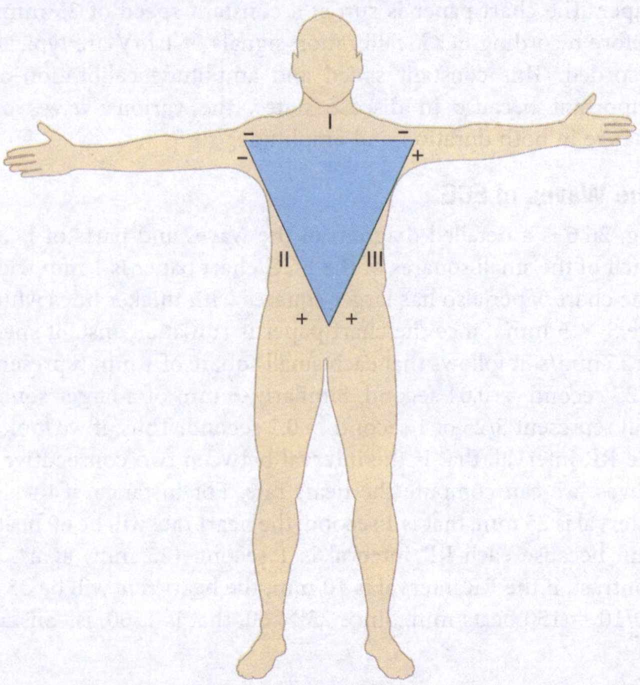

FIG. 26.5 Einthoven's triangle is a simplified representation of the placement of electrodes for leads I, II and III.

in the calculation, the heart rate can simply be calculated as 1500/RR interval in millimetres (1500 divided by RR interval). However, since the RR intervals vary with respiration, an average of several RR intervals is taken to calculate the heart rate.

Before we describe the different waves, let us remember the sequence of the conduction of the cardiac impulse. The cardiac impulse starts in the SA node, spreads throughout the atria, is delayed for a brief moment at the AV node (nodal delay) before it enters the bundle of His and the bundle branches and then spreads throughout the ventricular myocardium through the Purkinje's fibres. Thus, the atria get depolarized first followed by the ventricles and atrial repolarization occurs before ventricular repolarization.

In Fig. 26.6, we see that there are some waves that go up (positive) and some waves which go down (negative). The horizontal line which separates the positive and negative waves is called the *isoelectric line*. The first small positive wave is the P wave which reflects atrial depolarization, and the QRS complex represents the whole of ventricular depolarization. Atrial repolarization is not seen as a wave because it occurs at the same time as ventricular depolarization. Since the ventricular muscle mass is much more than that of the atria, the effect of atrial repolarization is hidden by ventricular repolarization. The T wave represents ventricular repolarization.

Apart from the waves of ECG, ECG is also described in terms of certain intervals or segments. Fig. 26.6 also depicts certain intervals and segments:

The PR interval (0.12–0.2 second) represents the time taken for atrial depolarization and nodal delay. The ST segment which follows ventricular depolarization is important because, as we will see later in the chapter, it changes when there is ventricular ischaemia (insufficient blood supply) and infarction (loss of blood supply leading to cell death).

Uses of ECG

ECG has many uses including the following:

1. **Calculation of heart rate:** This is possible since ECG is recorded at a constant speed of 25 mm/s. It is typically

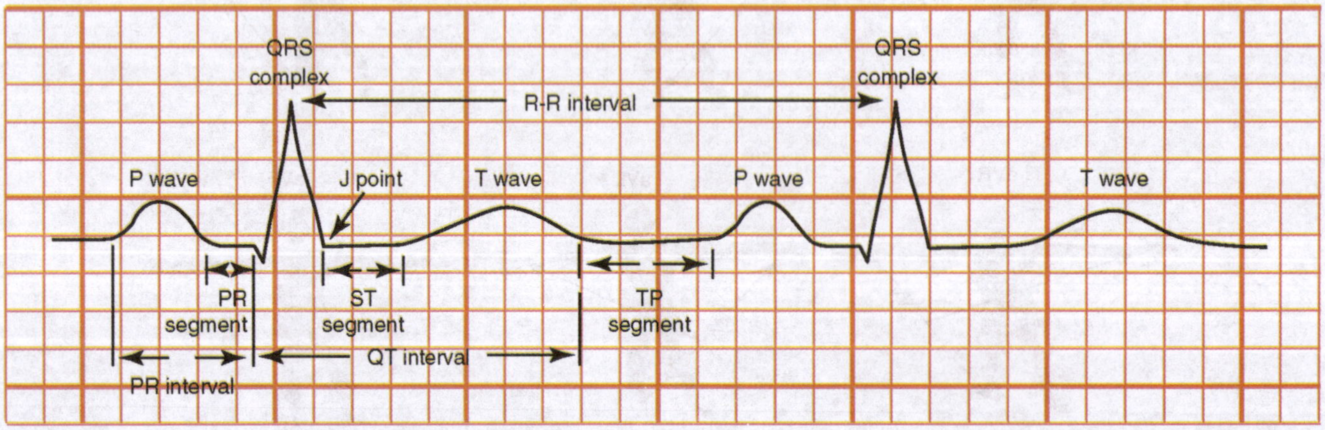

FIG. 26.6 A typical ECG showing the waves, intervals and segments.

calculated using the RR interval, that is the interval between two consecutive R waves as indicated earlier. While looking at ECG, we identify a 'sinus rhythm', that is a rhythm originating from the SA node, by the sequence of the waves in ECG. Thus, in a sinus rhythm, there is a P wave and every P wave is followed by a QRS complex. Fig. 26.7 shows three normal sinus ECG rhythms; panel A is the reference ECG. In panel B, we observe that the RR intervals are further apart than in panel A. This indicates that the heart rate is slower (bradycardia), and since every P wave is followed by a QRS complex it is a sinus rhythm and therefore called sinus bradycardia. In contrast, in panel C, the RR intervals are closer together than in panel A – the heart rate is therefore faster (tachycardia) and since every P wave is followed by a QRS complex it is a sinus rhythm and therefore called sinus tachycardia.

a. Sinus bradycardia (brady = slow) occurs when the heart rate falls below 60 beats/min. This is seen in sleep, at rest, in elite athletes, when the parasympathetic nervous system is activated and also in clinical conductions as in hypothyroidism.
b. Sinus tachycardia (tachy = fast) occurs when the heart rate goes above 100 beats/min. This is seen in exercise, in fever and when the sympathetic nervous system is activated (as during the fight-and-flight response).

In a **normal** recording of ECG, you will observe that the RR interval is not constant. The RR intervals tend to become shorter and then wider and this depends on the pattern of breathing. Thus, during inspiration, the RR intervals are closer, indicating an increase in the heart rate, while they are further part during expiration. This rhythm with an increased heart rate during inspiration and a slower heart rate during expiration is a normal rhythm of the heart and is called *sinus arrhythmia* (Fig. 26.8).

2. **Assessment of disturbances in the rhythm of the heart:** The normal rhythm of the heart is a sinus rhythm originating from the SA node and showing regular variations associated with respiration. However, there are conditions in which rhythms that originate from the SA node may not be conducted appropriately along the conduction pathway or when a site outside the pacemaker areas of the heart begins to set up an abnormal cardiac rhythm. These give rise to arrhythmias. While it is out of the scope of this book to discuss all arrhythmias, some of them are discussed as follows:
Conduction defects:
These are defects in the generation and transmission of the cardiac impulse from the SA node.

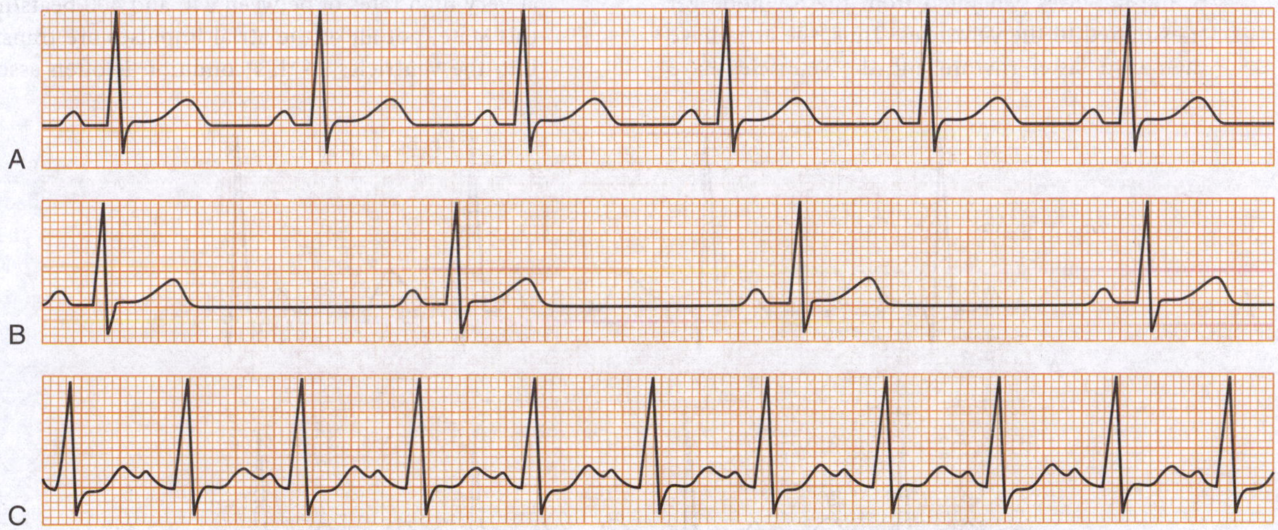

FIG. 26.7 (A) Reference ECG. (B) Sinus bradycardia. (C) Sinus tachycardia.

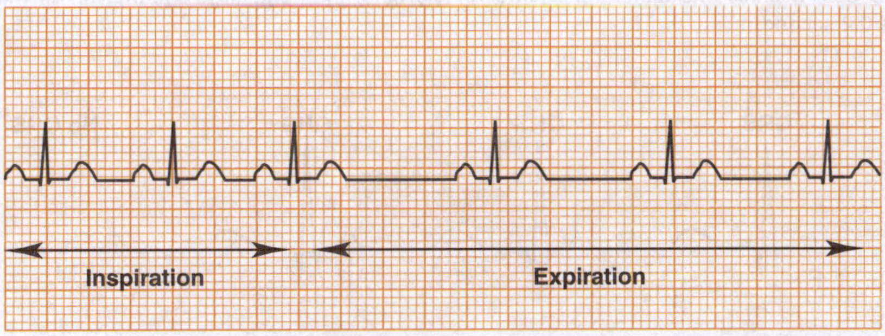

FIG. 26.8 Sinus arrhythmia.

- **a.** Sick sinus syndrome: In this syndrome, the SA node does not work properly. As a result, the heart rate may not be able to increase to certain stimuli like exercise and the person may have an abnormally high or low heart rate.
- **b.** AV block: This refers to a defect in the transmission of impulse from the atria to the ventricles. There are three different types of AV block:
  - **i.** *Type I AV block*: In this AV block, all the impulses that are generated in the SA node are transmitted to the ventricles. However, the transmission from the atria to the ventricles is delayed. We know this by looking at the PR interval which is the interval in ECG from the beginning of the P wave and the start of the QRS complex. This interval is normally 0.12–0.2 second. In type I AV block, this interval is prolonged as depicted in Fig. 26.9.
  - **ii.** *Type II AV block*: In this type of AV block, some but not all of the impulses that are generated in the SA node are transmitted to the ventricles. When the impulse is transmitted to the ventricle, the P wave will be followed by a QRS complex. When the wave is not transmitted, the P wave will not have a QRS complex following it as shown in Fig. 26.10.
  - **iii.** *Type III AV block*: This type of AV block is also called complete heart block. This is because none of the impulses generated from the SA node get transmitted to the ventricles. Thus, the atria have their own faster rhythm and the ventricles have their own slower rhythm and these two rhythms are not synchronized with each other. Thus, P waves are generated regularly and ventricular electrical complexes are also generated regularly, but slower and the relationship of the P wave with the ventricular electrical complexes is not fixed. A consequence of this is that the atria contract faster than the ventricles and therefore ventricular filling is ineffective since ventricular contraction does occur regularly after atrial contraction.

Other arrhythmias: Apart from conduction defects, there are many other arrhythmias that are encountered in patients. A detailed discussion of these is out of the scope of this chapter but these include the following: (1) *ventricular fibrillation* in which different parts of the ventricle are stimulated in small portions – this results in small separate parts of the ventricular muscle contracting at the same time rather than the entire ventricular muscle as a whole. In this situation, the ventricle is unable to function like a pump. The condition requires to be treated with an electrical device called a defibrillator. (2) *Ventricular asystole* is a condition in which there is no electrical activity in the heart. ECG appears as a flat line. (3) *Atrial flutter* is a condition in which the electrical activity of the atria is increased so that the atria begin to contract at very high rates of between 240 and 400 beats/min. In this state, not all of the atrial impulses are transmitted into the ventricles so this condition is often associated

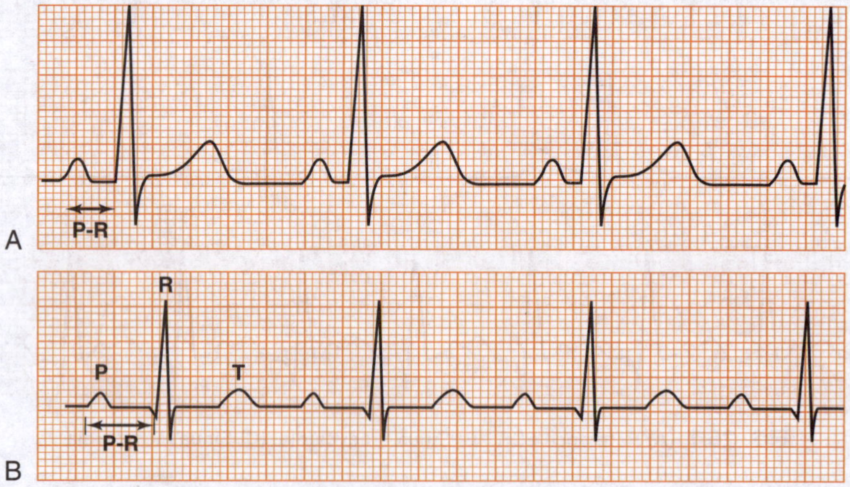

FIG. 26.9 (A) Normal ECG. (B) Type I AV block – note that the PR interval is greater than one large square. The normal PR interval is 0.12–0.2 second. The interval of a large square is 0.2 second.

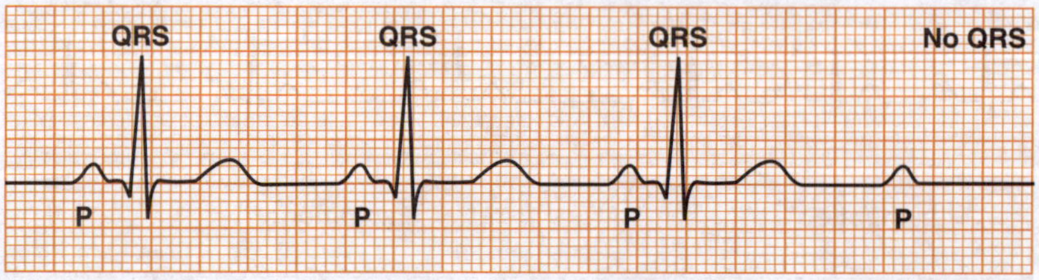

FIG. 26.10 Type II AV block.

with a type II AV block. (4) *Atrial fibrillation* is a condition in which different parts of the atria are stimulated in small portions so that separate parts of the atria contract at different times. This means that ventricular filling due to atrial contraction is reduced. You will understand this in relation to the cardiac cycle which is described in Chapter 27.

3. One of the common uses of ECG is to assess whether a person has had a heart attack (myocardial infarction, in which the blood supply to a part of the myocardium is completely stopped resulting in tissue death or necrosis) or ischaemia (reduced blood supply to a part of the heart). A depressed ST segment and inverted T wave at rest or during exercise may suggest myocardial ischaemia. ST segment elevation and pathological Q waves (deeper and wider than normal) are suggestive of myocardial infarction (Fig. 26.11). The leads that depict the abnormal ECG changes allow the location of the problem in the heart to be identified.
4. Since the waves of ECG reflect depolarization and repolarization, it stands to reason that these waves will be affected by the size of the atria and ventricles – the greater the size, the larger the waves. Thus, **ECG can also be used to assess atrial and ventricular hypertrophy** (increased muscle mass).
5. ECG can also be used to **monitor the effect of drugs** acting on the heart and also show changes with **electrolyte imbalance.**

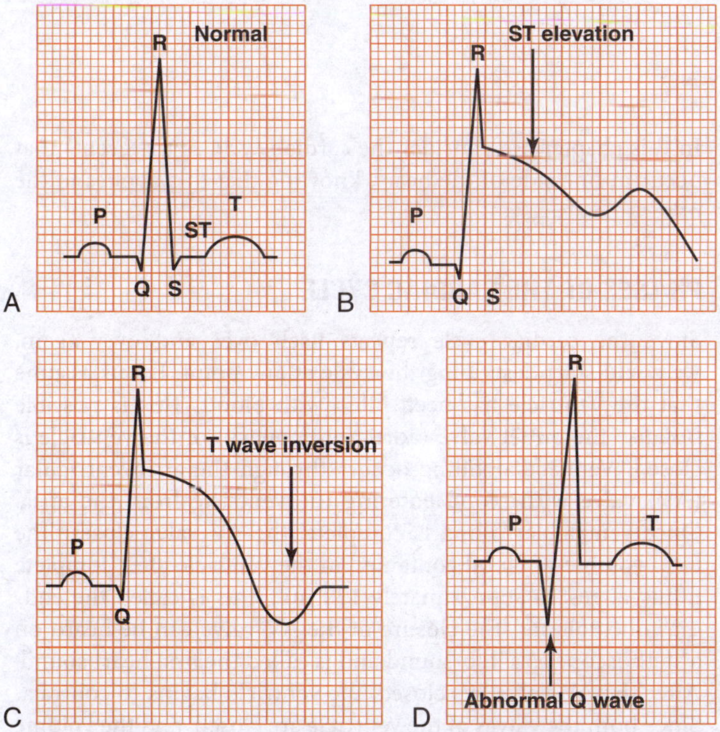

FIG. 26.11 ECG changes in myocardial ischaemia and infarction. (A) Normal ECG. (B) Elevated ST segment – compare this with the ST segment in panel A. (C) Inversion of T wave. (D) Pathological Q waves – notice the deep Q waves in comparison with the Q wave in panel A.

APPLICATIONS FOR NURSING

- Artificial pacemaker: For some individuals who experience cardiac arrhythmias, an external pacemaker may be required to 'override' the normal pacemaker of the heart, the SA node. The external cardiac pacemaker is a device that takes over the pacemaker function of the heart. The pacemaker has two parts: (1) an electrode that is inserted via a vein into the heart and (2) a pacemaker generator which has a battery and which creates the impulses which are transmitted to the heart via the electrode. The pacemaker generator is often implanted in the subcutaneous tissue of the heart. There are different types of pacemakers – some may include a single electrode while others may have more than one; some pacemakers are also dynamic and can alter the heart rate based on need. Pacemakers need to be checked at periodic intervals for the battery life and whether they are maintaining the pacemaking as they have been programmed to do.
- Defibrillator: This is a device that is used to restore the normal electrical rhythm of the heart by delivering an electric shock to the heart. It can be used in certain arrhythmias and when the heart stops contracting as may occur sometimes following a massive myocardial infarction. The use of a defibrillator in a timely and appropriate manner can be life-saving. Defibrillators are often therefore kept in places where people come in large numbers such as airports and malls. Healthcare professionals may be called over a public address system to help in the event of an emergency. Defibrillators nowadays are small in size and come with programmed instructions which allow their easy use.

SUMMARY

- The heart contains special cells called pacemaker (P) cells. These are found in the SA node (pacemaker of the heart) and AV node.
- The sequence of the conduction of the cardiac impulse is SA node → internodal pathways → AV node → bundle of His → left and right bundle branches → Purkinje's fibres.
- A conducting system is required:
  - To ensure rapid conduction
  - For sequential contraction of atria and ventricles
  - For synchronous contraction of the ventricles
- The main waves of ECG are the following:
  - P wave (atrial depolarization)
  - QRS complex (ventricular depolarization)
  - T wave (ventricular repolarization)
- Intervals and segments are useful in different situations:
  - PR (PQ) segment includes the time for AV nodal delay and is important in assessing conduction defects.
  - ST segment is assessed for elevation or depression in myocardial infraction and myocardial ischaemia.
- ECG is used to calculate the heart rate, assess rhythm of the heart, myocardial infarction and atrial and ventricular hypertrophy, among others.

CHAPTER REVIEW QUESTIONS

1. Describe the sequence of conduction of the cardiac impulse.
2. Draw and label a normal ECG and indicate what the waves represent.
3. List the functions of the ECG.
4. What do you understand by the following terms: (a) sinus bradycardia, (b) sinus tachycardia, (c) sinus arrythmia?

CHAPTER 27

The Cardiac Cycle

SPECIFIC LEARNING OBJECTIVES

At the end of this chapter, the student should be able to:

- List the phases of the cardiac cycle in sequence.
- Describe the volume, pressure and valvular changes that occur during the cardiac cycle.
- Describe the relationship between the waves of ECG in relation to the cardiac cycle.
- Describe the heart sounds and their relationship with the phases of the cardiac cycle.
- Describe the waves of the jugular venous pulse and outline its importance.
- Define cardiac output and list its determinants.
- Define venous return and list its determinants.

GLOSSARY OF TERMS

- **Cardiac cycle:** the repeated electrical and mechanical events of the heart
- **Systole:** contraction
- **Diastole:** relaxation
- **Isovolumetric:** having the same volume
- **Cardiac output:** volume ejected per ventricle per minute (resting value 5 L/min)
- **Stroke volume:** volume ejected per ventricle per contraction
- **Venous return:** the rate at which blood is returned to the heart

The heart contracts rhythmically and since the mechanical events of the heart follow the electrical events, it follows that the electrical events are also rhythmic. In Chapter 26, we described the waves of ECG which repeat themselves as a cardiac impulse travels from the SA node to activate the entire heart.

The cardiac cycle, therefore, is the repeated electrical and mechanical events of the heart. If the heart beats approximately 75 times a minute (i.e. 60 seconds), then the duration of each cardiac cycle will be 60/75 = 0.8 second. During a single cardiac cycle, the atria and the ventricles spend their time in contraction (systole) and in relaxation (diastole). The contraction and relaxation of the atria are referred to as atrial systole and diastole and that of the ventricle as ventricular systole and diastole.

The events of the heart, that is the left heart (left atrium and ventricle) and the right heart (right atrium and ventricle), are essentially the same. However, the pressures in the two ventricles are different, the right ventricular pressure being much lower than the left ventricle pressure. This is because the pressure gradient to drive blood through the pulmonary circulation is much lower than that required by the left ventricle to drive blood through the larger systemic circulation.

In this chapter, we consider the cardiac cycle as the events that occur in one side of the heart, knowing that this applies to the other side also.

PHASES OF THE CARDIAC CYCLE

Since the cardiac cycle repeats itself over and over again, we could start describing the cycle at any point. Let us assume that the ventricle has been filled with blood. This is possible because the outlet valve (aortic/pulmonary) of the ventricle is closed. Ventricular filling occurs through the atrioventricular (AV) valve with blood entering the ventricle from the atria. Once ventricular filling is complete, the AV valve closes. The total volume of blood contained in the ventricle after complete filling at rest is approximately 130 mL. This is called the end-diastolic volume. The closure of the AV valve can be heard on a stethoscope as a 'lub' sound and is called the first heart sound. After the AV valve has closed, the ventricle begins to contract. Since both the valves of the ventricle are closed, and the volume of blood in the ventricle remains the same, this phase of the cardiac cycle is called **isovolumetric (iso = same) contraction**. During this phase, the pressure in the ventricle rises sharply (Fig. 27.1).

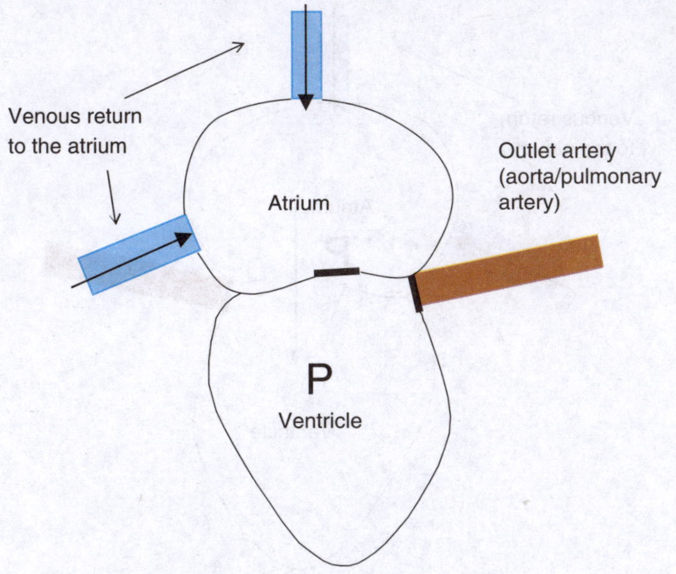

FIG. 27.1 Isovolumetric contraction.

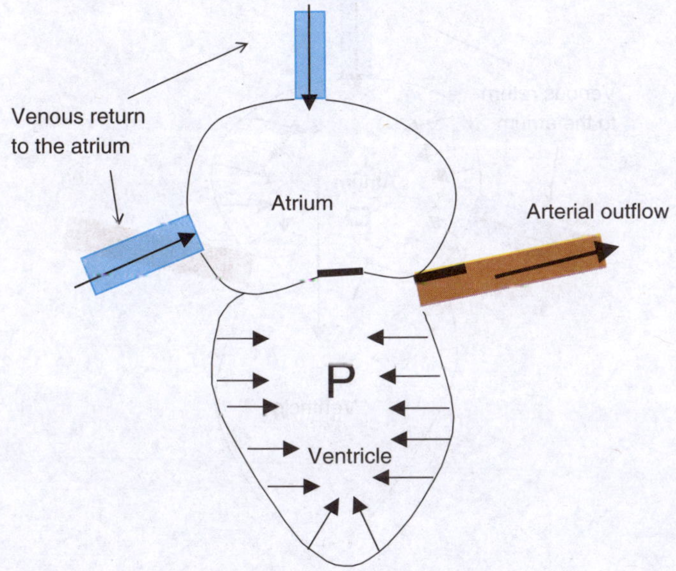

FIG. 27.2 Rapid ejection phase.

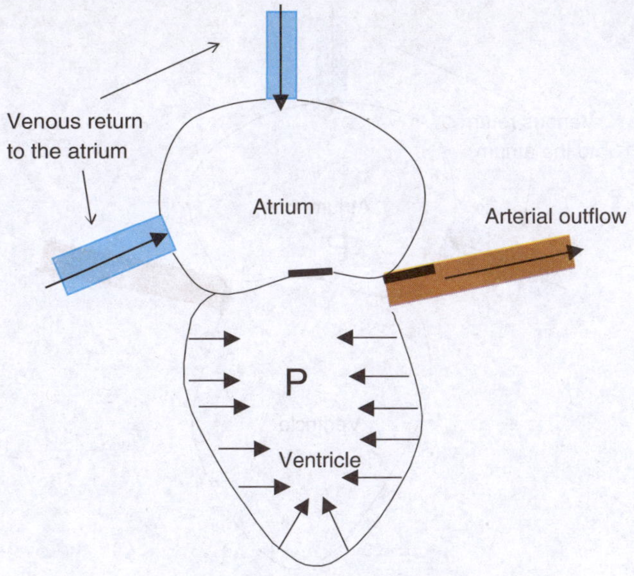

FIG. 27.3 Slow ejection phase.

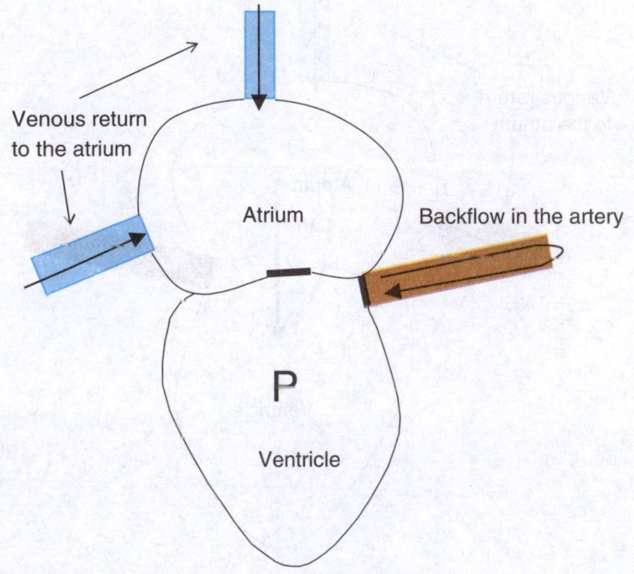

FIG. 27.4 Protodiastole.

As the pressure in the ventricle increases, it exceeds the pressure in the outlet artery (aorta/pulmonary artery). This causes the outlet valve (semilunar valve) to open. As the ventricle continues to contract, blood is ejected rapidly into the artery. This phase is called the **rapid ejection phase** (Fig. 27.2).

A fall in the pressure in the ventricle and a corresponding rise in the pressure of the artery causes a slowing of the ejection of blood from the ventricle into the artery. This is called the **slow ejection phase** (Fig. 27.3). The total volume of blood ejected during the rapid and slow ejection phases is about 70 mL at rest. The volume of the ventricle after the complete ejection of blood (i.e. at the end of systole) is called the end-systolic volume.

For a very short period, the pressure in the artery is greater than the pressure in the ventricle. This is because the pressure in the ventricle slowly decreases as blood is ejected from it. At the point when the pressure in the artery just exceeds the pressure in the ventricle, there is backflow of blood in the artery which causes the semilunar valve to shut. This closure of the semilunar valves can be heard on a stethoscope as a 'dup' sound. This phase of the cardiac cycle is called **protodiastole** (Fig. 27.4). Since the large arteries are elastic arteries, they expand when blood is ejected from the ventricles into them, and then like an elastic band, the elastic recoil of the arteries ensures that blood is pushed into the circulation even after ejection from the ventricle stops. This phenomenon of elastic recoil of the large arteries is called the *Windkessel effect*.

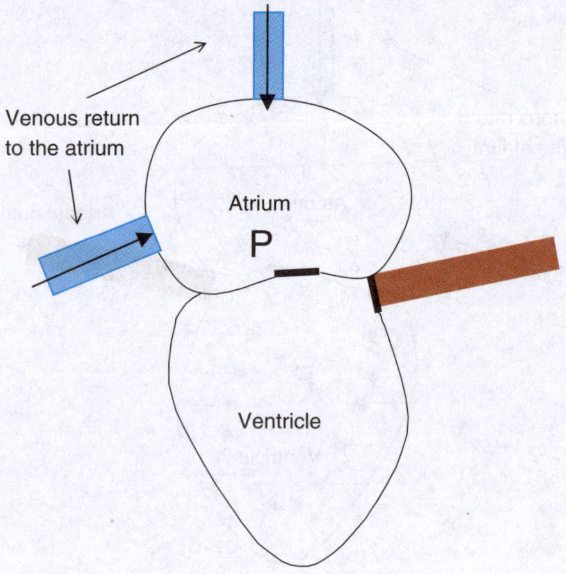

FIG. 27.5 Isovolumetric relaxation.

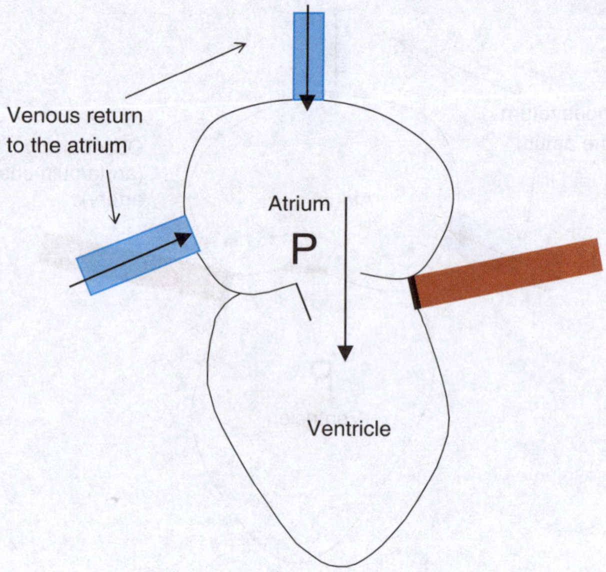

FIG. 27.7 Slow filling phase.

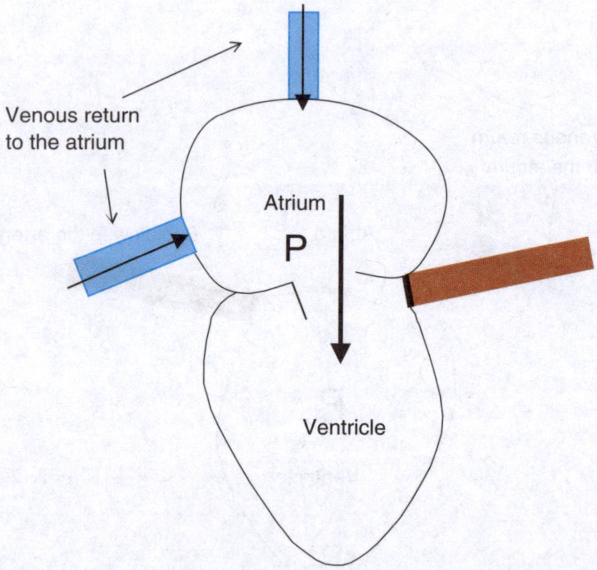

FIG. 27.6 Rapid filling phase.

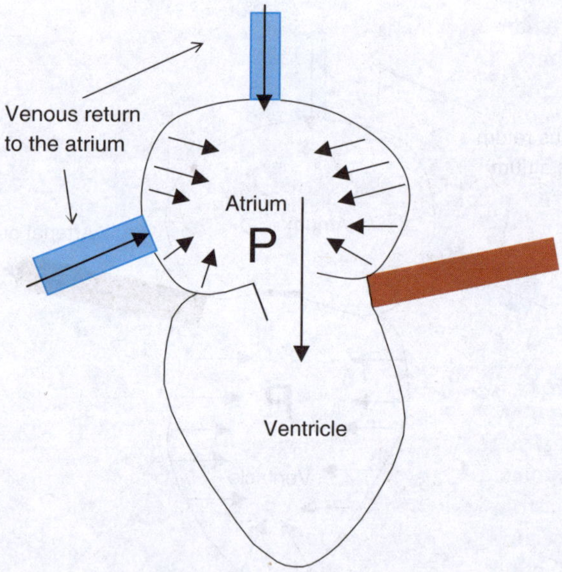

FIG. 27.8 Atrial systole.

Following protodiastole, both of the valves of the ventricle are now closed. The ventricle begins to relax. The amount of blood left behind in the ventricle after ejection is about 60 mL at rest (130 − 70). Since the ventricle is relaxing with a constant volume of blood contained within it, this phase of the cardiac cycle is called **isovolumetric relaxation** (Fig. 27.5). During this phase, there is a rapid decline in the pressure within the ventricle.

During the phases outlined earlier, venous blood continues to enter the atrium. As the atrium fills, the pressure within the atrium also increases. At some point, the pressure in the atrium exceeds the pressure in the ventricle – at this point, the AV valve opens. Blood now starts rapidly filling the ventricle. This phase is, therefore, called the **rapid filling phase** (Fig. 27.6). The turbulence created by the flow of blood is associated with the third heart sound. This is usually not heard in healthy individuals, although it may be heard in some children and young adults.

The initial rapid filling of the ventricle is followed by a slower filling as the pressure gradient between the atrium and the ventricle is reduced by the flow of blood. This phase is called the **slow filling phase** (Fig. 27.7). The rapid and slow filling of the ventricle together accounts for about 75% of ventricular filling at rest.

The final phase of ventricular filling is **atrial systole** or contraction (Fig. 27.8). This phase accounts for the remaining 25% of ventricular filling at rest. Thus, the biggest volume of

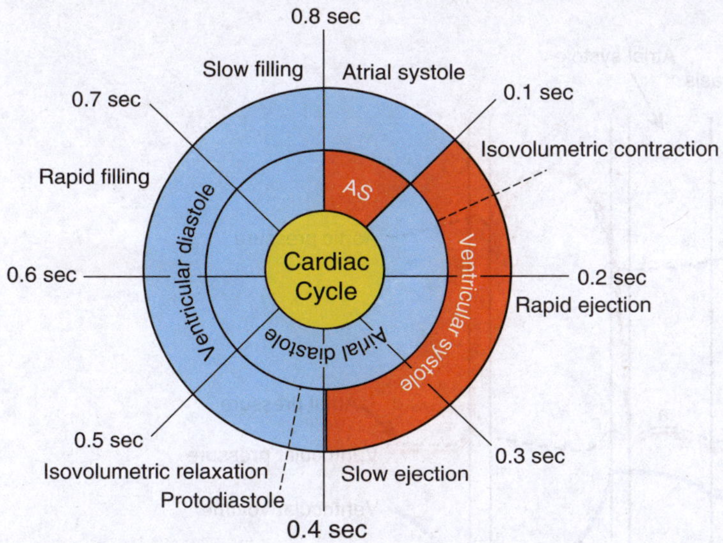

FIG. 27.9 Summary of the phases of the cardiac cycle.

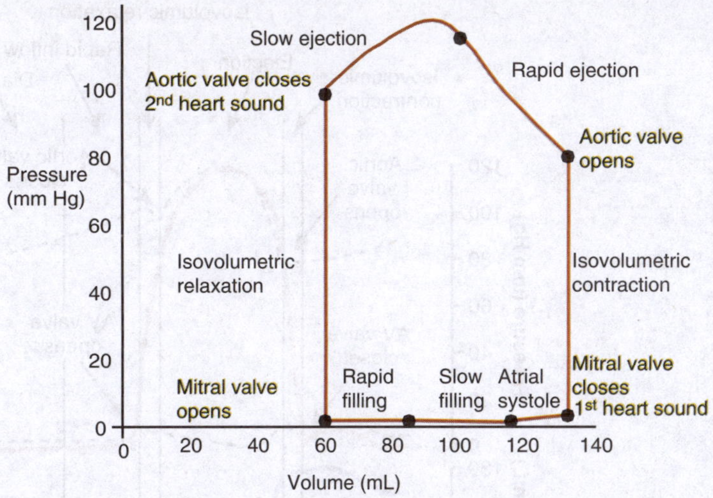

FIG. 27.10 Pressure–volume changes in the left ventricle during a single cardiac cycle.

ventricular filling is not due to atrial contraction but due to the movement of blood along a pressure gradient from the atria to the ventricles. The total volume of the ventricle at the end of diastole is called the end-diastolic volume. The turbulence created by the flow of blood into the ventricles due to atrial systole is associated with a fourth heart sound. This is rarely heard.

SUMMARY OF THE PHASES OF THE CARDIAC CYCLE

Fig. 27.9 summarizes the various phases of the cardiac cycle. This figure shows that systole and diastole are unequal; both for the ventricle and for the atrium. Thus, the ventricle spends approximately one-third (0.3 second) of the time in contraction or systole and two-thirds (0.5 second) of the time in relaxation or diastole. In contrast, the atrium spends only one-eighth (0.1 second) of the cardiac cycle in systole and seven-eighths (0.7 second) in diastole.

PRESSURE–VOLUME CHANGES DURING THE CARDIAC CYCLE

Fig. 27.10 summarizes the pressure–volume changes in the cardiac cycle of the left ventricle. It is clear from the diagram that during the three phases of ventricular filling, that is rapid filling, slow filling and atrial systole, the ventricular pressure remains close to 0 mm Hg. During these three phases, 70 mL of blood is added to the ventricle, approximately 75% of which is during the rapid and slow filling phases and the remaining 25% during atrial systole. Both isovolumetric phases are characterized by large changes in pressure. In the isovolumetric contraction phase, a filled left ventricle rapidly increases its pressure and then opens the aortic valve resulting in the ejection of blood. In the resting heart, the amount of blood ejected during the rapid and slow ejection phases is approximately 70 mL. The closure of the aortic valve (second heart sound) signals the start of the isovolumetric relaxation phase in which the pressure in the ventricle returns to a value close to 0 mm Hg.

ECG WAVES AND THE CARDIAC CYCLE

Change in electrical activity occurs before contraction and relaxation of the heart. In cardiomyocytes, the electrical effects are depolarization and repolarization. ECG represents the electrical activity of the whole heart at any point of time. Depolarization occurs before contraction (systole) and repolarization occurs before relaxation (diastole). Thus, the P wave of ECG which represents atrial depolarization occurs just before atrial systole phase of the cardiac cycle. The QRS complex which represents ventricular depolarization occurs just before and during the phase of isovolumetric contraction which is the first of three phases of ventricular systole. Finally, the T wave of ECG which represents ventricular repolarization occurs just before protodiastole. The electrical and mechanical events of the cardiac cycle are summarized in Wiggers' diagram, named after the person who created it. This diagram (Fig. 27.11) allows different events to be interpreted in relation to each other.

THE HEART SOUNDS IN THE CARDIAC CYCLE

While we have earlier mentioned the genesis or origin of the heart sounds, this subsection will re-emphasize these in a tabular form:

Heart Sound	Characteristics	Origin
First heart sound	'Lub' Low frequency	Closure of the AV valves
Second heart sound	'Dup' Higher frequency	Closure of the semilunar valves
Third heart sound	Low pitched	Turbulence of blood due to the rapid filling of the ventricles
Fourth heart sound	Low pitched	Turbulence of blood due to atrial systole

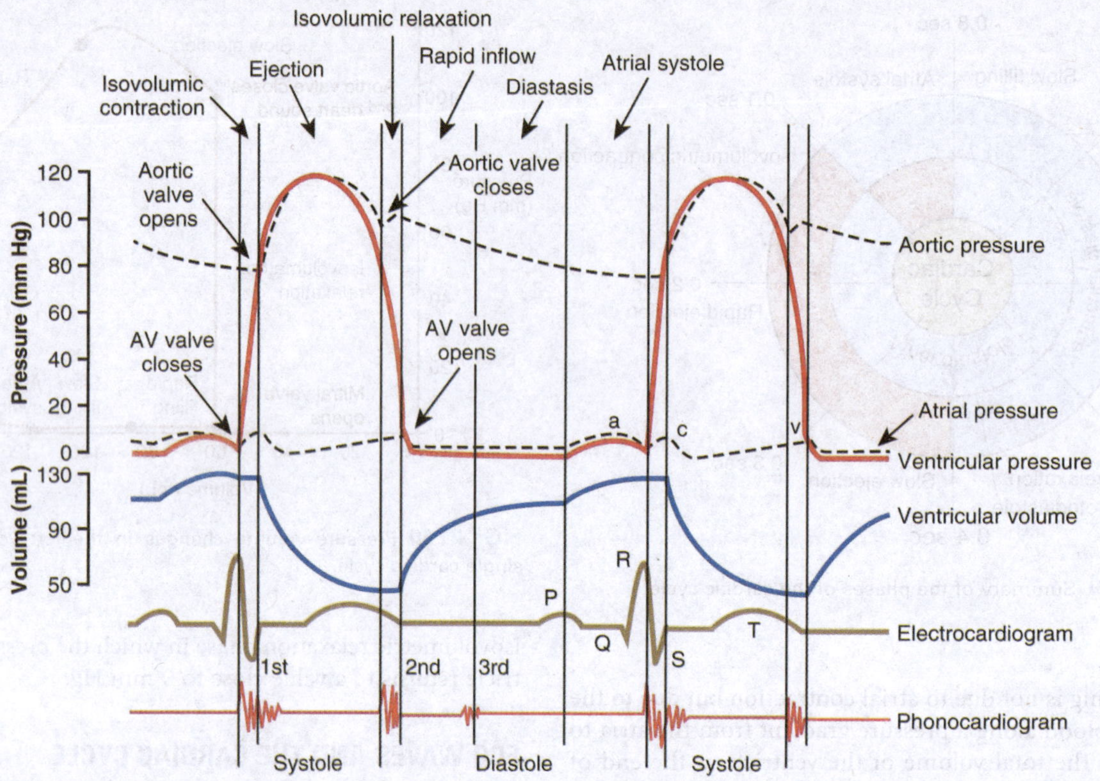

FIG. 27.11 Wiggers' diagram of the cardiac cycle showing simultaneous changes in ventricular volume and pressure, aortic pressure, atrial pressure, ECG and the heart sounds.

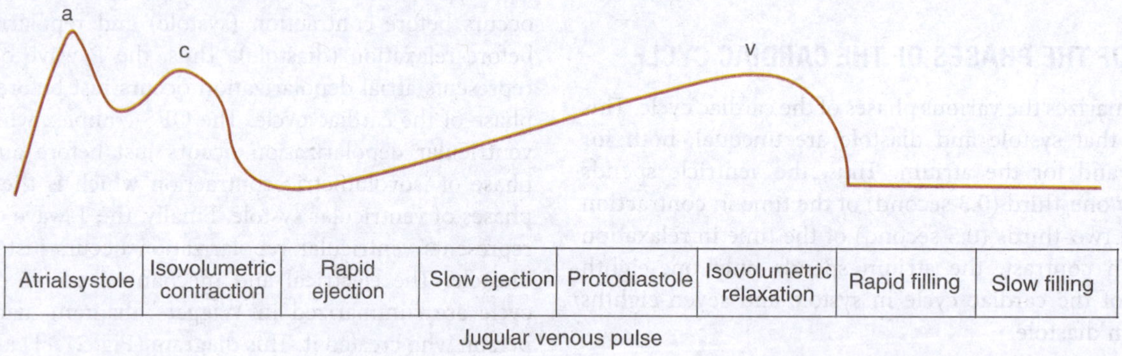

FIG. 27.12 The nature of the jugular venous pressure.

JUGULAR VENOUS PULSE

The internal jugular venous pulse reflects the pressure changes in the right atrium. It is examined on the right side since the right internal jugular vein is in a direct line with the superior vena cava and right atrium. Unlike the carotid artery pulse, the jugular venous pulse is better seen than felt (along the right side of the neck) and actually comprises multiple waves. The waves that are seen are depicted in Fig. 27.12. The figure shows the relationship between the waves of the jugular venous pulse and the phases of the cardiac cycle. The three waves that comprise the jugular venous pulse are the 'a' wave, the 'c' wave and the 'v' wave. The 'a' wave occurs because of increased pressure in the right atrium due to atrial contraction. The 'c' wave is a smaller wave which is due to an increase in atrial pressure since the AV valve bulges into the atrium during isovolumetric contraction; this is because of the large increase in pressure in the ventricle during this phase. The rapid decline after the 'c' wave is because of the decrease in ventricular pressure that occurs during ejection of blood from the ventricle. Finally, the 'v' wave is due to the gradual build-up of pressure in the right atrium due to atrial filling of blood via the superior and inferior vena cava. This pressure is rapidly reduced when the AV valves open and the blood in the atrium rapidly empties into the ventricles.

The jugular venous pulse is evaluated when there is heart failure involving the right side of the heart. This is discussed in greater detail in Chapter 33.

CARDIAC OUTPUT

During the cardiac cycle, blood is ejected from the ventricle into the artery. The amount of blood that is ejected per ventricle per minute is referred to as the cardiac output. In contrast, the amount of blood that is ejected per ventricle per contraction is called the stroke volume. We have already indicated that the amount of blood that is ejected per contraction, that is the stroke volume, is about 70 mL. Given that the heart rate (the number of contractions per minute) at rest is approximately 70, the cardiac output can then be calculated as the stroke volume × heart rate, that is 70 × 70 = 5 L, which is the resting cardiac output in an adult. Heart rate and stroke volume are the primary determinants of cardiac output and the cardiac output can be varied by altering one or both of these determinants. Cardiac output can increase four to five times above its resting level in very heavy activity.

REGULATION OF CARDIAC OUTPUT

Since heart rate and stroke volume are the primary determinants of cardiac output, cardiac output can be regulated by regulating its determinants.

Heart rate: Heart rate can be regulated by many factors.

1. Neural factors: The sympathetic nervous system which is responsible for the 'flight-and-fight' response increases the heart rate. In contrast, the parasympathetic nervous system which is typically activated by 'fear' reduces the heart rate.
2. Hormones: Many hormones also alter the heart rate. Thus, adrenaline (epinephrine) and thyroxine both increase the heart rate. In contrast, in those individuals who secrete less thyroid hormone (hypothyroidism), heart rate is slow.
3. Reflexes: The nervous control of heart rate is mediated through multiple reflexes. One of the important reflexes that alter heart rate that we will discuss further in Chapter 28 is the baroreflex, which helps to control blood pressure.

Stroke volume: Like heart rate, the stroke volume can be regulated by many factors. The stroke volume is increased or decreased by altering the amplitude (strength) of contraction of the ventricles.

1. Neural factors: The sympathetic nervous system increases the force of contraction of the ventricles and thus increases the stroke volume. The parasympathetic nervous system has a very sparse innervation of the ventricles.
2. Hormones: The hormones which increase heart rate, that is adrenaline and thyroxine, also increase the force of contraction of cardiac muscle.
3. The Frank–Starling mechanism: One of the factors which affect the force of contraction of a muscle fibre is the initial length of the muscle fibre. Starling's law states that the force of contraction of a muscle fibre is directly proportional to the initial length of the muscle fibre, within physiological limits. This is true for both skeletal muscle and cardiac muscle. The initial length of the cardiac muscle fibre depends on the extent to which it is stretched before it contracts. If the amount of ventricular filling during diastole is increased, the muscle fibre will be stretched more and will therefore contract more. The amount of ventricular filling (and therefore stretch of the cardiac muscle fibre) can be determined from the volume of the ventricle after filling of the ventricle is complete. This volume, as we have indicated earlier, is called the end-diastolic volume. Thus, for the heart, we can restate Starling's law to state that within physiological limits, the stroke volume is proportional to the end-diastolic volume. Since the ventricular filling acts on the heart even before it starts contracting, it is referred to as the *preload*.
4. Effect of *afterload*: This refers to the load that the heart needs to overcome once it begins to contract. It includes, for example, the aortic pressure for the left ventricle and the pulmonary pressure for the right ventricle. If the afterload is high, it means that the cardiac output will begin to fall and the ventricle will need to contract even harder in order to overcome the afterload. If the ventricle is contracting against a chronically increased afterload, the ventricle begins to hypertrophy (increase in size) as a way of contracting harder and overcoming the afterload.

VENOUS RETURN

While the different phases of the cardiac cycle are going on, blood is being constantly returned to the atria, via the inferior and superior vena cava for the right atrium and the pulmonary veins for the left atrium. Venous return is, therefore, the rate at which the venous blood returns back to the heart.

There are many factors which affect the venous return. Some of these include the following:

1. Blood volume: The greater the blood volume, the greater is the venous return. Blood volume in a typical adult is about 5 L, but it is more in people who are bigger. Blood volume may decrease during dehydration and is also altered in shock (Chapter 33) and in states in which there is fluid retention in the body, for example pregnancy.
2. Posture: When a person stands, there is venous pooling of blood and venous return to the heart is reduced. If a person who is standing lies down, the blood that had pooled due to gravity is now returned to the heart and venous return increases.
3. 'Muscle pump': Venous pooling in the extremities is reduced by muscle contraction. This is because muscle contraction squeezes the blood contained inside the veins and it is pushed towards the heart due to the presence of one-way valves in the veins of the extremities, which allow blood to flow only in one direction, that is towards the heart (Fig. 27.13).
4. 'Respiratory pump': The movement of the diaphragm up and down during respiration causes the intrathoracic and intra-abdominal pressures to change. Blood moves along

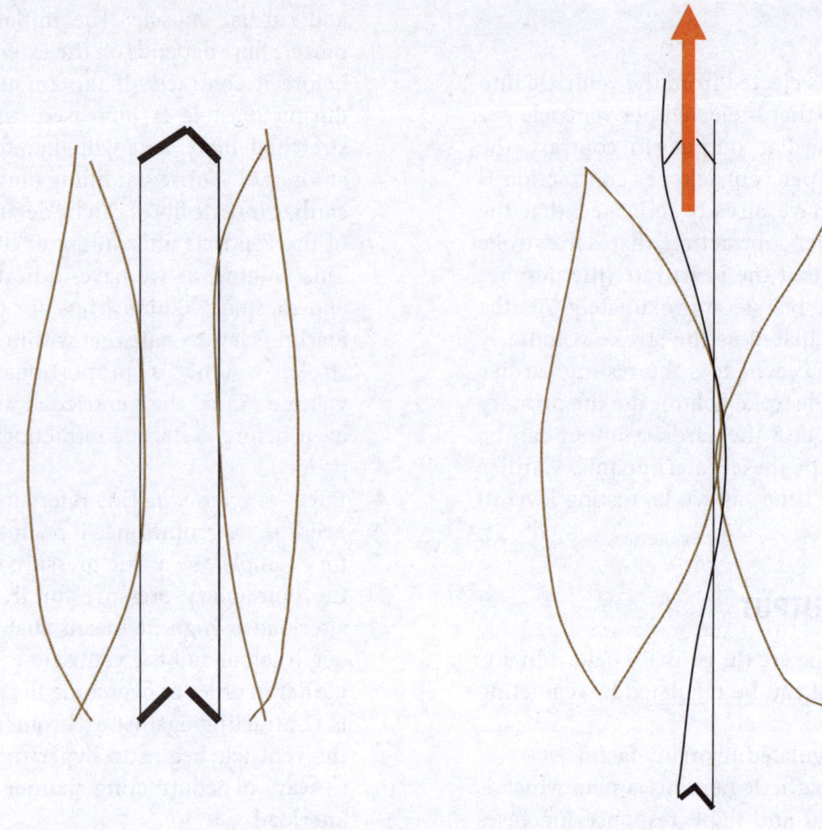

FIG. 27.13 The muscle pump and venous return. One-way valves allow blood to return to the heart when the muscle contracts.

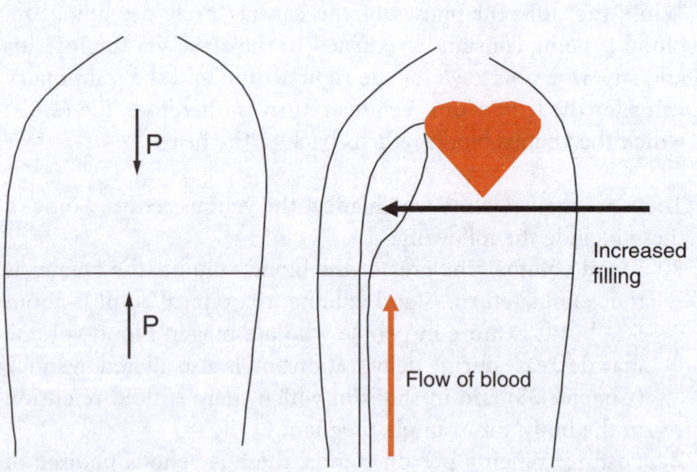

FIG. 27.14 The respiratory pump and venous return: inspiration.

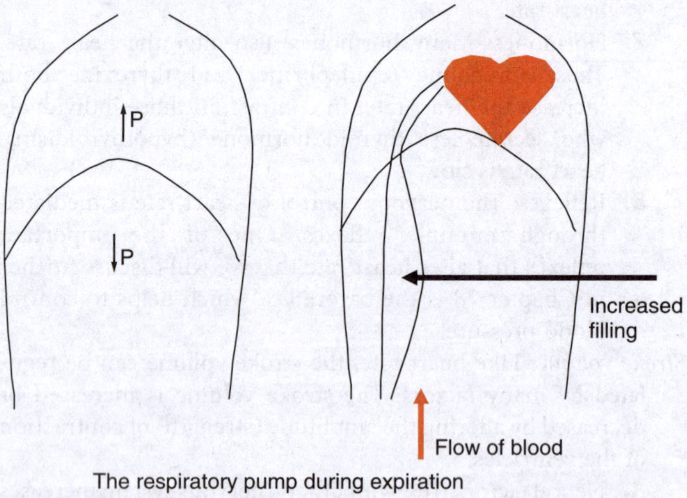

FIG. 27.15 The respiratory pump and venous return: expiration.

these pressure gradients towards the heart. During inspiration, the diaphragm moves down; because of this, the intrathoracic volume increases and the pressure decreases, while in the abdomen, the volume decreases and the pressure increases. There is, thus, a pressure gradient from the abdomen to the thorax which causes the blood to flow towards the heart (Fig. 27.14).

In contrast, during expiration, the diaphragm moves up, increasing the intra-abdominal volume while reducing its pressure. This creates a pressure gradient between the veins of the lower limbs and those of the abdomen, resulting in the movement of venous blood from the extremities into the large veins of the abdomen (Fig. 27.15).

5. Venoconstriction: This refers to the contraction of the veins. While the veins have relatively little muscle in their walls compared to the arteries, contraction of the veins, as, for instance, with sympathetic nerve activation, results in movement of blood towards the heart.

CLINICAL BOX

Syncope (Fainting)

Individuals who have been standing for a long time particularly in the heat may sometimes faint. This is because venous pooling in the extremities has severely reduced venous return to the heart. When a person faints and assumes a horizontal position, blood pooled in the veins rushes back to the heart. The person then gains consciousness.

Measures to take when a person faints:

1. If close by, support the individual so that the person does not injure himself or herself when falling.
2. Allow the person to lie down – this increases venous return; venous return can be further increased by raising the legs above the level of the heart while the person is lying down.
3. Clear the people around – so that there is plenty of fresh air.
4. If the weather is hot, give the person water to drink; the person may be dehydrated.
5. Once the person has gained consciousness, allow the person to sit for some time, and then stand, before walking. Ensure that you are by the person's side, in case he or she feels unsteady on his or her feet.
6. Enquire whether the person has any medical history – there are other reasons which can also lead to fainting.

APPLICATIONS FOR NURSING

- The nurse may be required to evaluate the jugular venous pulse to determine the response of patients with right heart failure to treatment.
- The nurse will be required to assist people when they have fainted. The mechanism of syncope and the simple measures that can be taken have been discussed earlier in the chapter.

SUMMARY

- The cardiac cycle is the repetitive electrical and mechanical events of the heart.
- The duration of the cardiac cycle at rest is 0.8 second, of which one-third (0.3 second) represents ventricular systole and two-thirds (0.5 second) represents ventricular diastole.
- Atrial systole is 0.1 second duration, while atrial diastole is of 0.7 second duration.
- The phases of the cardiac cycle in sequence are isovolumetric contraction, rapid ejection, slow ejection (ventricular systole) and protodiastole, isovolumetric relaxation, rapid filling, slow filling and atrial contraction (ventricular diastole).
- There are four heart sounds: the first heart sound is due to closure of AV valves; second heart sound is due to closure of the semilunar valves; third heart sound is due to rapid filling of the ventricles; fourth heart sound is due to atrial systole.
- Cardiac output is the volume of blood ejected per ventricle per minute. The resting value is 5 L/min. The primary determinants of cardiac output are heart rate and stroke volume (the volume ejected per ventricle per contraction). Therefore, cardiac output = stroke volume × heart rate.
- Venous return is the rate at which blood is returned to the heart. Among the determinants of venous return are blood volume, posture, muscle pump, respiratory pump and venoconstriction.

CHAPTER REVIEW QUESTIONS

1. List the phases of the cardiac cycle in order.
2. What are the heart sounds and how are they produced?
3. What is cardiac output and how is it regulated?
4. What is venous return? What are the factors that affect venous return?

CHAPTER 28

Haemodynamics and Blood Pressure

SPECIFIC LEARNING OBJECTIVES

At the end of this chapter, the student should be able to:

- Describe the basic relationship between pressure, flow and resistance.
- List the determinants of flow as given by Poiseuille's law.
- Distinguish between laminar and turbulent flow.
- Describe the pressure pattern along the circulatory tree.
- Describe the features of the microcirculation.
- Draw and label the arterial pulse pressure curve.
- Describe the determinants of arterial blood pressure.
- Describe the variations in blood pressure.
- Describe the regulation of blood pressure by the baroreflex.
- Describe the longer-term control of blood pressure.
- Describe the nature of the 'pulse' and its variations.

GLOSSARY OF TERMS

- **Blood pressure:** (unless otherwise specified refers to systemic arterial blood pressure) the lateral pressure exerted by the blood on the walls of the artery
- **Systolic blood pressure:** the highest pressure in the artery during systole (normal 120 mm Hg)
- **Diastolic blood pressure:** the lowest pressure in the artery during diastole (normal 80 mm Hg)
- **Pulse pressure:** the difference between the systolic and the diastolic pressure (normal 40 mm Hg)
- **Mean blood pressure:** calculated as diastolic blood pressure + 1/3 pulse pressure

The pumping of the heart allows the blood to enter the systemic and pulmonary circulations adequately. Ventricular pressure during systole provides the pressure gradient that drives blood flow through these circulations. The resistance offered to this flow of blood depends on a number of factors. These factors and those that maintain the blood pressure are discussed in greater detail in this chapter.

RELATIONSHIP BETWEEN PRESSURE, FLOW AND RESISTANCE

In physics, in the chapter on electricity, you would have studied the relationship between voltage, current and resistance. This relationship is given by the formula $V = IR$ and is termed Ohm's law. As an analogy of this law, the relationship between blood flow (as opposed to current), pressure (as opposed to voltage) and resistance can be described by the formula $\Delta P = QR$, where ΔP is the pressure between the two ends of a blood vessel, Q is the blood flow and R is the resistance to blood flow. This means that blood flow is directly proportional to the pressure gradient and inversely proportional to the resistance offered to the flow of blood. The entire blood flow through each of the circulations (pulmonary and systemic) is 5000 mL at rest and is the cardiac output.

Blood pressure is typically measured in mm Hg, while blood flow is expressed as mL/min. In order to describe blood flow to different organs of different masses (weights), blood flow is sometimes expressed as mL/g/min. This allows us to determine whether the blood flow per unit tissue is high or low. As an example, the blood flow to the cardiac muscle (coronary blood flow) at rest is about 250 mL/min. Since the heart weighs only 300 g, the blood flow per unit tissue is about 0.8 mL/g/min. In contrast, skeletal muscle receives about 1 L (1000 mL) of blood at rest in the average adult male, which is four times the blood flow to cardiac muscle. If, however, we assume that skeletal muscle is about 25 kg, then the blood flow per unit tissue is 0.04 mL/g/min which is very low compared to the blood flow in cardiac muscle. When skeletal muscle begins contracting, though, the blood flow to the active skeletal muscle mass can increase substantially.

POISEUILLE'S LAW

While $\Delta P = QR$, and therefore Q (blood flow) $= \Delta P/R$, blood flow is itself determined by various factors which are given by the following equation:

$$Q = \frac{\pi \Delta P r^4}{8\eta l}$$

This equation is derived from Poiseuille's law, where ΔP is the pressure difference between the two ends of the blood vessel, r is the radius of the blood vessel, η is the viscosity of blood and l is the length of the blood vessel. From the equation, we can see that blood flow is most affected by the radius of the blood vessel. Thus, if the radius of the vessel increases from 1 to 2, the effect on blood flow would be an increase from 1^4 to 2^4, that is a 16-fold increase (from 1 to $2 \times 2 \times 2 \times 2$). The viscosity of blood depends both on the cells that are contained within the blood and on the components of the plasma such as plasma proteins. An increase in the cell counts as well as an increase in the concentration of proteins can increase the viscosity of blood making it harder for the heart to pump the blood. In extreme situations, abnormal increases in the cells or plasma proteins can lead to what is called hyperviscosity syndrome.

If we substitute the determinants of Q in the equation $Q = \Delta P/R$, then the equation becomes: $(\pi \Delta P r^4/8\eta l) = \Delta P/R$.

Since ΔP cancels out, $R = 8\eta l/\pi \Delta P r^4$.

Thus, the resistance offered to blood flow is also strongly influenced by the radius of the blood vessel. Thus, as the radius of a blood vessel reduces, the resistance to blood flow increases.

PATTERNS OF BLOOD FLOW

There are two patterns of blood flow that occur in the circulation:

1. **Laminar blood flow:** It occurs when blood flows in a streamlined fashion. Observe Fig. 28.1. The top panel represents laminar flow. Here, each layer of blood maintains its fixed distance from the wall of the vessel. The central layers move faster than those in the periphery of the blood vessel. Laminar blood flow is seen throughout most of the circulation.
2. **Turbulent blood flow**: Represented in the lower panel of Fig. 28.1, it shows the movement of blood in all directions; this results in mixing of blood. The whorls of blood flow are called *eddy currents*. Turbulent blood flow is seen when the velocity of blood flow is high as in the ascending aorta, when blood flows through a constriction in the blood vessel or across tight (stenosed) valves in the heart.

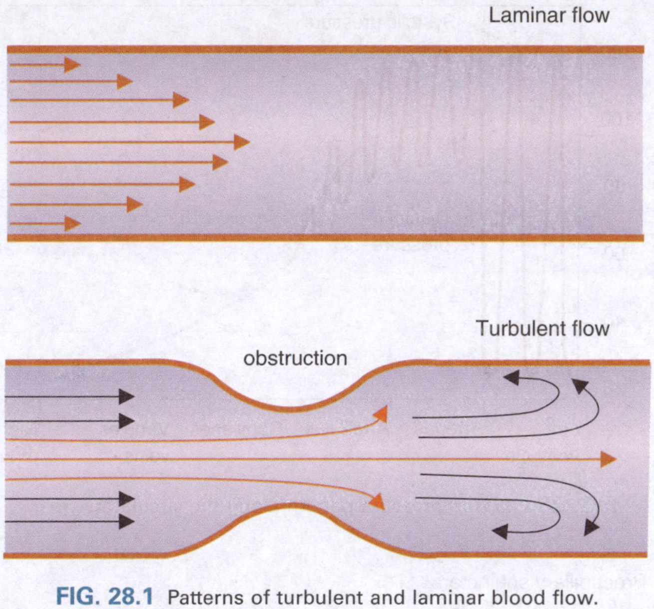

FIG. 28.1 Patterns of turbulent and laminar blood flow.

PRESSURE PATTERN ALONG THE CIRCULATORY TREE

The pressure in the circulatory system is not the same everywhere. Observe Fig. 28.2 carefully. In the ventricle where the pressure is generated, the pressures rise sharply during systole and reduce sharply during diastole to around 10 mm Hg. In the large arteries, pressure is still pulsatile but the pressure during diastole does not drop sharply and is maintained at about 80 mm Hg in the systemic circulation. The reason that the pressure does not fall further during diastole in these arteries is because of the resistance that is offered to blood flow by the muscular smaller arteries and arterioles. These vessels are the major site of the *peripheral resistance* to blood flow in the circulation. The total resistance offered by all the resistance vessels in the circulation to the flow of blood constitutes the *total peripheral resistance*. There is a sharp drop in pressure in the microcirculation so that in the capillary bed pressures range from 20 to 40 mm Hg. The pressure drops even further in the venules and the large veins. The right atrial pressures range from 2 to 5 mm Hg.

THE MICROCIRCULATION

The microcirculation is important because it is concerned with the most important functions of the tissues, the delivery of oxygen and nutrients and the removal of carbon dioxide and waste products. Fig. 28.3 illustrates the structure of the microcirculation.

The arteries terminate in muscular terminal arterioles. These in turn give rise to metarterioles. Metarterioles do not have thick muscle walls but instead have localized regions of smooth muscle thickening where capillaries are given off. These localized thickenings of smooth muscle are the *precapillary sphincters*. When the precapillary sphincters contract, blood flow into the capillary is reduced or stopped. The capillaries then enter a postcapillary venule. There are also some vessels in the circulation called

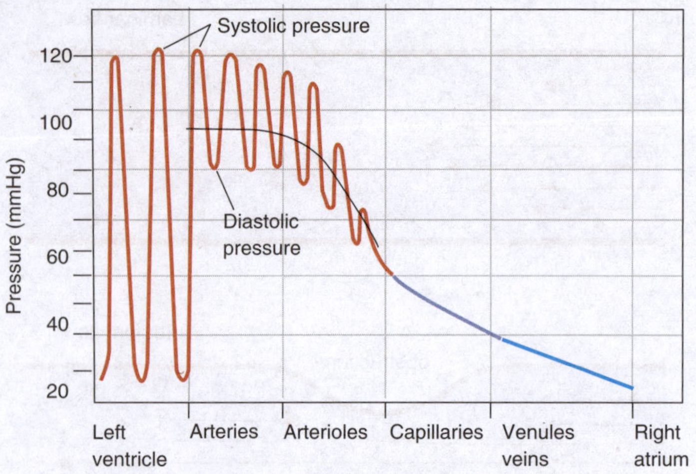

FIG. 28.2 Blood pressure pattern along the circulatory tree.

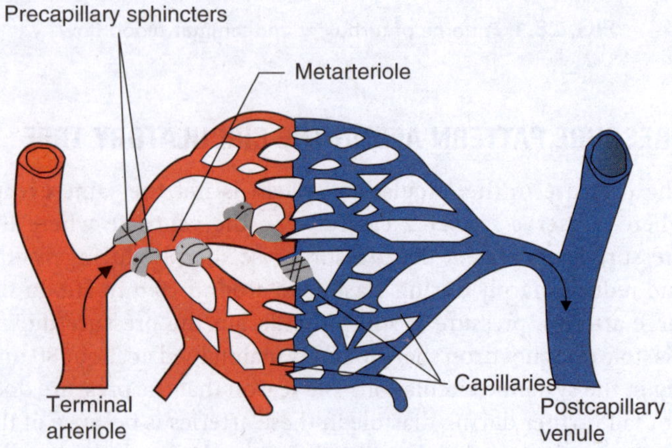

FIG. 28.3 The microcirculation.

'thoroughfare channels' or 'shunt vessels' which do not have precapillary sphincters and which can rapidly transfer blood from the metarteriole to the venule.

THE ARTERIAL PULSE PRESSURE CURVE

Since the pressure is not constant across the different vessels of the circulatory system, when we use the term 'blood pressure', we refer by default to the systemic arterial blood pressure. Other pressures in the circulation are usually specified by name – capillary pressure, venous pressure, etc. As shown in Fig. 28.2, the systemic arterial blood pressure varies between 120 and 80 mm Hg; it is high during systole and low during diastole. Unlike the diastolic pressure in the ventricle, however, which falls to around 10 mm Hg or lower, the diastolic pressure in the systemic arteries is maintained relatively high. *Arterial blood pressure is defined as the lateral pressure exerted by the blood on the arterial vessel wall.*

If we insert a small arterial catheter (tube) into a peripheral artery and connect it to a pressure measuring device, we will be able to observe the pulsatile nature of the blood pressure. A single arterial pulse pressure tracing is shown in Fig. 28.4.

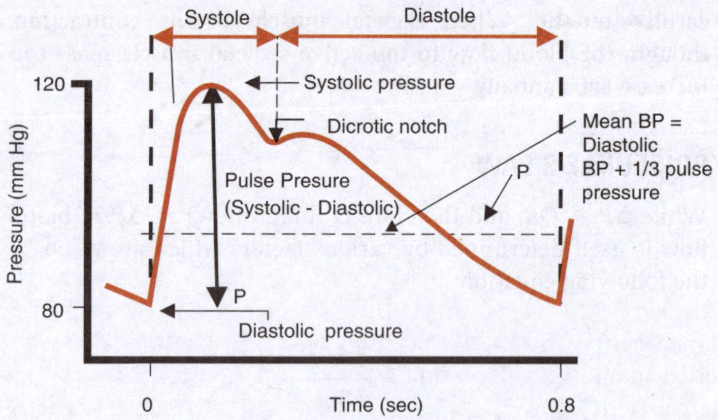

FIG. 28.4 The arterial pulse pressure trace.

You will observe in Fig. 28.4 that the arterial pulse pressure waveform varies between systole and diastole. The dicrotic notch is the point which marks (separates) these two phases. Systole is approximately one-third of the duration of the waveform and diastole is longer and is about two-thirds of the waveform. The highest pressure during systole is called the systolic pressure (120 mm Hg in the figure), while the lowest pressure during diastole is the diastolic pressure (80 mm Hg in the figure). The difference between the systolic and the diastolic pressure is called the pulse pressure (120 − 80 = 40 mm Hg).

The mean or average blood pressure is calculated as the diastolic pressure + 1/3 of the pulse pressure (80 + 13 = 93 mm Hg). Why do we use this complicated formula to calculate mean blood pressure? Why is mean blood pressure not equal to systolic + diastolic/2? The reason is that the duration of systole and diastole is unequal. In order to illustrate this, let us take another example of a blood pressure of 120/90 mm Hg. Since diastole is twice the duration of systole, we should calculate mean blood pressure by taking into account the fact that diastole is two times longer than systole. Thus, mean blood pressure will equal (2 × diastolic BP + 1 × systolic BP)/3 = (2 × 90 + 1 × 120)/3 = 100 mm Hg. If we apply the formula of diastolic + 1/3 pulse pressure, we get 90 + 1/3 of 30 mm Hg = 100 mm Hg!

DETERMINANTS OF BLOOD PRESSURE

Going back to the formula at the start of this chapter, ΔP (pressure) = Q (blood flow) × R (resistance to the flow of blood). For the whole of the circulation, Q is equal to the cardiac output. The difference between the pressure in the left ventricle and that in the right atrium is very large and the right atrial pressure is very small. We can therefore simplify the equation to read P (pressure) = cardiac output × total peripheral resistance.

The two major determinants of arterial blood pressure are therefore cardiac output and total peripheral resistance. Since blood pressure varies, that is systolic versus diastolic, one question is whether these two components of blood pressure always change in the same direction, that is if systolic blood pressure rises, will diastolic blood pressure also rise? The answer to this is 'no'. For instance, if a person is running a medium- to long-distance race and we take the blood pressure soon after the race, we will find that the systolic blood pressure rises, but the diastolic blood pressure may remain the same or even fall! This tells us that the systolic and diastolic blood pressure have different determinants.

Systolic blood pressure is largely determined by the cardiac output – the greater the amount of blood ejected into the arteries during ventricular ejection, the greater is the systolic blood pressure. There is another factor which can determine systolic blood pressure. In order to understand this, we need to go back to the nature of the large arteries which receive blood from the ventricle. Large arteries like the aorta are 'elastic arteries' – when blood is ejected into the artery, the artery, because of its elasticity, stretches. If the large artery was less elastic, that is stiffer, we would expect the pressure in the artery during ventricular ejection, that is systole, to rise even higher. This distensibility of the artery, that is the increase in the volume per unit change in pressure, is called arterial compliance. If arterial compliance is high, the vessel stretches more. When arterial compliance is low, it indicates that the artery is stiffer. In old individuals, the large arteries tend to be stiffer due to the deposition of cholesterol and calcium on the vessel wall – in these individuals, systolic pressure tends to be higher.

In contrast, the diastolic blood pressure is largely determined by the peripheral resistance. Resistance to blood flow is most affected by the radius of the arterioles which have a thick muscle wall.

VARIATIONS IN BLOOD PRESSURE

Blood pressure is not constant throughout the day. It changes due to a number of factors. These include the following:

1. The posture of the individual
2. Physical activity
3. Smoking and coffee intake
4. Ingestion of meals
5. Stress

In the longer term, blood pressure may be affected by factors such as the age of the individual, the dietary salt intake and the alcohol intake.

REGULATION OF BLOOD PRESSURE

Arterial blood pressure changes from moment to moment depending on our posture, activity and stress, among other things. However, changes in blood pressure are very rapidly brought back to normal. This is achieved through a reflex called the baroreflex (baro = pressure), and this constitutes the short-term regulation of blood pressure.

The Baroreflex (Short-Term Regulation of Blood Pressure)

Let us briefly revise the components of a reflex arc. These are the stimulus, the sensor (receptor), the sensory or afferent nerve, the integrating centre where information is processed, the motor (efferent) nerve and the effector organ.

The baroreflex can be understood in terms of the components of the reflex arc:

1. **Stimulus:** The stimulus which activates the baroreflex is a rise in arterial blood pressure.
2. **Receptors:** Blood pressure–sensing receptors (baroreceptors) are located in the arch of the aorta and the carotid sinus at the bifurcation of the common carotid artery. These two locations are important because they are close to where the pressure is generated in the first place, that is the ventricles, and so allow a rapid response to a change in pressure. The carotid sinus baroreceptors are also at a location that is critical for the blood supply to the brain (the internal carotid artery).
3. **The sensory (afferent) nerves:** The Hering branch of the glossopharyngeal nerve (IX cranial nerve) from the carotid sinus and the depressor nerve of the vagus (X cranial nerve) from the arch of the aorta carry the information from the baroreceptors to the brain (Fig. 28.5).
4. **Integrating centres:** The sensory nerves relay at the nucleus tractus solitarius. This is a common relay station for a lot of sensory information from different parts of the body. Once the information from the baroreceptors reaches here, it is sent to higher integrating centres in the brain including the *vasomotor centre*.
5. **Efferent nerves:** The response to the stimulus (i.e. a rise in blood pressure) is a withdrawal of sympathetic nerve activity to the blood vessels and the heart and an activation of the parasympathetic nervous system to the heart. The sympathetic nervous system is activated during the 'flight-and-fight' response. Thus, sympathetic nervous system activation results in an increase in heart rate and force of contraction of the heart, both of which increase the amount of blood ejected by the ventricle in a minute (cardiac output). Activation of sympathetic nerve fibres to the blood vessels results in vasoconstriction (contraction of the blood vessel) and a

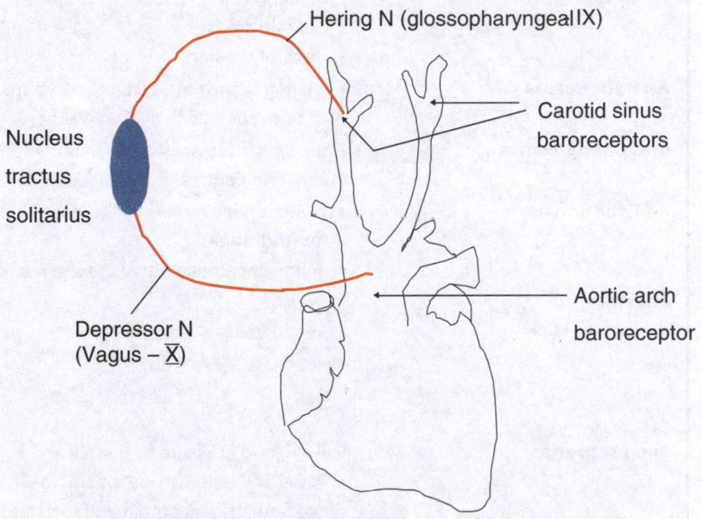

FIG. 28.5 Location and innervation of the baroreceptors.

rise in blood pressure. When there is a rise in blood pressure, the inactivation or withdrawal of the sympathetic nervous system results in a fall in heart rate and a decrease in the force of contraction of the heart which reduces cardiac output. Withdrawal of the sympathetic nervous system activity to the blood vessels results in vasodilatation and a decrease in the peripheral resistance. Since both cardiac output and peripheral resistance are determinants of blood pressure, a reduction in cardiac output and peripheral resistance will result in a fall in blood pressure. Activation of the parasympathetic nervous activity to the heart results in a further slowing of the heart rate.

6. **Effectors:** The effectors of the baroreflex as indicated in the previous section are the blood vessels and the heart since these two structures control peripheral resistance and cardiac output.

The baroreflex is summarized in Table 28.1.

Longer-Term Regulation of Blood Pressure

While the baroreflex is able to regulate blood pressure changes in the short term, experiments have shown that if the afferent nerves that carry information from the baroreceptors are cut, blood pressure rises and remains high for several days before returning back to normal, although with greater variability around the average blood pressure. This tells us that there is another mechanism or mechanisms that regulate blood pressure that are different from the baroreflex.

In the kidney, in the nephron is a structure called the juxtaglomerular apparatus (JGA). This is discussed in greater detail in Chapter 57. One of the types of cells which make up JGA is the juxtaglomerular cells which are located on the afferent arterioles of the glomerulus. These cells secrete a substance called renin. If there is a fall in blood pressure, the sympathetic nervous system is activated and this causes a release of renin. Renin helps convert angiotensinogen to angiotensin I. Angiotensin I is in turn converted to angiotensin II in the lungs due to the angiotensin-converting enzyme. Angiotensin II is a powerful vasoconstrictor and this helps to raise the blood pressure. In addition, angiotensin II also stimulates the release of a hormone called aldosterone. Aldosterone acts to increase salt and water reabsorption from the kidney and as a result increases blood volume which in turn increases blood pressure. The whole system is called the renin–angiotensin–aldosterone system (RAAS). These events are summarized in Fig. 28.6. When blood pressure is raised, RAAS is inhibited and the blood pressure will fall. When the blood pressure falls, the RAAS system is stimulated.

Another mechanism that helps to reduce blood pressure in the long term is *pressure natriuresis*. In this system, when the blood pressure is chronically raised, the kidneys excrete more water and sodium resulting in a fall of the blood pressure to its earlier level.

THE PULSE

You will be able to feel your own pulse over the radial artery at the lateral aspect of the wrist (Fig. 28.7). The tapping that you feel on the pulp of your finger is because the arterial pressure is not constant but rises and falls as depicted in Fig. 28.4. Thus, every time the pressure rises, you feel a tap on your finger. The pulse is used to determine the heart rate by counting the number of 'taps' that you feel in 1 minute. The arterial pulse can be felt in all major superficial arteries. These include the carotid arteries in the neck, the brachial artery and radial artery in the upper

Table 28.1 Components of the Baroreflex and Their Functions

Part of the Reflex Arc	Structures	Function
Stimulus		Increased blood pressure activates the baroreflex
Receptors	Baroreceptors: • Carotid sinus • Arch of the aorta	Sense the increase in blood pressure
Afferent nerves	• Hering branch of IX cranial nerve from carotid sinus • Depressor branch of X cranial nerve from aorta	Transmit the information of increased blood pressure to the brain
Integrating centre	Nucleus tractus solitarius – vasomotor centre/other integrating centres in the brain	Process the sensory information
Effector nerves	• Sympathetic nerves to the heart and blood vessels **(withdrawal)** • Parasympathetic nerves to the heart **(activation)**	Relay the information from the brain to the effector organs and produce the appropriate effects
Effectors	• Heart • Blood vessels (arterial)	Heart: A reduction in heart rate and force of contraction reduces cardiac output Blood vessels: Relaxation of vascular smooth muscle in the resistance arteries results in a fall in peripheral resistance
Final response	Fall in blood pressure to normal P = Cardiac output × peripheral resistance Since both cardiac output and resistance fall, blood pressure also falls	

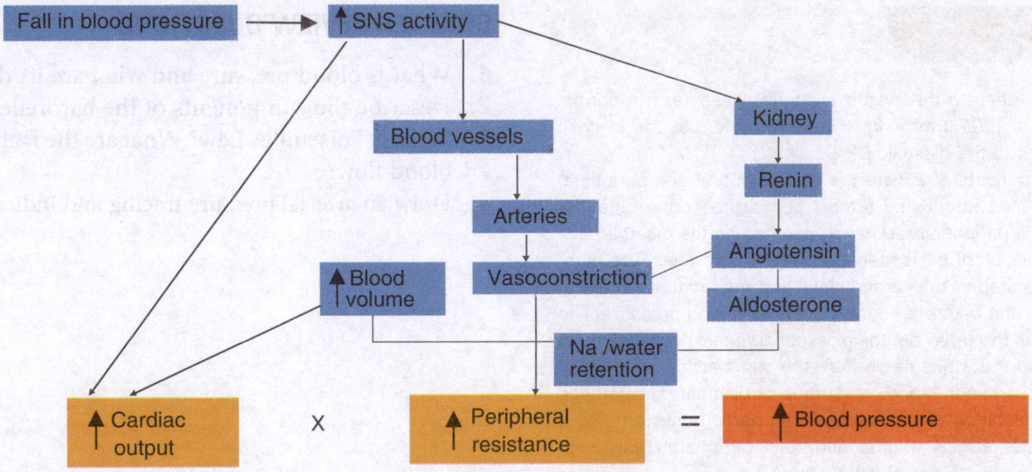

FIG. 28.6 Response to a fall in blood pressure.

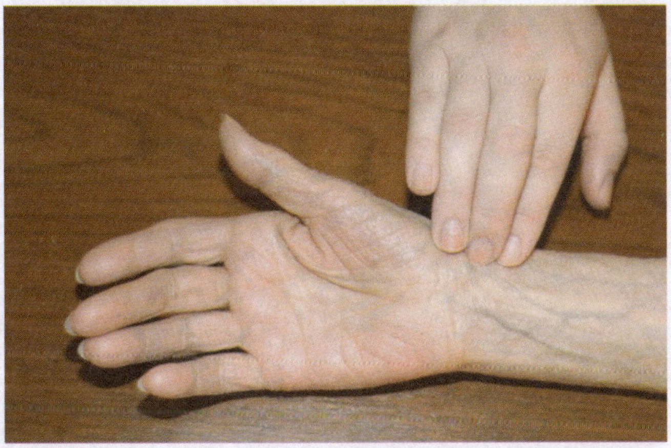

FIG. 28.7 The radial pulse. From: https://www.publiconsulting.com/wordpress/vitalsign/chapter/carotid-pulse/

limb, and the femoral, popliteal and posterior tibial and dorsalis pedis in the lower limb. However, the pulse during routine clinical examination is felt over the radial artery and sometimes over the carotid artery in the neck. Pulses are compared bilaterally (i.e. on both sides).

CLINICAL BOX

Examination of the Radial Pulse

Examination must be done after ensuring that the patient is resting and in a comfortable position and after performing hand hygiene. In order to examine the radial pulse, the pads (pulp) of three fingers are placed over the radial artery which runs on the lateral aspect of the wrist in continuity with the thumb as shown in Fig. 28.7. If you compress the outer two fingers slightly, you will be able to feel the pulse better in the middle finger. There are several things that you can learn from the pulse, some of which are described as follows:

- Heart rate: This is determined by counting the number of pulsations for 1 minute.
- Regularity of the pulse: This is determined by checking the rhythm of the pulse – under normal circumstances, the pulse will be regular and you may be able to appreciate some changes with respiration, that is when the patient is breathing in or out (typically heart rate increases with inspiration and decreases during expiration) – this may not always be appreciated while examining the pulse and is better recorded on an ECG.

CLINICAL BOX—cont'd

- Volume of the pulse: How strongly the 'tap' is felt is a reflection of the volume of the pulse. This is described on a scale of 0–4 (0, absent or unpalpable pulse; 1, thready, weak or diminished pulse that is difficult to palpate; 2, normal, easy to palpate pulse; 3, increased pulse; and 4, bounding pulse). Assessing the volume of the pulse requires practice to distinguish normal from weak or strong.
- *Variations in the peripheral pulse:* Variations in heart rate are seen in conditions which cause either a slowing of the heart rate (bradycardia) as, for instance, during sleep and hypothyroidism or an increased heart rate (tachycardia) as, for instance, during exercise, anxiety and hyperthyroidism.
- Variations in the volume of the pulse occur when there are large changes in cardiac output. For instance, a low-volume pulse may be seen in shock or myocardial infraction (Chapter 33). A high-volume, bounding pulse may be seen in exercise, anxiety and hyperthyroidism.
- There are many changes in the rhythm of the pulse – these are not discussed here.

APPLICATIONS FOR NURSING

- Blood pressure constitutes one of the vital signs of the patient. A nurse will be required to monitor the blood pressure of the patient.
- The nurse will be required to inform the doctor when blood pressure is abnormally low or high requiring action.
- It is important to understand the mechanism of the control of blood pressure since this is the basis of the action of blood pressure reducing medication. While a detailed discussion of antihypertensives (blood pressure–reducing medication) is beyond the scope of this chapter, some principles will be evident from the physiology of blood pressure discussed in this chapter.
- Some medications promote the excretion of sodium and water, reducing blood volume and blood pressure, since blood volume is a determinant of venous return which is a determinant of cardiac output which is a determinant of blood pressure.
- Some medications inhibit the angiotensin-converting enzyme which converts angiotensin I to angiotensin II. Since angiotensin II is a powerful vasoconstrictor and also stimulates aldosterone which causes salt and water retention, inhibition of both of these will reduce blood pressure.
- Other drugs can reduce cardiac output or peripheral resistance which will in turn reduce blood pressure.

SUMMARY

- Blood pressure refers to the systemic arterial pressure. The normal blood pressure is 120/80 mm Hg, where 120 refers to the systolic BP and 80 refers to the diastolic BP.
- The basic determinants of BP are the cardiac output and peripheral resistance. Cardiac output and arterial compliance determine the systolic BP, while peripheral resistance determines the diastolic BP.
- Short-term regulation of BP is mediated via the baroreflex. The baroreceptors are located at the carotid sinus and the arch of the aorta. The stimulus for the baroreflex is an increase in blood pressure. The afferent nerves in the reflex are the glossopharyngeal nerve from the carotid sinus and the vagus nerve from the aortic arch.
- The response to a rise in blood pressure is cardiac parasympathetic activation and inhibition of the sympathetic nervous system. As a result, heart rate, stroke volume and total peripheral resistance decrease resulting in a fall in blood pressure.
- Longer-term regulation of BP is mediated via the renin–angiotensin–aldosterone system.

CHAPTER REVIEW QUESTIONS

1. What is blood pressure and what are its determinants?
2. Describe the components of the baroreflex.
3. What is Poiseuille's Law? What are the factors that determine blood flow?
4. Draw an arterial pressure tracing and indicate its components.

CHAPTER 29

Regional Circulations

SPECIFIC LEARNING OBJECTIVES

At the end of this chapter, the student should be able to:

- Describe the distribution of blood in the major organs in absolute terms and as a percentage of the cardiac output.
- Describe the salient features of the following circulations:
  - Coronary
  - Cerebral
  - Renal
  - Cutaneous
  - Skeletal muscle
- Describe the concept of autoregulation of blood flow.

GLOSSARY OF TERMS

- **Autoregulation:** the maintenance of blood flow at fairly constant levels despite changes in perfusion pressure
- **Portal circulation:** two capillary beds in series (normally an arteriole leads to a capillary bed which then empties into a venule which drains into larger veins to be returned to the heart; in a portal circulation, the venous drainage of the first capillary bed then supplies a second capillary bed)

Once the blood is pumped from the left ventricle into the aorta, it goes to the organs of the body. The amount of blood that an organ receives varies, and is partly dependent on its size, but more on its function, and whether it is actively functioning or relatively quiescent (at rest). Thus, the metabolic rate of an organ partly determines its blood flow. For instance, the skeletal muscle of the body is about 40% of the body weight in an adult male and receives about 1 L of blood/min at rest, but this can increase many times when the muscle is actively working as, for instance, in a running race. In contrast, the heart is relatively small (about 300 g), about 1/100th of the mass of skeletal muscle, yet it receives about 250 mL/min at rest; in terms of the blood flow per unit gram of tissue, the blood supply to the heart is about 0.8 mL/g of tissue, while that of the skeletal muscle is about 0.04 mL/g. Thus, in terms of blood flow per unit gram of tissue, the blood flow to the heart at rest is 20 times higher than that of skeletal muscle!

In this chapter, we discuss the regional blood flow to different organs of the body. The pulmonary circulation, blood flow to the digestive system and the foetal circulation are dealt with in separate chapters. Fig. 29.1 illustrates the distribution of the blood flow at rest across different vascular beds in the body as a percentage of the cardiac output.

AUTOREGULATION OF BLOOD FLOW

In Chapter 28, we had indicated that $P = QR$, where P is the pressure, Q is the blood flow and R is the resistance. In other words, $Q = P/R$, that is the blood flow is directly proportional to the pressure gradient. In many vital organs, however, such as the heart, the kidneys and the brain, blood flow is maintained fairly constant despite variations in the pressure (between about 60 and 180 mm Hg). This is called autoregulation. The concept of autoregulation is illustrated in Fig. 29.2.

In Fig. 29.2, you will observe that at low pressures, blood flow increases as pressure increases. Between a range of approximately 60 and 180 mm Hg pressure, the blood flow is maintained more or less constant, although the blood flow is higher when the metabolic activity of the tissue is high and blood flow is lower when the metabolic activity of the tissue is low. When the pressure goes above 180 mm Hg, blood flow again increases as the pressure rises. Autoregulation of blood flow ensures that blood flow in vital organs is maintained despite wide variations in blood pressure.

CORONARY CIRCULATION

The heart is composed largely of muscle. The coronary blood circulation is that network of blood vessels that supplies the

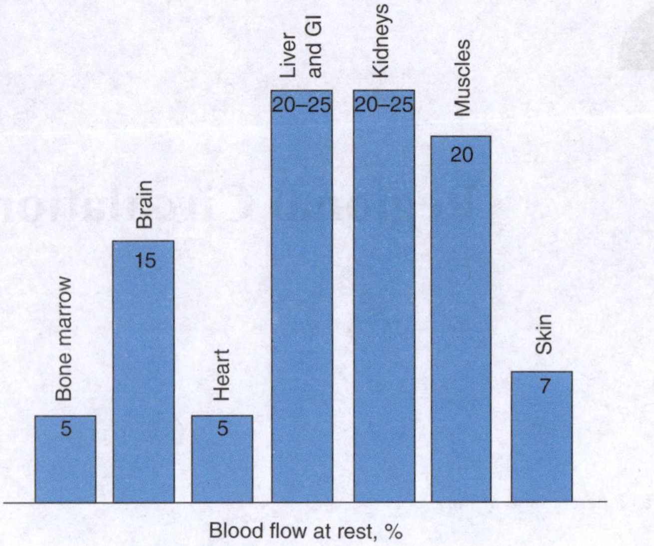

FIG. 29.1 Distribution of regional blood flow through key organs.

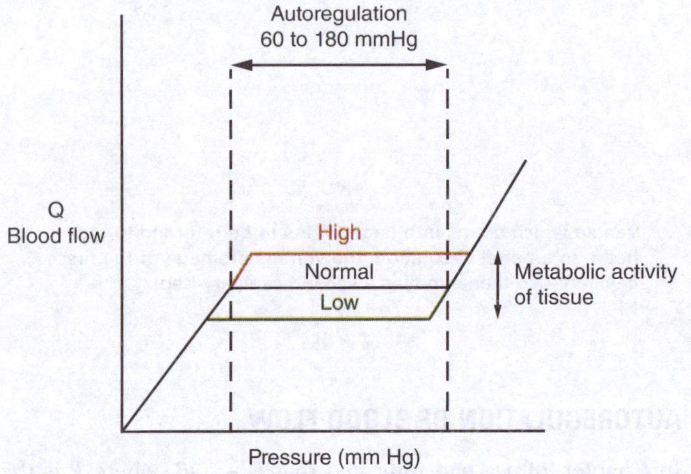

FIG. 29.2 Autoregulation of blood flow. Note that blood flow is autoregulated at different levels based on the metabolic activity of the tissue. The range of autoregulation is approximately 60–180 mm Hg, but differs from tissue to tissue.

heart itself. The arterial supply to the heart is from the left and right coronary arteries which arise from the root of the aorta. The blood then flows through the capillary network in the heart before emptying into the right atrium via the coronary sinus. Fig. 29.3 depicts the coronary circulation on the anterior and posterior surfaces of the heart.

Features of the Coronary Circulation

The coronary circulation is characterized by several special features:

1. Normal coronary blood flow is about 250 mL/min, that is about 5% of the cardiac output.
2. The capillary density in the coronary circulation is much higher than in other types of muscle. For example, the capillary density in the coronary circulation is eight times higher than that of skeletal muscle.
3. The blood flow through the coronary circulation is phasic. As the cardiac muscle fibres contract during systole, they compress the blood vessels contained within them. As a result, the blood flow almost stops during systole, while it is high during diastole when the cardiac muscle is relaxed. This biphasic pattern of blood flow is more in the left ventricle which is three times thicker than the right ventricle.
4. Although the left and right coronary arteries are a common feature across all individuals, the actual amount of blood flow delivered by each artery varies from individual to individual. Thus, in about 50% of persons, the right coronary is dominant; in 20%, the left coronary is dominant; and in the remaining 30%, both arteries deliver approximately the same amount of blood to the tissues. Dominance is based on which artery supplies the posterior one-third of the interventricular septum.
5. The coronary circulation shows autoregulation, that is the ability to maintain a near-constant blood flow despite a fluctuation in blood pressure (within a range).
6. Although coronary blood vessels are described as being end arteries (an artery that is the only supply of oxygenated blood to a portion of tissue), the small blood vessels of the

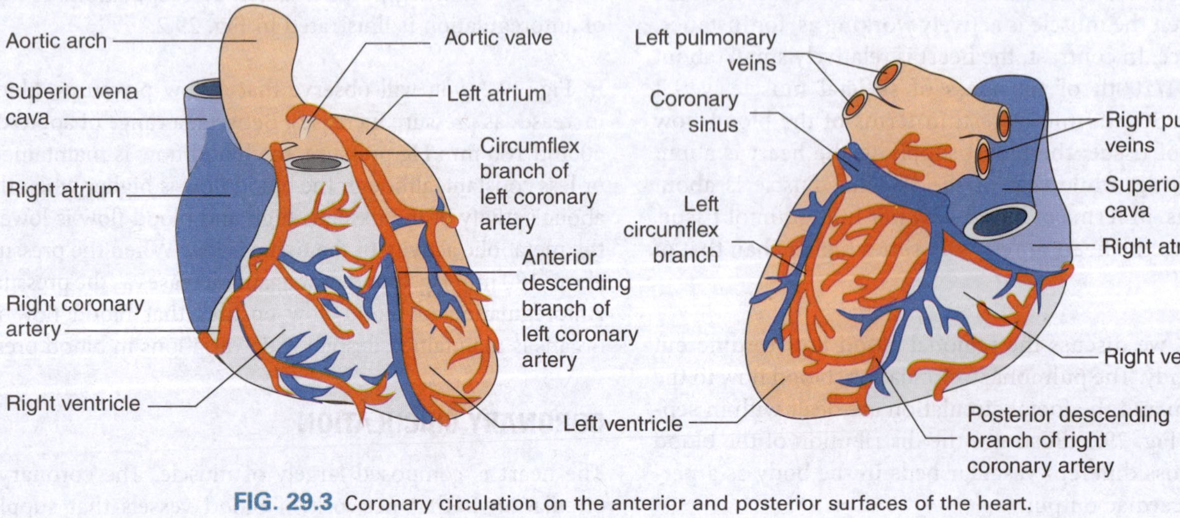

FIG. 29.3 Coronary circulation on the anterior and posterior surfaces of the heart.

coronary circulation form anastomoses with each other. These connections are called '*collaterals*'. When a blood vessel is blocked, these collaterals open up in an attempt to restore the blood supply to the area of muscle which has been deprived of its normal blood supply.

Regulation of Coronary Blood Flow

1. Coronary blood flow is closely linked to the metabolic activity of the heart. Thus, when the metabolic activity of the heart increases, the coronary blood flow also increases. This occurs because many metabolites are vasodilators – these include CO_2, reduced O_2, adenosine and nitric oxide (NO), among others.
2. Stimulation of the sympathetic nerves of the heart increases coronary blood flow. This, however, is not due to the direct action of the sympathetic nervous system on the blood vessels but more because the sympathetic nervous system increases both the heart rate and the force of contraction of the cardiac muscle (inotropy) and the resultant increase in metabolic activity increases coronary blood flow.

CLINICAL BOX

Coronary Heart Disease

Life expectancy has steadily increased. People are now increasingly adopting more unhealthy lifestyles with high-fat diets, low physical activity and increased smoking and tobacco use. These factors together with high blood pressure, increased body weight, diabetes and hypercholesterolaemia make individuals more prone to heart disease. Coronary heart disease includes those clinical conditions in which either the blood supply to the heart is insufficient to meet its metabolic demands or a coronary artery or its branches are blocked, cutting off the blood supply to a region of the heart. Ischaemic heart disease is an insufficiency of blood supply. Angina pectoris follows constriction of the coronary arteries. The person who has angina may experience chest pain on exertion which radiates to the side of the left arm or upwards into the neck. The pain usually lasts for a few minutes and may be relieved by rest. Myocardial infarction follows occlusion (blockage) of the coronary artery which affects the blood supply to a part of the myocardium; this can result in death of the tissues. The part of the myocardium that is affected can no longer take part in the pumping of the blood – this reduces the amount of blood that can be ejected by the ventricle. In addition, myocardial function can result in abnormal, sometimes fatal arrhythmias.

CEREBRAL CIRCULATION

The cerebral circulation refers to the blood flow to the brain. The brain in an adult weighs about 1.5 kg and receives about 15% of the cardiac output. This amounts to about 750 mL/min. The blood flow per gram of brain tissue is 750/1500 g, that is 0.5 mL/g of tissue. The brain receives its blood flow from the two internal carotid arteries and the two vertebral arteries which merge to form the circle of Willis at the base of the brain. The anterior, middle and posterior cerebral arteries originate from the circle of Willis and provide the blood flow to the cerebral cortex (Fig. 29.4). All parts of the brain do not receive blood equally. Instead, the cerebral blood flow is distributed to different parts of the brain depending on which part of the brain is active.

Features of the Cerebral Circulation

- Like the coronary circulation, the cerebral circulation displays 'autoregulation' – the ability to maintain near-constant blood flow in the face of changing pressures.
- While total cerebral blood flow is more or less constant, regional cerebral blood flow shows large variations in different parts of the brain and is highest where neuronal activity is highest.
- The brain has very poor tolerance to a lack of blood supply. Interruption of the blood flow to the brain for few seconds can result in a loss of consciousness.

Regulation of the Cerebral Circulation

1. The major regulation of cerebral blood flow is the regulation of the regional blood flow – increased neuronal activity is associated with an increase in local blood flow. This is mediated by various metabolites and other factors related to increased neuronal and metabolic activity including H^+ ions, K^+ ions and adenosine.
2. An important reflex that affects cerebral blood flow is *Cushing's reflex*. This reflex is activated when there is a rise in intracranial pressure. Intracranial pressure can rise if there is a tumour growing in the brain or if there is bleeding in the brain since the brain is enclosed in a rigid structure, the skull. When intracranial pressure increases, it compresses the blood vessels in the brain reducing cerebral blood flow. As a compensatory mechanism, there is a stimulation of the vasomotor area which increases the blood pressure in an attempt to overcome the pressure in the cerebral blood vessels and restore blood flow.

CLINICAL BOX: STROKE

Strokes are caused by either blockages or bleeds in the cerebral blood vessels. High blood pressure, smoking and increasing age are among the risk factors for stroke. Blockages in the cerebral arteries have much the same basis as the blockage that occurs in the coronary arteries in the heart, and are due to atherosclerotic plaques on the vessel wall. The consequence of a stroke is the impairment or loss of function related to the part of the brain that has been affected. A common type of stroke is that which is caused by blockage of the middle cerebral artery. This is associated with paralysis on the opposite side of the body – a condition called *haemiplegia*.

RENAL BLOOD FLOW

The renal blood flow accounts for about 20%–25% of the cardiac output, that is approximately 1250 mL/min. This is a very large blood flow for a very small organ; the kidneys are about 0.5% of the body weight. Yet, this is understandable, given that the kidney is responsible for the excretion of a large number of the metabolites in urine.

The kidney receives its blood via the renal artery, a branch of the aorta. The renal artery divides progressively to form the smaller branches and these terminate in *afferent arterioles* which form tufts of capillaries called the *glomerulus*. This is the site where filtration of blood, the first step in the formation of urine, takes

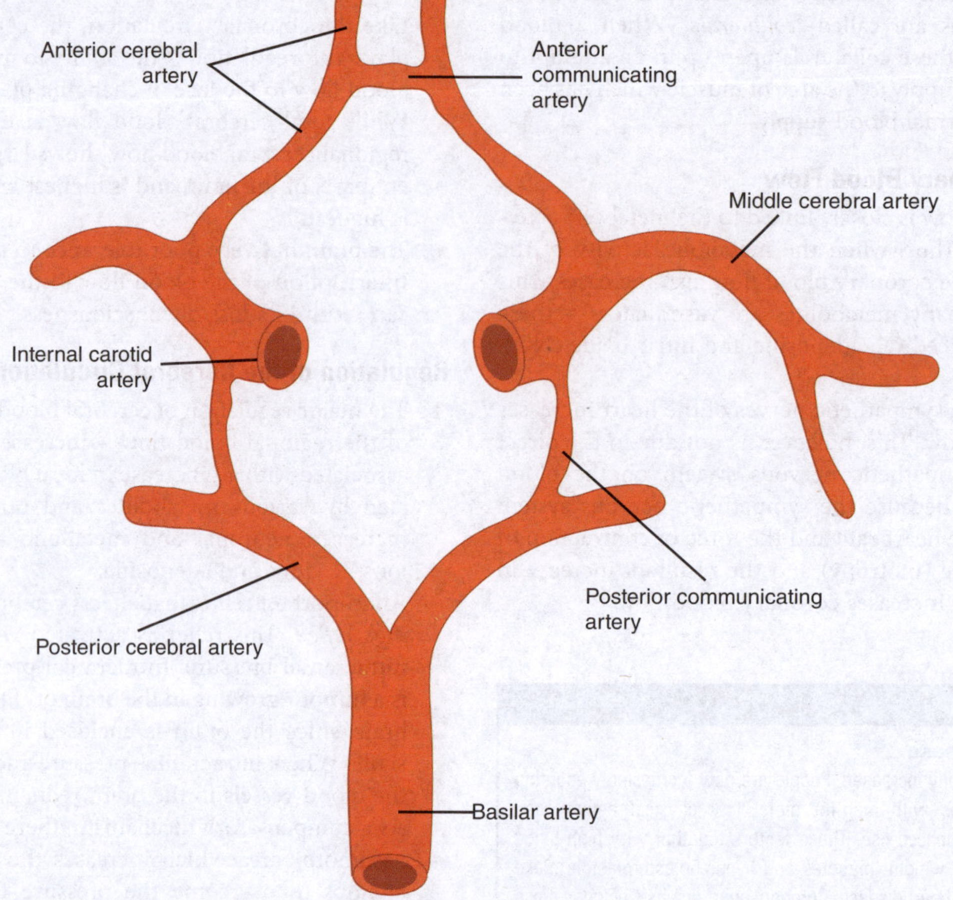

FIG. 29.4 The circle of Willis.

place and this will be discussed later (Chapter 58). After forming the glomerulus, the arteriole that emerges, called the *efferent arteriole*, goes on to form the peritubular capillary network that surrounds the renal tubules. Some nephrons, called juxtamedullary nephrons, have particularly long loops of Henle and are especially important in the concentration of urine. In these nephrons, the efferent arteriole gives rise to long straight vessels that follow the course of the loops of Henle; these are called the *vasa recta*. The arrangement of the blood vessels in the kidney is illustrated in Fig. 29.5.

Features of the Renal Circulation

1. The renal blood flow is very high given the small weight of the kidneys.
2. Like the coronary and cerebral circulation, the renal circulation exhibits 'autoregulation'.
3. The renal circulation is a portal circulation. A portal circulation has two capillary beds in series (one after the other). In the case of the kidney, the two capillary beds are the glomerulus and peritubular capillaries or the glomerulus and the vasa recta.

Regulation of the Renal Circulation

1. Although the kidney has one of the highest regional blood flows in the body, blood flow is not linked to metabolism. This is because the blood flow is so high that the kidney extracts only a small amount (less than 10% of the oxygen contained in the arterial blood) of the oxygen. Thus, there is a large oxygen reserve in the arterial blood, and the kidney can extract more oxygen when required at the same blood flow.
2. Stimulation of the sympathetic nerves supplying the kidney reduces renal blood flow substantially, but this does not appear to affect the amount of filtration that takes place at the glomerulus as much.

CUTANEOUS CIRCULATION

The primary function of the circulation of the skin is to maintain body temperature. It does this by regulating the amount of blood that is brought to the body surface where heat can be exchanged between the body and the surrounding environment. When the body is warm/hot and heat needs to be lost, cutaneous vasodilation brings a greater amount of blood to the surface for heat exchange. When the environment is cold and the body needs to conserve heat, there is cutaneous vasoconstriction – thus, little blood is available for heat exchange with the environment.

1. The amount of blood that flows through the cutaneous circulation varies; it can range from close to zero with severe vasoconstriction and as high as 7 L/min during extensive vasodilation.

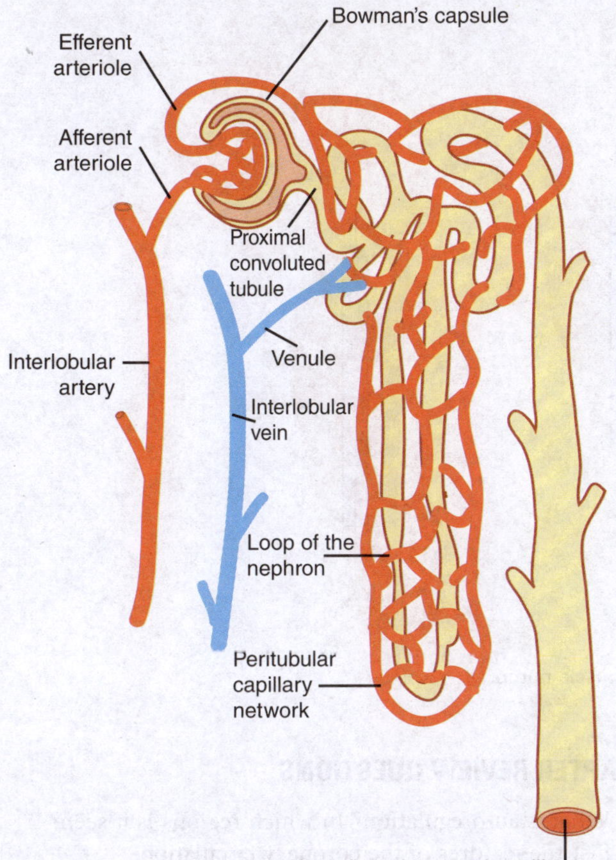

FIG. 29.5 Blood vessels related to the nephron in the kidney.

2. The whole of the cutaneous circulation does not vasoconstrict or vasodilate together – thus, regional areas of the skin may vasoconstrict or vasodilate. When we are exposed to cold, our hands or face which are not clothed feel very cold – this is because of local vasoconstriction.
3. The sympathetic nervous system is an important regulator of the cutaneous circulation and is responsible for the vasoconstriction of blood vessels.

The Triple Response

The triple response is a vascular response that is observed when a blunt object is firmly stroked against the skin. The three components of the response are the following:

1. Red line: This is because of capillary vasodilation due to the opening up of the precapillary sphincter.
2. Flare: The area around the red line becomes red because of a unique reflex called the axon reflex. This is illustrated in Fig. 29.6. The stimulus is the stroking of the skin firmly with a blunt object. This sensation is perceived by the receptor and is transmitted along the sensory nerve to the spinal cord. The sensory nerve also gives off a branch called a collateral which is directed to the blood vessels in the skin where the stimulus was applied. This causes vasodilation of the blood vessels.
3. Wheal: The area becomes elevated and swollen because fluid moves from the capillaries and venules into the tissue space.

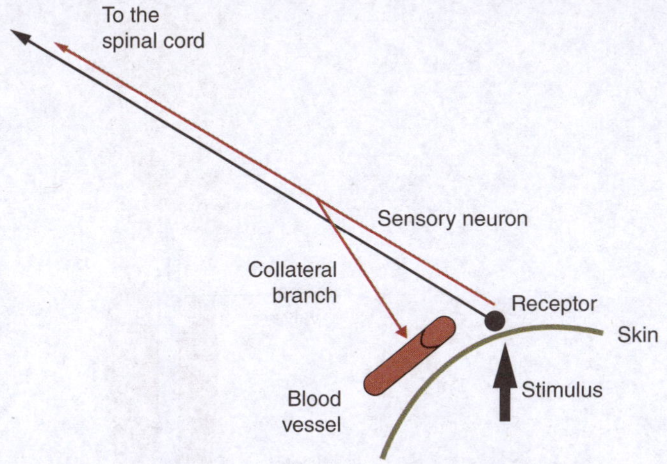

FIG. 29.6 The axon reflex as part of the triple response.

CIRCULATION TO SKELETAL MUSCLE

The blood flow to skeletal muscle varies. Thus, it can range from about 20% of cardiac output (i.e. 1 L/min) at rest to about 80% of cardiac output during heavy exercise. Remember that cardiac output itself rises from about 5 L/min at rest to about four to five times that amount (20–25 L) during heavy physical activity.

In skeletal muscle, the small blood vessels run parallel to the muscle fibres. The ratio of capillaries to muscle fibre is fairly constant at 1:1.

Features of Circulation to Skeletal Muscle

1. The amount of blood flow to skeletal muscle depends on the metabolic activity of the muscle. Vasodilation during increased metabolism is related to the increased concentration of various metabolites which cause blood vessels to vasodilate. These include CO_2, K^+, adenosine and H^+, among others.
2. During active contraction of skeletal muscle, blood flow to the muscle can be reduced. This is because the contraction of the muscle results in compression of the blood vessels. The extent of contraction determines the degree of compression of blood vessels. At around 70% of maximal contraction, compression is so severe that blood flow reduces close to zero. However, after a period of ischaemia (insufficiency of blood supply), the blood flow to the muscle increases. This is called *reactive hyperaemia*.
3. Contraction of the muscle, particularly in the extremities, plays an important role in increasing venous return to the heart. Thus, when the muscle contracts, veins are compressed and the blood is pushed towards the heart, aided by one-direction valves in the large veins. This is sometimes referred to as the *muscle pump* (Fig. 29.7).
4. Neural factors are important at rest. Sympathetic nerves are essentially vasoconstrictor and reduce blood flow to skeletal muscle. However, during the *flight-and-fight* response, hormones such as epinephrine (adrenaline) are released and these cause vasodilation and increased blood flow to the skeletal muscles.

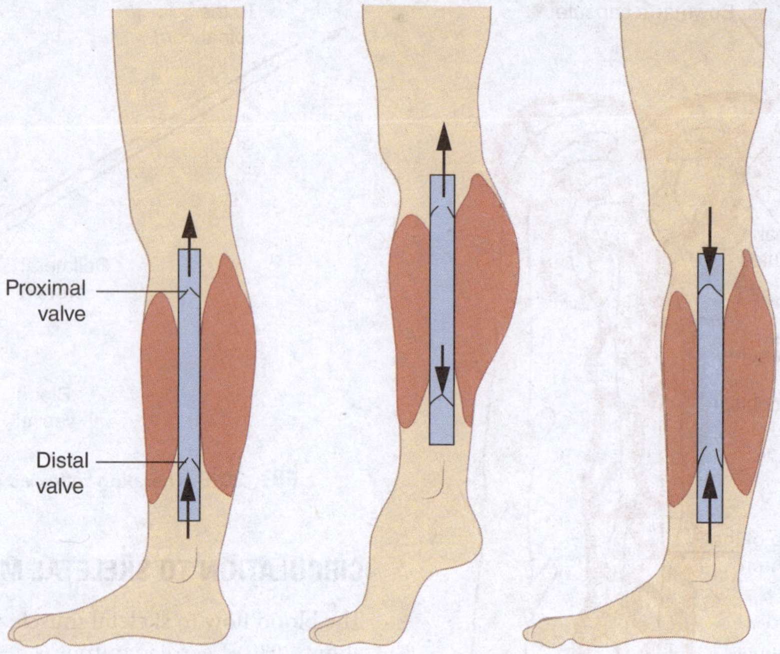

FIG. 29.7 The skeletal muscle pump.

APPLICATIONS IN NURSING

- The nurse will need to be aware of the pathophysiology of coronary heart disease and stroke and will need to monitor patients with these conditions.
- In the event of a myocardial infarction, the nurse is part of the resuscitation team and will need to administer cardiopulmonary resuscitation.

SUMMARY

- Regional blood is highly variable at rest; ranging from 5% of the cardiac output for the coronary circulation, 15% for the cerebral circulation and 20% for skeletal muscle to 20%–25% for the renal and splanchnic circulations.
- Autoregulation is the process by which regional flow is kept fairly constant despite changes in perfusion pressure. This is well developed in coronary, cerebral and renal circulations.
- Many regional circulations show large differences in blood flow at rest and during active states. For instance, skeletal muscle receives 20% of the cardiac output at rest but as much as 80% of the enhanced cardiac output during strenuous exercise.
- Portal circulations are those in which there are two capillary beds in series. They are seen in the kidney (glomerulus and peritubular network/glomerulus and vasa recta) and in the splanchnic circulation (GI capillary network and hepatic capillary network).

CHAPTER REVIEW QUESTIONS

1. What is autoregulation? In which regions is it seen?
2. List the features of the coronary circulation.
3. List the features of the cerebral circulation.
4. List the features of the renal circulation.

CHAPTER 30

Cardiovascular Homeostasis in Exercise and Posture

SPECIFIC LEARNING OBJECTIVES

At the end of this chapter, the student should be able to:

- Describe and explain the cardiovascular responses to exercise with specific reference to:
  - Cardiac responses
  - Blood pressure responses
  - Responses in regional blood flow
  - Regulation of cardiovascular function during exercise
- Differentiate between the cardiovascular responses to isometric and isotonic exercises.
- Describe cardiovascular homeostasis to change in posture.
- Describe and explain the basis of syncope.

GLOSSARY OF TERMS

- **Exercise:** structured physical activity with the aim of achieving some end point, for example fitness, better health and optimal performance
- **Isometric exercise:** exercise which does not involve the shortening of muscle – typically geared towards building up strength
- **Isotonic exercise:** exercise which involves shortening of muscle and the performance of work (this may involve small muscle groups or whole-body exercise, e.g. running and jogging)
- **Syncope:** a transient loss of consciousness due to a sudden fall in blood pressure and a reduction in cerebral blood flow
- **Postural hypotension:** a fall of greater than 20 mm Hg systolic or 10 mm Hg diastolic blood pressure during a change in posture from lying to standing within a 3-minute period

INTRODUCTION

Physical activity is any activity where we expend energy (the use of calories). Thus, physical activity may involve small amounts of energy expenditure while sitting at a desk or standing while other physical activities involve a large amount of energy expenditure, for example walking uphill with a load and playing competitive sports such as basketball or field hockey. Exercise is a structured physical activity which is performed to improve certain parameters, for example fitness, strength, mobility, health status and weight.

The first part of this chapter focuses on cardiovascular responses to a single bout of exercise, whether isotonic or isometric. We also briefly describe the long-term benefits of sustained exercise.

During the course of a day, we constantly change our body position (posture) – from lying to standing, sitting to standing, etc. During these times, there are large changes in the cardiovascular system. In the second part of this chapter, we describe how the body responds to changes in posture and what can happen if our responses are not suitable.

CARDIOVASCULAR RESPONSES TO WHOLE-BODY ACUTE ISOTONIC EXERCISE

- **Heart rate increases:** This is the result of several factors:
  - *Exercise pressor response*: It is a reflex that originates from the skeletal muscle that is being used. This results in an activation of the sympathetic nervous system and an inhibition of the cardiac vagal action (parasympathetic fibres). Both these effects result in an increase in heart rate.
  - *Central command*: Since heart rate begins to rise even before the exercise starts, it is believed that this is mediated by the brain and to some extent by the release of adrenaline in anticipation of the exercise.
- **Venous return increases:** As muscles begin to contract, they compress the blood in the veins which hold a significant part of the blood volume (muscle pump). Helped by the one-way valves in the limbs, the venous blood is pushed towards the heart. Increased respiration during exercise also propels blood to the heart because of the respiratory pump (discussed in Chapter 27).
- **Cardiac output increases:** The determinants of cardiac output are stroke volume and heart rate. We have already

discussed that the heart rate increases during exercise. When a person exercises, the exercising muscles act as a muscle pump and increase the venous return to the heart. This increase in venous return fills the ventricles with more blood during diastole. When the ventricles fill with more blood, they get stretched. Frank–Starling law states that the force of contraction of muscle is directly proportional to the initial length of the muscle fibre. Since the ventricles are filled with more blood with an increased venous return, they will be stretched more, and the initial length of the muscle fibres will be increased causing them to contract harder and increasing stroke volume. Stroke volume will also increase because the sympathetic nervous system is activated during exercise and these nerves have a stimulatory effect on the cardiac muscle causing them to contract harder. Chemicals, drugs and ions which increase cardiac contractility are called *positive inotropic* agents. Cardiac output can increase by an excess of four times its resting value in intense exercise.

- **Regional blood flow is redistributed:** During intense exercise, as much as 70%–85% of the cardiac output goes towards skeletal muscle while the blood flow as a percentage of cardiac output falls in the splanchnic (digestive tract and liver) circulation and to the kidneys. The increased blood flow to exercising muscle occurs because of intense vasodilation in exercising muscles. Blood flow to the heart in absolute amounts, that is mL/min, is increased in the coronary circulation while blood flow to the brain is maintained.
- **Blood pressure changes:** Since cardiac output is the determinant of systolic blood pressure and since cardiac output increases during isotonic exercise, systolic blood pressure is increased. In contrast, because there is such widespread vasodilation in skeletal muscle, the peripheral resistance (a determinant of diastolic blood pressure) may be reduced, and diastolic blood pressure may remain unchanged or even fall. A fall in diastolic blood pressure may also occur because the large amount of heat that is generated during exercise. The body needs to get rid of this extra heat – this happens through wide-spread cutaneous vasodilation which further lowers the peripheral resistance. The cardiovascular response to exercise is summarized in Fig. 30.1.

CARDIOVASCULAR RESPONSES TO ISOMETRIC CONTRACTION

The cardiovascular responses to isometric exercise differ from what is seen with isotonic exercise. However, to compare the two types of responses, it is important to look at exercises that involve similar muscle masses involved in the exercise. In isotonic exercise, diastolic blood pressure may not rise because of vasodilation in active skeletal muscle and the increase in cutaneous circulation (to dissipate the heat generated during exercise), both of which reduce the total peripheral resistance. In contrast, in isometric exercise, during the phase of sustained contraction, diastolic blood pressure may rise particularly when large muscle groups are involved because the contracting muscle compresses the blood vessels that are contained within the muscle, thereby increasing the peripheral vascular resistance.

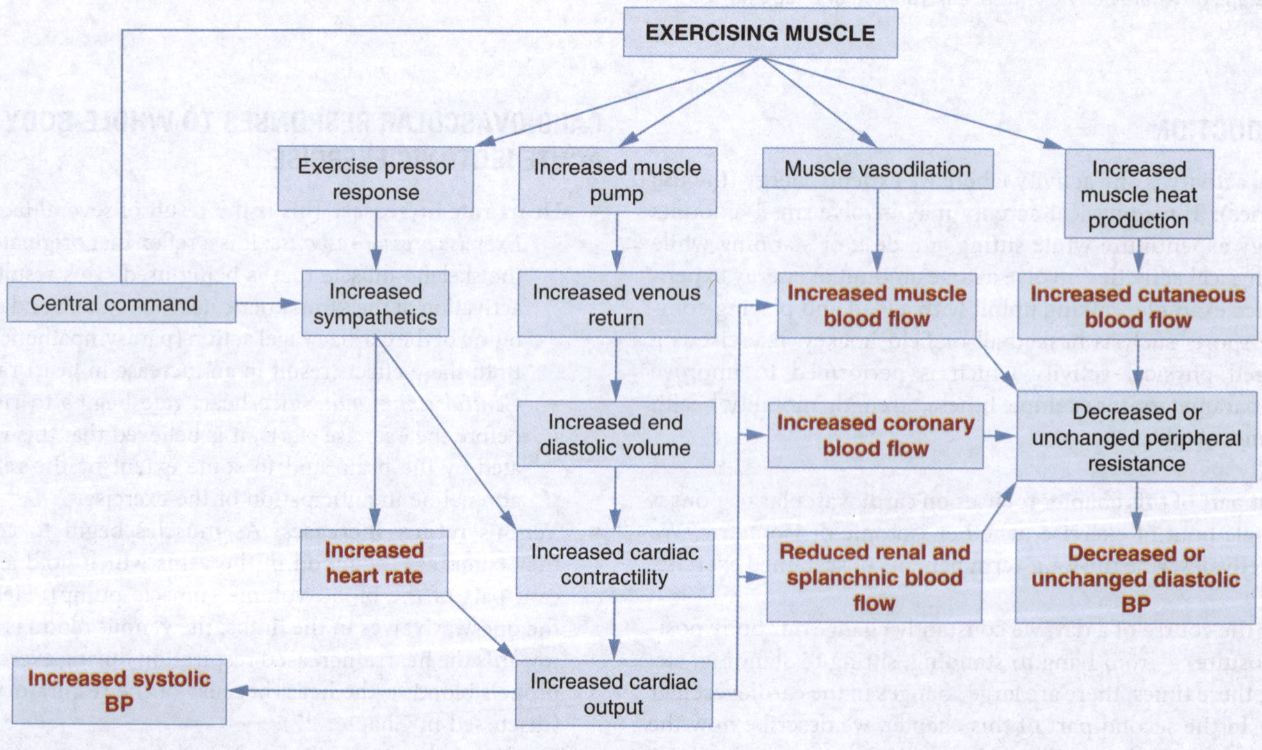

FIG. 30.1 Summary of cardiovascular changes to whole-body isotonic exercise. Notation in red indicates key changes related to heart rate, blood pressure and changes in regional blood flow.

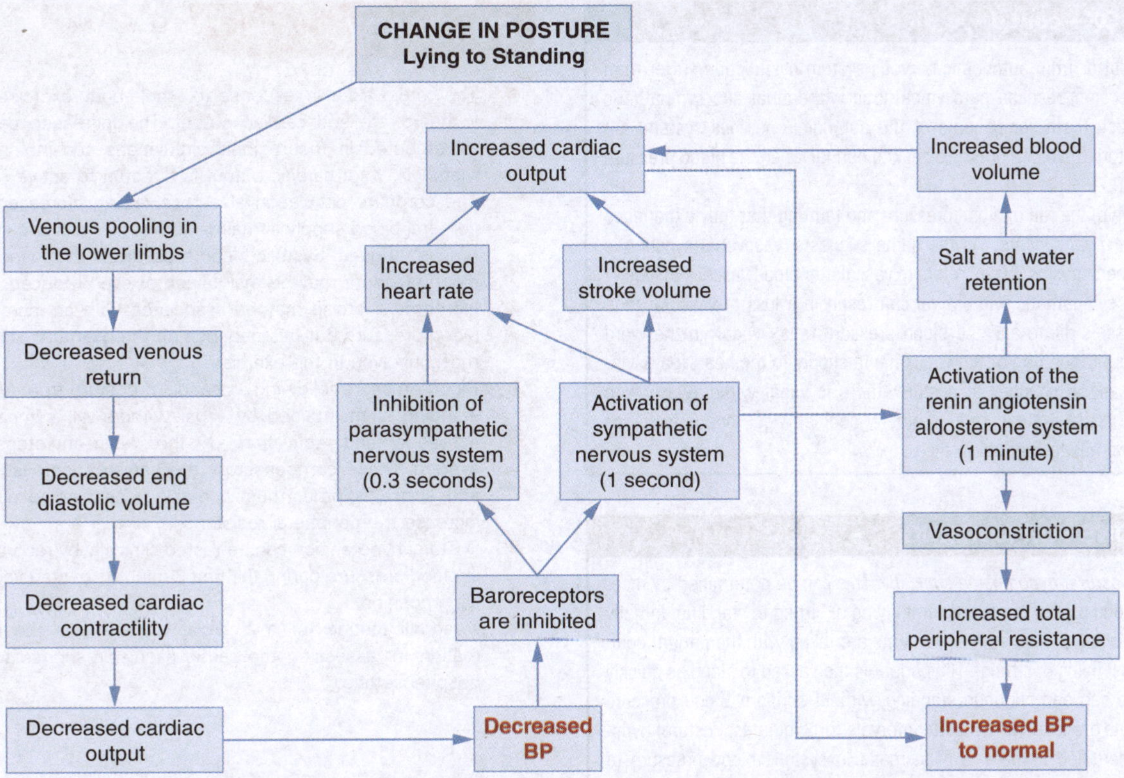

FIG. 30.2 Restoration of blood pressure following a change in posture from lying to standing up.

CARDIOVASCULAR RESPONSES TO CHANGE IN POSTURE

In this section, we describe what happens when a person who is lying down suddenly stands up. When we stand up, there is venous pooling in the lower limbs. This results in a decrease in venous return to the heart as a result of which there is less ventricular filling with blood. Lower ventricular filling means that the end-diastolic volume of the ventricle is lower and there is less stretch of the cardiac muscle fibres resulting in a decreased force of contraction (Frank–Starling law) and a reduced stroke volume which will reduce cardiac output and blood pressure (remember that cardiac output and total peripheral resistance are the major determinants of blood pressure).

As a result of the fall in blood pressure, the stretch on the baroreceptors is reduced. This results in an inhibition of parasympathetic nerve fibres to the heart in less than half a second. Normally, the vagus nerve (parasympathetic) to the heart slows down the heart rate. Thus, when it is inhibited, the heart rate rises. The rise in heart rate is also the result of an activation of the sympathetic nervous system which increases not only the heart rate but also the force of contraction of cardiac muscle increasing the stroke volume. The increase in both heart rate and stroke volume increases cardiac output (remember that cardiac output = stroke volume × heart rate). The activation of the sympathetic nervous system also activates the renin–angiotensin–aldosterone system. Angiotensin is a powerful vasoconstrictor which increases the total peripheral resistance while aldosterone causes salt and water retention increasing blood volume and venous return and thereby increasing cardiac output. The rise in cardiac output and total peripheral resistance restores the blood pressure back to normal after the fall in BP that occurred when changing the posture from lying to standing. These changes are summarized in Fig. 30.2.

CLINICAL BOX

Syncope

Syncope is defined as a temporary loss of consciousness due to a sudden fall in blood pressure which results in a reduced blood flow to the brain. We recognize this in common language as 'fainting'.

Causes of syncope include, among others, the following:

- Severe dehydration due to any cause.
- Sudden changes in posture, for example lying to standing or sitting to standing, in susceptible individuals.
- Cardiac arrhythmias resulting in ineffective pumping of the blood from the heart

Syncope and Posture

In normal healthy individuals, a shift from lying down to standing is not associated with any major problem – the blood pressure initially falls but in less than a second, as indicated in the earlier section, compensatory reflex mechanisms help to restore the blood pressure to normal. There are some individuals, however, who are especially prone to giddiness and fainting after a sudden shift in posture. This is called *postural hypotension*. These include, among others, the following:

- Elderly individuals.
- People suffering from autonomic nervous dysfunction (this is not that uncommon; e.g. we may see this as a complication of chronic, uncontrolled diabetes).
- Those on certain antihypertensive medications.

Continued

CLINICAL BOX—cont'd

People who suffer from autonomic nervous system dysfunction suffer from postural hypotension because parasympathetic withdrawal and sympathetic nervous activation (both components of the autonomic nervous system) are essential to restore the blood pressure back to normal when the blood pressure falls (see Fig. 30.2).

In elderly people, the fall in blood pressure and fainting that they experience is typically *vasovagal syncope*. As the name suggests, vasovagal syncope is related to two mechanisms. 'Vaso' refers to vascular or blood vessels. In elderly people, sudden sympathetic withdrawal can result in a loss of vascular tone – the blood vessels dilate and the blood pressure falls. 'Vagal' in the word 'vasovagal' refers to the role of the vagus nerve supply to the heart (parasympathetic). Normally in changes in posture, there is vagal withdrawal which contributes to the rise in heart rate. In elderly people, vagal tone is low – so vagal withdrawal has less effect in the elderly.

APPLICATIONS FOR NURSING

- *Measuring postural hypotension clinically.* This can be determined by measuring the blood pressure response from lying or sitting to standing. Initially at least two blood pressure measurements are taken with the patient comfortably at rest (lying or sitting). The patient is then asked to stand as quickly as he or she can and continue standing without support. Blood pressure measurements are taken at 1-minute intervals for 3 minutes. Postural hypotension is identified if there is a decrease in systolic blood pressure of 20 mm Hg or a decrease in diastolic blood pressure of 10 mm Hg within 3 minutes of standing when compared with blood pressure from the sitting or supine position. When performing this test, patients need to be instructed to sit immediately if they feel giddy at any time and the nurse needs to keep a careful watch on the patients to assist them to sit in the event that they feel faint or if their blood pressure falls excessively.
- *Exercise testing and exercise tolerance in clinical settings:* While exercise testing is done in several situations including to identify exercise tolerance in patients with chronic respiratory disorders, the most common form of exercise testing in the hospital is the treadmill test. In this test, patients walk on a treadmill where the speed and inclination of the treadmill is gradually increased. The patient's ECG is monitored to determine whether there are any ECG changes of myocardial ischaemia with increasing exertion.

SUMMARY

- The cardiovascular response to whole-body exercise is an increase in heart rate and cardiac output. The increased cardiac output is redistributed in the regional circulations such that nearly approximately 75% of cardiac output is directed to active skeletal muscle. The coronary circulation also receives an increased blood supply; cerebral blood supply is maintained while renal and splanchnic blood flow is reduced. Systolic blood pressure is increased while diastolic blood pressure may be maintained or even reduced.
- Isometric exercise may be associated with an increase in diastolic blood pressure but this depends on the quantum of skeletal muscle mass involved in the exercise.
- Blood pressure following a change in posture from lying or sitting to standing is maintained by vagal withdrawal, sympathetic nervous activation and activation of the renin–angiotensin–aldosterone system. These compensatory mechanisms increase the heart rate and stroke volume, thus increasing the cardiac output, and also increase the peripheral resistance.
- Postural hypotension can be tested clinically by recording the change in blood pressure during the first 3 minutes of standing from a sitting/lying position.
- Treadmill testing for myocardial ischaemia is the most common reason for assessing the cardiovascular response to exercise in a hospital setting.

CHAPTER REVIEW QUESTIONS

1. Describe the cardiovascular changes during isotonic exercise.
2. Describe the cardiovascular changes during isometric exercise.
3. Describe the cardiovascular changes when a person shifts from lying to standing.
4. What is syncope and what are some common causes?

CHAPTER 31

Cardiovascular Changes with Ageing

SPECIFIC LEARNING OBJECTIVES

At the end of this chapter, the student should be able to:

- Describe the cardiac changes that occur with ageing.
- Describe vascular changes with ageing.
- Describe alterations in regional blood flow that occur with ageing.
- Describe alterations in cardiovascular regulation with ageing.

GLOSSARY OF TERMS

- **Demographic transition:** a shift in population composition from younger individuals to older individuals
- **Epidemiological transition:** a shift in disease patterns from largely infectious diseases to a greater prevalence of noncommunicable diseases associated with ageing
- **Chronological age:** the age of the individual as calculated from the date and year of birth
- **Ventricular hypertrophy:** enlargement of the walls of the ventricle due to an increase in the size of the cardiac muscle cells (cardiomyocytes)
- **Aerobic capacity:** the maximum amount of oxygen that can be consumed during maximal exercise (this is largely a function of the heart and lungs and is sometimes referred to as cardiorespiratory fitness)
- **Autonomic failure:** a reduction in sympathetic or parasympathetic nervous activity or both, resulting in functional deficits

INTRODUCTION

The world has changed a lot in the last 100 years. At the time of India's independence in 1947, the average lifespan of an Indian was only 35 years. Birth rates were high and so were the deaths especially from infectious diseases. As a result, the elderly were a small percentage of the population. Since that time, birth rates have fallen and the lifespan has increased resulting in a rapidly growing aged population. It is estimated that by 2050, there will be more than 300 million people in India older than 60 years. The shift of the population from a relatively young population to a middle-aged and older population is referred to as the *demographic transition*. This has been accompanied by a disease (epidemiological) transition from largely infectious diseases to noncommunicable diseases, one of the risk factors of which is increasing age. Fig. 31.1 demonstrates these demographic and disease shifts diagrammatically. You will observe from the diagram that with time noncommunicable disease has increased and the number of elderly has also increased. The recent COVID pandemic has shown us that new infectious disease outbreaks will continue to happen.

This chapter focuses on what happens to cardiovascular physiology with ageing.

CLASSIFICATION OF AGEING

There is no clear definition of what is aged or elderly. This is because there are different ways of looking at ageing. One is *chronological age* – this refers to the age of the individual calculated from the date and year of his or her birth. The other approach is *biological ageing* – this recognizes that individuals are not simply their age – some older people may be more functional, physically and mentally, than much younger people. Older individuals of the same age may also differ in their functional abilities.

Although India recognizes that a person becomes a 'senior citizen' when he or she achieves the age of 60 years, there are many other classifications of ageing. Thus, people older than 60 years may be classified as young elderly, middle elderly or old elderly based on their actual age. Nomenclature differs based on different classifications: middle aged (45–59 years), elderly (60–74 years), old (75–90 years) and very old (older than 90 years). People may also be referred to as frail elderly if they are older than 60 years and if they have physical or cognitive (mental) difficulties. Despite all these classifications, it is important that older people are treated as individuals and that special care is taken to avoid the stigmatization of ageing, that is ageism.

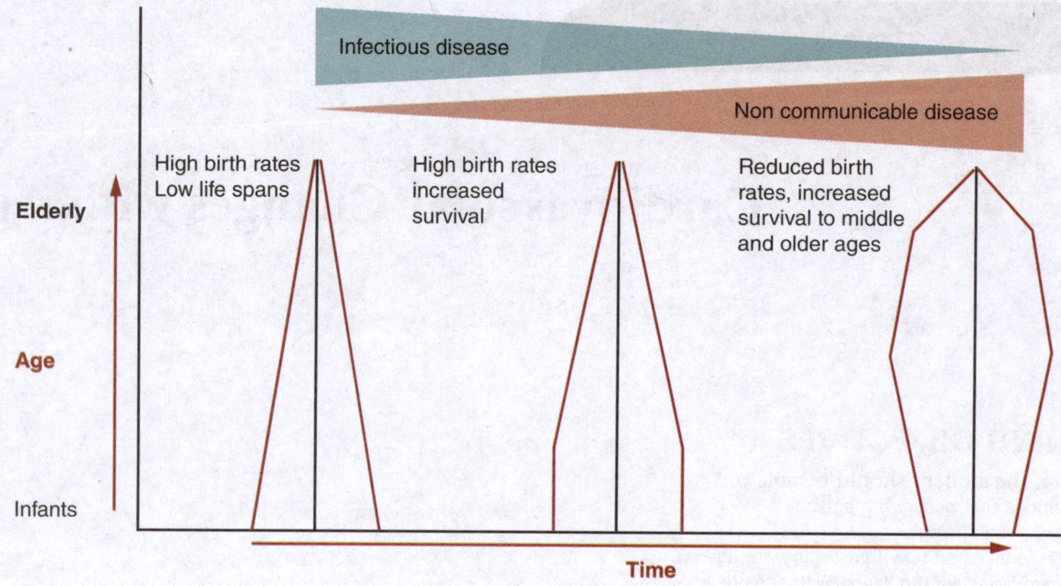

FIG. 31.1 Summary of the demographic and epidemiological transition over time. The COVID pandemic has shown us that despite the use of antibiotics and vaccines, infectious diseases are here to stay, although with lower rates, morbidity and mortality as in the past.

CARDIAC CHANGES WITH AGEING

The ageing heart undergoes several changes in both structure and function. These changes are not experienced by all aged individuals to the same extent but depend on genetics and health behaviours of the person. Health behaviours include smoking, alcohol consumption, amount of dietary salt intake and physical inactivity, among others. Individuals therefore vary in the changes that are seen.

Structurally, the heart may show the following:

- A reduction in the number of cardiomyocytes (cardiac muscle cells)
- A reduction in the number of pacemaker cells (SA and AV nodes)
- Thickening and calcification of the valves
- Hypertrophy of the left ventricle

Physiologically, the aged individual shows the following:

- A reduction in the maximal heart rate that can be achieved. A simple calculation is that the maximal heart rate is 220 − age (years). Thus, while a 20-year-old may be able to achieve a maximal heart rate of 200 beats/min, a 70-year-old may be able to achieve only 150 beats/min. This is associated with a decrease in aerobic capacity (cardiorespiratory fitness) of about 10% per decade.
- A reduction in the force of contraction of the heart.
- An increased risk of developing arrhythmias. Some of these arrhythmias may not be apparent until a routine ECG is done. An example of this is chronic atrial fibrillation. In this condition, the atrial electrical activity is erratic and uncoordinated as a result of which atrial contraction is not simultaneous or effective. This is important because the last 25% of ventricular filling with blood is due to atrial contraction.
- A decrease in the early diastolic filling of ventricles which is mediated largely by the pressure gradient between the atria and the ventricles.

VASCULAR CHANGES WITH AGEING

Ageing is also associated with structural and functional changes in the blood vessels.

Structurally, the blood vessels show the following changes:

- The blood vessels get stiffer. In individuals who have been hypertensive for some time, smooth muscle proliferation in the arteries make them less elastic. Blood vessels also get stiffer with age because of increased collagen deposition in the vessel wall and a loss of elastic fibres with age.
- The blood vessels may show atherosclerotic changes. Atherosclerosis is the deposition of fats and cholesterol of the arterial walls. These deposits are known as plaques. If plaques become large enough, they can obstruct blood flow (Fig. 31.2). This may be particularly important in certain regional circulations such as the heart where they can cause myocardial ischaemia and the brain where they cause strokes. Sometimes calcium may deposit in the plaques adding to the stiffness of the arteries. If a plaque breaks down, portions of the plaque may block arteries elsewhere.

Physiologically:

- The increased stiffness results in a loss of elasticity in the large arteries. In an earlier chapter, we discussed how blood that is ejected from the ventricle goes to the aorta (from the left ventricle) or the pulmonary artery (from the right ventricle). The elasticity of these vessels gives rise to the *Windkessel effect* in which the elastic recoil of the vessel wall propels the blood forward. When these

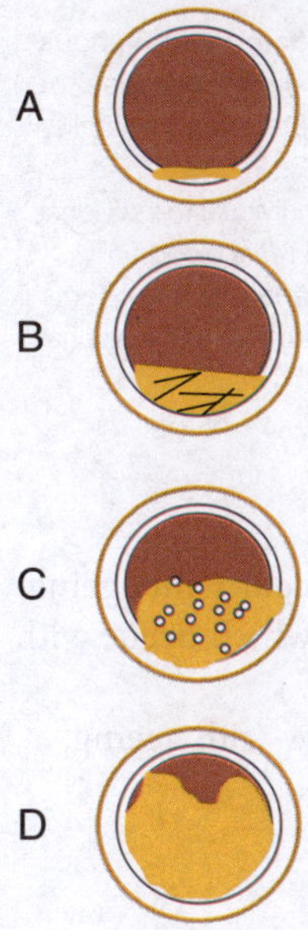

FIG. 31.2 Progression of an atherosclerotic plaque. (A) A fatty streak deposited where the endothelium is damaged.

(B) A fibrous plaque – deposition of collagen fibres in the plaque.

(C) Calcified plaque – figure shows 'spotty', early calcium deposits (calcification).

(D) A large plaque obstructing the flow of blood.

vessels become stiffer, they are not able to stretch and the pressure in the blood vessels during ejection of blood from the ventricle, that is systolic blood pressure, rises. This is why some elderly individuals show isolated systolic hypertension.

- Although blood pressure tends to rise with age, hypertension does not always increase with ageing. Studies in tribes which consume low salt intakes have shown that blood pressure remains fairly constant as people age.
- Valves in the veins of the legs may become incompetent. This results in venous pooling in the legs. The elderly may be more prone to develop large, tortuous veins in the lower limbs, a condition called *varicose veins.* The increased venous pressure because of venous pooling may also result in fluid shifting into the tissues so that some elderly show swelling of the feet towards the end of the day or after prolonged standing due to tissue oedema.
- The velocity of blood flow is slower with ageing. This may put elderly people at increased risk of formation of clots in the vascular system especially if they are bedridden or immobilized for long periods of time. The increased likelihood of intravascular clots is also increased because platelets in the elderly are more likely to aggregate together – a phenomenon called platelet aggregability.

CHANGES IN REGIONAL BLOOD FLOW

- Studies have shown that cortical cerebral blood flow (i.e. blood flow to the cerebral cortex) may be reduced with ageing. This reduction appears to be independent of the loss of neurons and grey matter that also occurs with ageing. The age-related decrease in regional cerebral blood flow appears to be greatest in those parts of the brain that are more metabolically active.
- Studies show that myocardial perfusion, that is coronary flow to the cardiac muscle, reduces after the age of 60 years.
- Ageing is associated with a reduction in renal blood flow, although this is highly variable between individuals. The decline is on average at the rate of about 10% per decade after the fourth decade. The reduction in blood flow is most pronounced on the outer aspect of the kidney, that is the cortex.

CHANGES IN CARDIOVASCULAR REGULATION

The autonomic nervous system plays an important role in regulating the cardiovascular system. The two parts of the autonomic nervous system are the sympathetic nervous system and the parasympathetic nervous system. Ageing is associated with a reduction in autonomic nervous activity. This may be due to the following:

- The normal process of ageing.
- The presence of other medical conditions such as diabetes which reduce the activity of the autonomic nervous system.

The reduction in autonomic nervous activity can affect cardiovascular function in various ways:

- An increased risk of postural hypotension. This is because the autonomic nervous system helps to restore the blood pressure during postural changes (lying/sitting to standing) as discussed in Chapter 30. The inability to regulate blood pressure may also be affected by the thickening of the arteries with ageing which makes the baroreceptors less sensitive to stretch (see Chapter 28 for a detailed discussion of the regulation of blood pressure).
- A reduced force of contraction of the heart. This may, in part, be due to the reduction in sympathetic nervous activity with ageing – sympathetic nerve fibres to the heart increase the force of contraction of the heart.

There are other regulatory processes which affect cardiovascular function and which are affected by ageing. These include various hormones including the renin–angiotensin–aldosterone system and molecules released from the endothelial lining of the blood vessels. A detailed discussion of these changes is beyond the scope of this chapter.

APPLICATIONS FOR NURSING

Nurses can play an important role in ensuring that the elderly maintain good cardiovascular health by ensuring that they (1) consume a healthy diet that has an adequate intake of vegetables and fruit, reduced refined sugars and less fats and oils; (2) adopt a physically active lifestyle; (3) take medications regularly for any comorbidities that they have such as diabetes and hypertension; and (4) get regular medical check-ups.

SUMMARY

- Ageing is a highly variable process between individuals and should not simply be seen as a function of the age of the individual (chronological age) but also in terms of function (biological age).
- Cardiac changes with ageing include a reduction in cardiomyocyte number, ventricular hypertrophy, reduction/alterations in pacemaker activity and thickening and calcification of the valves. This manifests as reduced cardiac contractility, increased risk of arrhythmias, reduced early diastolic filling and a reduction in maximal heart rate.
- Vascular changes with ageing include increased stiffness of arteries because of loss of elastic fibres, increased collagen deposition, atherosclerotic changes and, in the presence of chronic hypertension, smooth muscle proliferation. This can manifest as hypertension and the loss of the Windkessel effect as isolated hypertension. Venous valve incompetence can result in varicose veins and peripheral oedema due to increased venous pressure associated with venous pooling. Increased intravascular clots are more likely because of decreased velocity of blood flow and increased platelet aggregability with ageing.
- Regional blood flow changes are highly variable from individual to individual but may include a reduction in cerebral, coronary and renal blood flow.
- Autonomic nervous activity is reduced with ageing and this has effects on the regulation of cardiac function, vascular function and regional blood flow.

CHAPTER REVIEW QUESTIONS

1. Describe the changes in the heart which occur with ageing.
2. Describe the changes in the blood vessels which occur with ageing.
3. Describe the changes in regional blood flow with ageing.

CHAPTER 32

The Lymphatic System

SPECIFIC LEARNING OBJECTIVES

At the end of this chapter, the student should be able to:

- List the factors that influence the flow of fluid between the interstitial space and the vascular compartment.
- Describe the basic organization of the lymphatic system.
- Discuss the functions of the lymphatic system.
- Describe the factors that affect lymph flow.
- Define lymphoedema and list its common causes.
- Differentiate between peripheral oedema and lymphoedema.

GLOSSARY OF TERMS

- **Lymphoedema:** the accumulation of fluid in the tissues due to impaired lymphatic drainage
- **Starling's forces:** the pressures that operate to determine fluid shifts across two compartments and include the osmotic and hydrostatic pressures in each compartment (the osmotic pressure retains the fluid within a compartment while the hydrostatic pressure pushes fluid out of the compartment)

In the capillaries, there is an exchange of nutrients, gases and waste products. Thus, oxygen diffuses from the bloodstream into the interstitial spaces and the cells that make up the tissues, while the direction of the transfer of carbon dioxide is reversed, that is from the interstitial space and the cells back into the bloodstream. Nutrients move from the bloodstream to the tissues and waste products are removed from the tissues into the bloodstream. There is also a shift of fluids from the bloodstream to the interstitial space and vice versa.

FACTORS GOVERNING THE MOVEMENT OF FLUID IN THE CAPILLARY BED

The movement of fluid from the vascular compartment (vessels containing the blood) to the interstitial space is due to different pressures in these two spaces. There are essentially two types of pressures: the hydrostatic pressure (HP) and the osmotic pressure (OP). The hydrostatic pressure in a space tends to push water out of the space, while the osmotic pressure tends to retain water in the space. Each of the two spaces, that is the vascular space and the interstitial space, has its own hydrostatic pressure and osmotic pressure. Fig. 32.1 summarizes how these pressures work between the two compartments. These four pressures are collectively known as *Starling's forces*, in honour of the physiologist who showed their role.

As can be seen from Fig. 32.1, the hydrostatic pressures in the vascular compartment and the osmotic pressure in the interstitial space favour the movement of fluid from the vascular compartment to the interstitial space. In contrast, the hydrostatic pressure in the interstitial space and the osmotic pressure in the vascular space favour the movement of fluid from the interstitial space to the vascular compartment. Because the directions of these various pressures are different, the net filtration pressure (NFP) is given by the following formula:

$$NFP = (HPv + OPi) - (OPv + HPi)$$

where 'v' refers to the pressures in the vascular compartment and 'i' refers to the pressures in the interstitial compartment.

If NFP is positive, then there will be a movement of fluid from the vascular compartment to the interstitial space. If NFP is negative, there will then be a movement of fluid from the interstitial space to the vascular compartment.

Since exchange occurs in the capillary bed, we will refer to the pressures in this bed. The hydrostatic pressure in the capillary is between 20 and 25 mm Hg. In contrast, the interstitial pressure can be slightly negative in loose tissues such as the skin and positive in those tissues that are contained within a capsule or

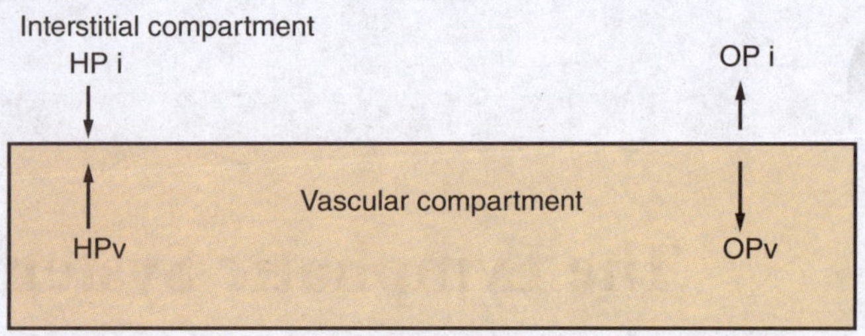

FIG. 32.1 Starling's forces that operate across the vascular compartment. HPi, hydrostatic pressure in the interstitium; HPv, hydrostatic pressure in the vascular compartment; OPi, osmotic pressure in the interstitium; OPv, osmotic pressure in the vascular compartment.

in a fixed space such as the kidneys and the brain. The plasma osmotic pressure is in excess of 25 mm Hg and is largely due to the albumin in the blood. In contrast, the interstitial osmotic pressure is much lower and is in the region of around 8 mm Hg.

When the capillary hydrostatic pressure is high, fluid tends to move out of the capillary into the interstitium. When the capillary osmotic pressure is low, fluid will again move to the interstitium.

ORGANIZATION OF THE LYMPHATIC SYSTEM

Most tissues of the body have lymph channels that drain excess fluid from the interstitial space into the bloodstream. The lymph channels drain into larger lymph vessels and pass lymph nodes on their way before draining into the venous part of the circulatory system. The lymph nodes are organized in clusters; the major groups are the cervical lymph nodes in the neck, the axillary lymph nodes in the armpit, the abdominal lymph nodes and the inguinal lymph nodes in the groin. Lymph, the fluid contained within the lymphatic vessels, from the lower part of the body and from the left side of the head, the left arm and parts of the chest drains into the *thoracic duct* which empties into the venous end of the circulation at the junction of the left internal jugular vein and the left subclavian vein (Fig. 32.2). Lymph from the remaining parts of the body drains into the *right lymph duct* which empties into the venous system at the junction of the right internal jugular vein and the right subclavian vein.

Although most of the venous volume consists of blood drained from capillary beds into the venules, about 10% of the venous blood consists of the fluid that returns to the veins via the

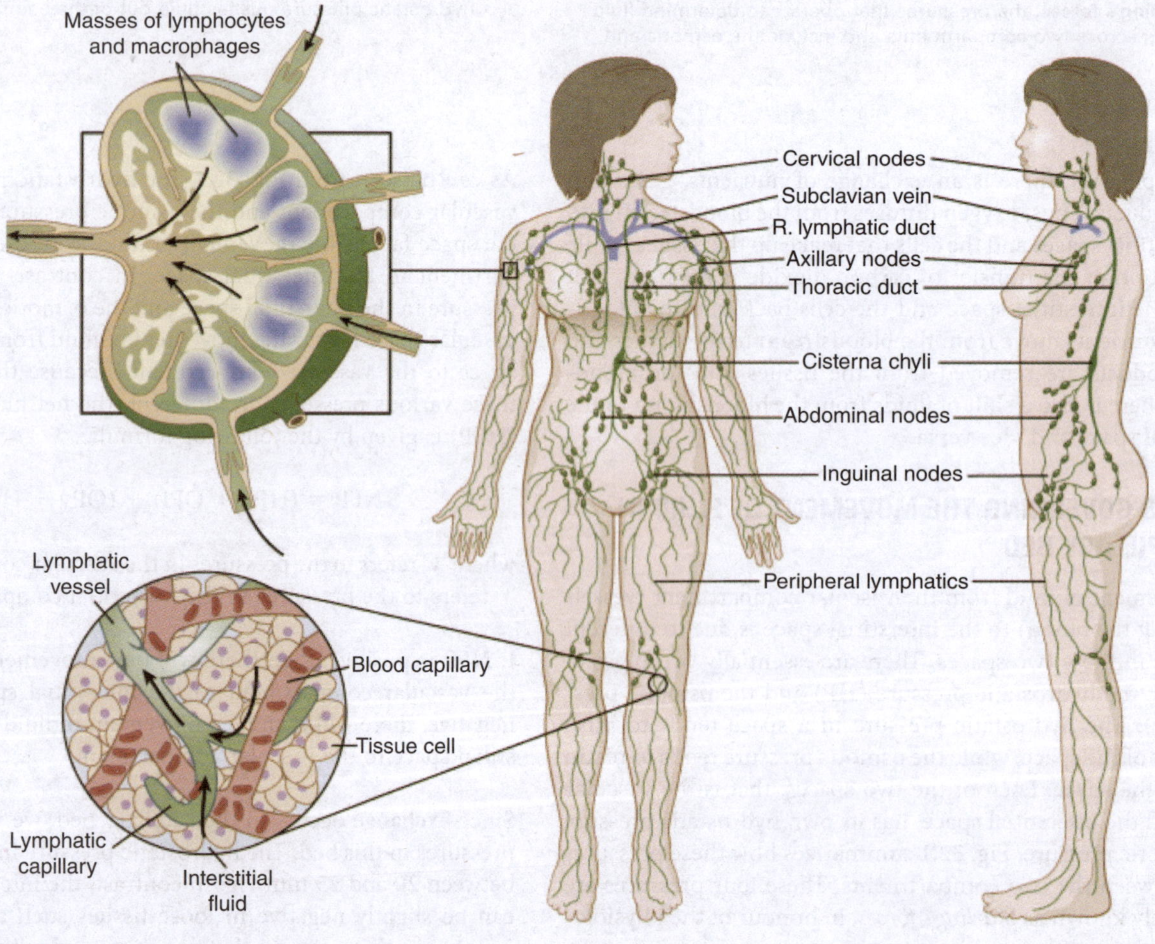

FIG. 32.2 Organization of the lymphatic system.

lymphatics. The protein content is highly variable in the lymphatics depending on the tissues that are being drained: in most tissues, it is about 2 g/dL which is less than one-third of the concentration in plasma, but it is about two to three times higher in lymph draining the liver and intestines. The total lymph flow is about 2–3 L/day.

FUNCTIONS OF THE LYMPHATIC SYSTEM

1. The lymphatic system is a means by which fluid from the interstitial space can empty into the blood.
2. Large molecules (including proteins), cells and particulate matter which cannot be removed directly from the interstitial space into the bloodstream are transported by the lymphatic system.
3. It plays an important role in the absorption of nutrients in the intestine, especially of fats.
4. Bacteria that are carried by the lymph are removed in the lymph nodes as part of the immune system of the body.

FACTORS THAT AFFECT LYMPH FLOW

The rate of lymph flow is not constant but depends on many factors:

1. The interstitial hydrostatic pressure: The greater the interstitial pressure within limits, the greater is the lymph flow. In fact, lymph flow can increase as much as 20 times based on the interstitial pressure alone.
2. The lymphatic vessels have smooth muscle in their walls. When the lymphatic vessel gets stretched, the smooth muscle contracts and this helps to propel the lymph forwards. This acts together with the valves that are present in the lymph channels.
3. External compression of lymphatics: This can also help to propel the lymph forwards and includes factors such as muscle contraction and movements of the body.

CLINICAL BOX

Lymphoedema

Lymphoedema is the accumulation of fluid in the tissues due to the inadequate drainage of interstitial fluid via the lymphatics. This can occur due to several reasons:

1. In some surgery for cancer, the lymph nodes in the axilla or in the femoral region are extensively dissected and removed. This disrupts the lymphatic drainage and the associated limb begins to swell.
2. In some tropical countries, the lymphatic vessels can be blocked by parasites as occurs in filariasis. These parasites are spread by mosquitoes. The characteristic feature is 'elephantiasis' – the limb and the skin covering it swells and thickens (Fig. 32.3).

Peripheral Oedema and Lymphoedema

Peripheral (vascular) oedema and lymphoedema can be differentiated based on their clinical presentation and the physiological mechanisms involved. The causes of peripheral oedema and lymphoedema are typically distinct. These are summarized in Table 32.1.

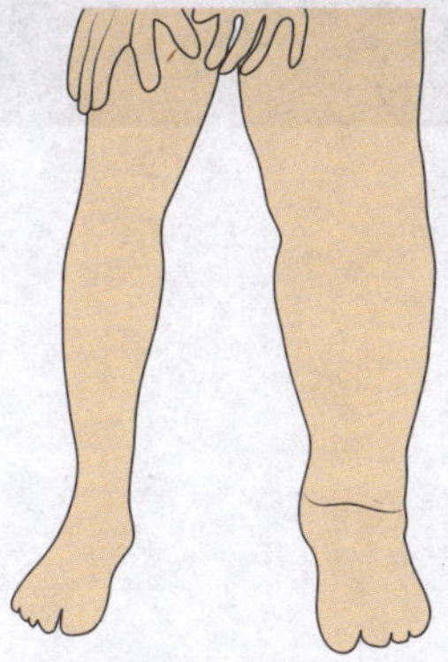

FIG. 32.3 Lymphoedema.

Table 32.1 Between Peripheral (Vascular) Oedema and Lymphoedema

	Peripheral (Vascular) Oedema	Lymphoedema
Location	Often bilateral	May involve one limb
Mechanism	Movement of fluid from the vascular compartment into the interstitial space	Obstruction to lymph flow
Nature of oedema	Pitting – pressing with a finger leaves a depression	Nonpitting
Causes	Congestive heart failure; incompetent venous valves resulting in increased venous pressure; hypoproteinaemia (dietary, hepatic, renal)	Obstruction to lymphatic vessels (e.g. filariasis); damage to lymphatic vessels following extensive surgery, e.g. resection of large cancers

APPLICATIONS IN NURSING

The nurse will need to educate patients on how to care for the limbs which have lymphoedema. This consists of the use of compressive bandages and care of the skin to prevent ulceration and infection, among others.

SUMMARY

- Movement of fluid in the tissues is the function of hydrostatic and osmotic pressures in the vascular compartment and in the interstitial space. These forces are referred to as Starling's forces.
- Total lymph flow is about 2–3 L/day.
- Functions of the lymphatic system include drainage of fluid and large molecules from the tissues, absorption of nutrients from the intestine and the carriage of bacteria to the lymph nodes.
- The rate of lymph flow depends on the interstitial hydrostatic pressure, the contraction of the lymphatic vessels and external compression.
- Lymphoedema is the accumulation of fluid in tissues due to impaired lymph drainage.

CHAPTER REVIEW QUESTIONS

1. Draw a diagram showing Starling's forces acting in a capillary bed. Indicate the direction of fluid movement for each of the pressures.
2. List the functions of the lymphatic system.
3. List the factors which affect lymph flow.

CHAPTER 33

Applications of the Cardiovascular System

SPECIFIC LEARNING OBJECTIVES

At the end of this chapter, the student should be able to:

- List the criteria for measuring blood pressure appropriately.
- Describe the principles of cardiopulmonary resuscitation.
- Define shock.
- List the causes of shock.
- Describe the pathophysiology of shock.
- Define heart failure and list the types of heart failure.
- Describe the basis of the clinical features of left and right heart failure.

GLOSSARY OF TERMS

- **Cardiopulmonary resuscitation:** repetitive chest compression and artificial respiration (often mouth-to-mouth) to maintain circulation and breathing
- **Shock:** a reduced perfusion of tissues associated with reduced blood pressure
- **Cardiac failure:** an inadequate pumping of the heart which is unable to meet the needs of the body

MEASUREMENT OF BLOOD PRESSURE

Blood pressure (BP) is one of the most common measurements done on patients. It is measured in different ways: (1) manually using a mercury sphygmomanometer (these are being phased out) and (2) automated digital BP devices. This section focuses on the precautions that are taken to obtain a good BP measurement. The procedure for taking BP is best demonstrated. The following should be kept in mind:

- Use a device that is in workable order and validated. In the case of automated devices, it is important to know that not all automated devices are accurate. Therefore, check for the approval of the device by the appropriate clinical association and check for data on validity.
- Since BP varies from moment to moment, explain the procedure to patient especially if they have not had a BP measurement before. Anxiety will raise BP. Therefore:
  - Check whether the patient has smoked or had a caffeinated beverage in the last 30 minutes as these can raise BP.
  - Ensure that the patient is seated or lying comfortably for at least 5 minutes before a measurement.
  - Use an appropriate-sized cuff for the patient (cuffs that are small or too big will give errors).
  - Take at least two measurements of BP.
- While recording BP in the patient's chart:
  - Note down the position of the patient (lying/sitting).
  - Note down the side where the measurement is recorded (left or right arm).
  - Record BP accurately – do not round off the BP measurement, for example, 118/78 rather than 120/80.

These precautions are necessary because BP is highly variable even in the same individual and different people may be taking BP of the patient on different occasions. Wrongly diagnosing a patient as hypertensive (i.e. with elevated BP) may result in starting of medications which are not needed.

PRINCIPLES OF CARDIOPULMONARY RESUSCITATION

Cardiopulmonary resuscitation (CPR) is a procedure that is used to keep the heart and respiration going until a medical team with adequate equipment and medications are available to take over. CPR is performed when the heart stops beating. This can happen following a cardiac arrest or when people who have drowned are rapidly taken out of the water. The actual procedure for CPR is best demonstrated, but the following principles apply. While performing CPR in a public space:

- Ask people in the area to stand back.
- Ask bystanders to call for an ambulance/medical help.
- Place the patient on a firm surface which will allow for compressions of the chest.
- Ensure that the airway is clear by tilting the neck back and pushing the chin up.
- Start chest compressions – this requires practice to perform them appropriately. Compressions are performed at the rate of 100–120 per minute, with the arms and forearms of the person performing the CPR straight rather than applying compression from the wrist. This will require a rocking motion. Compression manually presses the heart externally and helps to propel the blood through the circulation.
- Sustained CPR requires mouth-to-mouth respiration at more frequent intervals. After 30 compressions, give two rescue breaths using mouth-to-mouth technique.

Fig. 33.1 illustrates the principles of chest compression in CPR.

SHOCK

Shock is defined as the reduced perfusion (blood flow) of tissues usually associated with a reduction in BP. The pressure gradient is an important determinant of blood flow. Thus, when BP falls beyond a point where blood flow can be maintained by other mechanisms such as autoregulation in the heart, kidneys and brain, the blood flow to the tissues is reduced and the function of the tissues is affected.

Causes of Shock

There are many causes of shock and some of them are briefly described in this section.

1. *Hypovolaemic shock*: In this type of shock, there is a reduction in the blood volume. The normal volume is typically around 5 L in an adult male. However, the blood volume can fall in many conditions. These include acute blood loss associated with injury and severe bleeding, loss of plasma in extensive burns or loss of body water in severe dehydration. In these situations, the reduction in volume is associated with a reduction in venous return to the heart. The reduced venous return to the heart causes reduced ventricular filling and reduced cardiac output which will reduce the perfusion of tissues.
2. *Septic shock*: In this type of shock, the patient suffers from severe, extensive infection which spreads throughout the body and is carried by the blood. Toxins released by the bacteria and other products of tissue damage can result in a major fall in BP and reduced perfusion of the tissues.
3. *Anaphylactic shock:* This is an extreme allergic reaction in which histamine and other substances are released. Histamine causes dilation of blood vessels and increased vascular permeability. As a result of these two actions, BP falls and fluid moves out of the vascular compartment into the tissues, resulting in a fall in blood volume. This reduces venous return and ultimately cardiac output. Different people can be severely allergic to different things; some people may be allergic to injections like penicillin; as a result, a small test dose is always given before giving the full dose of the injection. Other people can be severally allergic to insect bites like bee stings or even constituents of food like peanuts or prawns.
4. *Neurogenic shock*: When we discussed the regulation of BP, we said that there are integrating centres in the brain as part of the baroreflex. In brain damage as occurs with head injuries, for instance, the areas of the brain responsible for the control of BP may be damaged. As a result, BP may fall and the perfusion of tissues is affected.
5. *Cardiogenic shock*: Perfusion of tissues is dependent on an adequate cardiac output. If the heart is unable to pump blood adequately as, for instance, following a heart attack, then BP will fall drastically and tissues will not be perfused.

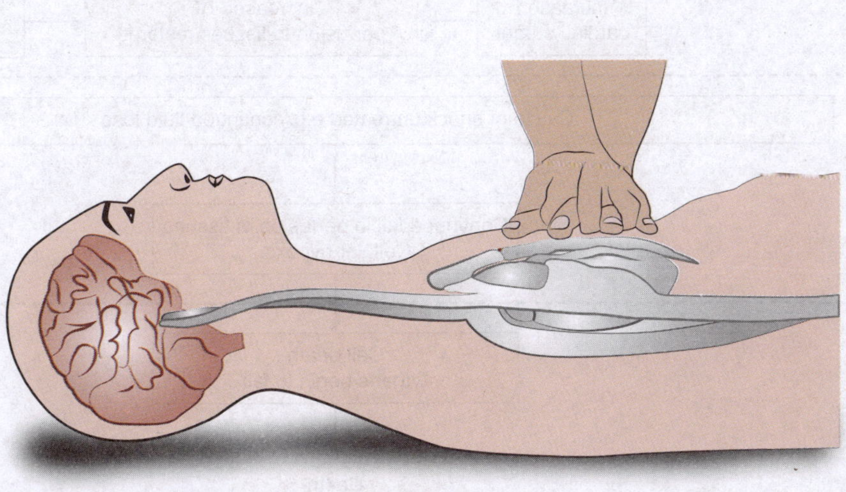

FIG. 33.1 Principle of chest compression during CPR.

Pathophysiology of Shock

Stages of Shock Depending on the severity of shock, shock can be divided into three different stages:

1. **Compensated shock:** When shock is not very severe, the body responds adequately by various mechanisms and the individual will recover, even in the absence of treatment. These mechanisms include the following:
   a. Activation of the sympathetic nervous system which ensures that BP is raised and that the heart pumps harder to maintain cardiac output.
   b. Activation of the renin–angiotensin system which also helps to maintain BP and which, through aldosterone, helps to retain salt and water and maintain the blood volume.
   c. Release of various stress hormones such as epinephrine (adrenaline) which ensures that the heart pumps faster and harder to maintain cardiac output and perfusion of the tissues.
   d. Release of the antidiuretic hormone from the posterior pituitary gland which ensures that the kidneys retain water and maintain blood volume.
2. **Progressive shock:** In this stage, shock is more severe, but timely treatment can ensure that the individual makes a recovery. Because of the sustained fall in BP, the function of the heart itself is impaired as the low BP also affects the coronary blood flow which supplies the heart. Other organs in the body may also begin to show reduced function. Rapid replacements of blood or intravenous fluids together with drugs that increase the contractility of the heart are helpful. Needless to say, the primary cause of the shock needs to be addressed.
3. **Irreversible shock:** In this stage, the patient does not recover and death ensues. The reduced blood flow for a prolonged period of time results in death of cells and organ failure.

The pathophysiology of shock is illustrated in Fig. 33.2.

HEART FAILURE

The inability of the heart to pump blood effectively to meet the needs of the body is called heart failure.

Causes of Cardiac Failure

The following are among the many causes of cardiac failure:

1. Coronary heart disease: Here the blockage of a coronary artery results in ischaemia and death of the myocardium supplied by the artery. As a result of this, the dead part of the

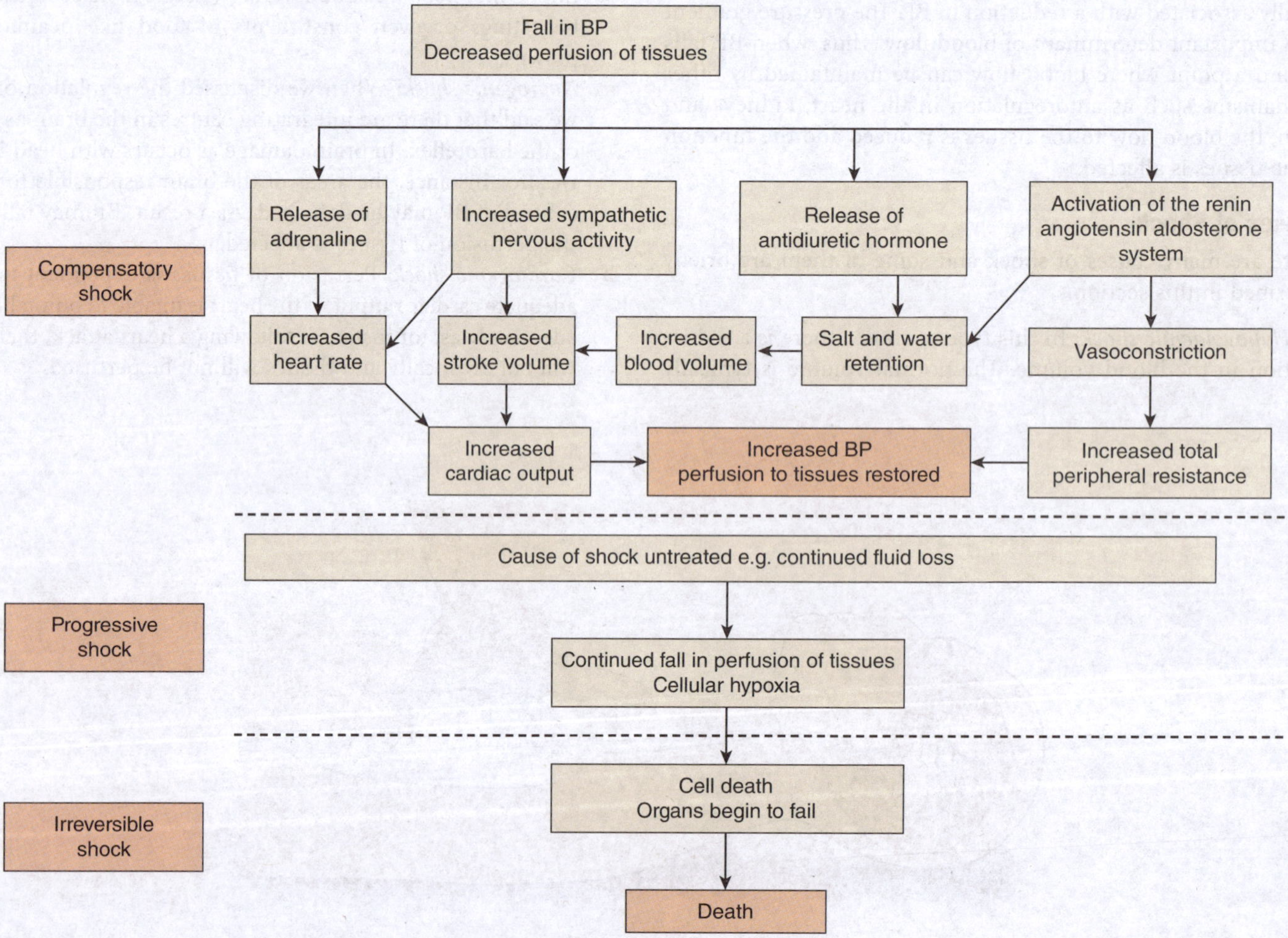

FIG. 33.2 The pathophysiology of shock.

myocardium becomes akinetic (without movement) during systole. As a consequence of this, the amount of blood that is ejected with each contraction (ejection fraction) is reduced.

2. Valvular heart disease: When the valves of the heart are either stenosed (tight) or incompetent (leaky), the pressure placed on the heart increases and this in time may lead to cardiac failure. A common cause of a valvular disease is rheumatic heart disease, the incidence of which is fortunately decreasing in India.
3. Cardiac myopathies: These are disorders of the cardiac muscle itself which result in inadequate pumping of blood.
4. Uncontrolled hypertension: When the heart has to pump against a high pressure, the load on the heart is increased. The heart compensates by increasing its size but if untreated leads to heart failure.

Left Heart Failure

In this condition, the left heart (left atrium and ventricle) is unable to pump blood adequately. As a result of this, there is an increase in blood behind the failing heart, that is in the pulmonary circulation. This is referred to as pulmonary congestion. Due to the sustained pulmonary congestion, there is then a transudation of fluid into the interstitium, a condition called pulmonary oedema. Patients with pulmonary oedema feel breathless even at rest and have a cough with pink, frothy sputum.

Right Heart Failure

In right heart failure, the right heart (right atrium and ventricle) is unable to pump blood adequately. As a result of this, there is an increase in the blood behind the failing right heart. Among the signs of right heart failure is an elevation in the jugular venous pressure (because of the increased back pressure); the right jugular vein is in direct continuity with the right atrium and therefore reflects the increased right atrial pressure. In addition, there is congestion in a number of tissues; among these is the liver, which is enlarged (hepatomegaly) as a result of the congestion and can be felt during an abdominal examination. The increased congestion behind the right heart results in transudation of fluid into the tissues. Right heart failure is characterized by peripheral oedema.

It is important to recognize that since the left and right hearts are two pumps in series, failure of one pump (heart) will, if sustained and untreated, inevitably result in failure of the other. Thus, initial left heart failure can ultimately lead to right heart failure since the right heart will have to pump against an increasing load due to the pulmonary congestion of left heart failure.

CLINICAL CASE PROBLEMS

(A) ***A 28-year-old man is brought into the emergency department. He had been riding his motorbike and had suffered an accident. The people who brought him in say that he had lost a lot of blood from a wound in the thigh and they bound his wound with a cloth. On examination, the man is unconscious, his BP is low and his pulse is rapid and thready.***

a. What condition is the person suffering from?
b. Describe the stages that the man will go through if he continues to bleed.
c. What needs to be done to prevent progression of the man's condition?

(B) ***A 76-year-old man who has been a chronic heavy smoker for 40 years has been experiencing breathlessness, weakness and swelling of the legs. He has been told that he is suffering from right heart failure.***

a. What is the reason for the swelling of his legs?
b. What other clinical signs will confirm the presence of right heart failure?

(C) ***A 60-year-old woman with a strong family history of heart disease suddenly collapsed in a shopping mall. She had been experiencing chest pain on exertion for some months which was relieved when she rested. She was shifted by bystanders in the mall to an ambulance and transported to the hospital.***

a. What procedure could have been done for her at the mall before the ambulance arrived?
b. Her ECG shows deep Q waves in some leads. What condition is she likely to have?
c. What is the basis of her condition?
d. What risk factors predispose an individual to develop her medical condition?

SELF-DIRECTED LEARNING

1. What are the risk factors for developing coronary heart disease that can result in a myocardial infarction?
2. What health behaviours can help prevent a heart attack?
3. What is secondary hypertension and what are some common causes?

WHAT YOU CAN LEARN FROM A HOSPITAL VISIT

1. Visiting a nursing station and ask the nurses what medicines/instruments they stock in their emergency trolley in case a patient suffers a heart attack in the ward. What are their uses?
2. Observe the nurses working in the emergency department. What roles/functions do they perform?

[illegible]

A 72-year-old man is brought to the emergency department. He had been [illegible] his grandchildren [illegible] the summer [illegible]. The people with him said that he [illegible] had [illegible] [illegible] [illegible] in the [illegible] and [illegible] the man is [illegible] and the [illegible] and [illegible].

1. [illegible]
2. [illegible]

[illegible]

3. A 75-year-old man [illegible] has been [illegible] years [illegible] and swelling of the [illegible] suffering from right heart failure.

[illegible]

[illegible] [illegible] [illegible] [illegible] [illegible] [illegible] [illegible] [illegible] [illegible] [illegible] [illegible] [illegible] [illegible] transported to [illegible].

[illegible]

[illegible]

[illegible]

[illegible]

1. [illegible] a [illegible]
2. [illegible]
3. [illegible]

[illegible]

[illegible]

[illegible] partly decreasing [illegible].

[illegible] heart failure.

Left Heart Failure

In this condition, the left [illegible] atrium and ventricle [illegible] sputum.

Right Heart Failure

[illegible] [illegible].

[illegible] [illegible] [illegible] [illegible] [illegible] [illegible] [illegible] [illegible] [illegible] [illegible] [illegible] [illegible] [illegible] [illegible] [illegible] [illegible] [illegible] [illegible] [illegible] [illegible].

5

SECTION

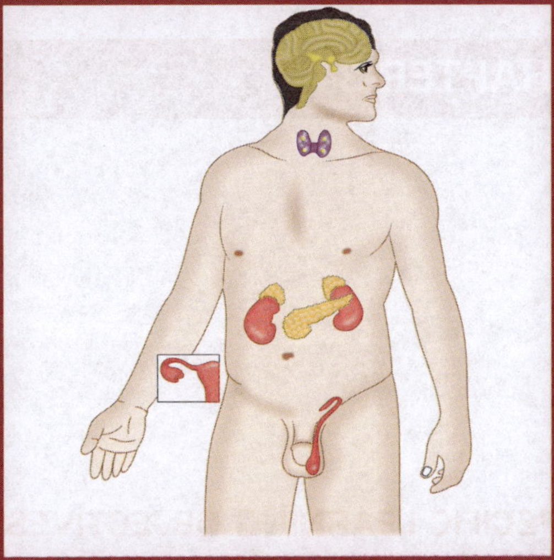

Blood

Section Outline

CHAPTER 34

Cellular and Noncellular Components of Blood

SPECIFIC LEARNING OBJECTIVES

At the end of this chapter, the student should be able to:

- Distinguish between plasma and serum.
- Classify the cellular components of the blood.
- List the major plasma proteins and describe their functions.

GLOSSARY OF TERMS

- **Plasma:** fluid portion of the blood obtained after centrifuging blood with anticoagulant
- **Serum:** plasma minus the clotting factors
- **Erythrocytes:** red blood cells
- **Leucocytes:** white blood cells
- **Thrombocytes:** platelets

In this chapter, we describe the constituents of blood and what their functions are. Some of the cellular components of blood are described in greater detail in subsequent chapters.

PLASMA AND SERUM

If blood is taken in a test tube which contains an anticoagulant (something that prevents clotting) and then spun in a centrifuge, we observe that the blood separates out into three distinct portions. The bottom layer consists of red blood cells (RBCs) which are tightly packed together. Above this is a thin whitish layer called the 'buffy coat' which consists of white blood cells and platelets. Right on top, occupying a little more than half the volume is a yellowish fluid called the plasma. In contrast, if a blood sample is taken in a test tube without any anticoagulant and allowed to stand for a while, we observe that a clot is formed and that this clot is surrounded by a clear yellow fluid which we call serum. Fig. 34.1 shows two test tubes, one with plasma and the other with serum.

What is the difference between plasma and serum? Plasma contains many substances; among them are clotting factors which are needed to form a clot. When blood is left standing without an anticoagulant, the clotting factors in the blood get used up during the formation of the clot. Thus, plasma minus the clotting factors is serum.

CELLULAR COMPONENTS OF BLOOD

The three major cellular components of blood are the erythrocytes (RBCs), white blood cells (leucocytes) and platelets (thrombocytes). The function of RBCs is to carry oxygen to the tissues and return carbon dioxide from the tissues to the lungs. We describe the function of RBCs in greater detail in Chapter 35. White blood cells are important to protect the body against germs. This is discussed in Chapters 36 and 39. Platelets play an important role in stopping bleeding during injury and during the subsequent formation of a clot. We will describe this in greater detail in Chapter 37.

Structure of RBCs

RBCs are small (~7 microns) biconcave cells. They do not have a nucleus and are rich in haemoglobin. Their primary function is to carry haemoglobin since haemoglobin by itself is toxic (harmful) to cells. RBCs are very flexible, and this allows them to change their shape so that they can squeeze through the capillaries where the greatest amount of gas exchange occurs. There are between 4.5 and 5.5 million RBCs/mm^3.

Structure of White Blood Cells

There are different types of white blood cells – all have nuclei, but some have granules in their cytoplasm (neutrophils, basophils, eosinophils) and some do not (monocytes, lymphocytes).

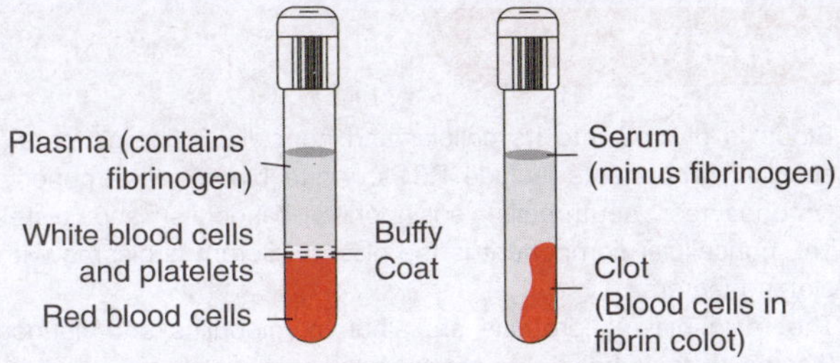

FIG. 34.1 Test tubes depicting the difference between plasma and serum.

The size of the different types of white blood cells varies widely – thus, small lymphocytes are just about the size of RBCs, while other cells like monocytes and neutrophils are much larger. There are between 4000 and 11,000 white blood cells/mm^3.

Structure of Platelets

Platelets are small fragments of cells about 2–4 microns in diameter. They do not have a nucleus. There are between 150,000 and 400,000 platelets/mm^3. Platelets have granules. When the contents of these granules are released, there are multiple effects. These include the following:

1. Local vasoconstriction (discussed in Chapter 37 which deals with the response to bleeding)
2. Wound repair (this is because platelets release growth factors such as platelet-derived growth factor)
3. Platelet aggregation and the formation of a platelet plug to stop bleeding

Fig. 34.2 depicts the cellular components of the blood.

NONCELLULAR COMPONENTS OF THE BLOOD

The noncellular component of the blood is the plasma and its constituents. An important constituent is the plasma proteins. These are proteins that circulate in the blood and perform various functions.

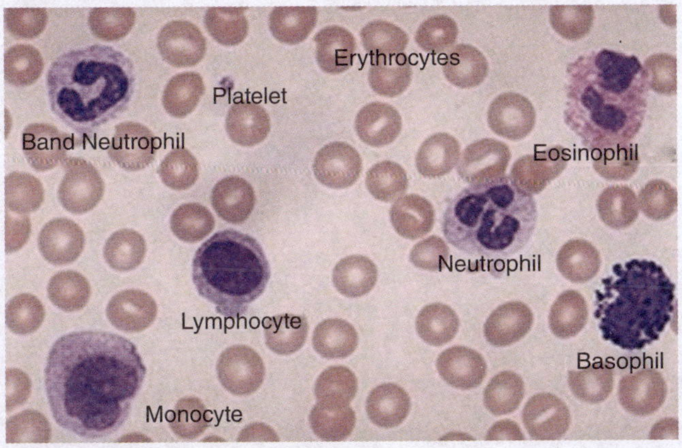

FIG. 34.2 A peripheral smear depicting the different cellular components of blood.

Plasma Proteins

The major plasma proteins are as follows:

1. Albumin (concentration 4.0–5.5 g%)
2. Globulins (concentration 1.5–3.0 g%)
3. Fibrinogen (concentration 0.3 g%)

There are also other plasma proteins. For example, fibrinogen is only one of the many clotting factors in plasma and there are many other proteins which serve specific needs, such as transport of specific substances in plasma.

The plasma proteins have many functions. These are:

1. **Osmotic pressure**: Plasma proteins, especially albumin, are osmotically active molecules. The normal osmotic pressure in the blood vessels is about 25 mm Hg. The osmotic pressure ensures that fluid is retained in the blood vessels. When there is hypoproteinaemia (reduced plasma proteins in the blood) as can occur with severe malnutrition, liver or kidney disease, fluid shifts from the blood vessels into the interstitial space resulting in oedema.
2. **Immunity:** Antibodies (immunoglobulins) are an important part of the body defence system. This is discussed in greater detail in Chapter 39.
3. **Coagulation:** Fibrinogen and other clotting factors in the blood are responsible for the generation of a clot. In the absence of one or more of these clotting factors, clotting is impaired, and minor injuries can result in prolonged bleeding. Details of this are discussed later in Chapter 37.
4. **Transport:** Plasma proteins help transport various substances in the blood. Some plasma proteins like albumin bind nonspecifically to many substances. Others like transferrin (iron) and ceruloplasmin (copper) have specific carrier roles.
5. Other functions of the plasma proteins include being:
   a. A protein reserve for tissue repair, etc.
   b. A buffer in acid–base balance
   c. Contribution to the viscosity of the blood

OVERALL FUNCTIONS OF BLOOD

Blood has several broad functions which will be discussed in greater detail in subsequent chapters of this section. These include the following:

1. Transport: This includes the transport of several substances:
   a. Oxygen and carbon dioxide
   b. Nutrients for tissue
   c. Waste products generated through metabolism in the tissues
   d. Hormones
2. Immunity: This occurs in many different ways:
   a. Phagocytosis as a function of several leucocytes
   b. Via different types of molecules in the blood. These include the following:
      i. Antibodies (immunoglobulins)
      ii. Cytokines

   iii. Other plasma proteins, for example complement proteins (see Chapter 39)
3. Haemostasis: The stoppage of bleeding, which occurs as a function of:
   a. Platelets
   b. Clotting factors
4. Maintenance of body temperature: Transport of warm blood to the skin surface and its dissipation by cutaneous vasodilation allows for loss of heat from the body. In contrast, vasoconstriction prevents warm blood from reaching the skin surface and body temperature is conserved.
5. Maintenance of acid–base balance in the body: This is achieved by the buffers present in blood, the carriage of carbon dioxide which is exhaled in the lungs, and the excretion of H^+ ions from the kidneys.

APPLICATIONS FOR NURSING

- The nurse may be required to take the appropriate sample (whole blood, plasma, serum) for laboratory investigations of the patient.
- The sources of blood for evaluation may be (1) venous; (2) capillary – using a finger puncture or a heel prick (in infants); or (3) arterial – as, for instance, to assess blood gases.
- Nurses must be aware of the normal ranges for the constituents of blood so that they can understand and interpret laboratory reports of patients.

SUMMARY

- Blood is divided into its cellular and noncellular components. The cellular components include RBCs, white blood cells (monocytes, lymphocytes, neutrophils, eosinophils, basophils) and platelets. The noncellular component is the plasma. Serum is plasma without clotting factors.
- The main plasma proteins are albumin, globulins and fibrinogen. Plasma proteins help (1) to establish the osmotic pressure within the blood vessels, (2) in immunity, (3) in clotting, (4) in transport of substances in the blood and (5) in acid–base balance, among others.
- The main function of RBCs is in carrying blood gases (oxygen and carbon dioxide), white blood cells help in immunity and platelets stop bleeding.

CHAPTER REVIEW QUESTIONS

1. List the cellular components of blood.
2. What are the plasma proteins? List the functions of plasma proteins.
3. Describe the overall functions of blood.

CHAPTER 35

Erythropoiesis: Functions of Red Blood Cell, Red Blood Cell Life Cycle

SPECIFIC LEARNING OBJECTIVES

At the end of this chapter, the student should be able to:

- Describe the steps in the formation of a red blood cell (RBC) (erythropoiesis) and the major changes that occur during this formation.
- List the factors that affect erythropoiesis.
- List the functions of haemoglobin.
- Describe the fate of RBCs.

GLOSSARY OF TERMS

- **Erythropoiesis:** the process of formation of RBCs
- **Jaundice:** a yellowish discolouration of the skin and mucous membranes due to elevated levels of serum bilirubin
- **Anaemia:** a reduced oxygen-carrying capacity of the blood due to alterations in the quantity or quality of RBCs and haemoglobin

In this chapter, we focus on the red blood cell (RBC) (erythrocyte), how it is formed, what its functions are, how it is broken down and the clinical conditions that are associated with RBCs.

ERYTHROPOIESIS

Sites of Erythropoiesis

- In the growing foetus, the yolk sac is the site of erythropoiesis till about 5 weeks of gestation. In fact, erythroid precursors (cells that give rise to the mature RBC) are the first blood cells to be seen in the foetus. Yolk sac blood islands containing erythroid cells are seen as early as 20–26 days of gestation.
- From 5 weeks to about 5 months, erythropoiesis takes place in the liver and spleen.
- From 5 months of gestation, erythropoiesis shifts to the bone marrow.
- Erythrocytes in the adult are formed in the red bone marrow:
  - Till 20–25 years, erythropoiesis is seen in the long bones such as the tibia and femur.
  - Erythropoiesis takes place in the flat bones such as the ribs, iliac crest and sternum throughout adult life into old age.

Stages of Erythropoiesis

The source of erythrocytes is a stem cell. A stem cell has two features:

1. It can replicate (renew; make more) itself.
2. It can differentiate into different cell lines. The stem cell from which erythrocytes are derived is called a pluripotent stem cell – pluripotent means capable of giving rise to different cell lines. Thus, the pluripotent stem cell that gives rise to erythrocytes also gives rise to white blood cells and platelets.

The pluripotent stem cell gives rise to other cells called the burst-forming unit (erythroid) and the colony-forming unit (erythroid), abbreviated to BFU-E and CFU-E, respectively. Fig. 35.1 shows the further steps in erythropoiesis. The cells that are formed are the pronormoblast, the early, intermediate and late normoblasts, the reticulocyte and finally the mature erythrocyte. The features of these cells are summarized in Table 35.1.

Summary of Changes During Erythropoiesis

During the process of erythropoiesis, the changes that occur in the structure of the cell are summarized as follows:

1. It becomes progressively smaller.
2. The nucleus condenses, becomes smaller and is finally extruded (thrown) out of the cell in the late normoblast stage.

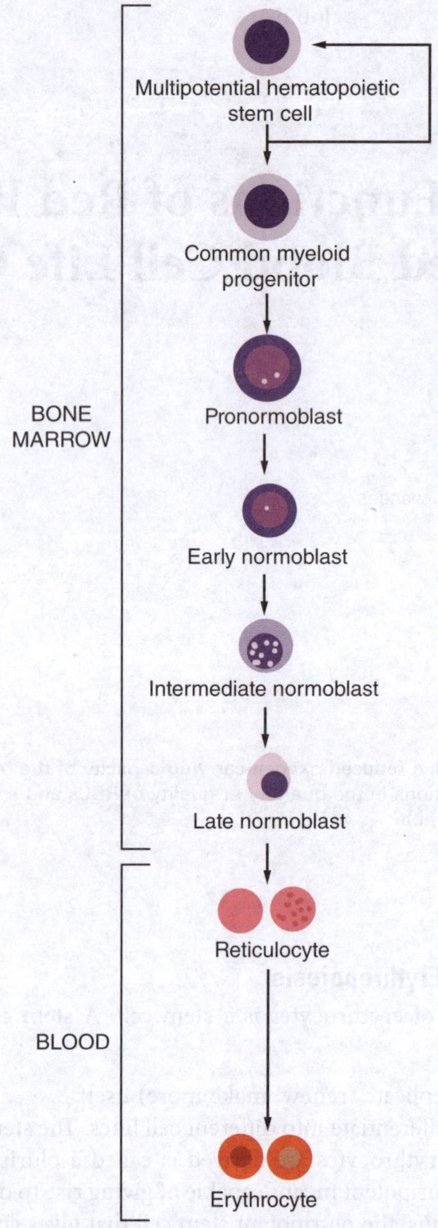

FIG. 35.1 Stages of erythropoiesis.

3. The staining of the cytoplasm of the cell changes from basophilic (bluish) to acidophilic (pinkish). This is because of haemoglobin, which appears in the intermediate normoblast stage.

The reticulocyte is the immediate precursor of the mature erythrocyte. Within its cytoplasm are small strands of remnant RNA. When erythropoiesis is increased, the number of reticulocytes in the blood also increases. Thus, the percentage of reticulocytes can be used to estimate the rate of erythropoiesis. The normal percentage of reticulocytes is 0.5%–2% of the total RBCs. Greater than 2% reticulocytes means increased erythropoiesis.

The mature erythrocyte or RBC appears like a biconcave disc, which is thinner in the centre and thicker at the periphery. It is about 7 microns in diameter. This shape of the erythrocyte increases the surface area of the cell and allows for more exchange of oxygen and carbon dioxide across the cell membrane. The erythrocytes are also flexible and this allows them to enter the capillaries which are small.

Table 35.1 Characteristics of Erythrocyte and its precursor cells.

Cell	Size (Microns)	Staining	Other Features
Pronormoblast	15–20	Basophilic	Has a well-defined nucleus with nucleoli
Early normoblast	14–17	Basophilic	Still mitotic Disappearance of nucleoli
Intermediate normoblast	10–15	Polychromatic	Haemoglobin starts appearing
Late normoblast	7–10	Largely eosinophilic	Pyknotic nucleus which gets extruded
Reticulocyte	~8	Eosinophilic, basophilic reticulum	Enters the circulation
Mature RBC	7.2	Eosinophilic	

Factors Affecting Erythropoiesis and Maturation of Erythrocytes

There are many factors which affect erythropoiesis. Some of the more important ones are discussed as follows:

1. **Hypoxia/erythropoietin:** A major function of the erythrocyte is the transport of oxygen which binds to haemoglobin contained within the erythrocyte. Thus, hypoxia (reduced oxygen at the level of tissues) would be expected to increase the production of erythrocytes and help increase oxygen delivery to the tissues. Thus, hypoxia causes the release of a hormone produced in the kidney called erythropoietin. Erythropoietin then stimulates erythropoiesis in the bone marrow. The liver can produce up to 10% of erythropoietin.
2. **Vitamin B_{12}** and folic acid: Because both of these are required for DNA synthesis, absence of these factors causes a failure of nuclear maturation and cell division.
   a. Vitamin B_{12} can be obtained from the diet in egg, fish, meat and dairy products. Vegans (vegetarians who do not consume milk or eggs) are at the risk of vitamin B_{12} deficiency. Vitamin B_{12} is absorbed at the terminal ileum. However, in order to be absorbed, vitamin B_{12} needs to first bind to intrinsic factor which is produced in the stomach. Thus, if enough vitamin B_{12} is being consumed in the diet, but there are problems with the secretion of intrinsic factor in the stomach or a disease of the terminal ileum, an individual can still be vitamin B_{12} deficient.
   b. Folic acid is present in a variety of nonvegetarian foods and especially in green leafy vegetables (the name folic acid is derived from the Latin word *folium* which means

leaf). However, a folic acid is destroyed in vegetables during cooking and in cereals during milling and baking. The duodenum and proximal jejunum are important sites of folic acid absorption, but absorption can occur along most of the intestine including the colon.

3. **Iron:** This is important for the formation of haemoglobin. Iron is present in a variety of nonvegetarian foods and also in green leafy vegetables. Cereals and millet (e.g. ragi) are also important sources of iron given the high carbohydrate intakes of Indians. Iron is absorbed throughout the small intestine. However, many factors can limit iron absorption. Some dietary factors such as phytates (present in wheat, and therefore important in chapati eaters) limit the absorption of iron. Ferric iron in the diet needs to be converted to its ferrous form to be absorbed; this requires acidification in the stomach (adding acid to diet, such as ascorbic acid [vinegar] and lemon juice [citric acid] may also enhance absorption of iron).
4. **Protein:** It is required for the formation of haemoglobin and for the structural proteins on RBC; protein deficiency can result in anaemia.
5. **Other factors:** These, among others, include vitamins A, C and E, other B vitamins and copper and hormones such as androgens and oestrogens.

HAEMOGLOBIN

Structure

Haemoglobin consists of four globular protein subunits linked to haem (hence the name haemoglobin). The haem portion contains the iron ion which is the site of binding for oxygen. There are different types of haemoglobin based on the nature of the protein subunits:

- In adults, there are two alpha and two beta subunits denoted as $\alpha_2\beta_2$.
- In the foetus, the haemoglobin is different and consists of two alpha and two gamma chains ($\alpha_2\gamma_2$).

Why is there this difference? Foetal haemoglobin (HbF) has a much stronger affinity (attachment) with oxygen than adult haemoglobin. This is important because oxygen content of the blood is much lower in the foetus than in the adult in whom oxygenation of blood occurs directly in the lungs. The higher affinity of HbF for oxygen thus allows haemoglobin to bind to oxygen at lower concentrations and transport oxygen in the foetal circulation.

Functions of Haemoglobin

1. **Transport of oxygen:** Haemoglobin carries about 97% of the oxygen in arterial blood. The remaining 3% is carried dissolved in plasma. Thus, if haemoglobin levels are reduced, transport of oxygen can be severely affected. One gram of haemoglobin carries approximately 1.34 mL of oxygen. Haemoglobin bound to oxygen forms oxyhaemoglobin.
2. **Transport of carbon dioxide:** One of the ways in which CO_2 is transported from the tissues to the lungs is combined with haemoglobin. Haemoglobin combined with CO_2 is called carbaminohaemoglobin. About 10% of carbon dioxide is carried this way.
3. **Buffer:** A buffer basically acts to maintain the pH constant so that a solution does not become too acidic or alkaline. Haemoglobin is capable of accepting H^+ ions when there is increased acidity and releasing H^+ ions when the pH rises (becomes more alkaline).

Normal Concentrations of Haemoglobin

The haemoglobin concentration in blood varies. Males tend to have a higher haemoglobin concentration than females. This is because:

1. In males, androgens stimulate erythropoiesis.
2. In females, there is a chronic loss of blood because of monthly menstrual periods.

The haemoglobin concentration in healthy adult males ranges from about 14 to 16 g/dL and for women between 13 and 15 g/dL.

Haemoglobin concentrations are typically used to screen for anaemia (a condition in which there is a reduced oxygen-carrying capacity of the blood due to problems in haemoglobin or in the erythrocyte). The World Health Organization (WHO) indicates that adult males with a haemoglobin concentration of $\geq$13 g/dL should be considered nonanaemic. The cut-off for pregnant women is $\geq$11 g/dL and that of nonpregnant women is $\geq$12 g/dL.

Fate of the Erythrocyte

RBC has a lifespan of about 120 days. RBCs are then destroyed by macrophages mainly in the liver and the spleen. The haemoglobin that is released into plasma is first bound to a plasma protein called haptoglobin. The globin part of the haemoglobin which is made up of amino acids is reutilized for protein synthesis by the body. The haem portion has two main parts – the iron is recycled in the body. The haem is metabolized, first to biliverdin (a yellow pigment) and then to bilirubin. Bilirubin is taken up in the liver where it is further metabolized (Fig. 35.2). This is discussed later in Chapter 40.

ANAEMIA

Anaemia is defined as a reduction in the oxygen-carrying capacity of the blood. This may occur because of a reduction in RBCs or because of a functional or structural defect in the haemoglobin. Details of the causes of anaemia and the characteristics of different types of anaemia are provided in Chapter 40.

JAUNDICE

Jaundice is a yellowish discolouration of the skin and mucous membranes due to elevated levels of serum bilirubin. Normal serum bilirubin levels are typically less than 1 mg/dL. It is important to remember that jaundice is a symptom, not a disease – the causes of jaundice are many, as we shall see later in Chapter 40.

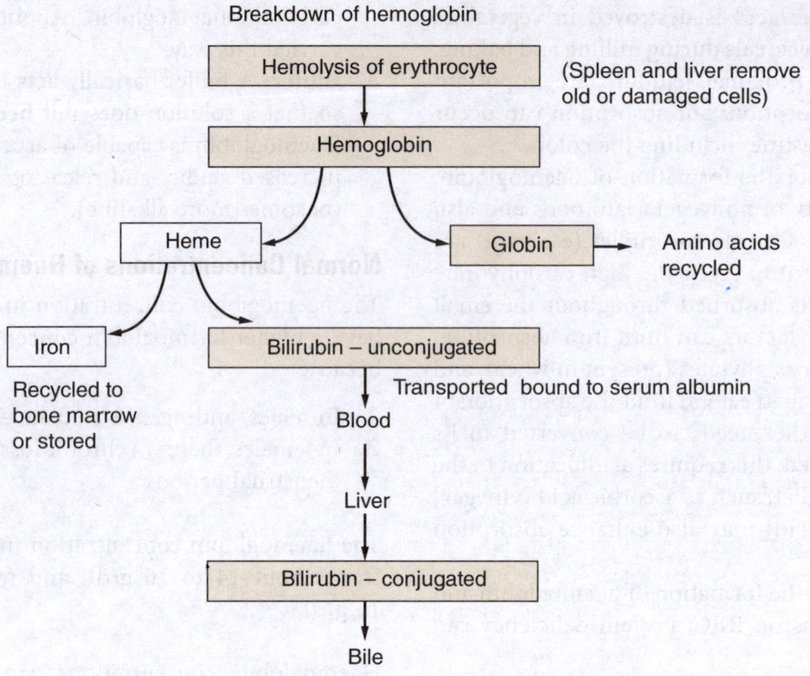

FIG. 35.2 Fate of haemoglobin following breakdown.

APPLICATIONS FOR NURSING

- The nurse may need to take part in screening camps for anaemia, since it is a major public health problem in the country.
- The nurse will need to provide health and nutritional advice to patients suffering from anaemia and jaundice.
- The nurse will need to educate close contacts of those suffering from jaundice about measures that they will need to take.

SUMMARY

- RBCs are derived from pluripotent stem cells and are formed in the following sequence: BFU-E, CFU-E, pronormoblast, early normoblast, intermediate normoblast, late normoblast, reticulocyte and mature erythrocyte. Reticulocytes and erythrocytes are seen in the peripheral blood. Haemoglobin appears in the intermediate normoblast.
- During erythropoiesis, cells become progressively smaller, the nucleus condenses and is extruded, haemoglobin is synthesized and increases in concentration, and the cytoplasm of the cells shifts from being basophilic to eosinophilic.
- Haemoglobin carries oxygen and carbon dioxide and also acts as a buffer in blood.
- Factors which affect erythropoiesis include hormones such as erythropoietin, androgens and oestrogen; vitamins such as B_{12} and folic acid; minerals such as iron and copper; and other nutrients such as proteins.

CHAPTER REVIEW QUESTIONS

1. Describe the stages of erythropoiesis.
2. What are the factors that regulate erythropoiesis?
3. Describe the structure and functions of haemoglobin.
4. What is the fate of the RBC?

CHAPTER 36

White Blood Cells (WBCs) – Formation, Types and Functions

SPECIFIC LEARNING OBJECTIVES

At the end of this chapter, the student should be able to:

- Describe the formation of leucocytes (white blood cells).
- Classify white blood cells.
- Describe each type of white blood cell in terms of its morphology and function.

GLOSSARY OF TERMS

- **Granulocytes:** those WBCs which have granules in the cytoplasm, that is neutrophils, basophils and eosinophils
- **Agranulocytes:** those WBCs which do not have granules in the cytoplasm, that is lymphocytes and monocytes
- **Cellular immunity:** an immune response that involves activation of the T lymphocytes and the release of cytokines
- **Humoral immunity:** an immune response that involves the production of antibodies from B lymphocytes and plasma cells
- **Cytokines:** proteins released by immune cells that affect cellular interactions and help mediate the immune response
- **Leukotrienes:** inflammatory molecules released by mast cells and basophils in response to allergens (molecules that trigger an allergic reaction)
- **Antigen:** a molecule or a part of a molecule that triggers an immune reaction

During our life, we are exposed to many bacteria, viruses and parasites. However, we rarely get very ill even though the air, water, soil and food we eat are full of microorganisms. This is because our body is normally able to defend itself from the harmful effects of these microbes. In the blood, one group of cells which help us defend ourselves from these microorganisms is the white blood cells (WBCs; leucocytes). In this chapter, we discuss what the different types of leucocytes are, how leucocytes are formed and what functions they perform.

CLASSIFICATION OF WHITE BLOOD CELLS

One of the ways of classifying different types of WBCs is based on morphology (appearance) under the microscope. Mature WBCs are classified based on whether they have granules in their plasma as granulocytes or agranulocytes. Granulocytes have granules in their cytoplasm – granules are particles in the cytoplasm which are visible on microscopy. They are most often secretory granules and appear as either fine or coarse granules under the microscope. The granules are of different composition in different cells. The three WBC granulocytes are neutrophils, basophils and eosinophils. Agranulocytes do not contain visible granules in their cytoplasm and include lymphocytes and monocytes. This classification of WBCs is represented in Fig. 36.1.

NORMAL COUNTS FOR WHITE BLOOD CELLS

Since WBCs play an important role in immunity to fight bacteria, viruses and parasites, the total WBC count and the counts of the different types of WBCs can rise rapidly. Low WBC counts can make a person more prone to infections. Table 36.1 highlights the normal cell counts and provides the nomenclature (names) for the conditions when the counts are high or low. The values that are provided may vary slightly between laboratories.

It is important to differentiate between leucocytosis and leukaemia. Leucocytosis is an increase in WBCs above the normal limit of 11,000/mm^3. This is often seen when there are bacterial infections. Leukaemia is an uncontrolled proliferation of WBCs (a form of cancer) in which apart from the cells listed in Table 36.1, there are also immature and abnormal WBCs.

CHARACTERISTICS OF WHITE BLOOD CELLS

In this section of the chapter, we describe the different types of WBCs and their functions. Using special stains, called the Romanowsky's stains, WBCs appear in various shades of blue and pink under the microscope. The acidic components of the cells take up the blue stain (methylene blue) while the basic

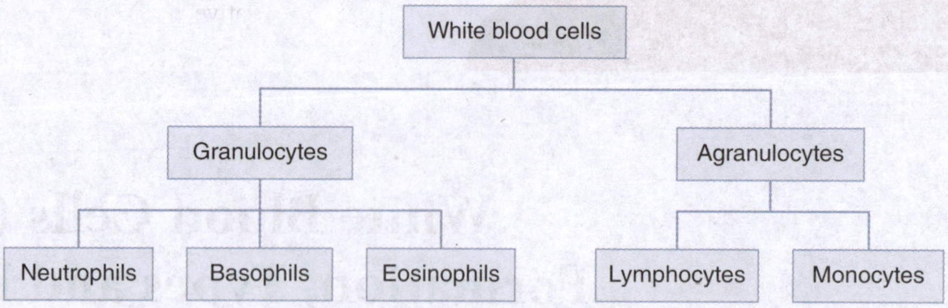

FIG. 36.1 Classification of WBCs.

Table 36.1 Normal Counts of the Different White Blood Cells

Cell	Normal Count (per mm³)	Differential Count (% of Total WBCs)	When Raised	When Low
Leucocytes	4000–11,000		Leucocytosis	Leucopaenia
Neutrophils	1600–6600	40–60	Neutrophilia	Neutropaenia
Lymphocytes	800–4400	20–40	Lymphocytosis	Lymphocytopaenia
Monocytes	80–880	2–8	Monocytosis	Monocytopaenia
Eosinophils	40–440	1–4	Eosinophilia	Eosinopaenia
Basophils	20–110	0.5–1	Basophilia	Basopaenia

components of the cells take up a pinkish colour (eosin). Thus, the nucleus which contains nucleic acids appears blue.

Agranulocytes

Lymphocytes

- *Morphology*: On microscopy, lymphocytes are classified as small or large lymphocytes based on their size. Fig. 36.2 illustrates a small and a large lymphocyte within the same field.
  - The small lymphocyte is approximately the same size as a red blood cell, while a large lymphocyte is 2–2.5 times bigger than a red blood cell.

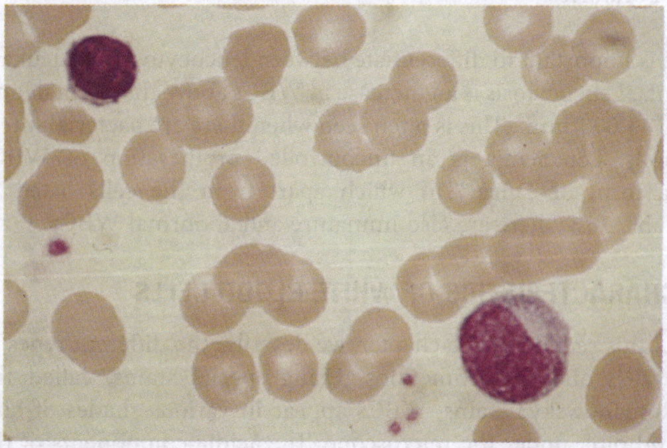

FIG. 36.2 Structure of lymphocytes. From: https://upload.wikimedia.org/wikipedia/commons/6/6f/ Small_%2B_Large_lymphocyte.JPG

  - Lymphocytes have a round nucleus which is surrounded by a relatively small amount of cytoplasm – in small lymphocytes, it may be just a rim. Thus, the nucleus-to-cytoplasm ratio is high.
  - There are no granules in the cytoplasm.
- *Lifespan*: This is highly variable – some lymphocytes have a lifespan of about a week while others may survive for many months and have the function of 'immune memory'.
- *Functions*: Lymphocytes have many functions in immunity. Apart from the classification of lymphocytes based on morphology, lymphocytes are also classified based on their function and how they are formed. Thus, lymphocytes are also classified as follows:
  - T lymphocytes, which are further classified as follows:
    - T-helper cells
    - T suppressor cells
    - Cytotoxic T cells
    - Memory cells
  - Natural killer (NK) cells
  - B lymphocytes

The different types of lymphocytes have different functions:

- T lymphocytes are involved in cell-mediated immunity: The helper and suppressor T cells help modulate the immune response. Many T cells release molecules called cytokines which help to direct the immune response. Cytotoxic T cells release granules which destroy cells and memory cells help the body to 'remember' prior exposure to microbes and to develop an effective immune response.

- B lymphocytes mediate humoral immunity involving antibodies (immunoglobulins), discussed in greater detail in Chapter 39.
- NK cells kill viruses and tumour cells without any prior activation.

Monocytes

- *Morphology*: The monocytes are the largest of the leucocytes. When they migrate to the tissues, they are called macrophages.
  - The size of the monocyte can reach as much as three times the size of an RBC, that is ~20 microns.
  - The cytoplasm is without any granules.
  - The nucleus is unilobar and is typically bean or kidney shaped.
- *Lifespan*: Most monocytes have a short lifespan in circulation of about 1 day. There are, however, some subpopulations of monocytes which can remain in circulation for several days.
- *Functions*: The monocytes have three broad functions:
  - Antigen presentation: Microbes have proteins on their cell surface called antigens. These antigens help to trigger the immune response. However, as part of the immune response, the monocytes/macrophages – process the antigens and present them to other immune cells.
  - Phagocytosis.
  - Production of cytokines.

Granulocytes

Neutrophils

- *Morphology*: A typical neutrophil is depicted in Fig. 36.3.
  - The size of a neutrophil is about 1.5–2 times the size of a red blood cell.
  - The cytoplasm has fine pinpoint granules.
  - The granules are described as azurophilic – neither the deep pink of eosin nor the blue of methylene blue in the stain.
  - The nucleus has lobes. The number of lobes varies and tells us the age of the neutrophil. Older neutrophils have more lobes. The relative number of neutrophils based on the number of lobes of the nucleus is called the Arneth's count. A shift to the left – that is many neutrophils with fewer lobes indicates an acute infective response in which many young neutrophils (with fewer lobes) are released into circulation.
- *Lifespan*: The lifespan of a neutrophil varies from a few hours to about 5–6 days. Once the neutrophil migrates into tissues, it survives for about 1–2 days.
- *Functions:* Neutrophils have a major antimicrobial role and they perform this using various processes:
  - Chemotaxis: Neutrophils move to a site of infection/ inflammation.
  - Phagocytosis: Neutrophils can engulf foreign particles and microbes and digest them. This is described in greater detail in Chapter 39.
  - Degranulation: Neutrophils release the contents of their granules and these have antimicrobial actions.
  - Neutrophil extracellular traps: Neutrophils release fibres with chemicals which help to traps microbes which are outside the cells (i.e. extracellular).

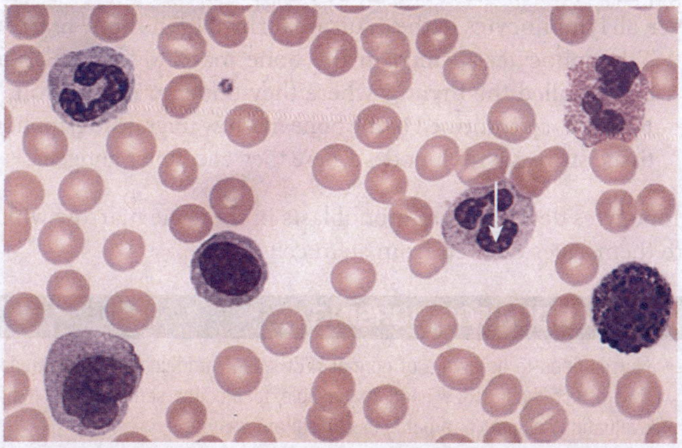

FIG. 36.3 Neutrophil on microscopy. From: https://www.rheumatologyadvisor.com/home/rheumatoid-arthritis-advisor/increased-neutrophil-activation-cell-death-in-rheumatoid-arthritis/

Eosinophils

- *Morphology*: Fig. 36.4 shows three eosinophils and one small lymphocyte in the lower right corner.
  - The eosinophil is about 1.5–2 times the size of a red blood cell (12–17 microns).
  - The nucleus is bilobed and described as 'spectacle-shaped'.
  - The cytoplasm is filled with coarse, pink, acidophilic granules.
- *Lifespan*: Eosinophils circulate in blood for about 8–12 hours but can survive many days in tissues.
- *Functions*: The functions of eosinophils are associated with the content of their granules.
  - Fighting viral infections: For example, eosinophil granules contain RNases which are effective against RNA viruses.

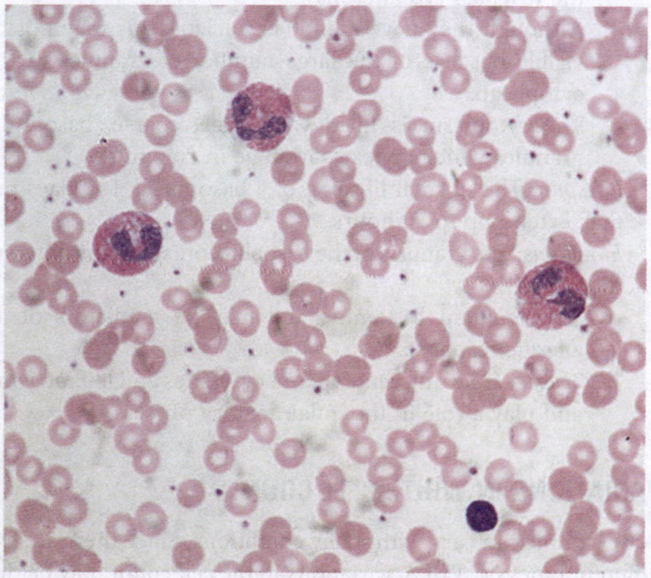

FIG. 36.4 Eosinophil on microscopy. From: https://en.wikipedia.org/wiki/Eosinophilia

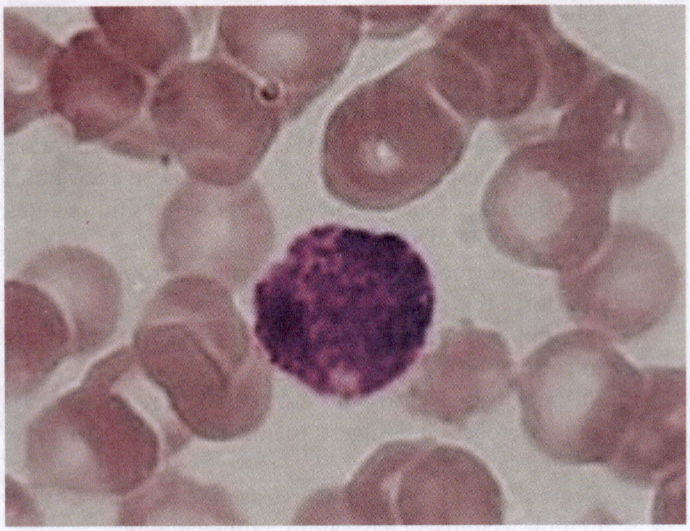

FIG. 36.5 Basophil on microscopy. From: https://en.wikipedia.org/wiki/Basophil#/media/File:Basophil.jpg

- Mediating allergic reactions: Major basic protein which is one of the components of the granules causes mast cell degranulation.
- Action against helminths and other intestinal parasites: Several contents of granules such as eosinophil peroxidase, eosinophil cationic protein and major basic protein can damage of the cell membrane of parasites and helminths.
- Mildly phagocytic.

Basophils

- *Morphology:* These are the most uncommon leucocytes and it is not uncommon not to find a basophil during a manual examination of a peripheral blood smear. A typical basophil is depicted in Fig. 36.5.
  - These are large cells which can be about twice the size of the RBC (14–16 microns).
  - Although they have a bilobed nucleus, this may not be visible because of the large number of granules in the cytoplasm.
  - The cytoplasm is filled with large, coarse, basophilic granules which appear dark blue in colour.
- *Lifespan*: The normal lifespan of a basophil is 1–2 days but may extend up to 70 hours.
- *Functions*: The granules of the basophil contain many different molecules:
  - They contain histamine and may be mediators of an allergic response.
  - They secrete different types of cytokines and leukotrienes and play a role in the inflammatory process.

VARIATIONS IN WHITE CELL COUNTS

WBC counts can vary with many conditions. Since there are five different types of WBCs, variations in the cell count may be due to any one or a number of them. The following are just a few of the most common variations:

Raised cell counts:

- Neutrophilia: seen in bacterial infections, especially when there is pus (pyogenic infections)
- Lymphocytosis: seen in viral infections and some chronic infections like tuberculosis
- Eosinophilia: seen in allergic conditions (hay fever, asthma, allergic skin conditions) and parasitic infections
- Monocytosis: seen in certain chronic infections, for example tuberculosis and malaria, and chronic inflammatory conditions
- Basophilia: relatively rare, seen in certain specific blood cancers

Reduced cell counts:

A decrease in the white cell count (leucopaenia) has many causes.
Reduced WBCs put individuals at higher risk of contracting infections.

- Radiation therapy: This is used to treat some cancers – when the radiation involves the bones – this may suppress formation of blood cells in the marrow.
- Chemotherapy: These are medications used to treat cancers. These medications may suppress all rapidly dividing cells including the cells in the bone marrow.
- Certain cancers which affect/invade the bone marrow can cause a reduction in blood cells.

FORMATION OF WHITE BLOOD CELLS

The process of development of WBCs is called leucopoiesis. WBCs are formed in the bone marrow from stem cells which are capable of self-renewal and differentiating into different cell lines. This differentiation allows different WBCs to be formed.

Granulopoiesis is the process of formation of granulocytes, that is neutrophils, eosinophils and basophils. The stem cells in the bone marrow give rise to differentiated cells such as the myeloblast, which in turn give rise to a promyelocyte and then myelocytes of different types which will separately give rise to the three granulocytes in peripheral blood.

The formation of lymphocytes is called lymphopoiesis. While lymphopoiesis in the foetus takes place in the foetal yolk sac and liver, all lymphocytes in the adult are formed in the bone marrow.

- T lymphocytes formed in the bone marrow migrate to an organ called the thymus where they undergo maturation.
- B lymphocytes formed in the bone marrow migrate to lymphoid tissue such as lymph nodes where they encounter antigens.

Monocytes develop from monoblasts in the bone marrow which are themselves derived from stem cells.

APPLICATIONS FOR NURSING

- Nurses need to be aware of normal WBC counts and common conditions that affect them. They need to be able to monitor serial blood count evaluations as part of a patient's clinical progress.
- Nurses need to be aware of the clinical features, signs and symptoms of possible infection in patients with low WBC counts – these include a large number of patients with cancer on radiotherapy or chemotherapy.

SUMMARY

- WBCs are classified as granulocytes (neutrophils, eosinophils and basophils) and agranulocytes (lymphocytes and monocytes).
- The normal total WBC count is 4000–11,000/mm^3; this count can be elevated (leucocytosis) or reduced (leucopaenia) and can reflect elevations or reductions in one or more of the five different WBCs.
- Lymphocytes classified as small and large on microscopy and as T, B and NK cells functionally play an important role in cell-mediated immunity (T cells) and humoral immunity (B cells).
- Monocytes are the largest WBCs which get converted to macrophages in the tissues. They are phagocytic, help to present antigens to other immune cells and produce cytokines.
- Neutrophils are the most abundant of WBCs. They increase in acute bacterial infections. They are phagocytic and help to destroy microbes through the release of the contents of their granules.
- Eosinophils act against viruses, helminths and parasites and mediate allergic reactions.
- Basophils are the least abundant of WBCs and mediate allergic reactions and release cytokines and leukotrienes that mediate inflammation.

CHAPTER REVIEW QUESTIONS

1. Describe with a diagram the appearance of the following cells under a microscope – (a) neutrophil, (b) eosinophil, (c) lymphocyte, (d) monocyte.
2. Which of the white blood cells show phagocytosis?
3. What are the functional types of lymphocytes and what is their function?
4. In which conditions is the total WBC count (a) raised, (b) decreased?

CHAPTER 37

Haemostasis

SPECIFIC LEARNING OBJECTIVES

At the end of this chapter, the student should be able to:

- Describe the structure, formation and functions of platelets.
- Describe the sequence of events that stop bleeding in response to an injury.
- Describe the coagulation pathways.
- Classify anticoagulants and describe their mode of action.
- Briefly describe some common bleeding and clotting disorders, specifically:
  - Thrombocytopaenic purpura
  - Haemophilia

GLOSSARY OF TERMS

- **Megakaryocyte:** a large bone marrow cell which gives rise to platelets
- **Thrombocyte:** platelet
- **Thrombocytopaenia:** a reduction in platelet count below 150,000/mm^3
- **Haemostasis:** stoppage of bleeding (not to be confused with homeostasis)
- **Platelet plug:** temporary haemostatic plug of aggregated platelets
- **Clot:** a permanent haemostatic plug with fibrin deposited into the platelet plug
- **Coagulation:** clotting
- **Fibrinolysis:** enzymatic degradation of a clot

We are subjected to all kinds of injuries during the course of a lifetime. This chapter addresses our responses to bleeding.

PLATELETS

Structure of platelets: The structure of a single platelet is depicted in Fig. 37.1.

- Platelets are small fragments of cells about 2–4 microns in diameter.
- They do not have a nucleus.
- Platelets have granules. There are different types of granules:
  - Dense bodies:
    - Approximately three to eight per platelet.
    - Contain serotonin, ADP, ATP, histamine and calcium.
  - Alpha granules:
    - These are the most abundant type of granules (50–80 per platelet).
    - These contain fibrinogen, von Willebrand's factor, platelet-derived growth factor, inflammatory proteins and angiogenic factors.
  - Lysosomal enzymes: Lysosomes contain enzymes called hydrolases which help to digest and degrade proteins.

Count: Between 150,000 and 400,000 platelets/mm^3. Ranges for the normal count vary between laboratories. A decrease in the platelet count is called thrombocytopaenia and an increase is called thrombocytosis.

Lifespan: In circulation, the lifespan is 5–7 days after formation. Platelets are removed from the bloodstream by macrophages and neutrophils and transported to the spleen where they are broken down.

Formation of platelets: Platelets are formed from large giant cells in the bone marrow called megakaryocytes through a process of fragmentation. A single megakaryocyte can give rise to as many as 1000 platelets.

Functions of platelets: When the contents of the platelet granules are released, there are multiple effects. These include the following:

1. Local vasoconstriction (discussed in the section 'Response to Bleeding')
2. Platelet adhesion, activation and aggregation and the formation of a platelet plug to stop bleeding
3. Providing the base on which a clot can be formed
4. Wound repair (this is because platelets release growth factors such as platelet-derived growth factor)

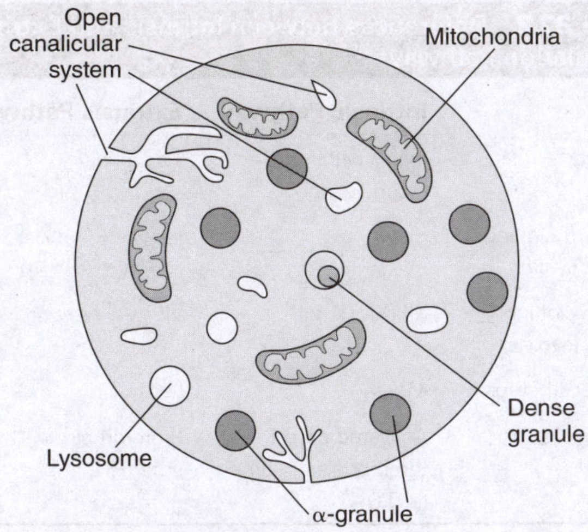

FIG. 37.1 Structure of a platelet.

RESPONSE TO BLEEDING

In this section, we will discuss what happens when there is bleeding and what steps the body takes to stop bleeding. Following injury, there are three steps which occur to control bleeding:

1. **Vasoconstriction of blood vessels:** Here, the blood vessel which has been injured/cut contracts. In the process, blood flow through the blood vessel reduces. Vasoconstriction occurs through multiple mechanisms:
   a. Mechanical injury to the blood vessel can cause the smooth muscle of the blood vessel to contract.
   b. The platelet releases certain vasoconstrictor substances such as serotonin from its granules.
   c. Injury can cause an activation of the sympathetic nervous system which can cause vasoconstriction.
2. **Formation of platelet plug:** Platelets are first activated, and then adhere to the injured site and to each other to form an aggregate. This is called a platelet plug or temporary haemostatic plug. If the injury is small, as, for instance, following a small cut or a needle or thorn injury, the platelet plug can stop the bleeding completely. This stoppage, however, is only temporary. Thus, if there is a repeated minor injury to the site, the platelet plug can be dislodged and bleeding can resume. The formation of a platelet plug occurs in three stages:
   a. **Adhesion** of platelets to exposed collagen in tissues that have been injured. The bridge between the platelet and the collagen is a substance called von Willebrand's factor which binds the platelet to the collagen and is released by the platelet granules.
   b. **Activation** of platelets – during this process, the platelet releases the contents of its granules.
   c. **Aggregation** of platelets – here, activated platelets attach to each other increasing the size of the 'platelet plug'.
3. **Formation of a clot:** In order to ensure more permanent stoppage of bleeding, a clot needs to form at the site of injury – this clot stabilizes the platelet plug through the deposition of a substance called fibrin. This requires the collective effort of many clotting factors which are activated through two different coagulation pathways which are described next.

CLOTTING FACTORS

There are many clotting factors which act to form a clot and these have traditionally been numbered using Roman numerals. When clotting is initiated, the clotting factors get activated. The active form is indicated by the lower case 'a' – thus, when factor XII is activated, we would represent it as XII_a.

The clotting factors are listed in Table 37.1.

COAGULATION CASCADE

Fig. 37.2 illustrates the coagulation cascades. They are called cascades because the activation of one factor leads to the activation of another, in sequence, until fibrin is formed.

From Fig. 37.2, you will observe that there are several components to the coagulation cascade:

1. There are two different mechanisms of activation of the coagulation cascade. The intrinsic pathway is activated when there is damage to the endothelial lining of the blood vessels. The extrinsic pathway is activated when there is tissue damage – this pathway involves fewer steps and is faster than the intrinsic pathway.
2. The clotting factors are sequentially activated. In the diagram, the blue boxes refer to the inactive clotting factor and the orange boxes refer to the active clotting factor.
3. Both the intrinsic and extrinsic pathways lead to a common, final pathway. The aim of coagulation is to allow for the deposition of fibrin in a stable clot.

Table 37.1 List of Clotting Factors

Clotting Factor	
I	Fibrinogen
II	Prothrombin
III	Tissue factor or tissue thromboplastin
IV	Calcium
V	Proaccelerin, labile factor
VI	This was originally thought to be a unique factor; it is now known to be activated factor V
VII	Stable factor, proconvertin
VIII	Antihaemophilic factor A
IX	Antihaemophilic factor B or Christmas factor
X	Stuart–Prower factor
XI	Plasma thromboplastin antecedent
XII	Hageman's factor
XIII	Fibrin-stabilizing factor

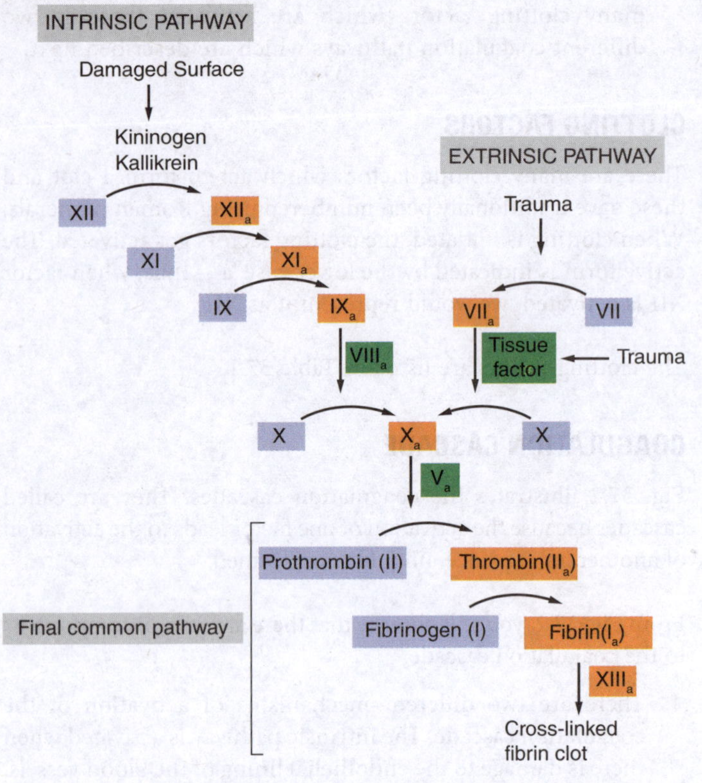

FIG. 37.2 The coagulation cascade.

4. Calcium ions are required in several stages of the coagulation cascade. This means that anything that reduces the availability of calcium ions will prevent coagulation.
5. The absence of a clotting factor will not allow the coagulation cascade to proceed and will thus prevent clotting.

Table 37.2 summarizes the differences between the intrinsic and extrinsic coagulation pathways.

ANTICOAGULANTS

Anticoagulants are substances which interfere with the process of clotting. These keep the blood fluid (in an unclotted state) – this is important in a variety of situations, for instance, during the storage of blood for blood transfusions, to prevent clot formation within the blood vessels of people who are bedridden and for storage of blood in laboratory analyses.

Anticoagulants work in different ways:

1. **Chelation of calcium ions:** Chelation is the process in which substances bind to a metal ion (in this case calcium) making it unavailable for reactions. We have already seen that calcium ions are required in several stages of the coagulation cascade. Thus, chelation of calcium ions prevents the steps in the coagulation cascade in which calcium ions are needed. Examples of anticoagulants that work this way are ethylenediaminetetraacetic acid (**EDTA**), sodium citrate and oxalates of sodium and potassium.

Table 37.2 Differences Between Intrinsic and Extrinsic Coagulation Pathways

	Intrinsic Pathway	Extrinsic Pathway
Activator	Injury within the blood vessel	Tissue injury
Speed of clotting after activation	Slow	Fast
Unique clotting factors involved	XII, XI, IX, VIII	VII
Number of steps	More	Less
Clotting test	Activated partial thromboplastin time (aPTT)	Prothrombin time (PT)

2. **Vitamin K antagonists:** Vitamin K is required for the formation of clotting factors II, VII, IX and X. Antagonists are substances which oppose the action of something else. Thus, antagonists of vitamin K oppose the action of vitamin K and prevent the formation of factors II, VII, IX and X and thus prevent clotting. Examples of anticoagulants that work this way are dicoumarol and warfarin.
3. **Prevention of the conversion of fibrinogen to fibrin:** This step occurs towards the end of the final common pathway of the coagulation cascade and is mediated by thrombin. Substances that prevent clotting by acting at this stage include heparin and hirudin.

THROMBOCYTOPAENIC PURPURA: AN EXAMPLE OF A BLEEDING DISORDER

Thrombocytopaenia is a reduction in the number of platelets below the lower limit of $150,000/mm^3$. Since platelets are required for the formation of the platelet plug to stop bleeding, these individuals have prolonged bleeding. This can be tested in a laboratory by assessing bleeding time. Bleeding time can be tested quite simply by performing a finger puncture with a lancet and then blotting the bleeding point every 15 seconds with a filter paper. The point at which no blood appears on the filter paper is the bleeding time. The normal bleeding time is approximately between 1 and 5 minutes. In thrombocytopaenia, patients may develop 'petechiae' which are small pinpoint bleeding spots beneath the skin. Spontaneous bleeding may occur in patients with platelet counts of less than $40,000/mm^3$.

HAEMOPHILIA: AN EXAMPLE OF A CLOTTING DISORDER

Classical haemophilia is a disease caused by the absence of factor VIII (antihaemophilic factor). Patients who suffer from this disease have prolonged clotting time. Patients with haemophilia may have excessive bleeding following injury, tooth extraction, surgery, etc., and may also develop spontaneous bleeding from the nose and in the urine and stools. Severe bleeding can be life threatening. Haemophilia is an X-linked recessive disease. This means that women can be carriers, since they have two X

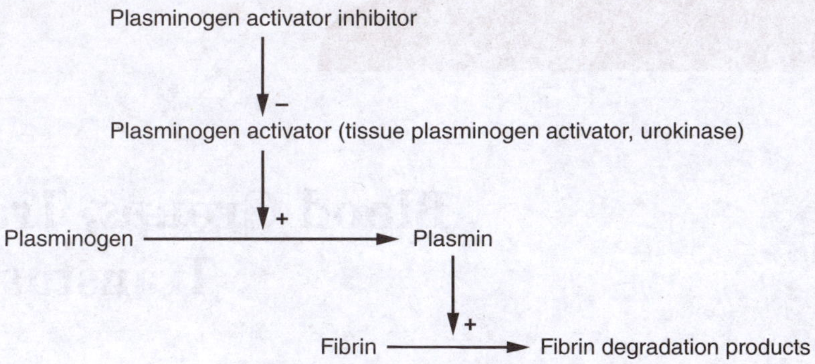

FIG. 37.3 Process of fibrinolysis.

chromosomes and one can be normal, while men will always have the disease if their X chromosome is affected.

There are three types of haemophilia:

- (Classical) Haemophilia A (deficiency of factor VIII, X-linked recessive)
- Haemophilia B (deficiency of factor IX, X-linked recessive)
- Haemophilia C (deficiency of factor XI, autosomal recessive)

Traditionally, clotting time was tested very simply in a laboratory; a drop of blood was drawn up into a capillary tube. After 1 minute, small segments of the tube were carefully broken off every 30 seconds until a fibrin thread was observed between the two broken segments of the tube. The normal clotting time using this method was between 3 and 7 minutes. Most hospitals no longer use this as a clotting test because it is not very accurate and does not indicate where the problem with clotting is. It has been replaced by other more accurate and specific tests which also allow the doctor to understand which clotting pathway is involved. Deficiency of specific clotting factors can be assessed by measuring the concentration of clotting factors in blood.

FIBRINOLYSIS

This is a process which involves the enzymatic breakdown of the fibrin clot once haemostasis is achieved. The steps involved in fibrinolysis are outlined in Fig. 37.3.

Plasminogen which is synthesized in the liver and circulates in the blood is important for fibrinolysis. Plasminogen gets converted to plasmin which acts on fibrin and breaks it down.

The conversion of plasminogen to plasmin occurs because of the presence of plasminogen activators such as tissue plasminogen activator which is present in various organs as well as the endothelium which lines the blood vessels. Plasminogen activators can themselves be inhibited by plasminogen activator inhibitors (PAI) of which there are several types. PAI are produced in several cells including vascular smooth muscle and the endothelium. If fibrinolysis does not occur, clots that form in blood vessels may occlude the blood vessel and these clots may break away from the vessel wall to form emboli and block other blood vessels.

APPLICATIONS FOR NURSING

- Nurses need to recognize the manifestations of bleeding and clotting disorders.
- Nurses need to interpret bleeding and clotting tests since many patients may be prescribed 'blood thinners' or anticoagulants.

SUMMARY

- Haemostasis is achieved by three processes: (1) vasoconstriction, (2) formation of a temporary haemostatic (platelet) plug and (3) formation of a clot.
- Formation of a platelet plug involves three processes: (1) adhesion to the injured surface, (2) activation of platelets and the release of granular contents and (3) aggregation of platelets.
- The coagulation (clotting) cascade consists of three parts: the intrinsic pathway activated by damage to the endothelium, the extrinsic pathway activated by tissue damage and a common final pathway.
- Reduction in platelet number (thrombocytopaenia) leads to a bleeding disorder, while the absence of a clotting factor (e.g. haemophilia – absence of factor VIII) leads to a clotting disorder. Bleeding disorders are characterized by a prolonged bleeding time, while clotting disorders are characterized by a prolonged clotting time.
- Anticoagulants prevent clotting. These include substances that (1) chelate Ca^{2+} ions; (2) interfere with the vitamin K–dependent production of factors II, VII, IX and X; and (3) interfere with the conversion of fibrinogen to fibrin.

CHAPTER REVIEW QUESTIONS

1. Describe the steps involved in the formation of a platelet plug.
2. What are the differences between the intrinsic and extrinsic pathway for clotting?
3. Classify anticoagulants and give one example of each.
4. Write a short note on (a) thrombocytopaenia, (b) haemophilia.

CHAPTER 38

Blood Groups, Transfusion and Transfusion Reactions

SPECIFIC LEARNING OBJECTIVES

At the end of this chapter, the student should be able to:

- List the different blood groups.
- State Landsteiner's law and explain its application.
- Describe the process for screening a potential blood donor.
- List the changes with storage of blood.
- Describe potential transfusion reactions.
- Describe Rh incompatibility of the newborn.

GLOSSARY OF TERMS

- **Agglutinogen:** antigen on the RBC cell membrane
- **Agglutinin:** antibody to an agglutinogen
- **Agglutination:** an antigen–antibody reaction visible microscopically
- **Major cross-matching:** mixing of donor's RBCs and recipient's plasma in a tube to check for agglutination
- **Minor cross-matching:** mixing of donor's plasma and recipient's RBCs in a tube to check for agglutination.

In Chapter 2, we discussed that proteins present on a cell membrane could function as antigens. If these antigens are located on viruses, bacteria, etc., they start a defence (immune) response which helps the body to get rid of these harmful organisms. However, antigens which are normally present on the cell membranes of the body are identified as 'self' – the body's immune system does not normally act against these antigens except in autoimmune diseases. The RBCs are the most numerous cells in the blood. Thus, during blood transfusion, it is important that the blood transfused from another person (donor) does not start an immune response in the person receiving the blood (recipient).

BLOOD GROUPS

RBCs, like other cells, contain antigens on its cell membrane. A person's blood group is determined by the antigens that are present on the RBCs. Karl Landsteiner, who won the Nobel Prize for Physiology and Medicine, described the ABO blood group system. After that, the Rh system was discovered. Since then, many 'minor' blood group systems have been described. However, we describe a person's blood group primarily on the basis of the ABO system and the Rh system.

Table 38.1 describes the antigens and antibodies that are present in the ABO and Rh systems. The antigen is sometimes called the agglutinogen, and the antibody the agglutinin.

Let us first look at the ABO system. The antigens and antibodies present in a person obey **Landsteiner's law**. This law has two parts:

Part 1: *If an antigen is present on the RBC, then the corresponding antibody in plasma is absent.* Thus, for blood group A, the antigen is A and the corresponding antibody would be anti-A, which is absent. In the same way for the AB blood group, the antigens present are both A and B, and both the corresponding antibodies (anti-A and anti-B) are absent. If the corresponding antibody was present, then the RBCs would be destroyed!

Part 2: *If an antigen is absent on the RBC, then the corresponding antibody is present in plasma.* This is illustrated by the blood group O. Blood group O does not have antigens of the ABO system, but it has both the antibodies (i.e. anti-A and anti-B). Note that Landsteiner's law is always stated with respect to the antigen – that is antigen present–antibody absent and antigen absent–antibody present.

Table 38.1 Distribution of Antigens and Antibodies in the Rh Factor and ABO Blood Groups

System	Group	Antigen (Agglutinogen)	Antibody (Agglutinin)
ABO	A	A	Anti-B
	B	B	Anti-A
	AB	A and B	–
	O	–	Anti-A and Anti-B
Rh	Rh+	D	–
	Rh−	–	–

The Rh system is different from the ABO system. People are classified on whether they have a D antigen (Rh +ve) or do not have a D antigen on their RBCs (Rh –ve). Unlike the ABO system, you will observe in Table 38.1 that the absence of an antigen D does not mean that the person will have anti-Rh (D) antibodies. In other words, the Rh system does not obey Landsteiner's law.

A person with O blood group is often called the **universal donor**. This is because the RBCs of a person with O blood group do not have A or B antigens. Thus, the antibodies in a person with A blood group (anti-B antibodies), B blood group (anti-A antibodies) and AB blood group (no AB antibodies) cannot react with the RBCs of an O group donor. Thus, people with O blood group (ideally Rh –ve) can give their blood to A, B, AB and O blood groups in an emergency – this is why they are called universal donors. This might seem strange, since a person with O blood group has anti-A and anti-B antibodies – these would be expected to react with the RBCs of the recipient if they are A, B or AB blood groups. In actual fact, the antibodies of the donor get so diluted within the blood of the recipient that such a reaction is unlikely. The dilution occurs because 1 pint (less than 500 mL) of donor blood gets mixed in 5000 mL (5 L) blood volume of the recipient.

In contrast, a person with AB blood group is called a **universal recipient**. Thus, people with A, B and O blood groups can donate blood to a person with AB blood group. This is because the person with an AB blood group does not have any antibodies that will react with the A and B antigens of the donor.

Why is it that the donor's antibodies are not as important as the recipient's antibodies? This is because the donor's antibodies are present in the fixed volume of blood to be transfused. When this is transfused, it is diluted in the recipient's blood volume. In contrast, a recipient can continue to produce antibodies against foreign antigens – so the immune response will be much greater. This is important when certain tests called 'cross-matching' are done before a transfusion. This is discussed later.

BLOOD TRANSFUSIONS

Patients may require blood transfusions for many reasons – they may need it at surgery, after an accident has resulted in blood loss, etc. In this section, we will review the steps that are taken prior to a transfusion and the complications that may occur with mismatched transfusions.

Screening of a Donor

A blood transfusion requires a donor.

As per the Government of India guidelines, a donor should:

- Be a healthy adult, mentally alert and physically fit
- Be between 18 and 65 years of age
- Have a normal blood pressure
- Be afebrile (without fever)
- Not be fasting and should have had a meal in the last 4 hours
- Not be involved in risky behaviours which might allow for transmission of blood-borne infections (e.g. sex workers, i.v. drug users)
- Have a haemoglobin level of ≥12 g%
- Not provide repeated donations less than 3 months (90 days) apart for males and 4 months (120 days) apart for females
- Provide not more than 350 mL of blood if between 45 and 55 kg, or 450 mL if greater than 55 kg body weight
- Provide written consent on an appropriate form

Blood from a donor is routinely screened for HIV, hepatitis B and C, malaria and syphilis.

Steps Prior to Transfusion

In order to transfuse blood, the donor blood group and the recipient blood group should be the same except in situations of extreme emergency when O Rh –ve blood may be transfused, since O Rh –ve is the universal donor.

Even if the blood groups of the donor and the recipient match, and the blood screening for infectious diseases is negative, blood is transfused only after performing 'cross-matching' tests. This is done because there are many minor blood groups which are not routinely tested for and immune reactions related to these antigens can occur. Cross-matching is of two types:

1. **Major cross-matching** is done with the donor's cells and recipient's plasma. It is called major since the antigens are on the donor's cells and the antibodies are generated by the recipient. In principle, the recipient can generate a sustained release of antibodies and this can result in a major immune reaction.
2. **Minor cross-matching** is done with the donor's plasma and recipient's cells. Here the immune response is likely to be minor since the amount of antibodies is limited in the volume of the donor's plasma and will be diluted in the much larger blood volume of the recipient. The two forms of cross-matching are summarized in Fig. 38.1.

CHANGES WITH STORAGE OF BLOOD

Blood is stored in the blood bank under the following conditions:

- Hypothermia: Lowered temperature (4°C) reduces the metabolic activity of the cells and helps to sustain them for a longer period of time.

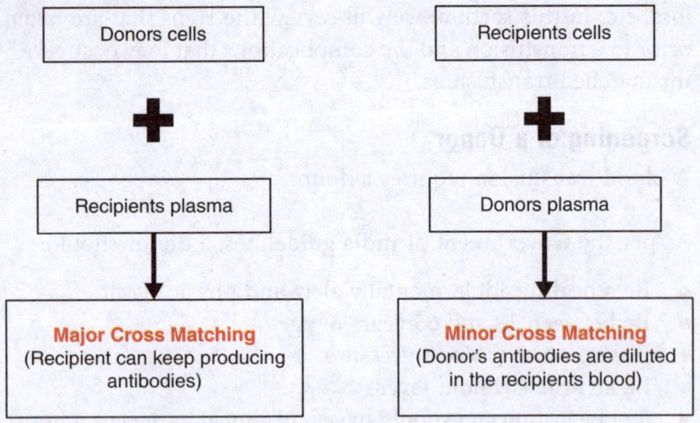

FIG. 38.1 Major and minor cross matching.

- Preservative: This contains several components and includes the following:
  - Citrate – acts as an anticoagulant
  - Phosphate buffer – to maintain the pH since lactic acid accumulates as a result of anaerobic glycolysis and unbuffered will lower the pH
  - Dextrose – to provide nutrients for the cells for energy

Even under these storage conditions, the cells undergo structural and functional changes.

Changes with storage include:

- Red blood cells show changes in shape and flexibility. Prolonged storage of RBCs results in reduced survival in the recipient following transfusion and a reduction in oxygen-carrying capacity.
- White blood cells become less functional within several hours of storage.
- Platelets are largely nonfunctional after 2 days.

These changes are the reason why fresh blood transfusions may be preferred in certain conditions and circumstances.

TRANSFUSION REACTIONS

1. **Mismatched (incompatible) blood transfusion:**
   Trigger: This reaction occurs when the wrong blood group is given to a person, for example blood group A blood is given to a blood group B person.
   Pathophysiology: The antibodies in the recipient attach on the antigens of the donor RBCs destroying them. In the example given earlier, anti-A antibodies in the plasma of the recipient would destroy the RBCs of the donor since the donor RBCs have A antigen on the cell membrane. The extent of the reaction will depend on the volume of the transfusion. The donor's cells will be destroyed and haemoglobin will be released into the circulation.
   Clinical features: In minor reactions, anaemia and jaundice may result. In more severe reactions, more haemoglobin is released from RBCs. Haemoglobin is toxic when freely circulating, and this can result in filtering of haemoglobin in the kidney and appearance of haemoglobin in the urine. The kidney can also be damaged resulting in renal failure and even death.
2. **Allergic reactions:**
   Trigger: Allergens (allergy-causing proteins) present in the donor blood.
   Pathophysiology: The recipient mounts an immune response against the allergens.
   Clinical features: These may be minor or severe. The patient may complain of itching of the skin, urticaria, wheezing, etc.
3. **Febrile reactions:**
   Trigger: Pyrogens (fever-causing molecules) present in the donor blood.
   Pathophysiology: The pyrogens interfere with temperature regulation resulting in a fever.
   Clinical features: The patient develops a fever which is clearly linked to the onset of the blood transfusion. This is usually not life threatening and can be managed by stopping the transfusion and giving paracetamol.

Rh INCOMPATIBILITY OF THE NEWBORN (ERYTHROBLASTOSIS FOETALIS)

- The Rh system is based on the presence of D antigens. Those with the D antigen are Rh +ve and those without the D antigen are Rh −ve.
- Rh incompatibility of the newborn occurs when the mother is Rh −ve and the baby is Rh +ve. We have earlier indicated that the Rh system does not follow Landsteiner's law. Thus, even when a person is Rh −ve, he or she does not automatically have the anti-D antibodies.
- If an Rh −ve person, however, is exposed to Rh +ve blood, he or she will develop anti-D antibodies.

Pathophysiology

When an Rh −ve woman is pregnant for the first time with an Rh +ve foetus, the mother does not automatically have anti-D antibodies. The first delivery is therefore usually uneventful. During the delivery of this first baby, however, it is possible that the mother gets sensitized (exposed) to the D antigen of the baby during the process of delivery. If this happens, the mother will now develop anti-D antibodies. If the mother now becomes pregnant a second time, again with an Rh +ve foetus, the anti-D antibodies of the mother can cross the placenta and destroy the Rh +ve foetal RBCs. This is shown in Fig. 38.2.

Clinical Features

The clinical features depend on the extent to which the red blood cells in the foetus are destroyed. The result of this might be an anaemia, jaundice, hydrops foetalis (in which the newborn has severe oedema and heart failure) or even death. The extremely high levels of bilirubin result in bilirubin being deposited in the brain, a condition called kernicterus. If the baby survives, mental retardation may be present.

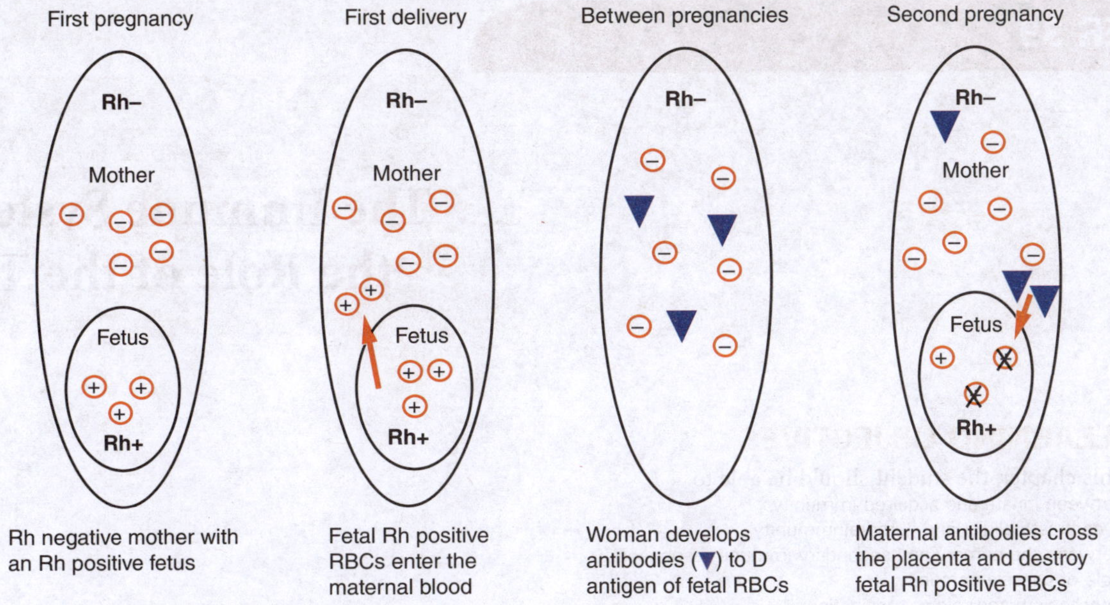

FIG. 38.2 Basis of Rh incompatibility of the newborn.

Prevention

After the first delivery, within 72 hours of the birth of a child, the mother can be administered anti-D antibodies through an injection. This prevents the mother from generating her own antibodies against the Rh antigen and the mother therefore remains unsensitized.

APPLICATIONS FOR NURSING

- The nurse will be required to ensure that the blood transfusion bag of the donor correctly matches the blood group of the recipient and that the preliminary evaluations of screening and cross-matching have been done.
- The nurse will be required to monitor blood transfusion for the evidence of any transfusion reaction.

SUMMARY

- The ABO system of blood groups is based on Landsteiner's law that indicates that the presence or absence of antigens on the RBC is associated with the absence or presence of antibodies in the plasma.
- O blood group is the universal donor and AB blood group the universal recipient.
- Cross-matching is the mixing of donor and recipient blood in a test tube prior to transfusion to check for any major immune reaction. Major cross-match is between donor's cells (RBCs) and recipient plasma. Minor cross-match is between donor's plasma and recipient cells.
- Transfusion reactions can occur due to a number of causes and may be a result of (1) mismatched transfusions, (2) febrile reactions and (3) allergic reactions, among others.
- Rh incompatibility of the newborn may result when the mother is Rh –ve and the foetus is Rh +ve.

CHAPTER REVIEW QUESTIONS

1. What are Landsteiner's Laws?
2. Prepare a table which shows the antigens and antibodies for A, B, AB and O blood groups
3. What are cross-matching reactions?
4. Describe the basis of Rh incompatibility of the newborn.

CHAPTER 39

The Immune System and the Role of the Thymus

SPECIFIC LEARNING OBJECTIVES

At the end of this chapter, the student should be able to:

- Distinguish between innate and acquired immunity.
- Compare and contrast cellular and humoral immunity.
- Distinguish between the primary and secondary immune responses.
- Discuss the role of passive immunity.
- Discuss the mechanism and role of vaccination.
- Define inflammation and list its components.
- List the functions of the thymus.

GLOSSARY OF TERMS

- **Immunity:** the ability of an individual to resist or overcome an infection
- **Antigen:** any molecule that can stimulate an immune response
- **Antibody:** also called immunoglobulin, produced by transformed B lymphocytes called plasma cells – are responsible for humoral immunity
- **Innate immunity:** uses cells and molecules that are already present in the body to help get rid of pathogens
- **Acquired immunity:** specific body defence response on exposure to pathogens or with immunization
- **Cell-mediated immunity:** immunity through T-lymphocytes
- **Humoral immunity:** immunity through antibodies (immunoglobulins)
- **Autoimmunity:** an immune response to the body's own cells (self-antigens), seen in a variety of autoimmune disorders
- **Vaccination:** stimulation of the immune system against a microbe using vaccines (vaccines are often, but not always, made from live, attenuated [weakened] microbes or dead microbes)

We are exposed to all kinds of organisms in the environment. Some are harmful, while others do not cause disease. The organisms may be visible only under a microscope (microorganisms) or they may be visible to the naked eye (worms, for instance). One of the functions of the body defence system (immune system) is to differentiate what is part of our bodies (self) and what is outside of our bodies which could cause disease (foreign). Once the immune system differentiates self from foreign, it is then possible for the immune system to respond appropriately.

The immune system has many functions:

1. It defends us from infective agents which may cause us harm.
2. It helps remove dead or damaged cells.
3. It constantly surveys our body for any mutant cell that can develop into a tumour and cause harm to the body (surveillance).

The immune system is not perfect. It does not succeed in getting rid of every microorganism that can cause harm. This is why we develop infectious diseases. In some situations, the body may be fooled into acting against our own cells (self), thinking them to be foreign. In this situation, we develop an autoimmune disease (auto = self). Myasthenia gravis (described in Chapter 52) is an example of such an autoimmune disease.

In this chapter, we discuss the parts of our immune system and how it acts. The different types of immunity are shown in Fig. 39.1.

INNATE IMMUNITY

This form of defence uses cells and molecules that are already present in the body to help get rid of pathogens.

The innate immune system of the body consists of the following components:

1. Physical barriers to disease
2. Phagocytosis
3. Complement system of proteins

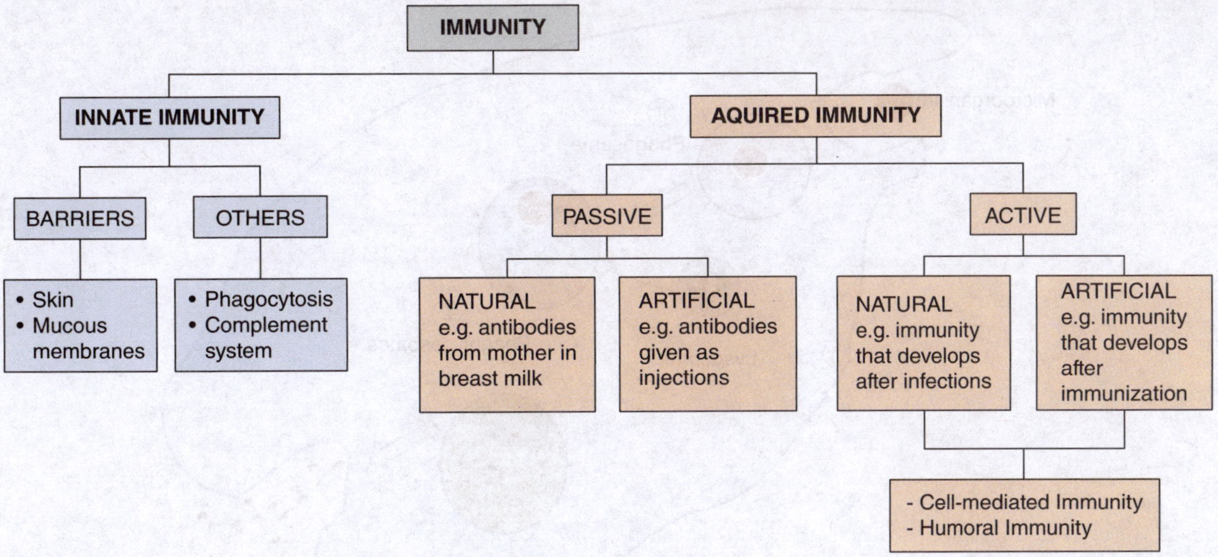

FIG. 39.1 Types of immunity.

Physical Barriers to Disease

Even before our immune cells act to contain an infection, the body is equipped with several physical barriers. These include the following:

1. Skin: Under normal circumstances, the skin is intact and continuous. Whenever we suffer from cuts and grazes, however, the continuity in the skin is broken and this provides an opportunity for microorganisms to enter the body.
2. Mucous membranes: These provide a physical barrier in the respiratory tract and the gastrointestinal and urinary tracts.
3. Secretions: Secretions such as tears, sweat and those of the stomach protect us from microorganisms because of either the pH or antibacterial components that they contain.
4. Helpful bacteria: We have microorganisms that live on the skin and in the gastrointestinal tract (commensals) that protect us from other harmful bacteria (pathogens).

Phagocytosis

Phagocytosis is the process by which a foreign cell or substance is engulfed by an immune cell, destroyed and then extruded. Among the white blood cells in the body, neutrophils and monocyte–macrophages are strongly phagocytic. Eosinophils are mildly phagocytic. Other cells which are capable of phagocytosis include dendritic cells, mast cells and natural killer cells.

The steps involved in phagocytosis include the following:

1. Attraction and movement of the phagocytic cell towards the pathogen.
2. Attachment to the pathogen and development of pseudopodia (foot-like processes which engulf the pathogen).
3. Complete engulfment of the pathogen (*phagosome*).
4. Fusion of lysosome with the phagosome to form a *phagolysosome*. The lysosome contains several enzymes which help to digest the pathogen.
5. Once the pathogen is digested, the degradation products are extruded from the cell by exocytosis.

The process of phagocytosis is depicted in Fig. 39.2.

Complement System of Proteins

Complement refers to a collection of about 20 plasma proteins. These proteins are activated sequentially on exposure to a foreign protein (antigen). The end result of the sequential activation of these proteins is **cell lysis**. However, the complement system also has other actions; these include, among others, the following:

1. Chemotaxis of white blood cells (chemotaxis is the directed migration of cells towards a site of injury, inflammation or infection)
2. Increased vascular permeability and other inflammatory effects (discussed later)
3. Facilitation of phagocytosis

ACQUIRED IMMUNITY

This type of immune response refers to the specific body defence response on exposure to pathogens or following immunization. Acquired immunity relies on lymphocytes rather than the phagocytic cells of innate immunity. There are two broad types of lymphocytes: these are the T lymphocytes which mature in the thymus and the B lymphocytes which mature in the bone marrow. Acquired immunity is of two types:

1. *Cell-mediated immunity* relies on activated lymphocytes to directly destroy pathogens.
2. *Humoral immunity* relies on the production of antibodies.

These two forms of acquired immunity are discussed in greater detail later in the chapter.

Cell-Mediated Immunity

This type of immunity is mediated by a specific lymphocyte called the T lymphocyte. On exposure to an antigen, the T lymphocytes proliferate and then circulate around the body. Antigens are molecules which produce an immune response and may

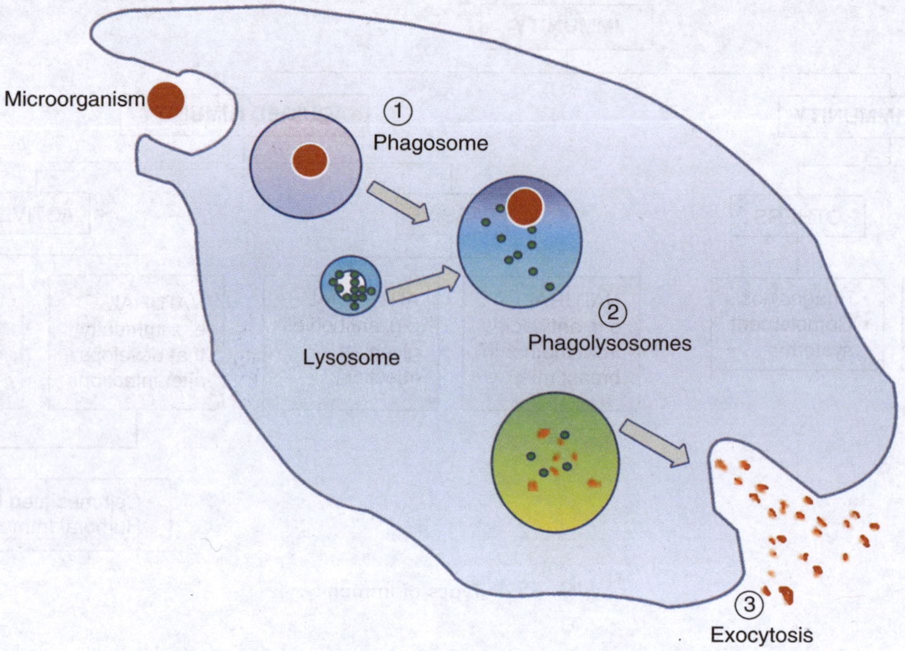

FIG. 39.2 Steps of phagocytosis.

be proteins on the surface of the pathogen. The T lymphocytes release chemicals called cytokines which enhance and modulate the immune response of the body. Cytokines include chemicals such as interferon γ and interleukins. Cytokines serve several functions:

1. They stimulate the growth and proliferation of T lymphocytes.
2. They promote the formation of antibodies.
3. They activate the macrophage system, both by attracting these phagocytic cells to the area they need to act and by increasing the efficiency of phagocytosis.

There are different kinds of T lymphocytes:

1. Helper T cells: These lymphocytes help to enhance the immune response in many different ways.
2. Cytotoxic T cells: These are sometimes referred to as 'killer' cells – they destroy pathogens by releasing perforins – these chemicals destroy the cell membrane of the pathogen and in the process kill these cells.
3. Suppressor T cells: These are capable of reducing the function of both the helper T cells and the cytotoxic T cells.

Humoral Immunity

In this form of immunity, antibodies are produced by transformed B lymphocytes called plasma cells. Antibodies act in several ways to protect the body:

1. They neutralize the toxins produced by the pathogens.
2. They can bind to antigens and activate the complement system.
3. They can bind to antigens and then increase their susceptibility to phagocytosis.

There are different types of antibodies. Antibodies are also called immunogobulins (Ig) and the different types are listed as follows:

IgM: This is largest immunoglobulin by molecular weight.
IgA: This is also called the secretory antibody since it appears in various body secretions, including breast milk.
IgG: This is the only immunoglobulin that is able to pass through the placental barrier.
IgD: Less is known about this compared to other immunoglobulins. We do know that it can trigger B lymphocytes.
IgE: This immunoglobulin binds to mast cells and mediates allergic responses.

Primary and Secondary Immune Responses

The antibody response to a first-time exposure of an antigen is called the primary immune response. When an individual has a subsequent exposure to the same antigen, the immune response that follows is called the secondary response. Fig. 39.3 illustrates these two responses.

As Fig. 39.3 shows, the following are the features of the primary response:

- It is slower.
- It is weaker (note the higher antibody concentration for the secondary response).
- It involves IgM antibodies (as compared to IgG antibodies in the secondary response).

The secondary immune response is quicker and higher because memory cells developed during the first antigen exposure allow a faster and more targeted response during subsequent exposures.

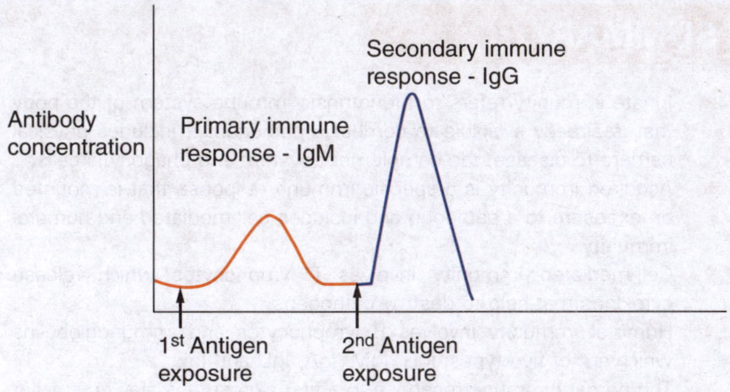

FIG. 39.3 The primary and secondary immune responses.

PASSIVE IMMUNITY

This is the transfer of ready-made antibodies to an individual. The purpose is to enhance the individual's defence. Here, the individual does not mount an active immune response (the individual does not mobilize cells or produce antibodies), therefore the term passive. There are essentially two types of passive immunity:

1. Natural: This occurs, for instance, from the mother to the foetus or to the newborn child. The antibodies from the mother can be transferred across the placenta to the foetus, although these are restricted to IgG, which are the only immunoglobulins that can cross the placenta. Antibodies can also be transferred in the breast milk during lactation.
2. Artificial: Here antibodies are prepared artificially and then administered to an individual. They are used both for the treatment and for the prevention of disease.
   a. Artificial passive immunity can be used in the treatment of a variety of diseases such as diphtheria, tetanus and botulism. The use of convalescent plasma for COVID-19 is another example of artificial passive immunity. Here, plasma from patients who have recovered from COVID-19 and which is rich in antibodies is given to other patients to boost their immunity and help them fight the disease.
   b. It can also be used to prevent disease. For instance, if an Rh –ve mother gives birth to an Rh +ve child, the mother is given antibodies against the D antigen of the baby's red blood cells. This ensures that the mother does not get sensitized to the D antigen. If this was the case, she would then mount a high immune response the second time she had an Rh +ve child and this would result in disease in the child, called Rh incompatibility of the newborn.

VACCINATION (IMMUNIZATION)

Vaccination is the process by which an individual is administered an antigen so that the resultant immune response helps the individual to develop protection against a pathogen. The antigen may be alive but inactivated (not infective) or it may be attenuated (i.e. with reduced infectivity).

While the number of available vaccines has grown in the last few years, among the vaccines that are administered to children are the following:

1. Bacille Calmette-Guerin (BCG) – against tuberculosis
2. Hepatitis B
3. Oral polio vaccine
4. DPT (diphtheria, pertussis and tetanus)
5. *Haemophilus influenzae* type B
6. Rotavirus
7. MMR (measles, mumps, rubella)
8. Varicella (chickenpox)
9. Typhoid
10. Japanese B encephalitis (in selected high-burden districts)
11. Pneumococcal conjugate vaccine

INFLAMMATION

This is an immune response of the body to various exposures such as pathogens, injury, chemical irritants and foreign bodies. The aim of inflammation is to:

- Eliminate the exposure.
- Limit the cell damage.
- Promote tissue repair.

Inflammation is characterized by certain typical signs (Fig. 39.4):
- Redness (rubor)
- Swelling (tumour)
- Increased temperature at the site of the inflammation (calor)
- Pain (dolour)
- Loss of function, depending on the extent of inflammation

In medical terminology, inflammation of a tissue or organ is denoted by the ending 'itis'. Thus, hepatitis is inflammation of the liver, pancreatitis is inflammation of the pancreas, etc.

THYMUS GLAND AND IMMUNITY

The thymus is a lymphoid gland situated in the upper chest just behind the sternum. It is filled with immature T lymphocytes. The thymus gland is most active during childhood and gradually gets filled with fatty tissue in adults.

Functions of the thymus include the following:

1. T-lymphocyte development: This occurs after lymphocyte precursors produced in the bone marrow enter the thymus gland. Thymopoiesis is the process whereby the whole range of T lymphocytes develops within the thymus. During this process, the lymphocytes acquire their cell membrane–specific receptors.
2. T-lymphocyte maturation: during this process cells are presented with 'self' antigens. Those that react strongly undergo apoptosis (cell death); this reducing the chance of auto-immune reactions.
3. T-lymphocyte export: Once T lymphocytes are mature, they leave the thymus gland and populate other lymphoid tissues in the body.

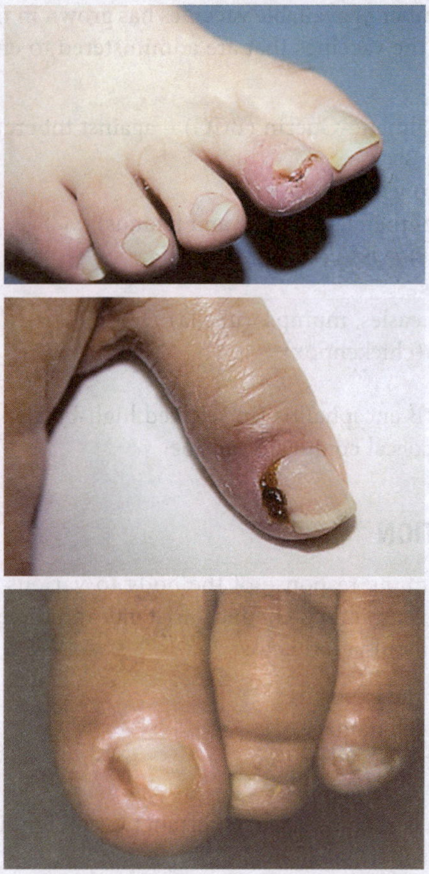

FIG. 39.4 An example of inflammation.

APPLICATIONS FOR NURSING

- The nurse will be required to identify and monitor response to treatment in the event of an infection or inflammation.
- Nurses will need to administer vaccines – the expanded programme of immunization (i.e. which vaccines and when they have to be administered) is beyond the scope of this book. Nurses will need to educate parents on the need to ensure complete immunization of their children.

SUMMARY

- Innate immunity refers to the intrinsic immune system of the body that is already available to combat a pathogen. It includes physical barriers to disease, the complement system and phagocytic cells.
- Acquired immunity is a specific immune response that is mounted on exposure to a pathogen and includes cell-mediated and humoral immunity.
- Cell-mediated immunity involves T lymphocytes which release cytokines that help to destroy pathogens.
- Humoral immunity involves B lymphocytes and immunoglobulins which are of five types: IgG, IgM, IgA, IgD and IgE.
- The primary immune response to a first exposure is slower, smaller and mediated by IgM as opposed to the secondary immune response which is mediated by IgG.
- Passive immunity is the transfer of ready-made antibodies to an individual. This can be natural, for example mother to child during breastfeeding, or artificial, that is administration of prepared antibodies.
- Inflammation is the immune response of the body that aims to eliminate a variety of harmful exposures including pathogens. It is characterized by swelling, redness, increased temperature, pain and loss of function.
- Vaccination is a process in which an individual is exposed to an antigen in order to induce an immune response that will protect the individual from the disease.
- The thymus gland is important for the development, maturation and export of T lymphocytes.

CHAPTER REVIEW QUESTIONS

1. What is innate immunity? How does it work?
2. Describe the process of phagocytosis.
3. Differentiate between cell-mediated and humoral immunity.
4. What are the functions of the thymus gland?

CHAPTER 40

Application of the Physiology of Blood

SPECIFIC LEARNING OBJECTIVES

At the end of this chapter, the student should be able to:

- Define and classify anaemia.
- Define and classify jaundice.
- Distinguish between bleeding disorders and clotting disorders.
- Describe the process of disseminated intravascular coagulation.
- List some common immune deficiency states.
- Describe the immune basis of transplantation.

GLOSSARY OF TERMS

- **Jaundice:** a yellowish discolouration of the skin and mucous membranes due to elevated levels of serum bilirubin
- **Anaemia:** a reduced oxygen-carrying capacity of the blood due to alterations in the quantity or quality of RBCs and haemoglobin
- **Transplantation:** the transfer of a tissue or an organ from one part of the body to another (e.g. skin grafts) or from one person to another

This chapter describes some applications of the physiology of blood in clinical medicine which you will see in the hospital.

ANAEMIA

Anaemia is a reduced oxygen-carrying capacity of the blood due to alterations in the quantity or quality of RBCs and/or haemoglobin. There are different types of anaemia which are summarized in Table 40.1.

Types of Anaemia

Anaemia can be classified in different ways:

1. **Based on aetiology (cause):**
   a. *A defect in the production of RBCs*: This can occur because the body does not produce enough erythropoietin. This can occur when there is kidney damage as in chronic renal failure, since most of the erythropoietin is produced in the kidney. It can also occur when nutrients needed for cell division or for the formation of haemoglobin are not available in the amounts that are needed. Thus, anaemia can result from deficiency of iron, vitamin B_{12}, folic acid, etc. Since RBCs are produced in the bone marrow, disease conditions that affect the bone marrow such as some cancers, or some treatments which reduce bone marrow function, like radiation and chemotherapy for cancers, can also result in anaemia.
   b. *An increased destruction of RBCs (haemolysis) or blood loss.* This can occur when there are defects in the structure of the RBC or of haemoglobin. The RBC is normally a biconcave disc. In rare diseases, the shape of the RBC may be altered and the RBC is spherical (spherocytosis). As a result, the RBC is more fragile and gets destroyed (lysed) more easily. Defects in haemoglobin may also cause increased lysis of the RBC. An example of this is sickle cell anaemia, in which the glutamic acid is replaced by valine in the sixth position of the β chain of haemoglobin. The RBC becomes more rigid, becomes sickle shaped and is more easily lysed.
   c. *Acute or chronic blood loss*: It can also result in anaemia. Acute blood loss occurs when there is injury such as following a road traffic accident. Chronic blood loss can occur in many conditions. In some women, menstrual blood loss is very heavy (menorrhagia) and this can result in anaemia. Hookworm infection of the intestine is another cause of chronic blood loss. Hookworm enters the skin in the larval stage and is therefore more frequently seen in children and adults who walk barefoot. Once in the intestine, the worms suck blood through the mucosa of the intestine resulting in chronic blood loss.

Table 40.1 Types of Anaemia

Based on aetiology (cause)	1. Decreased production of RBCs a. Decreased erythropoietin from kidney b. Nutrient deficiency (iron, vit B12, folic acid, etc.) c. Bone marrow dysfunction (radiation, chemotherapy, etc.)
	2. Increased destruction of RBCs a. Abnormal RBC structure (e.g. spherocytosis) b. Defective haemoglobin (e.g. HbS – sickle cell)
	3. Acute or chronic blood loss
Based on morphology\ (appearance)	1. Microcytic – hypochromic anaemia a. Small RBCs, less stained, e.g. iron deficiency
	2. Normochromic – normocytic anaemia a. RBCs are normal in size and staining, e.g. acute blood loss
	3. Macrocytic anaemia a. RBCs are larger than normal, e.g. vitamin B12 and folic acid deficiency

This is why deworming is often a part of the treatment of anaemia in children.

2. **Based on morphology (appearance) of the RBC:** RBCs are described in terms of their cell size and the staining characteristics of the cell. When a cell is of normal size, it is called 'normocytic'. If an RBC is smaller than normal it is called 'microcytic', while a larger than normal RBC is called 'macrocytic'. In a similar way, a cell which has normal staining (because of the concentration of haemoglobin) is called 'normochromic' (chroma = colour in Greek). If a cell has reduced staining, it is called 'hypochromic' and suggests that there is a reduced concentration of haemoglobin in the cell.
   a. *Microcytic–hypochromic anaemia*: This is often seen in iron-deficiency anaemia, although there are other causes. The RBCs are smaller than normal and stain more lightly. Iron deficiency can occur because:
      i. There is inadequate iron in the diet (i.e. a nutritional anaemia).
      ii. There is inadequate absorption of iron (i.e. reduced bioavailability).
      iii. There is increased demand for iron. This can, for instance, occur in pregnancy, in which the demand for iron needs to take care not only of the pregnant woman but also of the growing foetus.
      iv. There is increased loss of iron – since a significant portion of iron is contained within the haem part of haemoglobin, increased blood loss (menorrhagia, hookworm infection, etc.) will result in iron deficiency.
   b. *Normocytic–normochromic anaemia:* This is typically seen in situations in which there is significant ACUTE blood loss. If the patient did not have any other anaemia at the time of blood loss, the existing RBCs in the blood will be of normal size and staining.
   c. *Macrocytic anaemia:* This is often seen in vitamin B_{12} and folic acid deficiency. A deficiency of these factors may result from inadequacy in the diet or inadequate absorption. A particular form of vitamin B_{12} deficiency anaemia is called pernicious anaemia. As indicated earlier, vitamin B_{12} first needs to combine with intrinsic factor (produced in the stomach) before it is finally absorbed in the terminal ileum. Absence of intrinsic factor therefore limits vitamin B_{12} absorption.

Haemoglobinopathies:

This is a term that is used to refer to a group of diseases which have an 'abnormal' haemoglobin. Sickle cell anaemia is one such condition. However, there are other conditions as well. In an earlier section, we indicated that the normal adult haemoglobin is $\alpha 2\ \beta 2$ based in the protein subunits. Thalassaemia refers to a condition in which one or more types of these subunits are decreased. Beta-thalassaemia is a condition in which the β subunits are not synthesized and α-thalassaemia refers to the condition in which the α subunit is not synthesized. In both these conditions, the individual suffers from anaemia because of the abnormal haemoglobin. These conditions are genetically determined and manifest early in life.

JAUNDICE

Definition

Jaundice is a yellowish discolouration of the skin and mucous membranes due to elevated levels of serum bilirubin. Normal serum bilirubin levels are typically less than 1 mg/dL. It is important to remember that jaundice is a symptom, not a disease – the causes of jaundice are many, as we shall see later in this section.

Pathophysiology of Jaundice

Since the increased levels of serum bilirubin are the reason for the yellowish discolouration of the skin and mucous membranes, it is important that we understand the metabolism of bilirubin.

Haem in haemoglobin is broken down to biliverdin and then to bilirubin. This bilirubin is called unconjugated bilirubin. Unconjugated bilirubin is not water soluble and binds itself to albumin. For this reason, unconjugated bilirubin is not seen in the urine. Unconjugated bilirubin is then taken up into the liver where it is conjugated with glucuronic acid – this conjugated bilirubin is water soluble and is excreted in the bile through the bile duct. On reaching the intestine, the conjugated bilirubin is converted to stercobilinogen which gives the stool its colour. A small portion of the stercobilinogen is reabsorbed into the blood and is excreted in the urine as urobilinogen. These steps in the metabolism of bilirubin are illustrated in Fig. 40.1.

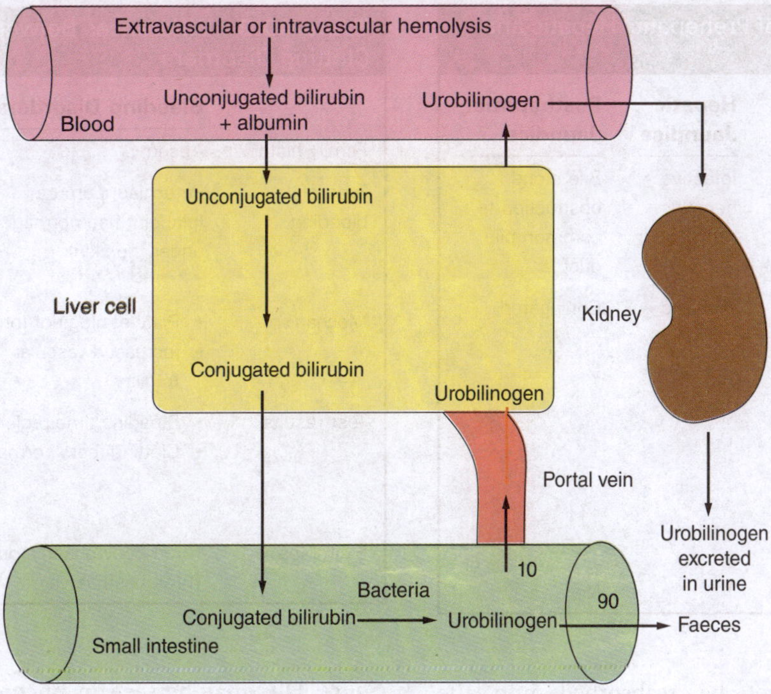

FIG. 40.1 Metabolism of bilirubin.

Types of Jaundice

There are three types of jaundice based on how the metabolism of bilirubin is affected.

1. ***Prehepatic (haemolytic) jaundice:***
   a. In this type of jaundice, there is excessive destruction of RBCs. As a result of this, more haem is broken down and more bilirubin is produced.
   b. The type of bilirubin is unconjugated bilirubin which does not appear in the urine.
   c. Since more and more bilirubin is being processed in the liver, more conjugated bilirubin will be excreted into the bile duct and then into the intestine where it is converted into stercobilinogen.
   d. Since a portion of this larger amount of stercobilinogen is absorbed into the bloodstream and then excreted into the urine, urine urobilinogen levels will be elevated.
2. ***Hepatic jaundice:***
   a. This is the jaundice that occurs when the liver is directly affected as in infective hepatitis.
   b. Since the liver cells are themselves involved, uptake of unconjugated bilirubin, conjugation of bilirubin and excretion of bilirubin are all affected.
   c. This type of jaundice is characterized by a mixed bilirubin pattern sometimes called biphasic (i.e. both unconjugated and conjugated bilirubin).
   d. The conjugated bilirubin appears in blood as backflow since the liver cells (hepatocytes) swell, blocking the excretion of conjugated bilirubin.
   e. Since conjugated bilirubin levels are elevated in blood and since conjugated bilirubin is water soluble, it will appear in the urine.
   f. A characteristic feature of hepatic jaundice is that some of the hepatocytes which are swollen will rupture (break) and will release their contents into the bloodstream. These contents include enzymes present in the cells. Thus, hepatic jaundice is characterized by high levels of liver enzymes in the blood. These liver enzymes are aspartate transaminase (AST) (also called serum glutamic oxaloacetic transaminase [SGOT]) and alanine transaminase (ALT) (also called serum glutamic pyruvic transaminase [SGPT]).
3. ***Posthepatic jaundice:***
   a. In this jaundice, the excretion of conjugated bilirubin through the common bile dust is blocked. This can happen with bile stones which block the common bile duct or, for instance, with cancers in the area, which can also cause blockages.
   b. In this type of jaundice, conjugation of bilirubin occurs but excretion is impaired. The backflow and back pressure of bile in the common duct result in damage to hepatocytes and conjugated bilirubin then overflows into blood. Since it is water soluble, this bilirubin will appear in urine.
   c. Because of the damage to hepatocytes caused by the back pressure of bile, hepatic enzymes will also appear in the blood but in lower concentrations than what is seen with hepatic jaundice.
   d. There are two additional characteristic features of posthepatic jaundice:
      i. Urobilinogen is absent in urine. This is because stercobilinogen is not produced in the intestine because conjugated bilirubin does not reach the intestine

Table 40.2 A Comparison of Prehepatic, Hepatic and Posthepatic Jaundice

	Prehepatic Jaundice	Hepatic Jaundice	Posthepatic Jaundice
Example	Haemolytic anaemia	Infective hepatitis	Bile stone obstruction to common bile duct
Type of hyperbilirubinaemia	Unconjugated	Biphasic	Conjugated
Bilirubin in the urine	No	Yes	Yes
Increased liver enzymes	No	↑↑↑	↑
Increased biliary tract enzymes	No	No	↑↑↑
Urine urobilinogen	↑↑↑	↑	No

Table 40.3 Differences Between Bleeding and Clotting Disorders

	Bleeding Disorders	Clotting Disorders
Family history	Absent	Present
Type of bleeding	Petechiae, purpura (pinpoint haemorrhages under the skin)	Larger volumes of bleeding (under the skin and into the joints)
Mechanism	• Platelet plug not formed • Increased vascular fragility	Fibrin clot not formed
Test results	• Bleeding time prolonged • Clotting tests normal	• Bleeding time normal • Clotting tests abnormal
Examples	Thrombocytopaenic purpura Thrombasthaenia	Haemophilia

and therefore cannot be reabsorbed into the bloodstream.

ii. The pressure of the bile in the common bile duct (above the obstruction) damages the cells lining the common bile duct. These cells contain some specific enzymes, including alkaline phosphatase (ALP). Thus, obstructive jaundice is characterized by the appearance of bile duct–specific enzymes in the blood.

Table 40.2 summarizes the differences between prehepatic, hepatic and posthepatic jaundice.

BLEEDING AND CLOTTING DISORDERS

The process of haemostasis (stoppage of bleeding) is discussed in Chapter 37. In that chapter, we described thrombocytopaenic purpura as an example of a bleeding disorder and haemophilia as an example of a clotting disorder. There are some differences between bleeding disorders and clotting disorders which are summarized in Table 40.3.

Not all bleeding disorders are due to a reduction in platelet number. Increased fragility of the blood vessels wall can also result in bleeding. In other situations, the platelet count may be normal but the platelets may not function normally and unable to carry out their normal functions of adhesion, activation and aggregation – one such condition with dysfunctional platelets is *thrombasthaenia*.

Disseminated Intravascular Coagulation

In the previous section, we described the general differences between bleeding disorders and clotting disorders. There are other conditions in which the clotting system in the body can be affected. One such condition is disseminated intravascular coagulation (DIC).

Cause: DIC may be seen in uncontrolled sepsis (blood-borne infections). It may also be seen in certain cancers.

Pathophysiology: Tissue damage due to the underlying disease, for example sepsis, can release tissue factor which activates the extrinsic coagulation pathway. The coagulation cascade goes into a positive feedback loop which results in intravascular clots. The use of the clotting factors for the intravascular clots may finally result in a nonavailability of clotting factors in the blood.

Clinical features: The formation of intravascular clots may result in reduced blood flow to different organs resulting in further tissue damage and organ failure. In the later stages, the reduction in clotting factors can result in bleeding under the skin and in other organs. Thus, the patient may experience haematuria (blood in the urine) or bleeding from the rectum or vagina, among others.

IMMUNE DEFICIENCY STATES

There are some conditions where the immunity of a person is reduced. When this happens, the person is at increased risk of developing infections.

There are several causes of immunodeficiency:

1. *Malnutrition*: Protein–energy malnutrition is associated with multiple problems in the immune system. Cell-mediated immunity is impaired as also components of innate immunity such as phagocytosis and complement function. In addition, micronutrient deficiencies, such as those of zinc, selenium, iron and multiple vitamins including vitamins A, D and B_6, among others, are associated with immune dysfunction. Malnutrition increases the risk of several diseases including tuberculosis. There is a vicious cycle wherein malnutrition increases the risk of infection and infection itself increases malnutrition. In developing countries, where

malnutrition affects a large number of infants and growing children as well as the elderly, this is a serious problem.

2. *Infections*: Infections such as HIV/AIDS reduce immunity. In HIV, the virus destroys helper T cells (discussed earlier) and therefore impairs cell-mediated immunity. This makes the individual more susceptible to infections and certain cancers.
3. *Therapy:* Certain therapies (treatments) such as radiation therapy or chemotherapy which are used to treat cancers result in a reduction in the immune response. These therapies kill not only the cancer cells but other rapidly dividing cells as well. Thus, cells which are produced as part of the immune response are also affected. White blood cell counts need to be monitored carefully in patients who are undergoing these therapies.
4. *Corticosteroids*: These hormones are produced naturally in the body but are also administered as medication in a variety of clinical conditions. These steroids have multiple effects on the immune system, among which (1) they suppress T and B cells, (2) they also suppress the action of macrophages and (3) they cause eosinopaenia (a reduction in the eosinophil count). While these steroids may be used to treat inflammatory and allergic conditions, suppression of the immune system means that these patients need to be monitored carefully for any infection.
5. *Cancer*: Some cancers may spread to or originate from the bone marrow. Since the bone marrow is the site of production of the white blood cells, production of these cells may be impaired and patients suffer from immune deficiency.

IMMUNITY AND TRANSPLANTATION

Today, transplantation of organs has become more common. Among the organs that are transplanted are the kidney, heart and liver. The person who donates the organ is called a 'donor' and the person who receives the organ is called the 'recipient'. A knowledge of immunity during transplantation helps to show several points about immunity. It helps us understand how the body differentiates between 'self' and 'foreign', what tests can be done to get as close a 'match' as possible during transplantation and what measures can be taken to reduce 'rejection' of a transplanted organ.

There are different types of transplantation:

- *Autograft*: From one part of the body to another part of the body of the same person, for example skin grafts
- *Isograft*: Between genetically identical individuals (e.g. identical twins)
- *Allograft*: Between members of the same species
- *Xenograft*: Between members of different species

How Does the Body Recognize What Is 'Self' and What Is 'Foreign', and What Is the Basis of 'Transplant Rejection'?

The cells of our body contain antigens called self-antigens. The antigens responsible for rejection of a transplanted tissue are called histocompatibility antigens. There are many histocompatibility antigens but the one most involved in rejection is the major histocompatibility complex (MHC), also called the human leucocyte antigen (HLA) system. The HLA system is inherited and this makes family members more likely to be HLA identical, thus reducing the chances of a transplant rejection.

When Can a Transplant Be Rejected?

Transplants can be rejected at various stages:

- *Hyperacute* rejection refers to the rejection of the graft in a matter of minutes to hours.
- *Acute rejection* typically occurs during the first 6 months following a transplant.
- *Chronic rejection* may occur several months to years after a transplant.

How Can Transplant Rejection Be Reduced?

Transplant rejection can be reduced in essentially two ways:

1. Carefully matching the donor and the recipient
2. Suppressing the recipient immune system following the transplant

APPLICATIONS FOR NURSING

- The nurse may need to take part in screening camps for anaemia, since it is a major public health problem in the country.
- The nurse will need to provide health nutritional advice to those patients suffering from anaemia and jaundice.
- The nurse will need to educate close contacts of those suffering from jaundice about measures that they will need to take.

SUMMARY

- Anaemia is Classified based on morphology into normocytic, microcytic and macrocytic anaemias. It is also classified based on aetiology into anaemias caused by reduced production and those caused by increased destruction and blood loss.
- Jaundice is of three types: prehepatic, hepatic and posthepatic. These types of jaundice can be differentiated based on biochemical profiles.
- Immune deficiency states are those conditions in which the immune response of an individual is reduced, for example in malnutrition, HIV–AIDS, cancer, radiation and chemotherapy.

CHAPTER REVIEW QUESTIONS

1. What is anaemia? Classify anaemia by (a) aetiology, (b) morphology.
2. What is jaundice? Differentiate between the different types of jaundice.
3. Differentiate between bleeding and clotting disorders.
4. What is disseminated intravascular coagulation?

CLINICAL CASE PROBLEMS

(A) ***A 4-year-old boy is brought to the hospital by his mother. She says that he has become weak and is breathless when he runs a short distance. His conjunctiva and nail beds are pale and an examination of his stool reveals a heavy infestation of hookworms.***

a. What condition is the boy suffering from?
b. Define the condition.
c. Deficiency of what substance has caused the problem?
d. What changes do you expect to see in his RBCs?

(B) ***A 10-year-old child with a history of a viral fever which started a few days before presents with a 'rash'. The bleeding time is prolonged and the platelet count is low.***

a. What is the condition that the child is suffering from?
b. What is the normal platelet count?
c. What is the name given to the 'rash' on the skin?
d. What do you expect to see with the clotting tests?

(C) ***A 20-year-old college student has been eating street food on a regular basis. She presents to the hospital with yellowish discolouration of the eyes (jaundice), nausea and vomiting and the passage of very high-coloured urine.***

a. Define jaundice.
b. What type of jaundice is she likely to have?
c. How would you confirm the type of jaundice she has and exclude the other types of jaundice?

SELF-DIRECTED LEARNING

1. Describe iron metabolism, iron deficiency and its consequences.
2. What are the different types of hepatitis?

WHAT YOU CAN LEARN FROM A HOSPITAL VISIT

1. Visit the blood bank – go through a blood donor form. Check how blood is stored in the blood bank.
2. Visit the clinical pathology laboratory – check what haematology tests are done in your hospital.

6
SECTION

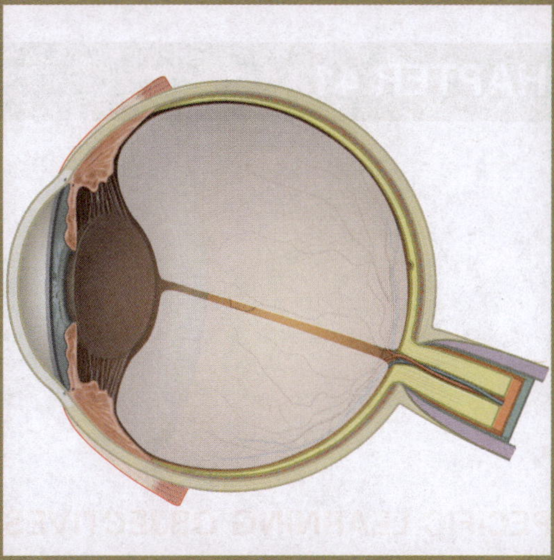

The Endocrine System

Section Outline

CHAPTER 41

The Hypothalamus, Pituitary and Pineal Glands

SPECIFIC LEARNING OBJECTIVES

At the end of this chapter, the student should be able to:

- List the characteristics of a hormone.
- Describe the relationship between the hypothalamus and the pituitary.
- List the hormones produced by the hypothalamus and state their functions.
- List the pituitary hormones and state their functions.
- Describe with an example 'negative feedback'.
- List the functions of the pineal gland.

GLOSSARY OF TERMS

- **Endocrine:** relating to hormones and the glands that synthesize or secrete them
- **Neuroendocrine reflex:** a reflex which is mediated by nerves and hormone (the sensory nerve typically conveys information of the stimulus which then results in the secretion of the hormone and an action)
- **Negative feedback:** a process in which the system responds in an opposite manner to the perturbation (stimulus) (with regard to hormones, an increase in the concentration of hormone results in effects which attempt to lower the concentration of the hormone)
- **Second messenger:** chemical released following the binding of a hormone with its receptor, which mediates the action of the hormone

The term 'hormone' was first used by a scientist called Starling, who together with Bayliss discovered the first hormone, secretin.

A hormone is a chemical substance which:

1. Is produced in ductless glands
2. Is released in small quantities
3. Is carried in circulation
4. Acts at a distance from its site of secretion
5. Performs its action by acting on specific receptors

TYPES OF HORMONES

Hormones vary in chemical structure and can be classified as follows:

1. *Steroid hormones* include cortisol, aldosterone, testosterone, oestrogens and progesterone.
2. *Peptide hormones* some of which are prolactin (PRL), oxytocin, antidiuretic hormone (ADH), calcitonin, insulin, glucagon, parathormone and renin.
3. *Amines* which include thyroxine and epinephrine (adrenaline). Norepinephrine is mainly a neurotransmitter but in high circulating concentrations can act as a hormone.

TYPES OF HORMONE RECEPTORS

As mentioned earlier, hormones act by binding with specific proteins called receptors. These receptors are:

1. *Cell membrane receptors*: water-soluble hormones such as peptide and amine hormones bind to them.
2. *Cytoplasmic receptors*: lipid-soluble hormones which cross the cell membrane such as steroid hormones, thyroid hormone and vitamin D act on them.
3. *Nuclear receptors*: lipid-soluble hormones may also interact directly with the DNA in the nucleus.

SECOND MESSENGERS

Once a hormone binds to its receptors, it releases other chemicals in the cell. These include, for instance, calcium ions, cyclic adenine and guanine monophosphate (cAMP and cGMP), inositol triphosphate and diacylglycerol. The chemicals that are released inside the cell are called *second messengers* (the hormone is the first messenger) and help to mediate the actions of the hormone on the target cell.

GENOMIC AND NONGENOMIC EFFECTS OF HORMONES

Hormones which are lipid soluble and cross the cell membrane may mediate their actions through two effects:

- Genomic effects are the result from the hormone binding to the DNA to start protein synthesis.
- Nongenomic effects are those actions which are independent of transcription, translation and protein synthesis. These can include, for example, the following:
  - Opening of ion channels on the cell membrane
  - Activation of second messengers within the cell

Nongenomic effects act faster than genomic effects.

The hypothalamus and the pituitary gland are an important part of the endocrine system. Later you will learn that the hypothalamus has many other functions. In this chapter, you will learn about the close interaction that the hypothalamus has with the pituitary gland in the release of hormones.

Fig. 41.1 shows the location of the hypothalamus. You will observe that it is located below another part of the brain called the thalamus and above the pituitary gland.

THE ENDOCRINE ROLE OF THE HYPOTHALAMUS

The hypothalamus has two endocrine functions:

1. It produces releasing and inhibitory hormones that control a part of the pituitary gland called the anterior pituitary. The anterior pituitary itself produces many hormones.
2. It synthesizes hormones which are transported to and then released from another part of the pituitary gland called the posterior pituitary gland. These hormones are sometimes called posterior pituitary hormones, but they are actually synthesized in the hypothalamus and only released from the posterior pituitary gland.

The hormones that are released from the hypothalamus that control the anterior pituitary gland are as follows:

1. Thyrotropin-releasing hormone (TRH)
2. Corticotropin-releasing hormone (CRH)

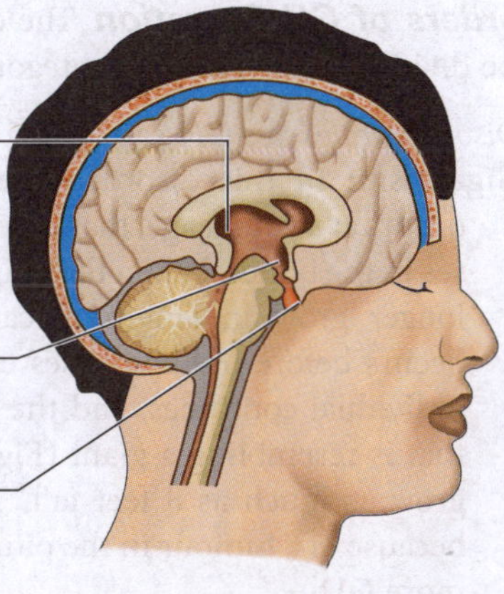

FIG. 41.1 The location of the hypothalamus and the pituitary gland.

Table 41.1 Summary of the Linkages Between the Hypothalamus and the Anterior Pituitary Gland

Hypothalamus	Action	Anterior Pituitary Hormone
Growth hormone–releasing hormone	STIMULATION	Growth hormone
Thyrotropin-releasing hormone	STIMULATION	Thyroid-stimulating hormone
Corticotropin-releasing hormone	STIMULATION	Adrenocorticotropin
Gonadotropin-releasing hormone	STIMULATION	Luteinizing hormone
Prolactin inhibitory hormone	INHIBITION	Prolactin

3. Growth hormone–releasing hormone (GHRH)
4. Gonadotropin-releasing hormone (GnRH)
5. Prolactin inhibitory hormone (PIH)

These hormones either release other hormones from the anterior pituitary gland or inhibit the release of hormones from the anterior pituitary gland. This is summarized in Table 41.1.

The hypothalamus also produces hormones which are released from the posterior pituitary gland. These hormones are as follows:

1. Oxytocin
2. Vasopressin (also called ADH)

We will discuss the actions of these two hormones later in the chapter.

HOW DO THE HYPOTHALAMIC HORMONES REACH THE PITUITARY GLAND?

There are two ways in which the hypothalamic hormones reach the pituitary gland:

1. **Hypothalamic–hypophysial portal blood vessels:** These are blood vessels which come from the lower hypothalamus and enter the anterior pituitary gland (Fig. 41.2). Thus, hormones produced by the neurons of the hypothalamus which act on the anterior pituitary gland are transported through these blood vessels. Since the anterior pituitary is rich in glandular cells which produce their own hormones, this part of the pituitary gland is sometimes referred to as the *adenohypophysis* (adeno = related to a gland).
2. In contrast, the so-called posterior pituitary hormones (oxytocin and ADH) are produced by neurons in the hypothalamus which extend right into the posterior pituitary gland. Here they release the hormones into blood vessels in the posterior pituitary and are then carried to other parts of the body (Fig. 41.3). Because the neurons from the hypothalamus project right into the posterior pituitary gland, this part of the pituitary gland is called the *neurohypophysis*.

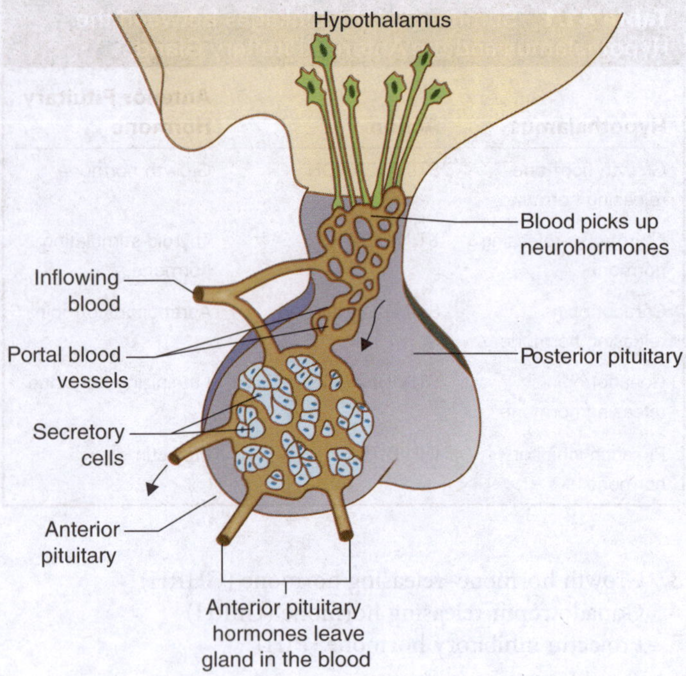

FIG. 41.2 The hypothalamic–hypophysial portal system.

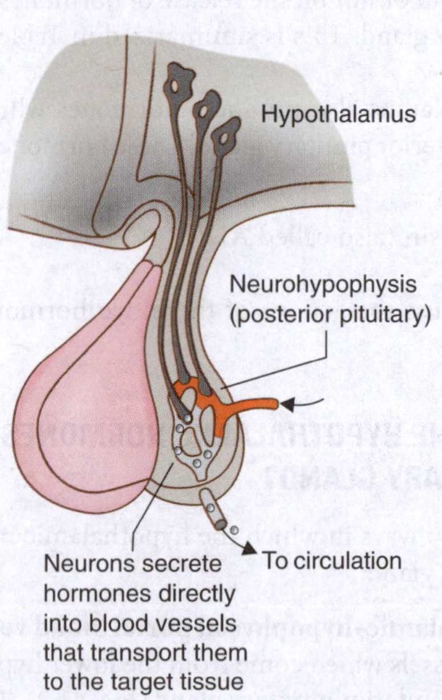

FIG. 41.3 The neurohypophysis.

HORMONES OF THE ANTERIOR PITUITARY GLAND

The hormones produced by the anterior pituitary gland are as follows:

1. Growth hormone (GH)
2. Adrenocorticotropin (ACTH) which acts on the adrenal cortex to stimulate the release of glucocorticoids
3. Thyroid-stimulating hormone (TSH) which acts on the thyroid gland to stimulate the release of thyroxine
4. Gonadotropic hormones include luteinizing hormone (LH) and follicle-stimulating hormone (FSH), which act on the ovaries and testes
5. Prolactin (PRL) which acts on the breasts (mammary glands)

Each of these hormones has a corresponding 'releasing' or 'inhibitory' hormone produced in the hypothalamus.

Growth Hormone

All anterior pituitary hormones with the exception of GH exert their effects by acting on other endocrine glands/tissues.

Site of production: GH is produced by specific cells in the anterior pituitary gland called somatotropes.

Chemical nature: GH is a protein which has 191 amino acids.

Actions: GH acts to promote growth. It does this by acting through other substances in the periphery called somatomedins or insulin-like growth factors.

Increasing growth

1. It stimulates cartilage and bone growth.
2. It causes an increase in organ size (organomegaly).
3. It increases muscle mass.

At a cellular level, GH increases growth by:

1. Increasing the size of cells
2. Increasing mitosis

Metabolic Actions

1. It increases body protein by:
   a. Increasing transport of amino acids into cells
   b. Increasing protein synthesis
2. It uses up fat stored in the body by increasing the breakdown of fats (lipolysis).
3. It conserves carbohydrates by decreasing the uptake of glucose by the cells. As a result, glucose may increase in blood. In conditions in which excessive GH is produced, the person may develop diabetes mellitus. It is for this reason that GH is called a 'diabetogenic' hormone.

Regulation of GH Secretion GH is secreted throughout the life cycle of an individual. However, the secretion of GH in elderly individuals is much lower than that during the active phase of growth. In addition, more GH is secreted in response to acute stimuli such as exercise, hypoglycaemia (decreased glucose levels in the blood), starvation and stress.

Disorders of GH Secretion The disorders of GH secretion can be divided into two broad categories:

1. *Disorders of excess GH secretion:*
   Gigantism: In this disorder, the excess secretion of GH occurs at a young age, that is before the closure of epiphyses in the bones. When the epiphyses close, bones can no longer grow in length. Because excess GH secretion occurs before the epiphyses close, linear growth of the individual continues, and the person becomes very tall, that is resembling a giant (Fig. 41.4). Some people may grow as much as 8 feet tall. This condition may occur because of a tumour in the pituitary gland which secretes more GH.
   Acromegaly: In this disorder, there is increased secretion of GH in adulthood after the epiphyses are closed. Although

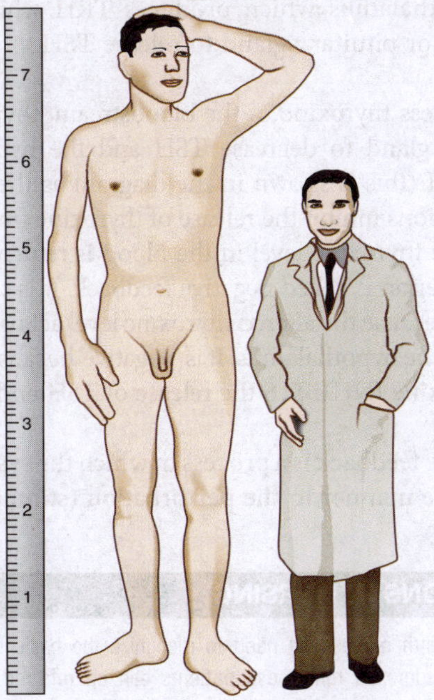

FIG. 41.4 Gigantism.

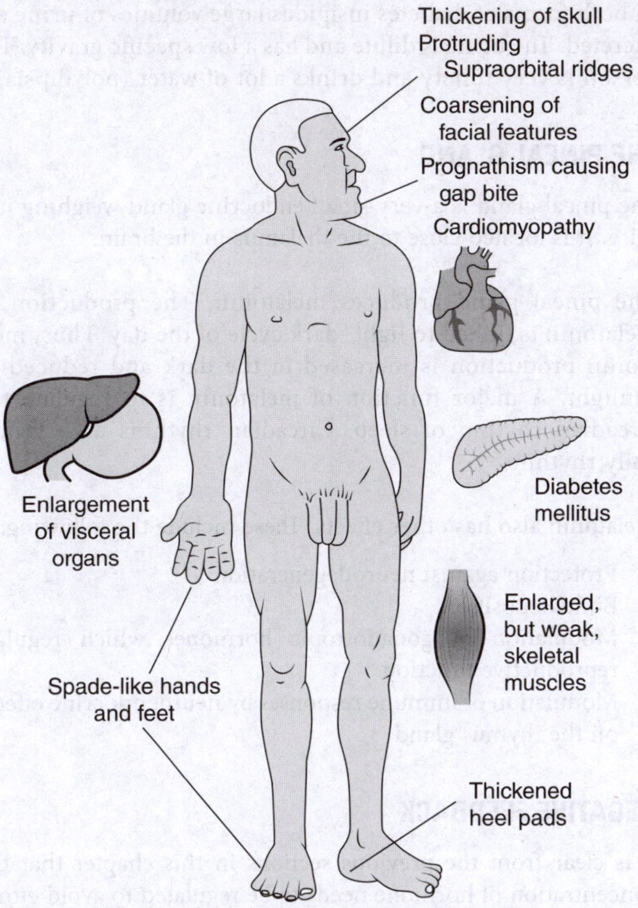

FIG. 41.5 Acromegaly.

there is no further linear growth, the bones widen and the individual has a protruding jaw (prognathism) and thickening of the other bones of the face, hands (spade-like hands) and feet (Fig. 41.5). The organs (e.g. liver and kidneys) are also enlarged. The person may also develop diabetes mellitus.

2. *Disorders of decreased GH secretion:*
   Dwarfism can result either because less GH is secreted or because the somatomedin (insulin like growth factor) is not produced. This is what happens in the case of the African pygmy.

POSTERIOR PITUITARY HORMONES

The two posterior pituitary hormones are actually synthesized in nerve cells in the hypothalamus and released into the bloodstream in the posterior pituitary gland from where they are transported to other parts of the body.

Oxytocin

Oxytocin has two major actions in the body:

1. **Contraction of the pregnant uterus:** When the cervix begins to dilate and the head of the baby moves downwards, oxytocin is released. This results in the contraction of the uterus and helps in the birth of the baby. In this situation, the release of oxytocin is an example of a positive feedback loop. Dilation of the cervix releases oxytocin which causes the uterus to contract which pushes the baby down and further dilates the cervix. The feedback is stopped when the baby is born and there is no further stretch of the cervix.
2. **Milk ejection by the breasts:** Milk ejection is initiated by the suckling of the baby on the breast. This causes oxytocin to be released. The oxytocin causes a contraction of the myoepithelial cells surrounding the alveoli of the breasts and results in milk flow.

Both these reflexes are referred to as *neuroendocrine reflexes* because sensory signals for the release of oxytocin are conveyed to the brain via nerves resulting in the release of a hormone.

Vasopressin (ADH)

This hormone has two actions which are best remembered by the two names that the hormone has:

1. **Vasoconstriction:** Here, the hormone acts on the arteries and causes them to contract. In the process, blood pressure is increased (i.e. vasopressor action).
2. **Antidiuretic action:** The hormone acts on the late distal convoluted tubule and collecting duct of the nephron in the kidney to increase water reabsorption – thus, urine volumes are decreased.

Diabetes insipidus (should not be confused with diabetes mellitus) is a disorder with two causes:

1. Less ADH is secreted (central diabetes insipidus) or
2. ADH is normally secreted but is unable to act on its receptors in the nephron (nephrogenic diabetes insipidus).

In both forms of diabetes insipidus large volumes of urine are excreted. The urine is dilute and has a low specific gravity. The person is very thirsty and drinks a lot of water (polydipsia).

THE PINEAL GLAND

The pineal gland is a very small endocrine gland weighing just 0.1 g. It is located close to the thalamus in the brain.

The pineal gland produces melatonin. The production of melatonin is linked to light–dark cycle of the day. Thus, melatonin production is increased in the dark and reduced in sunlight. A major function of melatonin is to regulate the circadian rhythm of sleep. Circadian rhythms are cyclical daily rhythms.

Melatonin also has other effects. These include the following:

- Protection against neurodegeneration
- Bone deposition
- Modulation of gonadotropic hormones which regulate reproductive function
- Modulation of immune responses by neuroendocrine effects on the thymus gland

NEGATIVE FEEDBACK

It is clear from the previous sections in this chapter that the concentration of hormone needs to be regulated to avoid either an excess or a decrease in the hormone, both of which can cause serious problems. This is achieved through a process called 'negative feedback'. In order to illustrate this, we can take the example of a hormone like thyroid hormone (thyroxine) which is secreted from the thyroid gland located in the neck (Fig. 41.6).

We already know that the concentration of thyroxine depends on three different structures. These include:

- the thyroid gland itself where thyroxine is synthesized and then secreted,
- the pituitary gland which produces TSH which stimulates the thyroid gland to release thyroxine and
- the hypothalamus which produces TRH which stimulates the anterior pituitary gland to release TSH.

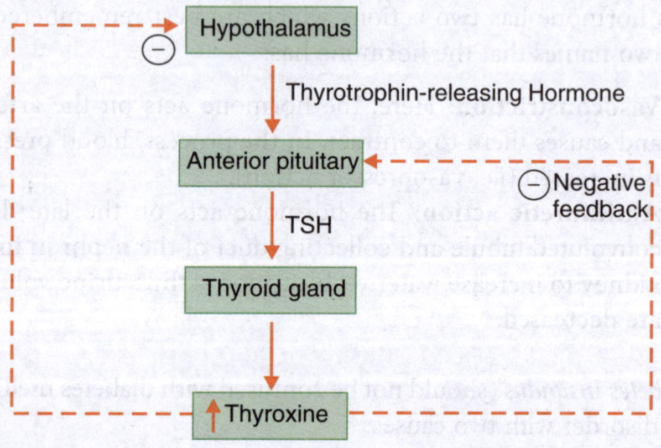

FIG. 41.6 An illustration of negative feedback using the example of thyroid hormone. The dashed lines show inhibition.

If there is excess thyroxine in the bloodstream, thyroxine acts on the pituitary gland to decrease TSH and the hypothalamus to decrease TRH (this is shown in the diagram as the dashed line). These two actions inhibit the release of thyroxine from the thyroid gland and the thyroxine level in the blood is returned to normal. This phenomenon is called negative feedback. It is clear that there is 'feedback' because the altered thyroxine level acts on the pituitary gland and on the hypothalamus. It is 'negative' because an increased level of thyroxine INHIBITS the release of TSH and TRH.

Thus, negative feedback is a process in which the system responds in an opposite manner to the perturbation (stimulus).

APPLICATIONS IN NURSING

Community health nurses will need to recognize the basic features of key endocrine disorders so that these patients can be referred for treatment. Features of other endocrine disorders are described in subsequent chapters. It would also be useful for nurses to be able to interpret the values of different hormones in blood in order to monitor response to treatment.

SUMMARY

- The hypothalamus and pituitary gland are an important part of the endocrine system. The hypothalamus produces releasing and inhibitory factors that control the secretion of hormones from the anterior pituitary gland. These are GHRH, CRH, GnRH, TRH and PIH.
- The hypothalamus also synthesizes hormones which are released from the posterior pituitary gland (oxytocin and ADH) and are sometimes called the posterior pituitary hormones.
- The anterior pituitary gland produces growth hormone, ACTH, LH, FSH, TSH and prolactin.
- Growth hormone stimulates bony, muscle and organ growth. It has several metabolic actions – it utilizes fats, synthesizes proteins and preserves carbohydrates. It is diabetogenic. Excess growth hormone secretion is associated with gigantism (if excess secretion occurs in childhood) and acromegaly (if excess secretion occurs in adulthood). Reduced action of growth hormone is associated with dwarfism.
- Oxytocin promotes contraction of the uterus during labour and the milk ejection reflex during lactation.
- Vasopressin (ADH) is a vasoconstrictor and reduces the excretion of water in the urine. Reduction in ADH secretion or its action can result in diabetes insipidus. There are two forms of diabetes insipidus – central and nephrogenic.
- The pineal gland through melatonin regulates the circadian sleep cycle. Its other proposed actions include protection against neurodegeneration, bone deposition, regulation of gonadotropic hormones and modulation of thymic immune function.

CHAPTER REVIEW QUESTIONS

1. List the hypothalamic hormones.
2. What are the hormones produced by the anterior pituitary gland and what are their functions?
3. What are the functions of growth hormone?
4. What is the role of the pineal gland?

CHAPTER 42

The Thyroid Gland

SPECIFIC LEARNING OBJECTIVES

At the end of this chapter, the student should be able to:

- List the hormones secreted by the thyroid gland.
- Describe the steps in the synthesis of T3 and T4.
- List the actions of thyroid hormones.
- Describe how the secretion of thyroid hormones is regulated.
- List and briefly describe disorders of thyroxine secretion.

GLOSSARY OF TERMS

- **Hypothyroidism:** an underactive thyroid gland in which less thyroid hormone is secreted
- **Hyperthyroidism:** an overactive thyroid gland in which excessive thyroid hormone is secreted
- **Goitre:** an enlargement of the thyroid gland

The thyroid gland is situated in the front of the neck just below the larynx (Fig. 42.1). It is a butterfly-shaped gland which weighs between 15 and 20 g in an adult.

HORMONES OF THE THYROID GLAND

The thyroid gland secretes three hormones. These are:

1. Thyroxine (T4)
2. Triiodothyronine (T3)
3. Calcitonin

Of these, calcitonin is concerned with the regulation of calcium levels in the body and we will discuss its role in Chapter 43.

SYNTHESIS OF T4 AND T3

The microscopic structure of the thyroid gland is shown in Fig. 42.2.

The thyroid gland is made up of large numbers of closed follicles filled with a substance called colloid. The major component of colloid is thyroglobulin, which plays an important role in the synthesis of T3 and T4. The follicle is lined by cuboidal epithelial cells, also called glandular cells. These cells are the site of production of thyroglobulin which is secreted into the colloid and T3 and T4 which are secreted into the blood vessels.

The synthesis of T3 and T4 occurs in five steps as follows:

1. **Iodide trapping:** Iodine is needed for the synthesis of T3 and T4. In earlier times, people living in the Himalayan mountains were deficient in iodine because of their diets and developed a swelling of the thyroid gland called a goitre. Today, this problem has been reduced because salt is enriched with iodine (iodized salt). Iodides are absorbed in the gastrointestinal (GI) tract and transported in the blood to the thyroid gland. In the thyroid gland, the iodide is transported across the cell membrane into the glandular cell against its concentration gradient by a special protein transporter. This is why the process is called iodide trapping. The iodide transporter is a sodium–iodide symporter (both sodium and iodide moving into the cell). Approximately 20% of the iodide that is available in blood is removed by the thyroid gland with each passage. The free iodide concentration in the thyroid gland is between 20 and 50 times higher than in plasma.
2. **Oxidation of the iodide ion:** This step is needed because it is only the oxidized form of iodide that combines with the amino acid tyrosine. This is described in a later step.
3. **Organification of thyroglobulin:** Thyroglobulin which is present in the follicles of the thyroid gland is rich in the amino acid tyrosine. It is the most important protein in the thyroid gland and is important for the synthesis and

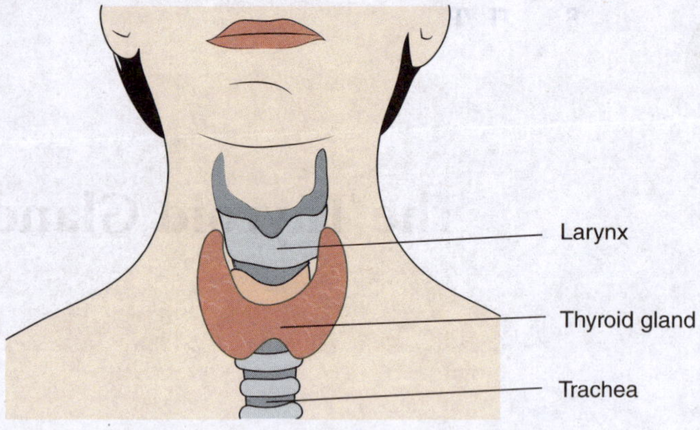

FIG. 42.1 Location of the thyroid gland.

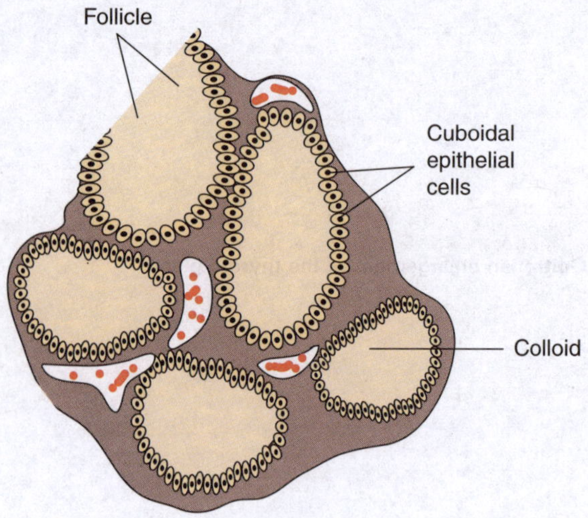

FIG. 42.2 Microscopic structure of the thyroid gland.

storage of thyroid hormones. Oxidized iodine in the presence of an enzyme (thyroid peroxidase) combines with tyrosine to form monoiodotyrosine (MIT) (one iodine with tyrosine) and diiodotyrosine (DIT) (two iodines with tyrosine).

4. **Coupling reaction:** Here, one MIT and one DIT are coupled to form triiodothyronine (T3). Note that T3 denotes that there are three iodines in the molecule. Similarly one DIT and one DIT combine to form thyroxine (T4) which contains four iodines in the molecule.
5. **Secretion of T3 and T4 into the blood:** This occurs by a process of exocytosis.

COMPARISON OF T3 AND T4

Both T3 and T4 have similar actions in the body, but there are some differences:

1. T4 is secreted into blood in greater quantities than T3.
2. T3 is biologically more active than T4.

REGULATION OF SECRETION OF T3 AND T4

The concentrations of T3 and T4 levels in the blood are regulated by *negative feedback*. Examine Fig. 42.3. You will observe that the hypothalamus releases thyrotropin-releasing hormone (TRH) which stimulates cells in the anterior pituitary to release thyroid-stimulating hormone (TSH). TSH in turn acts on the thyroid gland and stimulates the release of the thyroid hormones T3 and T4. If the concentration of T3 and T4 rises in the blood, it inhibits the secretion of TRH as well as TSH. The T3 and T4 levels are thus maintained at fairly constant levels.

When assessing thyroid function biochemically, T3, T4 and TSH are typically measured as this tells us the status not only of the thyroid gland but also of the regulatory system via the pituitary gland.

ACTIONS OF T3 AND T4

The thyroid hormones have many actions affecting all systems of the body. Some of the more prominent actions are as follows:

1. **Growth:** T3 and T4 have important actions in growing children. They promote skeletal growth. In addition, T3 and T4 are critical for the development of the brain in the foetus and in the early years following birth. Children who are thyroid hormone deficient at birth, and who are not detected and treated, may suffer from mental retardation.
2. **Metabolism:** T3 and T4 stimulate carbohydrate and fat metabolism and increase the basal metabolic rate. The basal metabolic rate is the minimal metabolic rate that is required to sustain life when a person is at rest. It is measured in the morning in the fasted condition, about 10–12 hours after the last meal, with the person lying down but awake, in a thermoneutral room.

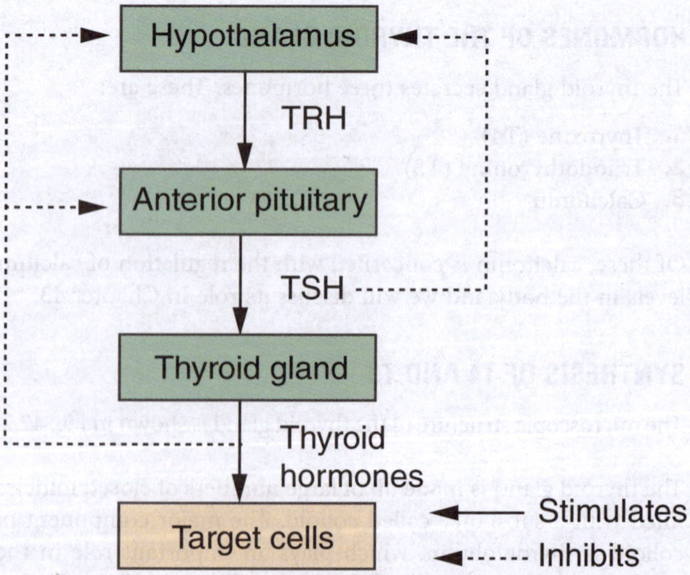

FIG. 42.3 Regulation of thyroid hormone secretion.

Thyroxine affects carbohydrate metabolism in the following way. It increases:

a. Glucose uptake by the cells
b. Glycolysis and gluconeogenesis

Thyroxine has many effects on fat metabolism which include the following:

a. Mobilization of fat tissue
b. Increased concentrations of free fatty acids in plasma
c. Increased oxidation of free fatty acids

3. **Cardiovascular system:** T3 and T4 increase the heart rate and the force of contraction of the heart. As a result of these actions, the cardiac output also increases.
4. **Respiration:** T3 and T4 increase the rate and depth of breathing and the utilization of oxygen (because of the increased metabolic rate of the body).
5. **GI system:** T3 and T4 increase appetite and food intake and also increase the secretion of digestive enzymes. They also increase gut motility.
6. **Others:** Thyroid hormones are required for normal muscle and sexual function and for normal cerebral activity.

DISORDERS OF THYROID HORMONE SECRETION

1. **Excess thyroid hormone secretion:**

Hyperthyroidism (thyrotoxicosis, Graves' disease): Patients with hyperthyroidism have high circulating levels of T3 and T4. Hyperthyroidism can occur because of a tumour in the thyroid gland, among other reasons. In some situations, the thyroid gland may be visibly enlarged – this is called a goitre. Patients tend to have a multitude of symptoms and signs (Fig. 42.4):

a. Excitability and nervousness.
b. Intolerance to heat (this is partly due to the fact that the basal metabolic rate in these individuals is increased) and sweating.
c. Mild-to-moderate weight loss despite a good appetite.
d. Diarrhoea which may vary from mild to severe.
e. Muscle weakness.
f. Palpitations – when measured the heart rate is found to be high.
g. Tremors in the hands.

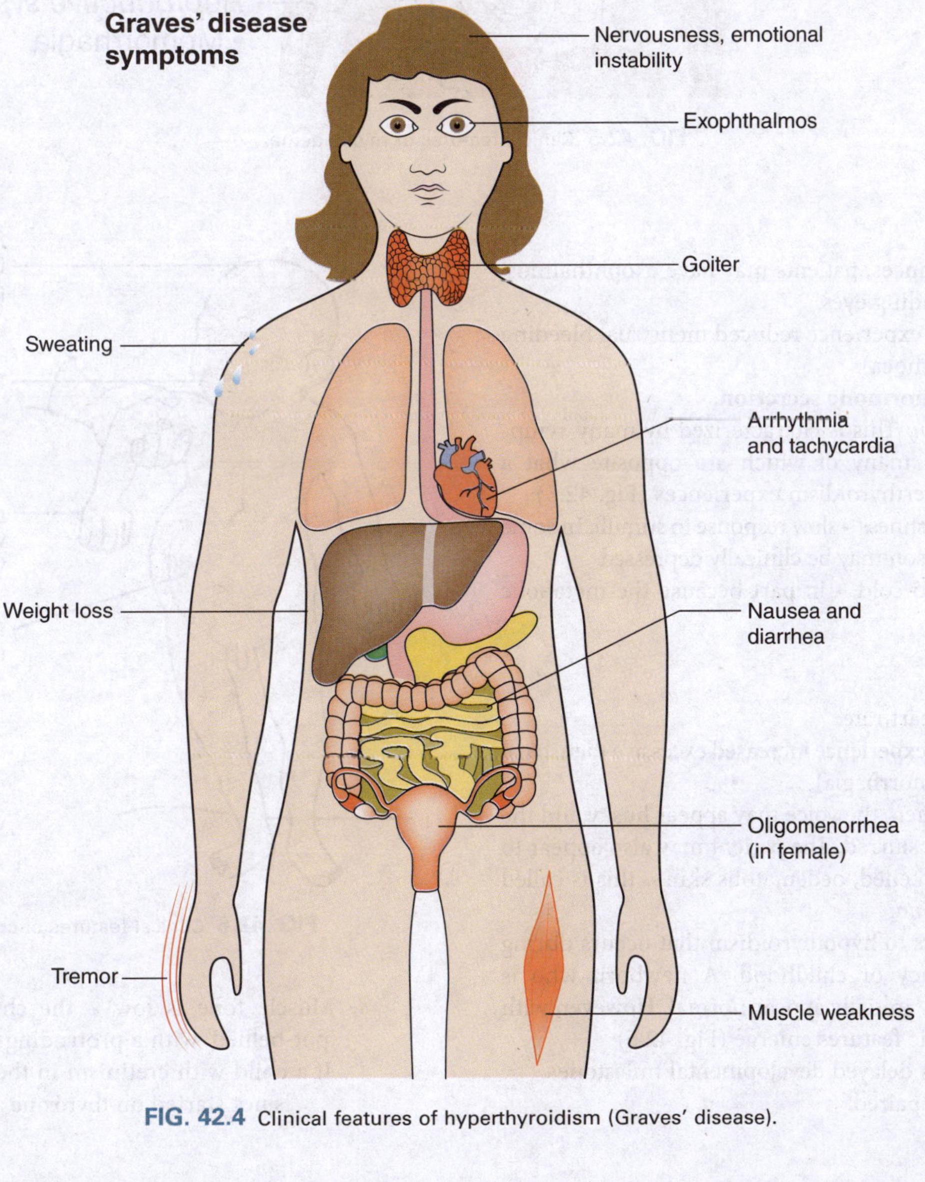

FIG. 42.4 Clinical features of hyperthyroidism (Graves' disease).

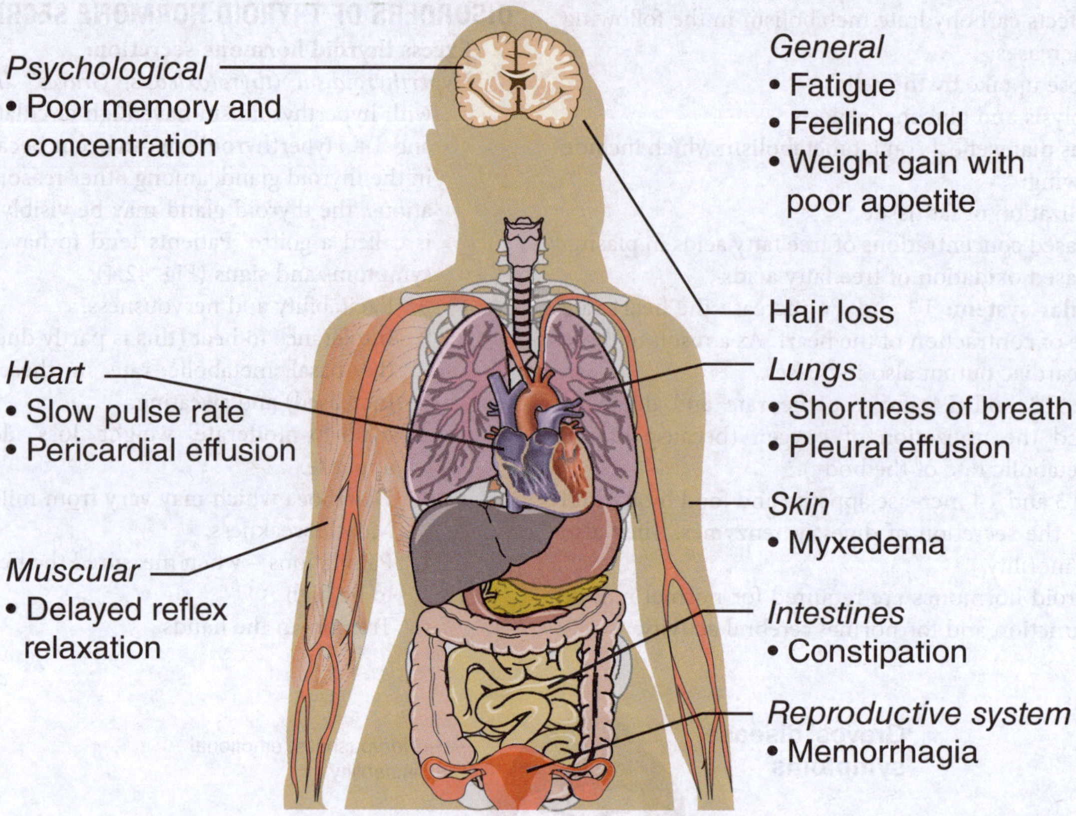

FIG. 42.5 Clinical features of myxoedema.

h. In some instances, patients may have exophthalmos, that is protruding eyes.

i. Women may experience reduced menstrual bleeding (oligomenorrhoea).

2. **Decreased thyroid hormone secretion:**

Adult hypothyroidism: This is characterized by many symptoms and signs, many of which are opposite what a patient with hyperthyroidism experiences (Fig. 42.5):

a. Mental sluggishness – slow response to stimuli. In some cases, the person may be clinically depressed.

b. Intolerance to cold – in part because the metabolic rate is low.

c. Weight gain.

d. Constipation.

e. Decreased heart rate.

f. Women may experience increased excessive menstrual bleeding (menorrhagia).

In some women, the voice may appear husky and the speech is slurred. The patient may also appear to have thickened, oedematous skin – this is called *myxoedema*.

Cretinism: This refers to hypothyroidism that occurs during foetal life, infancy or childhood. A newborn who is hypothyroid may initially appear normal. However, with time, more classic features emerge (Fig. 42.6):

1. The child has delayed developmental milestones.
2. Growth is impaired.

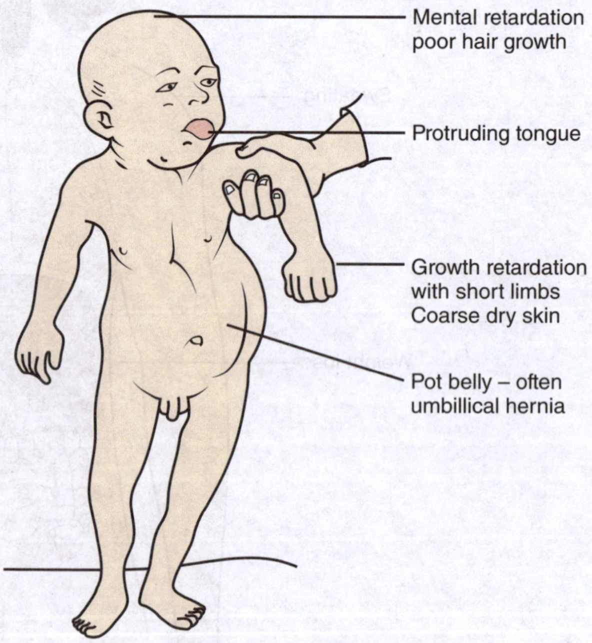

FIG. 42.6 Clinical features of cretinism.

3. Muscle tone is low – the child is typically short, 'pot-bellied' with a protruding tongue.

If a child with cretinism in the first 6 months of life is not started on thyroxine as medication, there is a strong chance that mental retardation will occur. This is because thyroid hormones are essential for brain development and for the myelination of nerves. It is for this reason that many doctors suggest screening for thyroid hormone levels at birth.

EFFECT OF DRUGS, TOXINS, DIET, CHEMICALS AND THE ENVIRONMENT ON THYROID FUNCTION

- Environmental conditions are known to affect thyroid hormone function. For instance, exposure to cold increases TSH and thyroid hormone secretion. In contrast, starvation and protein–energy malnutrition are associated with lower circulating levels of T3. Overfeeding results in increased conversion of T4 to T3.
- Physical and emotional stress can result in an increased secretion of thyroid hormones, but this is likely to be temporary.
- Lithium which is a drug used in psychiatry can interfere with the release of thyroid hormone from the thyroid gland.
- Certain foods can interfere with thyroid synthesis or function. However, they do not exert major effects in the normal amounts that they are consumed. Foods include cassava, cabbage, and cauliflower.
- Certain antidiabetic (sulphonylureas), antituberculosis and anticonvulsant drugs may interfere with thyroid hormone synthesis.

APPLICATIONS FOR NURSING

- The nurse needs to be aware of the symptoms and signs of patients with disorders of thyroid hormone secretion as these can affect the vital signs of the patient. Thus, in hypothyroidism, a patient may have below normal temperature, decreased breathing, low blood pressure, low blood sugar and slow heart rate (bradycardia), and may also appear unresponsive or less responsive to questions or instructions. The patient experiences being cold and may require extra blankets even if the room temperature does not appear low.
- In contrast, a patient with hyperthyroidism may have higher than normal temperature, increased breathing, high blood pressure and fast heart rates (tachycardia), and may appear very anxious. The patient experiences being warm even when the room temperature is low and may wish to throw off bed covers and blankets.
- Nurses need to be aware that certain medications may interfere with thyroid hormone synthesis and function.

SUMMARY

- The thyroid gland produces three hormones: thyroxine (T4), triiodothyronine (T3) and calcitonin.
- Circulating levels of T3 and T4 are regulated by negative feedback involving the anterior pituitary (TSH) and the hypothalamus (TRH).
- Thyroxine increases metabolic rate and the metabolism of carbohydrate and fat, heart rate and the contractility of the heart, GI secretions and motility and respiration, among others. Thyroxine is also important for skeletal growth and brain development.
- An increase in thyroxine secretion in adulthood results in hyperthyroidism (thyrotoxicosis, Graves' disease), while a reduced secretion results in hypothyroidism.
- Cretinism is hypothyroidism in foetal life, infancy or childhood. It is important to detect hypothyroidism in the newborn at birth and to start treatment early to prevent mental retardation.

CHAPTER REVIEW QUESTIONS

1. Describe the steps involved in the synthesis of T3 and T4.
2. Describe the actions of thyroxine.
3. Describe the regulation of T3 and T4 by negative feedback.
4. What are the clinical features of adult (a) hyperthyroidism, (b) hypothyroidism?
5. What is cretinism? What are the clinical features?

CHAPTER 43

The Parathyroid Gland and Calcium Balance

SPECIFIC LEARNING OBJECTIVES

At the end of this chapter, the student should be able to:

- List the basic functions of calcium in the body.
- Outline briefly the metabolism of calcium in the body.
- List the hormones involved in calcium balance and their respective roles. Specifically describe the formation and actions of:
  - Parathormone
  - Vitamin D
  - Calcitonin
- Explain the calcium–phosphate interrelationship.
- Describe the consequences of hypocalcaemia.
- Describe briefly disorders of the parathyroid gland.
- Explain briefly what rickets is.
- Write a short note on osteoporosis.

GLOSSARY OF TERMS

- **Hyperparathyroidism:** an increased secretion of parathormone from the parathyroid glands
- **Hypocalcaemia:** a reduction in circulating calcium levels (normal ~10 mg/dL)
- **Carpopedal spasm:** a spasm of the muscles of the hand and feet due to hypocalcaemia
- **Rickets:** a decrease in mineralization of bone in children due to the deficiency of vitamin D
- **Osteoporosis:** a condition commonly seen with increasing age characterized by brittle bones due to the loss of matrix in the bone

Calcium concentrations in blood are very closely regulated. The normal calcium concentration in blood is about 10 mg/dL. About 40% of calcium in blood is bound to plasma proteins and 10% to phosphates while the remaining calcium (50%) is in ionized form. In this chapter, we describe how calcium which is important for many functions is regulated by different hormones.

FUNCTIONS OF CALCIUM

Calcium is involved in a large number of physiological processes that are essential to the functioning of the body:

1. development of bone and the maintenance of bone density.
2. development of teeth.
3. contraction of all types of muscles (i.e. skeletal, smooth and cardiac).
4. essential factor in blood clotting (one of the ways in which anticoagulants work is to chelate calcium ions and thus prevent clotting).
5. second messenger within cells acted upon by hormones.
6. affects nerve excitability.
7. exocytosis of neurotransmitters and hormones.

BASIC CALCIUM METABOLISM

Dietary Calcium

Calcium is present in our normal diets. Sources of calcium include milk and other dairy products, green leafy vegetables, peas, lentils and beans. Nonvegetarian sources include meat, fish, shrimps and crabs. The normal recommended daily allowance for calcium in the diet in India is about 600 mg/day in adult men and women. Growing children require more calcium for bone growth and in these children the daily need goes up to

800 mg/day. Pregnant and lactating mothers have the highest need for calcium – 1200 mg/day.

Fate of Calcium

Once consumed in the diet, approximately 35% of the calcium is absorbed in the intestines, while most of the rest is excreted in faeces. About 10% of the ingested calcium is excreted in the urine. Approximately 99% of the calcium in the body is stored in the bones and teeth.

HORMONES INVOLVED IN THE REGULATION OF CALCIUM

There are mainly three hormones that regulate calcium levels. These are:

1. Parathormone which increases blood calcium levels.
2. Activated vitamin D3 (1,25-dihydroxycholecalciferol) which also increases blood calcium levels.
3. Calcitonin which decreases blood calcium levels.

We will discuss each of these hormones in greater detail later in the chapter.

SITES OF CALCIUM REGULATION

There are also three main sites where the hormones that regulate calcium act. These are:

1. Intestine: The site of calcium absorption from the diet.
2. Kidney: The site of the excretion of 10% of the ingested calcium. Ninety-nine per cent of the fluid that is filtered in the Bowman's capsule of the kidney is reabsorbed; 90% is reabsorbed in the early nephron while 10% is reabsorbed in the late distal convoluted tubule and the collecting duct.
3. Bone: The major site of storage of calcium in the body. One of the major forms of calcium storage in the bone is hydroxyapatite which is a crystalline salt of calcium and phosphate and is given by the formula: $Ca_{10}(PO_4)_6(OH)_2$. Bone deposition is mediated by cells called osteoblasts while bone resorption is mediated by cells called osteoclasts.

PARATHORMONE

Formation

Parathormone is produced in the parathyroid glands. The parathyroid glands are four in number and are embedded in the posterior surface of the thyroid gland (Fig. 43.1).

Actions of Parathormone

The main function of parathormone is to increase the circulating level of calcium in the blood. It does this in two direct ways:

1. It increases calcium absorption from the bone.
2. It decreases the excretion of calcium by the kidney.

It also increases the absorption of calcium from the intestine, but this is an indirect effect and is mediated by 1,25-dihydroxycholecalciferol which is activated by parathormone in the kidney. This is discussed later in this chapter.

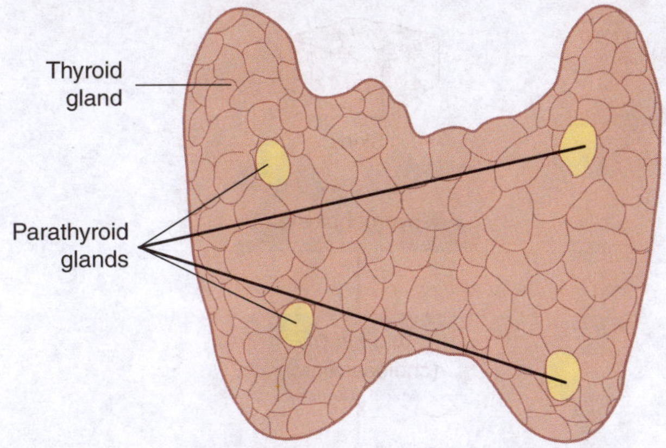

FIG. 43.1 Anatomical location of the parathyroid glands (back view).

Regulation of Parathormone

Increased secretion of parathormone occurs when there is a decrease in the concentration of calcium in the blood. In contrast, parathormone secretion is inhibited when the concentration of calcium increases in the blood. An increased calcium concentration can occur in many situations, for example when the dietary consumption of calcium is high or when there is demineralization of bone following prolonged immobilization or bed rest.

VITAMIN D – 1,25-DIHYDROXYCHOLECALCIFEROL

Formation

There are three steps in the formation of the active form of vitamin D (Fig. 43.2):

1. Cholecalciferol is formed in the skin through the action of the ultraviolet rays of the sun on 7-dehydrocholesterol. The extent to which cholecalciferol is formed depends on the duration and intensity of sunlight, the extent of clothing, the pigmentation of the skin, age of the individual and the use of sunscreen are associated with reduced formation of cholecalciferol in the skin.
2. Cholecalciferol that is formed in the skin enters the circulation and is converted to 25-hydroxycholecalciferol in the liver.
3. The addition of another OH group in the kidney results in the formation of 1,25-dihydroxycholecalciferol. This step is dependent on parathormone. In the absence of parathormone, no 1,25-dihydroxycholecalciferol is formed. This is the most active form of vitamin D.

Actions of Activated Vitamin D

Vitamin D increases circulating calcium levels through two main actions:

1. The main action is the increased absorption of calcium in the intestine: all segments of the small intestine, the

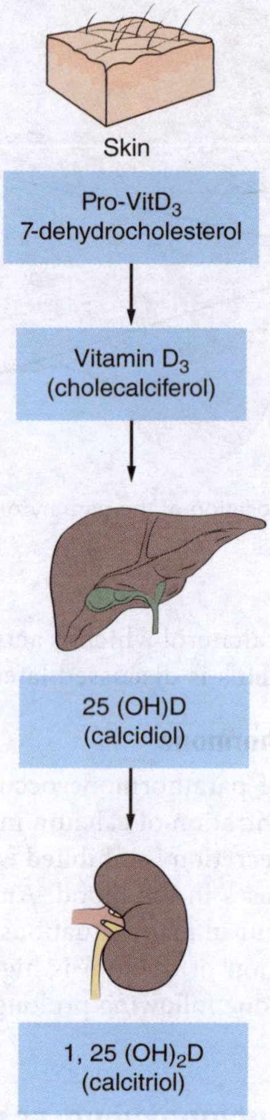

FIG. 43.2 Formation of vitamin D.

duodenum, jejunum and ileum have a high absorptive capacity for calcium, resulting in approximately 35% absorption of the ingested calcium.

2. A mild effect on the reabsorption of calcium at the distal convoluted tubule in the kidney.

CALCITONIN

Formation

Calcitonin is formed by special cells called parafollicular cells (also called C cells) in the thyroid gland (Fig. 43.3). The thyroid gland has large amounts of colloid which are surrounded by cuboidal epithelium (the follicular cells). The parafollicular cells are so named because they lie beside the follicular cells (para = beside, near).

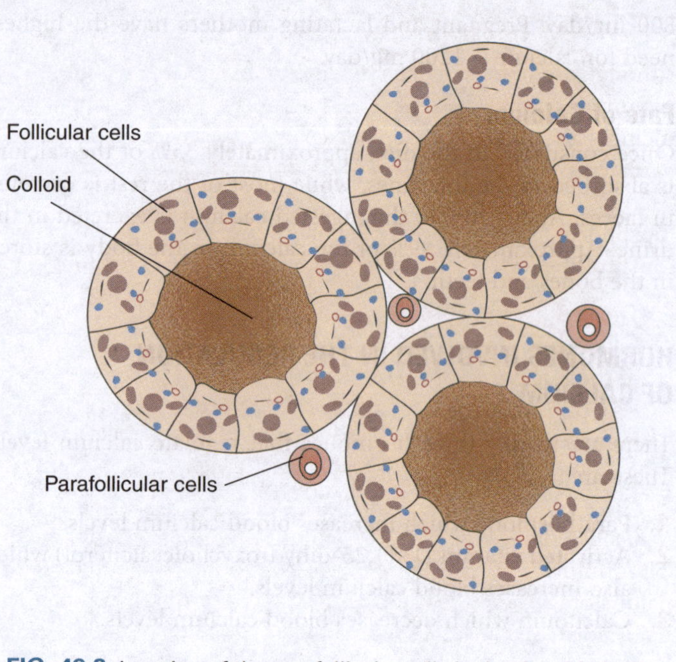

FIG. 43.3 Location of the parafollicular cells in the thyroid gland.

Actions of Calcitonin

Unlike parathormone and vitamin D which increase circulating calcium levels, calcitonin *decreases circulating calcium levels.* The major site of calcitonin action is the bone, where it decreases the resorption of calcium from the bone. It has minor action on the intestine (inhibits absorption) and kidney (inhibits reabsorption).

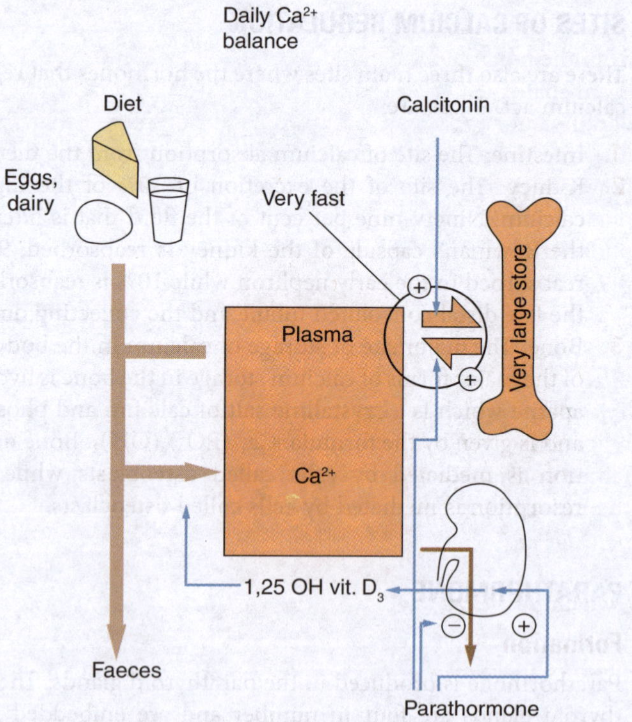

FIG. 43.4 A summary of the actions of hormones maintaining calcium balance.

Regulation of Calcitonin

The primary stimulus for the release of calcitonin is an increased concentration of circulating calcium.

Fig. 43.4 summarizes the actions of the hormones in regulating circulating calcium levels.

CALCIUM–PHOSPHATE INTERRELATIONSHIPS

Although we have discussed the metabolism and regulation of calcium in isolation so far, it is important to recognize that calcium and phosphate metabolism are closely linked and regulated.

Phosphorus, primarily as phosphate ions, has important functions in the body. These, among others, include the following:

1. The production of ATP which is used for energy.
2. In protein synthesis (phosphorus is an important component of the nucleic acids DNA and RNA).
3. As phospholipids in many situations including cell membranes.
4. As a buffer in blood to neutralize acids.

While 99% of calcium is stored in bone and teeth, approximately 85% of inorganic phosphate is stored in bone. Thus, bone is the major storage site for both calcium and inorganic phosphate. The major form in which calcium and phosphate is deposited in the bone is as a combination of calcium and phosphate called hydroxyapatite: $Ca_{10}(PO_4)_6(OH)_2$.

Parathormone which increases circulating calcium levels also regulates phosphate levels. When parathormone releases calcium from the bone into the bloodstream, it also releases phosphate – given that calcium and phosphate are in combination in bone. Parathormone also increases the absorption of phosphate in the intestine. These two actions increase phosphate levels in blood; however, parathormone also inhibits the reabsorption of phosphate in the kidney as a result of which there is increased loss of phosphate in the urine and there is a small **drop** in circulating phosphate levels.

HYPOCALCAEMIA

Two clear features of hypocalcaemia are increased nerve irritability and sustained contraction of muscle (tetany). The sustained contraction of muscles may take the form of a spasm of the muscles of the hand and feet which is therefore called *carpopedal spasm* (Fig. 43.5).

Two clinical tests illustrate the increase in nerve irritability and muscle dysfunction in hypocalcaemia. In Fig. 43.5, you will observe that when the side of the face is tapped, the muscle on that side of the face contracts. This is because the tapping irritates the facial nerve which runs below the skin in that region and results in the contraction of the muscles supplied by the facial nerve. This sign is called *Chvostek's sign*. Similarly, the muscles of the hand go into spasm during hypocalcaemia when a blood pressure cuff is inflated over the arm – this is *Trousseau's sign*. There may also be changes in the voice due to laryngospasm and diminished or absent deep tendon reflexes (like the knee jerk).

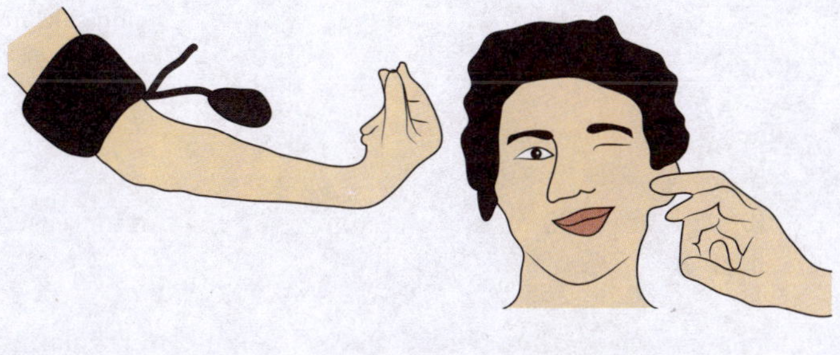

FIG. 43.5 Clinical features of hypocalcaemia.

DISORDERS OF SECRETION OF PARATHORMONE

Excess Secretion

Excess secretion of parathormone is referred to as *hyperparathyroidism*. This may occur if there is a tumour in the parathyroid glands (primary hyperparathyroidism) and when there is sustained hypocalcaemia as a result of which parathormone secretion is increased due to negative feedback (secondary hyperparathyroidism).

Since parathormone mobilizes calcium from the bone to sustain circulating calcium levels, the patient may complain of bony pain and may have fragile bones which fracture easily. The patient may also experience muscle weakness. Changes in emotional state are not uncommon and in severe cases, the problem can be life threatening. While parathormone generally increases calcium reabsorption in the kidney, high sustained circulating levels of calcium with hyperparathyroidism mean that more calcium will be lost in the urine and this can give rise to kidney stones.

Decreased Secretion

If parathormone secretion is reduced, the circulating calcium level drops and the patient will experience all the features of hypocalcaemia.

RICKETS

This results from a decreased calcification of bone and was identified in children who were vitamin D deficient. Children with this disorder may have bony deformities such as 'bow legs' and 'knock knees' among other skeletal deformities. There may also be a swelling of the joints of the costochondral junctions (the joints between the ribs and the cartilage at the front of the rib cage) – the so-called 'rachitic rosary' (Fig. 43.6). Children may complain of muscle weakness and may have a tendency to fracture their bones easily. Vitamin D deficiency in adults results in a condition called *osteomalacia*. Osteomalacia is characterized by bone pain partly in weight-bearing areas and an increased risk for fractures.

OSTEOPOROSIS

This is the most common bone disorder in adulthood. This is a condition in which the bones become more brittle because of a loss of tissue (matrix).

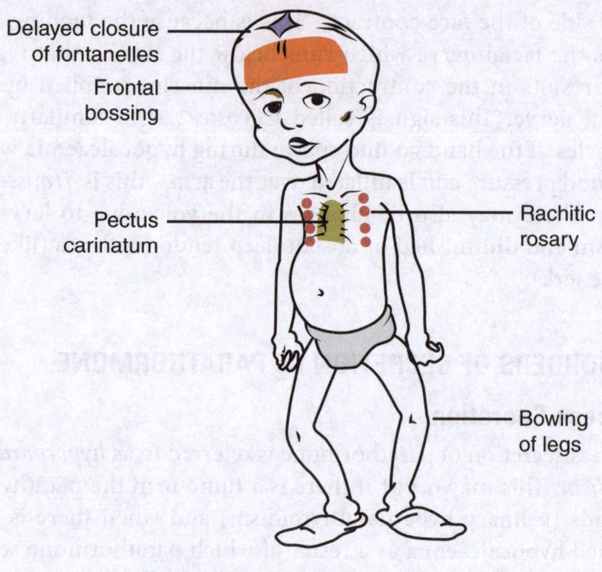

FIG. 43.6 Features of rickets.

Risk factors for osteoporosis:

- Older age
- Prolonged, low calcium intakes
- Physical inactivity, prolonged immobilization or bed rest
- Postmenopausal women (in women, oestrogen prevents bone breakdown but this can change dramatically after menopause)
- Low testosterone levels (this can occur in males with ageing or in people who receive treatments for prostate cancer, which lower the concentrations of testosterone)

Clinical features:

- Increased risk of fractures (in the elderly, this may involve the hip and can result in prolonged recovery times)
- Collapse of vertebra resulting in a loss of height and a 'hunchback' (kyphosis)

Prevention:

Osteoporosis can be prevented by adopting a proper and healthy lifestyle. This includes the following:

- Eating a nutritious diet rich in protein and calcium.
- Taking calcium and vitamin D supplements when prescribed.
- Adopting a more physically active lifestyle.
- Maintaining an optimal body weight (both underweight and overweight increase the likelihood of osteoporosis and fractures).

APPLICATIONS FOR NURSING

- Conditions such as rickets and osteoporosis require lifestyle and nutritional counselling. Nurses should be able to provide culturally appropriate dietary and physical activity counselling to patients.
- Nurses need to be aware of the symptoms and signs of hypocalcaemia and need to monitor muscle function, breathing, cardiac function and mental status since all these can be affected in hypocalcaemia.

SUMMARY

- Calcium is important for multiple processes in the body including development of teeth and bones, muscle contraction, nerve excitability and transmission of impulses across synapses, in blood clotting, etc.
- Circulating levels of calcium are regulated by three hormones: parathormone and vitamin D increase calcium levels while calcitonin decreases calcium levels.
- The maintenance of calcium levels occurs by the hormones acting at three sites: (1) intestine to control absorption of calcium from the gut, (2) kidney to control the rate at which calcium gets excreted in the urine and (3) bone to regulate the rate at which calcium gets mobilized from bone or deposited in bone.
- Hypocalcaemia results in muscle spasm and increased nerve excitability. Two signs which are elicited clinically to determine hypocalcaemia include Chvostek's sign and Trousseau's sign.
- Disorders of calcium metabolism include those involving parathormone (hyperparathyroidism and hypoparathyroidism) and vitamin D (rickets and osteomalacia).

CHAPTER REVIEW QUESTIONS

1. What are the functions of calcium in the body?
2. List the three hormones that regulate plasma calcium levels.
3. Describe the synthesis of vitamin D.
4. Describe the actions of parathormone.
5. What are the features of hypocalcaemia?

CHAPTER 44

The Endocrine Pancreas

SPECIFIC LEARNING OBJECTIVES

At the end of this chapter, the student should be able to:

- Describe the functional anatomy of the endocrine pancreas. List the hormones produced by the endocrine pancreas.
- Describe the actions of insulin.
- Describe the regulation of insulin secretion.
- Describe the actions of glucagon.
- Describe the role of somatostatin in relation to glucagon and insulin secretion.
- List the types of diabetes mellitus and describe their clinical features.

GLOSSARY OF TERMS

- **Hypoglycaemia:** a condition characterized by an abnormally low level of blood glucose
- **Insulin resistance:** a reduced response of the body to insulin resulting in increased blood glucose levels
- **Diabetes:** two types of diabetes – diabetes insipidus due to a deficiency in secretion or action of antidiuretic hormone and diabetes mellitus characterized by an abnormal elevation in blood glucose due to inadequate secretion of insulin or due to resistance to insulin action

Diabetes is characterized by elevated blood glucose levels. The number of people with diabetes is increasing throughout the world. Developing countries have undergone an economic and nutritional transition (with increased intake of fat, refined sugars, salt, energy-dense foods and reduced physical activity) and a demographic transition (with increasing lifespans). These countries have some of the greatest increases in diabetes in their populations. In this chapter, how blood glucose is controlled in the healthy individual and what happens when these regulatory processes break down have been discussed.

The pancreas is an important exocrine organ secreting a large number of enzymes which are important for the digestion of the food. In addition, the pancreas also secretes hormones – this is what we call the endocrine pancreas.

The endocrine pancreas consists of the islets of Langerhans. There are about 1–2 million of these in the pancreas. The structure of an islet of Langerhans is depicted in Fig. 44.1.

Fig. 44.1 shows that most of the pancreas consists of acini which secrete the enzymes important for the digestion of foods. The islet of Langerhans consists of several cells. These include the alpha cells which secrete a hormone called glucagon, the beta cells which secrete insulin and the delta cells which secrete somatostatin. Of these cells, the β cells are the highest number, accounting for about 60% of the islet cells, α cells account for about 25% of the cells and δ cells for 10%. There are also other cells in the islet. These cells are arranged close to each other and affect each other's secretion.

INSULIN

Insulin is a peptide hormone which acts on receptors on the cell membrane. Insulin receptors are found in many tissues including the liver, muscle and white adipose tissue. The major action of insulin is anabolic (building up of energy stores and tissues). In muscle, insulin increases glucose uptake. Since insulin is secreted into the portal circulation (the liver receives a dual blood supply from the hepatic artery and the portal vein), the liver is exposed to high levels of insulin (twice that of insulin concentration in the systemic circulation). The action of insulin on the liver shows all its anabolic effects with a synthesis of the major macromolecules – glycogen, lipid and protein. In adipose tissue, insulin inhibits lipolysis (breakdown of lipids) as a result of which plasma fatty acid concentration reduces.

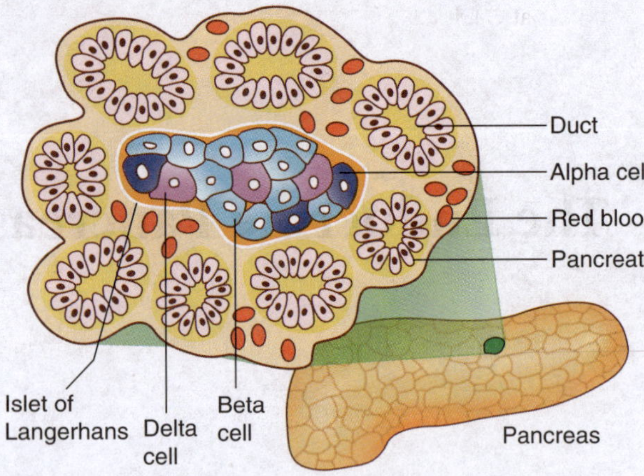

FIG. 44.1 Microscopic structure of the pancreas indicating acini and the islets of Langerhans.

Summary of Actions

1. Blood glucose: Insulin *lowers blood glucose levels*. This it does in several ways:
   a. It increases the uptake of glucose in the peripheral tissues especially in the muscle. Glucose is taken into cells through the action of special proteins on the cell membranes called glucose transporters (GLUT). There are different types of GLUT proteins. Of these, GLUT-4 is the transporter for glucose in muscle, the major site of glucose uptake from the blood. Seventy-five per cent of the glucose that is taken up the muscle goes into storage through the process of glycogen synthesis.
   b. It prevents the release of glucose into the circulation by inhibiting glycogenolysis (the breakdown of glycogen into glucose) and gluconeogenesis (the synthesis of glucose from amino acids and fatty acids).
   c. It stimulates glycogen synthesis – in which glucose is used to form the storage molecule glycogen.
   d. It promotes the conversion of excess glucose into fatty acids.
2. Protein metabolism: Insulin promotes protein synthesis and storage.
3. Fat metabolism: Insulin prevents the breakdown of fat (lipolysis) and promotes synthesis (lipogenesis) and storage of fat.
4. Apart from its metabolic effects, insulin also reduces the concentration of potassium (K^+) in the blood by stimulating the uptake of K^+ ions by cells in the muscle and liver.

Control of Insulin Secretion

Insulin increases when there is an increase in blood glucose. Under physiological conditions, this occurs after a meal. Increased fatty acids and amino acids in the blood also increase insulin secretion from the β cells of the pancreas independent of blood glucose levels.

Several hormones stimulate insulin secretion. These include glucagon, growth hormone and cortisol.

When a meal is eaten, insulin levels begin to rise even before the nutrients are absorbed and before the blood levels of glucose, fatty acids and amino acids increase. This suggests that some factors in the gastrointestinal (GI) tract influence insulin secretion. Several GI hormones are now known to increase insulin secretion and include gastrin, cholecystokinin and gastric inhibitory peptide.

Three of the factors which reduce insulin secretion are (1) a decreased blood glucose, (2) fasting and (3) somatostatin.

COUNTER-REGULATORY HORMONES

Just as insulin reduces blood glucose levels, there are some hormones which increase blood glucose levels. These include:

1. growth hormone,
2. cortisol, epinephrine (adrenaline) and
3. glucagon.

These hormones are called counter-regulatory hormones because they counter the actions of insulin. Glucagon is discussed further in the next section of this chapter.

GLUCAGON

Actions

Glucagon increases the blood glucose levels. It does this in different ways:

1. It increases gluconeogenesis, that is the formation of glucose from amino acids and fatty acids.
2. It causes glycogenolysis (breakdown of glycogen) in the liver.

Glucagon has other effects, the most important of which is that it promotes lipolysis (breakdown of fats) resulting in the release of fatty acids.

Control of Glucagon Secretion

In contrast to insulin, increased blood glucose levels inhibit glucagon secretion, while fasting stimulates glucagon secretion.

Earlier we had indicated that the α, β and δ cells of the islets of Langerhans were located close to each other and could regulate each other. Fig. 44.2 illustrates how this happens.

As can be seen from Fig. 44.2, glucagon stimulates the secretion of both insulin and somatostatin (green lines), while somatostatin inhibits the secretion of both insulin and glucagon (red lines). Insulin is also inhibitory to glucagon.

DIABETES MELLITUS

Forms of Diabetes Mellitus

There are two forms of diabetes mellitus: type I and type II. These two forms have very different characteristics and alterations in physiology.

Type I diabetes mellitus has the following characteristics, among others:

1. It occurs early in age, most often in childhood.
2. The individual is typically thin.
3. Blood glucose levels are elevated.
4. Plasma insulin levels are low or absent.

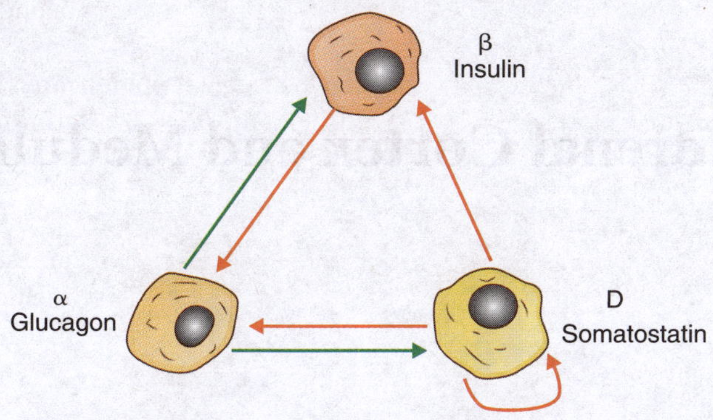

FIG. 44.2 Interactions between the cells of the islets of Langerhans.

5. The low/absent insulin levels suggest that this is the key problem and that the individual might be unable to produce sufficient insulin. Patients with type I diabetes mellitus respond to the administration of insulin.

Type II diabetes mellitus has the flowing characteristics:

1. It usually occurs in middle age and in older individuals. However, in recent times, type II diabetes is increasingly being seen in overweight and obese children as well.
2. The individual is usually overweight or obese. In adults, this is determined by calculating the body mass index (BMI) as the weight (kg)/(height)^2 (m). In adults, a BMI of 25 has been conventionally considered overweight, and a BMI of 30 and above as obesity. There has been a suggestion that the BMI cut-off needs to be lowered for South Asians since they are at an increased risk of complications of overweight/obesity at a lower BMI.
3. Insulin levels are normal or high during the initial course of the disease.
4. Plasma glucose levels are elevated.
5. The normal/high insulin levels suggest that the individual is producing sufficient insulin but is resistant to the action of insulin which is circulating in the blood. This is called insulin resistance. In insulin resistance, despite high levels of insulin in the blood, glucose uptake into tissues is reduced, as in glycogen synthesis. Suppression of lipolysis is also reduced. Individuals with type II diabetes mellitus can increase the sensitivity of insulin by losing weight and by exercising. Losing weight and exercising result in a movement of insulin receptors to the cell membrane – the increased number of insulin receptors increases insulin action. Patients with type II diabetes respond to a variety of oral medications which bring down the circulating levels of glucose, although they may also need to be treated with insulin at a later stage.

Long-Term Complications of Uncontrolled Diabetes Mellitus

Chronically elevated blood glucose levels tend to damage the blood vessels. This results in microvascular disease (involving small blood vessels) and macrovascular disease (involving arteries). Microvascular disease results in damage to the retina (diabetic retinopathy), kidney (diabetic nephropathy) and nerves (diabetic neuropathy). Macrovascular disease results in an increased risk of coronary artery disease (resulting in myocardial infarction) and cerebrovascular disease (resulting in strokes).

In addition to the long-term complications listed earlier, patients with uncontrolled diabetes also have an increased risk of infections. These include respiratory infections, including tuberculosis, skin infections and urinary infections, among others. The reasons for this are many and involve both reduced cellular and humoral immunity. Thus, uncontrolled diabetics produce lower levels of interleukins (cytokines) in response to infection, show reduced chemotaxis and phagocytic activity, and have reduced mobilization of neutrophils to the sites of infection, among many other changes in the immune system.

APPLICATIONS FOR NURSING

- Nurses will routinely give patients their medication including insulin. Under these circumstances, nurses should be aware of the effects of excess insulin administration which essentially resembles hypoglycaemia but can be associated with coma if circulating glucose levels drop too low. The features of hypoglycaemia include hunger, weakness, nervousness, tremors and increased sweating. If blood glucose levels drop further, the person may experience seizures, unconsciousness and even coma. A person who develops hypoglycaemia should be immediately given sugar to eat or other carbohydrates including sugary juices, which may be available. Severe hypoglycaemia needs to be treated under medical supervision.
- Nurses need to be aware that diabetics can go into coma not only if there is severe hypoglycaemia but also if there are prolonged and high elevations of blood glucose.
- An important role of the nurse in diabetes is to counsel the patient with regard to (1) changes in diet and regularity of meal timings, (2) need for regular physical activity, (3) need for regularity of treatment, (4) need for weight loss (if type II) and (5) need to be aware of complications of diabetes and how to deal with them.

SUMMARY

- The islets of Langerhans are the endocrine portion of the pancreas and secrete insulin (β cells), glucagon (α cells) and somatostatin (δ cells).
- Insulin causes a reduction in blood glucose levels by increasing glucose uptake in tissues. It is also an anabolic hormone which promotes glycogen synthesis, protein synthesis and lipogenesis.
- Glucagon increases blood glucose levels and is a counter-regulatory hormone to insulin together with growth hormone, cortisol and epinephrine.
- Somatostatin is inhibitory to both glucagon and insulin.
- Diabetes mellitus (DM) is of two types: type I DM is characterized by a lack of insulin, while in type II DM there is insulin resistance.

CHAPTER REVIEW QUESTIONS

1. Describe the actions of insulin.
2. Describe the actions of glucagon.
3. What are the counter-regulatory hormones for insulin? What action do they have in common?
4. Differentiate between type I and type II diabetes mellitus.

CHAPTER 45

Adrenal Cortex and Medulla

SPECIFIC LEARNING OBJECTIVES

At the end of this chapter, the student should be able to:

- Describe the functional anatomy of the adrenal gland in relation to endocrine physiology.
- List the hormones that are produced by different parts of the adrenal gland.
- Describe the actions of mineralocorticoids.
- Describe the actions of glucocorticoids.
- Describe the control of secretion of glucocorticoids through the hypothalamo–hypophysial–adrenal axis.
- Describe the clinical features of Cushing's syndrome.
- Briefly describe the Addison's disease, Conn's syndrome and adrenogenital disease.
- Describe the actions of adrenaline.
- Briefly describe the features of pheochromocytoma.
- Define stress. Describe the body's response to stress.

GLOSSARY OF TERMS

- **Glucocorticoids:** a class of steroid hormones secreted from the adrenal cortex which have metabolic (carbohydrate, protein and fat) and anti-inflammatory effects, for example cortisol
- **Mineralocorticoids:** a class of steroid hormones secreted by the adrenal cortex which regulate salt and water balance, for example aldosterone
- **Hypernatraemia/hyponatraemia:** a rise/fall in circulating sodium concentrations
- **Hyperkalaemia/hypokalaemia:** a rise/fall in circulating potassium concentrations
- **Catecholamines:** a class of substances that includes epinephrine, norepinephrine and dopamine

The adrenal glands are located at the superior poles of the kidney. Each adrenal gland weighs about 5 g. The gland is divided into an outer cortex and an inner medulla (Fig. 45.1).

The cortex is about 80% of the adrenal gland, and the medulla is 20%. Each of the portions of the adrenal gland secretes different hormones. The adrenal cortex itself is further divided into three distinct zones:

1. An outer *zona glomerulosa*
2. A middle *zona fasciculata*
3. An inner *zona reticularis*, which lies adjacent to the adrenal medulla

HORMONES SECRETED BY THE ADRENAL GLAND

The adrenal gland secretes multiple hormones (Fig. 45.2).

Adrenal cortex:

- Zona glomerulosa: aldosterone (a mineralocorticoid)
- Zona fasciculata: cortisol (a glucocorticoid)
- Zona reticularis: androgens

Adrenal medulla produces catecholamines (i.e. norepinephrine and epinephrine).

HORMONES OF THE ADRENAL CORTEX AND ASSOCIATED CLINICAL CONDITIONS

Actions of Mineralocorticoids (Aldosterone)

Aldosterone is the major mineralocorticoid in humans and is secreted from the zona glomerulosa of the adrenal cortex. Aldosterone has the following major effects:

1. **Retention of sodium:** Aldosterone stimulates the reabsorption of sodium in the distal convoluted tubule and collecting duct of the nephron in the kidney. It does this by exchanging sodium ions for potassium ions. Thus, aldosterone reduces the excretion of sodium in the urine.
2. **Excretion of potassium:** Aldosterone increases the excretion of potassium in the urine because when it reabsorbs sodium in the nephron, it exchanges the sodium for potassium (Fig. 45.3).
3. **Maintenance of the extracellular fluid volume and blood pressure:** When sodium is retained, water is also retained.

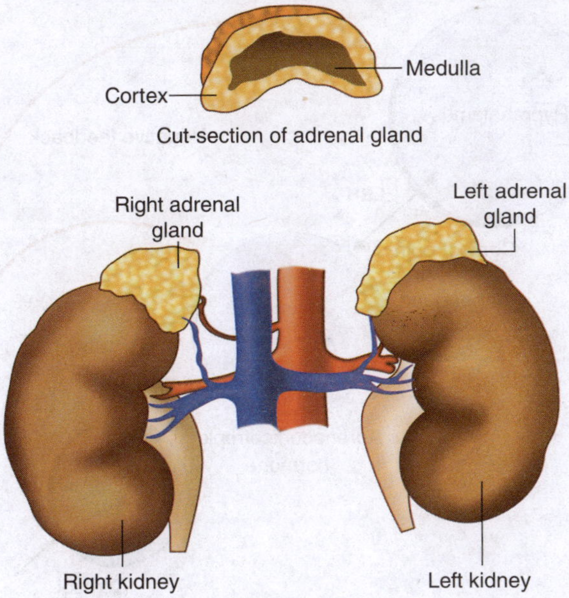

FIG. 45.1 Location of the adrenal glands.

This results in an increase in the blood volume and the blood pressure.

4. **Action on the sweat glands and salivary glands**: Aldosterone increases the reabsorption of sodium and the excretion of potassium in each of these glands. In addition, aldosterone also increases the absorption of sodium in the large intestine.

Regulation of Aldosterone Secretion An increase in the potassium concentration in the extracellular fluid increases the secretion of aldosterone, while an increase in sodium concentration decreases the aldosterone secretion. This makes sense, because when potassium concentration is high, aldosterone increases the excretion of potassium restoring potassium concentration back to normal. In contrast, an increase in sodium concentration reduces aldosterone secretion (resulting in an increase in sodium excretion); otherwise, more sodium would be retained and this would increase sodium concentrations even further. Thus, the factors that affect the secretion of aldosterone are:

Increasing aldosterone secretion:
- High plasma potassium
- Low plasma sodium
- Angiotensin II (this was discussed in Chapter 28)
- Low blood pressure

Decreasing aldosterone secretion:
- High plasma sodium
- Low plasma potassium
- High blood pressure

Actions of Glucocorticoids (Cortisol)

Glucocorticoids have many actions. It is beyond the scope of this book to discuss all of them in detail. Some of the more important ones are listed here.

Metabolic actions:

1. *Carbohydrates*: Cortisol is anti-insulin in nature. Insulin helps to lower blood glucose levels. Therefore, cortisol acts to increase blood glucose levels (hyperglycaemia) by increasing glucose production (gluconeogenesis). Due to hyperglycaemia, there is a compensatory increase in circulating insulin levels which attempt to lower the blood glucose.
2. *Proteins*: Since cortisol increases gluconeogenesis, that is the production of glucose primarily from amino acids, it means that proteins are broken down to release amino acids for this purpose. Thus, cortisol increases proteolysis in skeletal muscle.
3. *Fats*: Cortisol is a lipolytic hormone, which mobilizes fatty acids from the adipose (fat) tissues to the liver where they are utilized in gluconeogenesis – the production of glucose.

Anti-inflammatory actions:

Cortisol inhibits inflammatory and allergic reactions in the body. It does this through a number of mechanisms some of which are (1) reducing the circulating number of lymphocytes, eosinophils, monocytes and basophils; (2) causing an involution (reduction in size) of the lymph nodes and thymus, thus deceasing the antibody production; and (3) decreasing the permeability of capillaries and therefore reducing the movement of fluid from the blood vessels into the tissue spaces.

Cortisol is a stress hormone:

During periods of chronic stress, whether physical or psychogenic, cortisol secretion is increased. While cortisol ensures the availability of substrates such as glucose for survival, the anti-inflammatory and immune-lowering

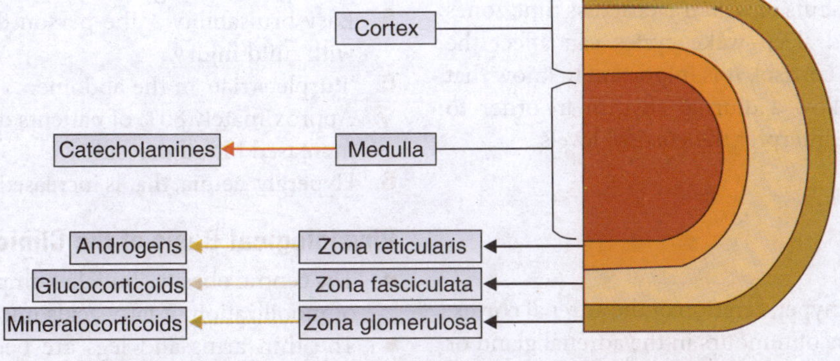

FIG. 45.2 The source of hormones from the adrenal glands.

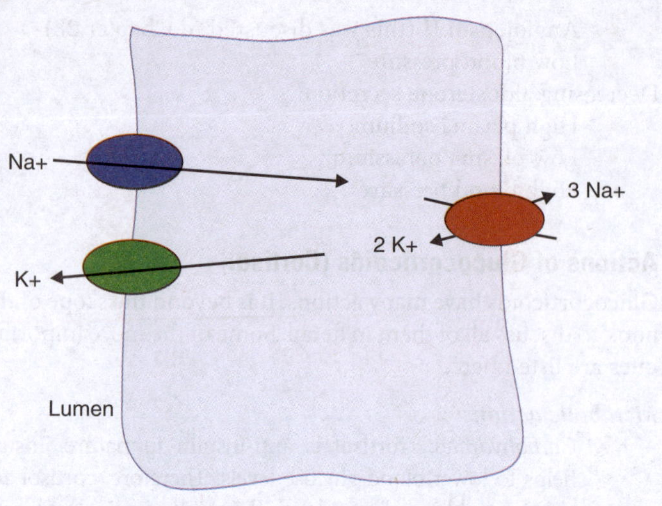

FIG. 45.3 Action of aldosterone in the nephron.

effects of glucocorticoids result in a suppression of the immune response and an increased likelihood of infections.

Gastrointestinal effects:
Cortisol increases gastric acid secretion, as a result of which prolonged elevations in cortisol or the use of glucocorticoids in medication may result in gastric ulcers.

In addition to the above-mentioned effects, cortisol also has some mild mineralocorticoid action which may be significant when cortisol is secreted in excess quantities.

Regulation of Glucocorticoid Secretion Glucocorticoid secretion is regulated through a number of negative feedback loops which involve the hypothalamus, the anterior pituitary gland and the adrenal cortex. This is illustrated in Fig. 45.4. As can be seen from the figure, the hypothalamus releases corticotropin-releasing hormone (CRH) which stimulates the anterior pituitary to release adrenocorticotropic hormone (ACTH) which in turn stimulates the secretion of cortisol from the adrenal cortex. Circulating cortisol inhibits the further release of both ACTH and CRH in negative feedback loops.

Cortisol secretion shows a strong diurnal variation (i.e. a variation during the 24-hour day–night cycle). Thus, cortisol levels are high in the morning and low in the evening. For people who work on intermittent night shifts or who travel across time zones with 'jet lag', the disrupted sleep–wake cycles can affect the normal diurnal variation in cortisol. It is important to know that cortisol levels in blood follow a diurnal rhythm in order to sample blood correctly and interpret the cortisol levels.

CUSHING'S SYNDROME

Cause

1. This condition is due to hypersecretion of the adrenal cortex. This can happen because of tumours in the adrenal gland or in the pituitary.

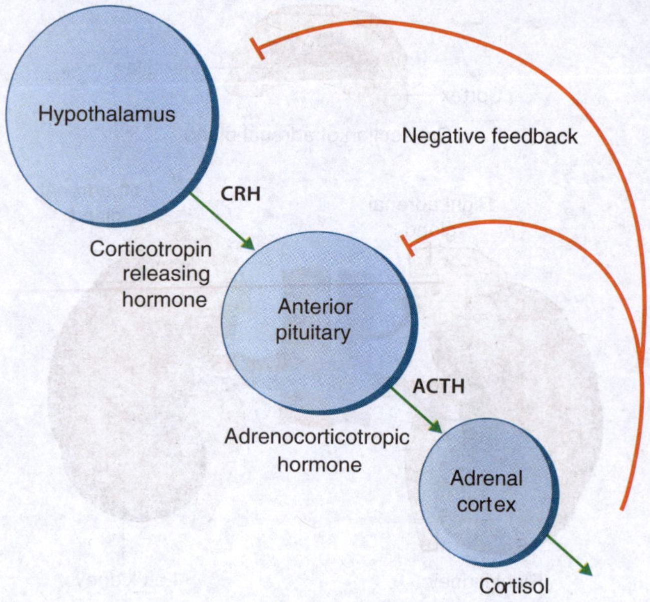

FIG. 45.4 The hypothalamo–pituitary–adrenal axis.

2. If there is a tumour in the pituitary gland, ACTH may be secreted in excess resulting in excess production of cortisol by the adrenal cortex.
   Thus, high levels of ACTH and cortisol suggest a pituitary cause, since if the tumour was in the adrenal cortex, cortisol would be high, but ACTH would be low because of the negative feedback.
3. Cushing's syndrome may also be seen when patients have been on long-term glucocorticoids as medications to suppress chronic inflammations.

Features

A person with Cushing's syndrome develops features which are primarily the result of excess circulating cortisol and has a typical appearance as shown in Fig. 45.5.

The person has:

1. 'Moon face'.
2. 'Buffalo hump' characterized by the deposition of fat at the back of the neck.
3. Central obesity – that is accumulation of fat in the abdominal region.
4. Thin arms and legs.
5. Easy bruisability – the person develops bruises in the skin with mild injury.
6. 'Purple striae' in the abdomen.
7. Approximately 80% of patients develop hypertension, that is increased blood pressure.
8. Hyperglycaemia, that is increased circulating levels of glucose.

Physiological Basis of the Clinical Features

- The central obesity, 'buffalo hump' and 'moon face' are a result of mobilization of fatty acids into these regions of the body.
- The thin arms and legs are because of the breakdown of proteins in muscles and muscle wasting.

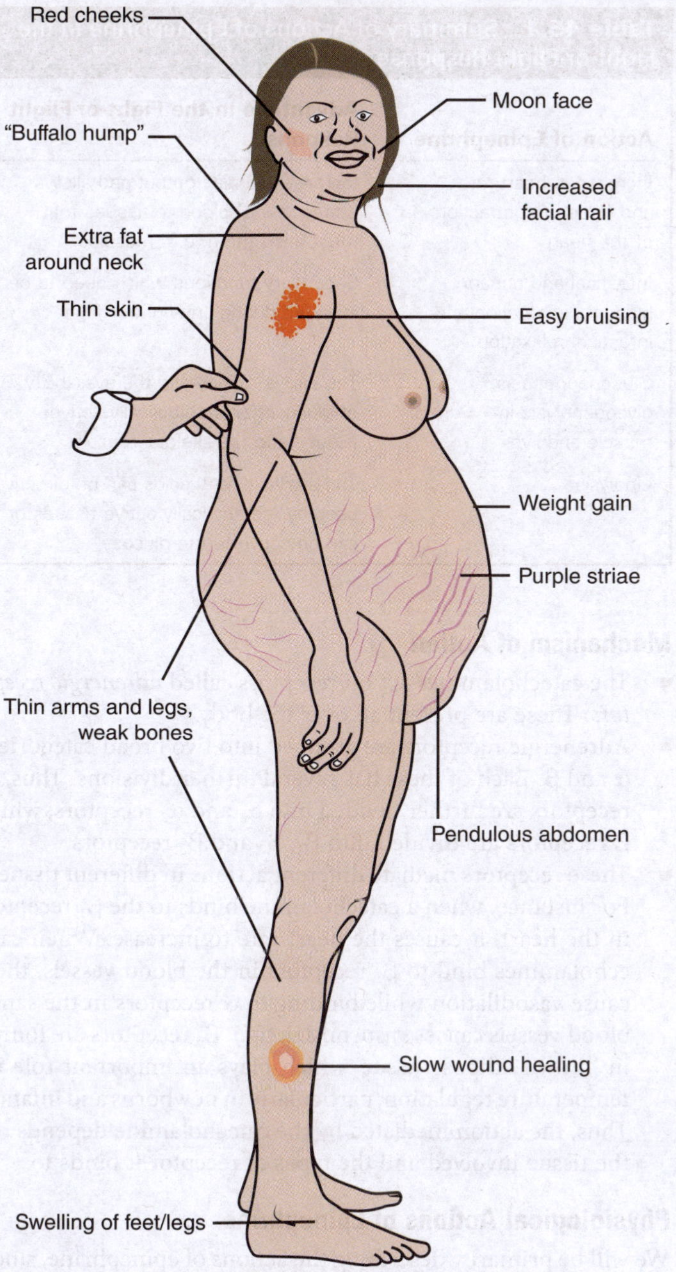

FIG. 45.5 Clinical features of Cushing's syndrome.

- The easy bruising is a result of weakness of the vessel walls.
- The purple striae are a result of decreased collagen synthesis resulting in thin and fragile skin.
- The hypertension is due to the mineralocorticoid effect of cortisol which results in a retention of sodium and water.
- Hyperglycaemia is due to the effect of cortisol on carbohydrate metabolism; increased gluconeogenesis and reduced glucose utilization of glucose in the cells resulting in increased circulating glucose levels.

ADDISON'S DISEASE

Cause

This condition is due to adrenal insufficiency – that is the adrenal cortex is unable to produce sufficient adrenocortical hormones.

Clinical Features

A patient with Addison's disease has the following clinical features, among others:

1. Fatigue and weakness
2. Loss of appetite
3. Various symptoms related to the gastrointestinal tract such as vomiting, nausea, diarrhoea, constipation and abdominal pain
4. Dizziness
5. Hyperpigmentation

Physiological Basis of the Clinical Features

- The deficiency of mineralocorticoids results in loss of sodium and water in the urine. As a result of this, the blood pressure falls and the patient may experience dizziness.
- The loss of sodium may also contribute to the muscle weakness as also a decrease in secretion of androgens.
- The hyperpigmentation of the skin is caused by stimulation of the melanocortin receptor in the skin by the high circulating corticotropin concentrations (corticotropin concentrations increase as a negative feedback because of low circulating levels of cortisol).
- Patients may also experience hypoglycaemia because of a deficiency of cortisol.

CONN'S SYNDROME

Cause

This is usually the result of a small tumour affecting the zona glomerulosa which results in the secretion of high amounts of aldosterone.

Clinical Features

The clinical features are related to increased mineralocorticoid effects. Thus, there is:

1. increased sodium and water retention resulting in increased blood pressure (hypertension). The increased sodium levels in the blood are called hypernatraemia.
2. There is also a loss of potassium, a condition called hypokalaemia which may be associated with severe muscle weakness and sometimes paralysis.

ADRENOGENITAL SYNDROME

Cause

This is usually due to a tumour of the adrenal cortex which results in excess secretion of androgens. Androgens are the masculinizing hormones so the features that are seen are related to this.

Clinical Features

In a female (Fig. 45.6):

1. Growth of facial hair
2. Deep voice
3. Male distribution of hair in the body

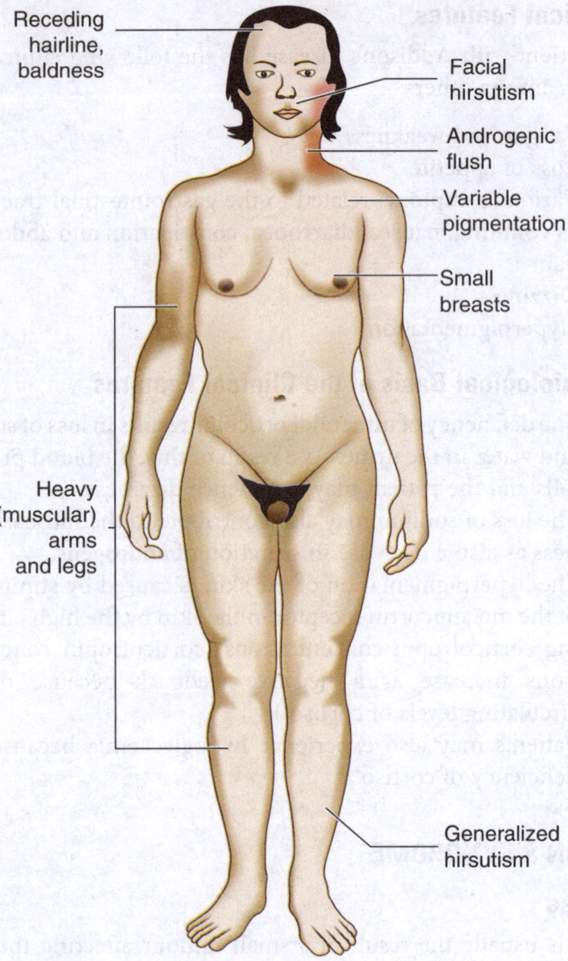

FIG. 45.6 Clinical features of adrenogenital syndrome.

4. Growth of clitoris to resemble a penis
5. Amenorrhoea – absence of menstrual cycles

In a male before puberty: rapid development of the male sex organs, that is enlarged penis.

HORMONES OF THE ADRENAL MEDULLA

The adrenal medulla produces 'catecholamines'. There are two catecholamines that are produced:

1. Epinephrine (adrenaline) which accounts for about 80% of the secretion of the adrenal medulla.
2. Norepinephrine (noradrenaline) which accounts for about 20% of the secretion of the adrenal medulla (norepinephrine is primarily a neurotransmitter and is found in neural tissues and in the brain).

Stimuli for Release

These hormones are 'stress hormones' and released in response to a variety of stimuli including pain, fear, trauma, anxiety, anger, haemorrhage, extremes of temperature and severe exercise. The response to stress is called the *'fight-or-flight response'*.

Table 45.1 Summary of Actions of Epinephrine in the Fight-or-Flight Response

Action of Epinephrine	Advantage in the Fight-or-Flight Response
Increase in heart rate and force of contraction of the heart	Increases cardiac output and allows better flow of blood to tissues that most need them, e.g. muscles
Intestinal and urinary bladder constriction and intestinal relaxation	Secondary functions which need to be inhibited during any fight or flight
Gluconeogenesis, glycogenolysis in muscle and liver	The aim is to increase the availability of glucose for metabolically active tissues such as skeletal muscle
Lipolysis	The available fatty acids can be directly used by metabolically active tissues or can be converted to glucose

Mechanism of Action

- The catecholamines act on receptors called *adrenergic receptors*. These are present all over the body.
- Adrenergic receptors are grouped into two broad categories: α and β. Each of these has several further divisions. Thus, α receptors are further divided into α_1 and α_2 receptors, while β receptors are divided into β_1, β_2 and β_3 receptors.
- These receptors mediate different actions in different tissues. For instance, when a catecholamine binds to the β_1 receptor in the heart, it causes the heart rate to increase. When catecholamines bind to β_2 receptors in the blood vessels, they cause vasodilation while binding to α receptors in the same blood vessels causes vasoconstriction. β_3 receptors are found in 'brown adipose tissue' which plays an important role in temperature regulation, particularly in newborns and infants. Thus, the action mediated by the catecholamine depends on the tissue involved and the types of receptor it binds to.

Physiological Actions of Epinephrine

We will be primarily describing the actions of epinephrine, since it is the primary hormone of the adrenal medulla. There are differences in the actions produced by epinephrine and norepinephrine because, while these catecholamines act on both receptors, epinephrine has a preference for β receptors while norepinephrine has a preference for α receptors.

The overall actions of adrenaline can best be understood in terms of the fight-and-flight response and some of these are summarized in Table 45.1. A complete list of actions across tissues together with the type of receptor involved can be obtained from reference books.

PHEOCHROMOCYTOMA

Cause

This is a clinical condition characterized by an increased secretion of catecholamines. This may be from the adrenal medulla but also from cells called chromaffin cells which are found in close proximity to the sympathetic nervous system.

Clinical Features

It is characterized by a range of symptoms which reflect the widespread distribution of adrenergic receptors across the body. These include the following:

1. Palpitations (an awareness of a fast, irregular and strong heartbeat)
2. Anxiety
3. Chest pain
4. Tremors
5. High blood pressure

APPLICATIONS FOR NURSING

Nurses should be aware that synthetic corticosteroids (glucocorticoids) and epinephrine are used extensively as medication because of their extensive effects on the body.

- Corticosteroids are used in conditions characterized by inflammation and in severe allergic disorders since they have anti-inflammatory effects and suppress the immune systems.
- Epinephrine is used, among others, to relieve severe bronchospasm associated with anaphylaxis since epinephrine causes bronchodilation. Because of its effects on the heart, it can also be used to restore cardiac rhythm after cardiac arrest (when the heart has stopped beating).
- Nurses must also be aware that corticosteroids when used as medication for prolonged periods of time can give rise to features that resemble Cushing's syndrome. It is important therefore to elicit the medication history of patients.

You will learn more about these medications later in your nursing course.

SUMMARY

- The adrenal gland secretes multiple hormones. Aldosterone, glucocorticoids and androgens are secreted from the adrenal cortex, from the zona glomerulosa, zona fasciculata and zona reticularis, respectively. Catecholamines (epinephrine and norepinephrine) are secreted from the adrenal medulla.
- The major action of the mineralocorticoids (aldosterone) is to retain sodium and excrete potassium while acting on the distal part of the nephron in the kidney.
- The major actions of the glucocorticoids are to increase glucose levels, mobilize fats, break down proteins, reduce inflammation and suppress immunity, among others.
- The regulation of circulating glucocorticoids (cortisol) is via the hypothalamo–hypophysial–adrenal axis: multiple negative feedback effects that involve CRH, ACTH and cortisol.
- Adrenal gland abnormalities of hormone secretion of the adrenal gland include (1) hypersecretion of the adrenal cortex – Cushing's syndrome; (2) reduced secretion from the adrenal cortex – Addison's disease; (3) excessive secretion of aldosterone – Conn's syndrome; and (4) excessive secretion of androgens – adrenogenital syndrome.
- The adrenal medulla secretes epinephrine and norepinephrine. These catecholamines produce their actions by acting on adrenergic receptors of which there are two primary types: α and β.

The actions of adrenaline are best understood in terms of the fight-and-flight response. Excess production of epinephrine may result in pheochromocytoma.

CHAPTER REVIEW QUESTIONS

1. Describe the parts of the adrenal gland and list the hormones produced by each part.
2. Describe the actions of aldosterone.
3. Describe the actions of glucocorticoids.
4. Describe the actions of epinephrine

CHAPTER 46

Applications of the Endocrine System

SPECIFIC LEARNING OBJECTIVES

At the end of this chapter, the student should be able to briefly describe the role of hormones in relation to:

- Cardiovascular function
- Weight balance
- Foetal growth and development
- Ageing
- Stress

GLOSSARY OF TERMS

- **Hyperlipidaemia:** an increase in the circulating fat particles (i.e. in the blood) which include cholesterol and triglycerides
- **Palpitations:** an uncomfortable awareness of one's own heartbeat because of irregularity or rapid heart rate
- **Ventricular hypertrophy:** thickening of the wall of the ventricle due to an increase in its mass
- **Hypertension:** an abnormal increase in the systemic arterial blood pressure
- **Stress:** the response of the body to an increased demand which may be physical, social or psychological
- **Stressor:** an event or situation which evokes a stress response

CARDIOVASCULAR MANIFESTATIONS OF ENDOCRINE DISORDERS

Various endocrine disorders affect the cardiovascular system. The functional and clinical manifestations that are seen depend on several factors which include how much the hormone level is increased or decreased, the duration of the illness and whether the illness has been treated.

Thyroid hormones:

The thyroid hormones (T3 and T4) increase the heart rate (positive chronotropy) and the force of contraction (positive inotropy) of the heart. Thyroid hormones also influence the function of the vascular smooth muscle that forms a part of the blood vessel wall. In hypothyroidism, the cardiac output may fall as much as 30%–40% of its normal value. Hypothyroidism is also associated with hyperlipidaemia (an increase in the circulating levels of lipids). In hyperthyroidism, there is an increased heart rate which may manifest as palpitations – an uncomfortable awareness of one's own heart rate often manifesting as a 'racing' heart or 'skipped beats'. The person may also experience arrhythmias such as atrial fibrillation. Cardiac output may increase substantially. The increased force of contraction of the heart can lead to ventricular hypertrophy and, if left untreated, to heart failure.

Hormones of the adrenal gland:

The adrenal cortex secretes both cortisol and aldosterone. Excess secretion of cortisol (seen in Cushing's syndrome) is associated with central obesity and hypertension. Excess aldosterone secretion is also associated with hypertension because of the increased salt and water retention. The hypertension may lead to left ventricular hypertrophy. Excessive secretion of adrenaline seen in pheochromocytomas may be associated with arrhythmias and hypertension – the rise in blood pressure may be sustained or 'paroxysmal', that is sudden periods of raised blood pressure in between periods of normal blood pressure. This is because adrenaline may be released in 'bursts'.

Insulin:

Insulin has direct effects on the heart and blood vessels. In healthy individuals, it increases heart rate and the force of cardiac contraction so that both stroke volume and cardiac output increase. Insulin also causes vasodilation of blood vessels resulting in a fall in peripheral resistance and a reduction in blood pressure. In insulin resistance, these effects seen in healthy individuals are reduced.

Oestrogen:

Women in the reproductive age group appear to be protected against cardiovascular disease compared to men of the same age. Part of the reason is due to the actions of oestrogen. Oestrogen improves the lipid profile in the blood with a reduction in the LDL cholesterol ('bad' cholesterol) and an increase in the HDL cholesterol ('good' cholesterol). Oestrogen also has direct beneficial effects on the cardiac muscle cells – counteracting the effect of oxidant damage to the heart. Oestrogen helps to maintain the ability of blood vessels to relax and vasodilate.

HORMONES AND WEIGHT BALANCE

We derive our energy (calories) from the food that we consume. This represents the energy intake. We expend or use the energy that we consume in various ways.

1. Even when we are resting, our body is constantly expending calories – for the beating of the heart, the expansion of the lungs and to move ions in and out of cells, among others. This expenditure of energy constitutes the resting metabolic rate. When we record this rate, the first thing in the morning, when we are awake but lying down, emotionally calm and in a thermoneutral environment (neither warm nor cold), we call the rate of energy expenditure the basal metabolic rate.
2. We also expend energy when we are physically active and when we consume food (because although we derive our energy from food, we also spend energy to break down food during digestion and absorption and then convert this food into its storage forms).

If we add up all the ways we expend energy, we get our total energy expenditure. When the body weight is stable, our energy intake is equal to the energy expenditure. If the energy intake is higher than the energy expenditure (when we eat too much), or if the energy expenditure is lower than the energy intake (when people are physically inactive, for instance), we gain body weight. If, however, energy intake is low (as in starvation or undernutrition) or if energy expenditure is very high, a person may lose body weight (Fig. 46.1).

Hormones and weight:

Thyroxine and adrenaline are among the major hormones that increase energy expenditure or the 'burning of calories'. Several hormones affect the storage of fat in our bodies. Insulin is a potent hormone that stimulates lipogenesis – the formation of fat. In contrast, both growth hormone (released from the anterior pituitary) and leptin (released from adipose tissue) inhibit lipogenesis.

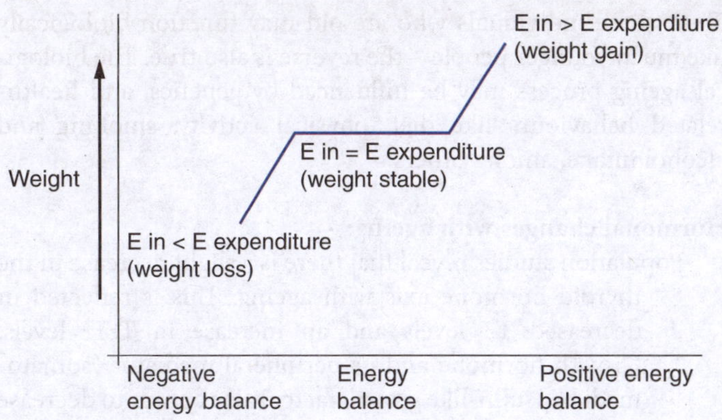

FIG. 46.1 Relationship between body weight, energy intake and energy expenditure.

HORMONES – FOETAL GROWTH AND DEVELOPMENT

The developing foetus is influenced by both maternal and foetal hormones. The period of gestation associated with the start of secretion of foetal hormones varies for different hormones. Prior to foetal hormone secretion and until the secretion is sustained at significant levels, maternal hormones which cross the placental barrier also play a major role.

One of the major areas of foetal growth and development is the brain and neuronal networks.

Thyroxine:

Thyroxine (mainly T3) has receptors in neurons and in supporting glial cells in the brain called oligodendrocytes. These receptors start appearing around the 10th week of gestation and increase in number after that. T3 is important for several processes including the growth and development of neural tissue (neurogenesis), neuronal migration, neuronal and glial cell differentiation (there are different types of glial cells with different functions), myelination of nerves (which allows them to transmit information faster) and synaptogenesis (the connections between neurons).

Adrenal hormones:

The foetal adrenal gland starts producing cortisol in appreciable quantities only from around 22 weeks of gestation. Cortisol acts via glucocorticoid receptors which are found on neural and glial cells across the brain, and importantly in the limbic system, that part of the brain which regulates emotion. Excessive stress during pregnancy and the exposure of the foetal brain to high levels of cortisol can increase the risk of cognitive problems after birth as well as affective problems such as schizophrenia, attention-deficit/hyperactivity disorder, antisocial behaviour, increased vulnerability to post-traumatic stress disorder, anxiety disorders, learning difficulties and depression, among others. Other hormones which can affect neuronal development in the foetus include sex steroids, oxytocin and melatonin.

Intrauterine growth retardation (IUGR) is defined as the inability of the foetus to achieve its full growth potential (genetically determined size) and this may be associated with neurodevelopmental abnormalities.

HORMONES AND AGEING

Ageing is a highly variable process between individuals. The chronological age of the person (i.e. his or her calculated age from birth) does not always reflect the biological ageing process.

Thus, some individuals who are old may function biologically like much younger people – the reverse is also true. The biological ageing process may be influenced by genetics, and health-related behaviours like diet, physical activity, smoking and alcohol intake, among others.

Hormonal changes with ageing:

Population studies reveal that there is a slight decrease in the thyroid hormone axis with ageing. This is reflected in decreased T3 levels and an increase in TSH levels. Growth hormone and its peripheral mediator (somatomedin/insulin-like growth factor) also appear to decrease with ageing. The diurnal variation in cortisol is reduced with ageing – this has been associated with decreased physical and cognitive performance.

In males, the reduction in androgen levels with ageing is associated with a reduction in muscle mass and a lowering of bone density. In women, the postmenopausal reduction in oestrogen levels also has a major effect on bone density – osteoporosis increases and this increases the risk of fractures related to falls. Bone health in the elderly is further compromised because of reduced vitamin D levels with ageing. Vitamin D is important for the absorption of calcium from the intestine. Growth hormone reduction also contributes to decreased bone health.

Glucose levels in the blood may increase modestly with ageing after the fourth decade. This may, in part, be related to reduced insulin secretion but also lower glucose uptake in the tissues. The lower uptake may, in part, reflect lower muscle mass with ageing (since muscle is a major site of glucose uptake) and increased fat deposits.

HORMONES AND STRESS

Types of stress:

Stress refers to the added demands that are placed on the body. Stressors include all events or situations that cause stress and can be of different types: (1) physical stress includes things like infection, haemorrhage and pain due to any cause; (2) psychological stress includes events that cause extreme anxiety or distress; and (3) social stress includes a variety of stressors such as death of a close friend or family member or loss of a job. Clearly certain stressors cannot easily be classified into one category or another, for instance, death in the family may be a social stress as well as a psychological stress.

Stress responses:

The response to stress occurs in two phases:

1. The immediate response to stress is the activation of the sympathetic nervous system and a release of adrenaline from the adrenal medulla. The effects of this include increased alertness, an increase in the heart rate and the force of contraction of the heart, a mobilization of energy sources in the body and an activation of the immune system.
2. When stress is sustained, the adrenal cortex begins to release cortisol. Cortisol also mobilizes the energy sources of the body but when cortisol levels remain high for prolonged periods of time, they suppress the immune system of the body.

APPLICATIONS FOR NURSING

- The nurse needs to be aware that apart from the classical features of the excess or reduced secretion of individual hormones, hormones affect the functioning of all organ systems of the body.
- The nurses because of their close interaction with patients may be more aware of any chronic stress that the patient is undergoing. This is important because chronic stress is associated with various clinical manifestations including heart disease, depression, behavioural disorders, obesity and exacerbation of asthma, among others.

CLINICAL CASE PROBLEMS

(A) ***A 40-year-old woman comes to the outpatient department with a history that she has been steadily losing weight. Although the weather has become cold, she feels warm. Her eyes are protruding and when you take her pulse, you find that her resting pulse is 100 beats/min. You also notice that she has a tremor in her hands.***

a. What condition is the woman likely to be suffering from?
b. Which endocrine gland is involved?
c. What are the metabolic actions of the hormone involved?
d. List the steps in the synthesis of the hormone.

(B) ***A 60-year-old woman reports that she has been on corticosteroids for a long time because of multiple joint pains and swelling. She noticed that her face has become 'puffy' and that she has been putting on weight around the abdomen.***

a. Which endocrine gland in the body produces glucocorticoids?
b. What are the metabolic actions of this hormone?
c. What are the immune effects of corticosteroids?
d. What condition arises due to excess secretion of this hormone in the body?

(C) ***A 70-year-old woman had a fall in the bathroom and fractured the neck of femur on the right side.***

a. What condition might she have had to increase the risk of fracture?
b. What are the main hormones that control calcium balance in the body and how do they act?
c. What can be done to improve bone health in the elderly?

SELF-DIRECTED LEARNING

- Find out some common conditions for which corticosteroids are prescribed to patients.
- Read about the complications of poorly controlled diabetes mellitus.

WHAT YOU CAN LEARN FROM A HOSPITAL VISIT

- Find out which endocrine assays are done in your hospital and how they are interpreted.
- Visit the medicine/endocrinology outpatient department of your hospital. What are the complications that long-standing diabetics commonly come with?
- Find out the different types of 'insulin' that are stocked the pharmacy. How do they differ?

7

SECTION

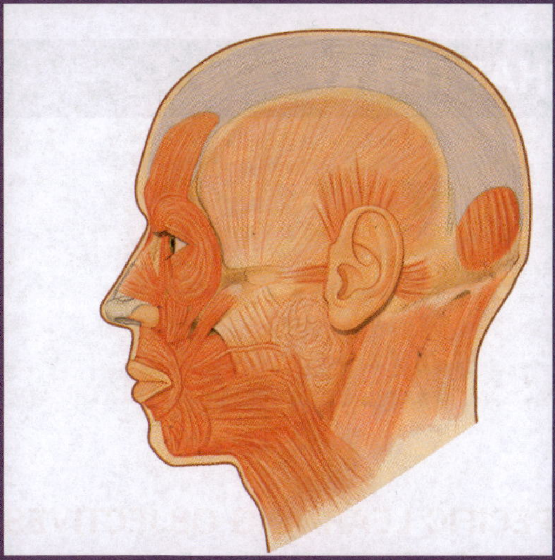

The Sensory Organs

Section Outline

CHAPTER 47

Functions of Skin

SPECIFIC LEARNING OBJECTIVES

At the end of this chapter, the student should be able to:

- Describe the functional anatomy of the skin.
- List the functions of the skin.
- Describe each function of the skin in brief.
- List the changes that occur in the skin with ageing.

GLOSSARY OF TERMS

- **Epidermis:** the outermost layer of the skin
- **Dermis:** situated just below the epidermis, this layer contains a variety of structures including connective tissue, blood vessels, sebaceous and sweat glands, nerves and hair follicles
- **Piloerection:** hair 'stands on end'; the erection of hair that accompanies exposure to cold
- **Sensation:** in medicine, sensation is the registration of nerve signals that originates from sensory receptors (in the skin, these receptors include those of pain, temperature, touch and pressure)
- **Thermoregulation:** the maintenance or regulation of body temperature (normal temperature is 98.6°F [37°C])

The skin covers our bodies and is the largest organ in the body in terms of surface area. It covers an area of approximately 20 square feet!

The skin is divided, as can be seen in Fig. 47.1, into three broad layers:

- Epidermis
- Dermis
- Subcutaneous adipose tissue (hypodermis)

The main cells of the epidermis are the keratinocytes, while the uppermost layer of epidermis, the stratum corneum, is made of a protein called keratin. Within the epidermis are the cells which give colour to our skin, called melanocytes.

The dermis, which is the layer below the epidermis, contains nerve endings, other skin receptors, sweat glands and sebaceous glands (which give the skin its oily appearance), hair follicles and blood vessels.

The subcutaneous adipose tissue layer provides insulation to the body and prevents heat loss. This layer varies in thickness in different parts of the body. It is especially thick, based on the weight of the person, in the abdomen and the buttocks.

FUNCTIONS OF THE SKIN

The skin has many functions, some of which are listed as follows:

1. Protection
2. Thermoregulation
3. Sensation
4. Excretion
5. Endocrine role

These functions are discussed in greater detail in the next section of this chapter.

PROTECTIVE ROLE OF THE SKIN

The skin protects the body in many different ways:

1. **As a physical barrier:** The topmost layer of the skin is the epidermis. This physical barrier of the skin has many roles:
   i. It prevents the entry of the microorganisms that may be harmful to the body.
   ii. It forms a waterproof layer; thus, fluids from outside cannot enter the body through the skin, nor can fluids from the body escape directly through the skin except through specialized glands.
   iii. The skin protects the body from physical and mechanical injuries. The thickness of the skin varies in different

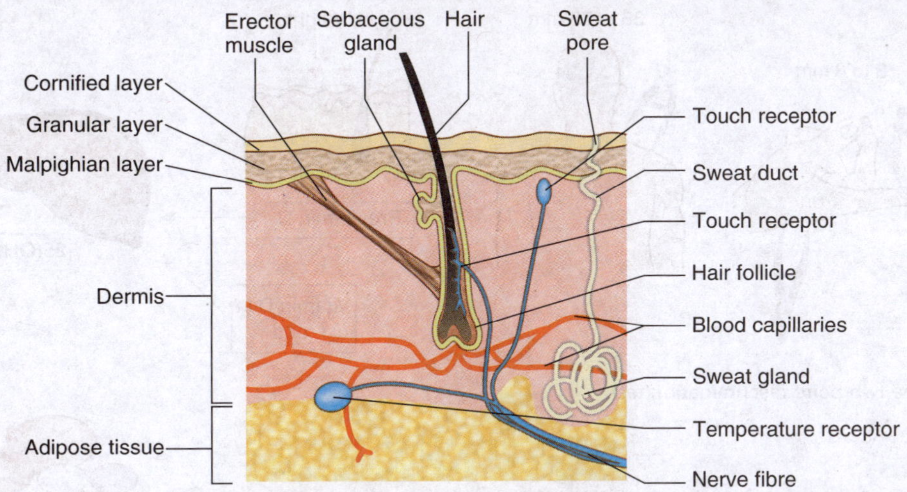

FIG. 47.1 The layers of the skin.

locations of the body. Thus, while the skin over the palms is relatively thin and soft, the skin over the soles of the feet is much thicker especially in people who walk barefoot.

iv. The skin also protects us from the harmful effects of UV radiation of the sun. There is a large variation in the colour of the skin and darker skins protect against UV radiation, largely through the pigment, melanin.

2. **As an immune barrier:** The skin contains different cells which are phagocytic (i.e. cell eating) and which also help to increase the immune response of body. This helps us to prevent or react to infections. Among the more important cells for this function are the macrophages and dendritic cells.

THERMOREGULATION

The skin plays an important role in temperature regulation of the body. It does this in different ways, four of which are described:

1. **Sweating:** In hot weather, we sweat much more. This also happens when we exercise and heat is generated within the body. Sweat is made up mainly of water and some electrolytes including sodium, potassium and chloride. As sweat evaporates, it cools the body surface.
2. **Change in blood flow in the skin:** In order for the body to lose heat to the surrounding environment, heat needs to be exchanged between the body and the environment. When the weather is hot or when the body temperature rises, the skin blood vessels vasodilate (i.e. become larger in diameter). This brings warm blood being to the surface of the skin where heat can be lost to the environment. In contrast, when the weather is cold, the blood vessels in the skin vasoconstrict (become smaller in diameter). This means that less blood is brought to the surface of the skin and therefore less heat is lost from the body. In other words, heat is conserved (retained) within the body. These changes are summarized in Fig. 47.2.

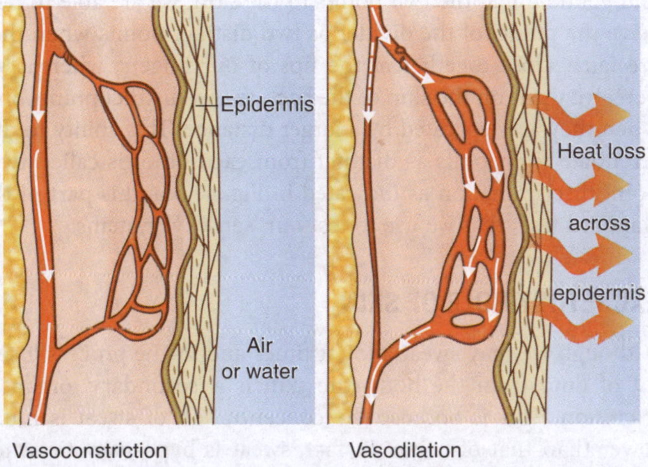

FIG. 47.2 The role of cutaneous vasoconstriction and vasodilation in temperature regulation.

3. **Piloerection:** We know that the hair on our forearms stands up (piloerection) if we feel cold. This process is important for conservation of heat in animals such as primates which have a lot of hair but is of limited use in humans since the amount of hair on the skin in humans is relatively less.
4. **Subcutaneous adipose fat as an insulation layer:** This layer prevents, partly, the heat from escaping from the body. Research studies have shown that chronically undernourished people may be unable to maintain their body temperatures, in part, due to a decrease in the subcutaneous fat layer.

ROLE OF SKIN AS A SENSORY ORGAN

Our skin has very many different kinds of sensors (receptors) which allow us to perceive different sensations. Thus, located within the skin are receptors for pain, cold and warmth, touch and pressure, among others. Not all parts of the skin are as sensitive as others. Thus, for example, the lips are more sensitive to sensations than our feet. The receptors which allow us to

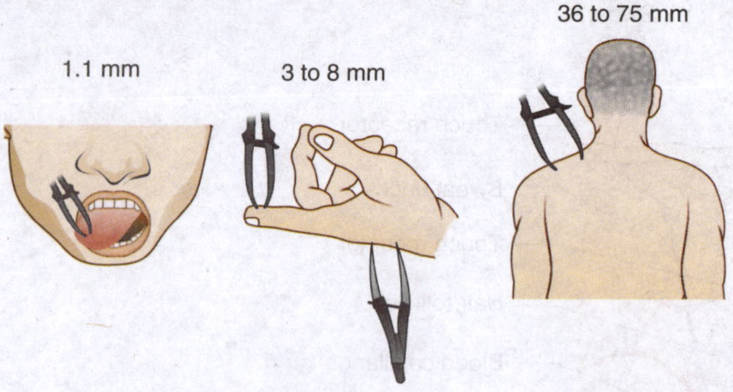

FIG. 47.3 The two-point discrimination test.

perceive sensation are located in the dermis at different depths as indicated in Fig. 47.3. Our ability to differentiate between two points on the surface of the skin also varies in different parts of the body. Thus, if we take blunt dividers from a geometry box and gentle touch the two points to the skin, we are able to perceive the points of the divider as two distinct points when they are fairly close together at the tips of our fingers, whereas we perceive them on the skin of the back as two distinct points only when they are separated by a larger distance. This ability to differentiate two points as distinct from each other is called two-point discrimination as indicated in Fig. 47.3 and is part of the standard tests that we use to test our 'sensory' systems.

EXCRETORY ROLE OF SKIN

Although we may sweat a lot at times and in the process lose a lot of fluid from the body, the skin is a 'secondary' organ of excretion. This is because the concentration of sweat is much lower than that of urine. In fact, sweat is hypo-osmotic when compared to plasma, that is it is less concentrated. The volume that we sweat depends on many factors, including the ambient (environmental) temperature and the generation of 'body heat'. When the weather is hot, adults can lose up to 10–12 L of sweat per day.

ENDOCRINE ROLE OF SKIN

The skin starts the production of vitamin D in the body. In order for vitamin D to be fully active, it must undergo chemical changes in its structure in the liver and kidney. However, the starting point is the skin. On exposure to sunlight (UV radiation), a chemical compound called 7-dehydrocholesterol (7-DHC) is converted to previtamin D3. This is the compound that is further modified in the liver and kidney (Fig. 47.4). Vitamin D is important because it helps to maintain calcium levels in the body mainly by increasing the absorption of calcium in the intestine.

In the skin, vitamin D production depends on many factors including the duration of exposure to the sun, the geographical location on the earth, the type of season, the time of day, the use of sunscreen and the type of clothing used.

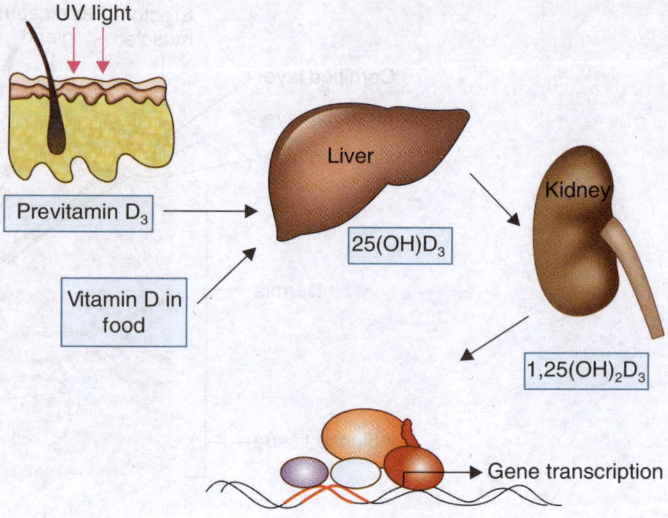

FIG. 47.4 The role of the skin in the production of vitamin D.

CHANGES IN SKIN WITH AGEING

Ageing is associated with changes in all layers of the skin which result in different manifestations:

1. Both the epidermis and the dermis decrease in thickness with ageing. The reduced cell turnover that occurs with ageing results in decreased wound healing.
2. Melanocyte density tends to decrease with ageing but this affects exposed and nonexposed areas of the skin differently.
3. Hair growth decreases with ageing and grey hair begins to appear because of decreased melanin production within the hair follicle.
4. Sebum production from the sebaceous glands decreases with ageing – the skin becomes dry.
5. The number and function of sweat glands decrease with ageing.
6. 'Photoageing' refers to the ageing of the skin due to sun exposure and is characterized by dryness of the skin, loss of elasticity and irregular pigmentation.

APPLICATIONS IN NURSING

One of the clinical situations that a nurse will need to face is that of extensive burns. In this situation, skin is lost from the surface of the body and several problems can result. The nursing plan for a patient with burns will depend on the cause of the burns, the extent of the burns, the part of the body affected and the depth of the burns. A loss of skin cover of about 15% in adults or 10% in children will require careful intravenous fluid replacement. This is because fluid loss will occur wherever the skin has been damaged or lost due to the burns. Thus, a nurse will need to maintain carefully a chart for fluid balance (intake/input and losses). In addition, the loss of protective skin cover makes the patient more susceptible to infections. Nursing care must take this into account. There are many other issues to deal with, which is beyond the scope of this textbook. These issues are highlighted in the context of the functions of the skin.

SUMMARY

The skin is an important organ in the body. It plays an important role in mechanical and immune protection, temperature regulation, excretion and sensation, and as an endocrine gland in the production of vitamin D.

CHAPTER REVIEW QUESTIONS

1. Explain how the skin helps in 'protection'.
2. How does the skin help in thermoregulation?
3. What are the receptors located in the skin?
4. What are the changes that occur in the skin with ageing?

CHAPTER 48

Physiology of Vision

SPECIFIC LEARNING OBJECTIVES

At the end of this chapter, the student should be able to:

- Draw and label a diagram of the cross-section of the eye.
- List the extraocular muscles and describe the movement that each performs.
- List the parts of the eye that light passes through in sequence before reaching the retina.
- Distinguish between rods and cones, the receptors in the eye.
- Distinguish between light and dark adaptations.
- Describe the features of accommodation.
- Trace the pathway for vision from the retina to the cortex and describe the common errors that are associated with disruptions of this pathway.
- Describe the effects of ageing on vision.
- Describe how visual function can be tested with regard to the following:
  - Visual fields
  - Visual acuity
  - Pupillary reflexes
  - Colour vision
  - Movements of the eye

GLOSSARY OF TERMS

- **Accommodation:** changes that occur in the eye when a person focuses from a distant object to a nearby object
- **Light adaptation:** the process by which the eye adapts when a person moves from a dark area to bright light
- **Dark adaptation:** the process by which the eye adapts when a person moves from bright light to a darkened area
- **Strabismus:** a condition in which the eyes are not normally aligned – commonly called squint
- **Scotoma:** loss of a part of the visual field

The eye allows us to see clearly and recognize objects in three dimensions (i.e. including depth) and to distinguish colours. The eye is located in the orbit, a bony shell that is open in front – this protects the eye from injury.

FUNCTIONAL ANATOMY OF THE EYE

Fig. 48.1 illustrates the cross-section of the eye. You will observe from this figure that the eye is not spherical.

The outer covering of the eye is the transparent cornea in front which is attached to a white, fibrous coat called the sclera, around the rest of the eye. The muscles that control the movements of the eye (extraocular muscles) are inserted into the sclera. Covering the cornea and the sclera is a mucous membrane called the conjunctiva. The conjunctiva may appear red in colour during an inflammation called conjunctivitis. Conjunctivitis can result from viral or bacterial infections as well as allergies.

In the posterior part of the eye, there are two layers inner to the sclera. The first layer is the highly vascular (filled with blood vessels) choroid which provides nutrition to the eye. The innermost layer is the retina, which we will discuss in greater detail later.

The eye is divided into two large parts:

The anterior part which is located in front of the iris and lens (Fig. 48.1) contains a clear fluid called the aqueous humour.

The posterior part of the eye located behind the lens and the iris is filled with a jelly-like mass called the vitreous humour.

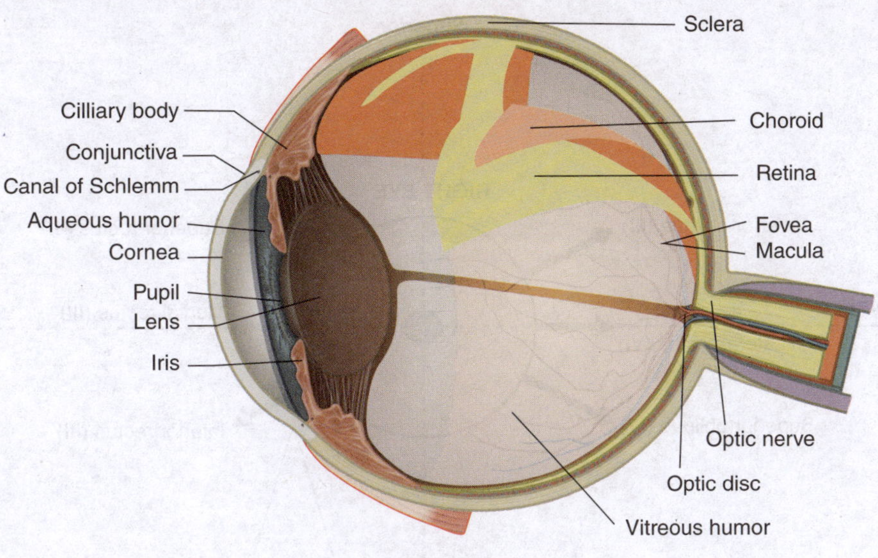

FIG. 48.1 Cross-section of the eye.

The lens is biconvex in shape. It is enclosed in a tough capsule and is held in place by a suspensory ligament that is attached to the choroid body. The choroid body consists of the ciliary muscle. When the ciliary muscle contracts, the lens becomes more convex – this allows the lens to bend the light rays more so that they are focused on the retina.

The iris projects from the ciliary body and covers a part of the lens. It is made up of muscle. The circular central part through which light enters the inner eye is called the pupil. The iris is pigmented and gives the 'eye' its colour. The muscles of the iris are arranged so as to increase or decrease the size of the pupil (Fig. 48.2).

Thus, when the circular muscles of the iris contract, they make the central pupil smaller (miosis). When the radial muscle fibres contract, the pupil becomes larger (mydriasis).

THE EXTRAOCULAR MUSCLES AND MOVEMENTS OF THE EYE

We are able to move our eyes because of extraocular muscles which are inserted into the sclera of the eye. These various muscles are depicted in Fig. 48.3. The extraocular muscles of the eye are controlled by three cranial nerves (III – oculomotor; IV – trochlear; VI – abducens). All extraocular muscles are supplied by the third cranial nerve except the lateral rectus, which moves the eye outwards (laterally) and is supplied by the abducens nerve; and the superior oblique which is supplied by the trochlear nerve.

The movements of the eye can be tested by asking the patient to look straight ahead and then follow the index finger of an examiner in all quadrants of the visual field. Fig. 48.4 illustrates which muscles of the eye are involved for different movements.

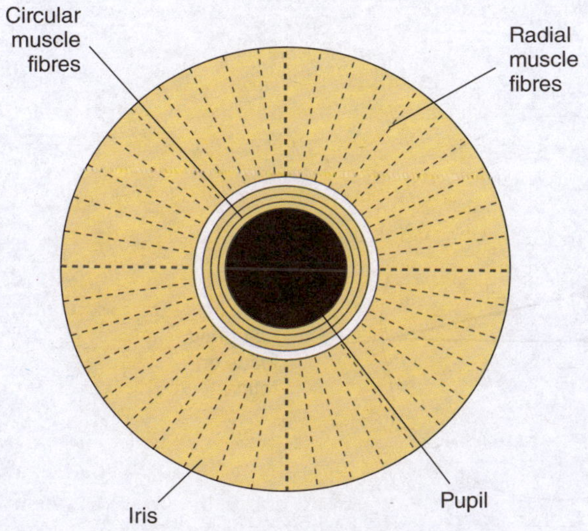

FIG. 48.2 The arrangement of the muscles of the iris.

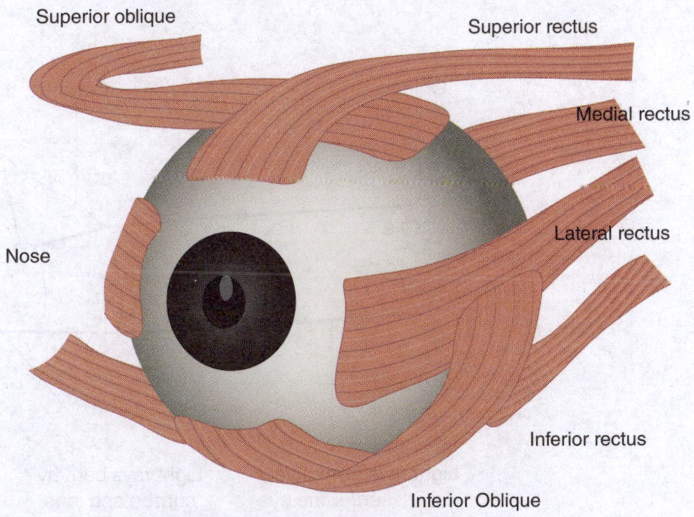

FIG. 48.3 The extraocular muscles of the eye.

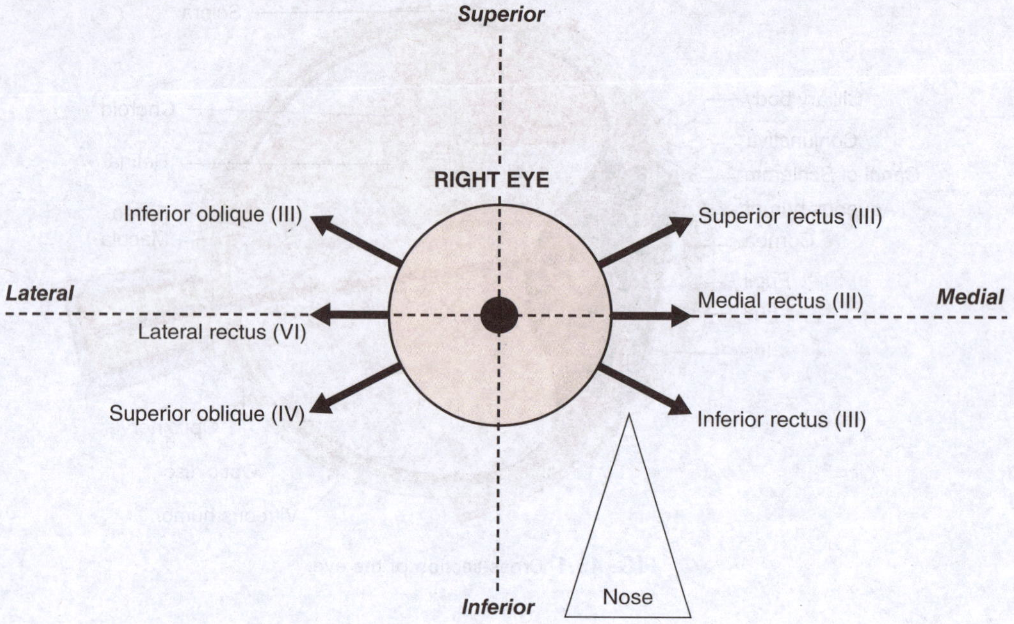

FIG. 48.4 Movements of the extraocular muscles of the eye.

A summary of the actions of the extraocular muscles is given below:

- The lateral rectus turns the eyeball laterally.
- The medial rectus turns the eyeball medially.
- The superior rectus turns the eye upwards and medially.
- The inferior rectus turns the eye downwards and medially.
- The superior oblique turns the eye downwards and laterally.
- The inferior oblique upwards and laterally.

THE PATH OF LIGHT IN THE EYE

In order for us to see an object, the ray of light needs to pass through the eye and form an image on the retina, where these signals are detected and then passed on to the brain for processing.

As a ray of light passes through the eye, it gets bent (i.e. it undergoes refraction). The various media that light needs to pass through before it reaches the retina are as follows:

1. Cornea
2. Aqueous humour
3. Lens
4. Vitreous humour

This passage of light is depicted in Fig. 48.5.

About two-thirds of the refractive power of the eye is provided by the cornea and one-third by the lens. The refractive power of the lens is not fixed but can be altered because the curvature of the lens can be increased by the contraction of the ciliary muscles.

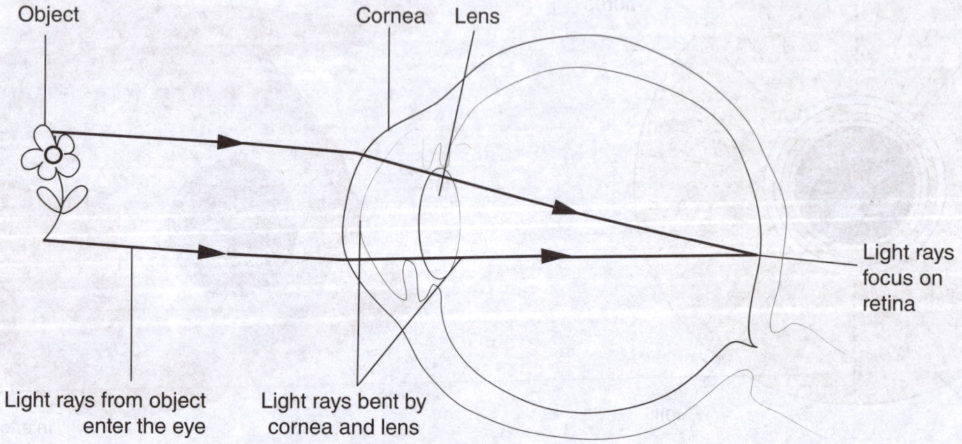

FIG. 48.5 The pathway of light entering the eye.

THE RECEPTORS OF THE EYE

Once the image falls on the retina, it needs to be detected. This is possible because the retina contains the sense organs of the eye. These are the *rods* and *cones*. The rods are especially helpful when we see in the dark (scotopic vision), while the cones are more active when it is bright (photopic vision) and also help us to differentiate colour.

The rods and cones are different in structure and both contain special pigments that are sensitive to light. These pigments undergo changes when they are exposed to light and then stimulate the nerve fibres that leave the eye and go towards that part of the brain which processes visual information. A comparison of the rods and cones is provided in Table 48.1.

Rods and cones are named because of the shape of their cells as illustrated in Fig. 48.6.

On the retina is a region called the fovea – this is the region of maximum density of cones per unit area. It is the area where detail (visual acuity) of objects is maximum. It is also the region from where close to 50% of the nerve fibres that travel in the optic nerve arise. The fovea is located about 2 mm away from the optic disc. The area around the fovea contains a yellow pigment and is thus called the yellow spot.

Table 48.1 Comparison Between the Rods and the Cones

	Rods	Cones
Number	20 times more than cones, i.e. 120 million in each eye	6 million in each eye
Most active	In dim light (i.e. night vision)	In bright light
Characteristics	Discern coarse detail	Discern fine detail, colour vision
Pigment	Rhodopsin	Cone pigments (blue, green and red sensitive)

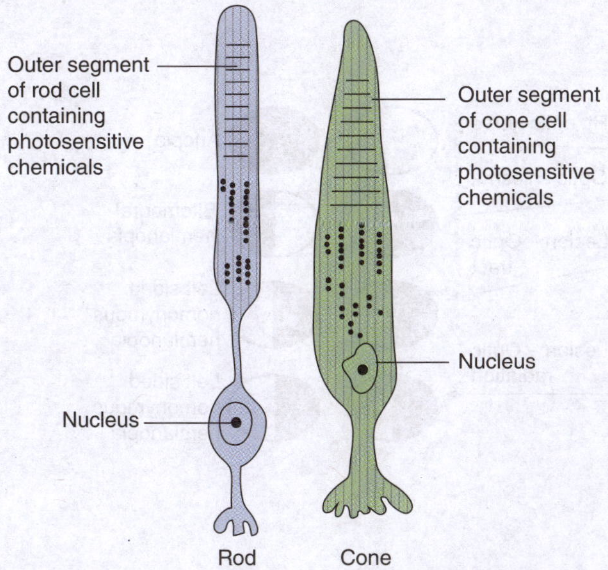

FIG. 48.6 The receptors (rods and cones) of the retina.

There is a part of the retina where there are no rods or cones. This occurs at the optic disc, where the optic nerve arises. Images that fall on this part of the retina will not be sensed and give rise to a *blind spot*.

LIGHT AND DARK ADAPTATIONS

If you move from a dark room into bright light (like when you come out of a movie theatre), you will feel that the light is very bright. You will probably blink and screw up your eyes to limit the amount of light entering the eye. After about 5 minutes, the eyes now seem to adapt to the bright environment – this is called *light adaptation*.

In contrast, when you have spent a lot of time in bright light and you suddenly enter a dark room, you find that you are initially unable to see very much. Slowly, over a period of time, you are able to see more and more details in the dark room. This process is called *dark adaptation* and takes about 20 minutes to be complete.

ACCOMMODATION

This is the process by which the eye adapts when you are looking at a distant object and then suddenly start seeing something very close, in front of the eye. You can test for accommodation by asking a person to look into the distance and then asking him or her to focus on your finger which you hold up in front of his or her eyes.

When a person tries to refocus on a nearer object, the rays of light initially meet behind the retina resulting in blurred vision. After a brief moment, however, the object becomes clear – this is because the ciliary muscle contracts and the lens becomes more convex allowing the rays of light to be focused on the retina (Fig. 48.7).

While the major change in accommodation is an increase in the convexity of the lens, there are actually three changes which occur:

1. An increase in the curvature of the lens
2. A convergence of the eyes
3. Miosis (pupils become smaller)

THE VISUAL PATHWAY

Once the image is received on the retina, information is then transmitted along the optic nerve (i.e. the second cranial nerve) to the part of the cortex where visual information is processed. Fig. 48.8 depicts the visual pathway from the two eyes.

The area from which we perceive visual information is called the visual field. This is basically the area we can see. For each eye, the field of vision that is closer to the nose is called the nasal field, while the area that is towards the outer parts of our vision is called the temporal field. The nasal visual field projects on the temporal part of the retina, while the temporal visual fields project on the nasal parts of the retina.

Information from each eye is first conveyed to the **optic nerve**. Thus visual information from the left eye is carried in the left optic nerve and that from the right eye in the right optic nerve. Now look at Fig. 48.8 carefully. You will observe that all the fibres of the optic nerve do not remain on the same side of the brain. Thus, the optic nerve fibres that carry information from the temporal part of each retina remain on their respective sides. However, the nerve fibres which carry information from the

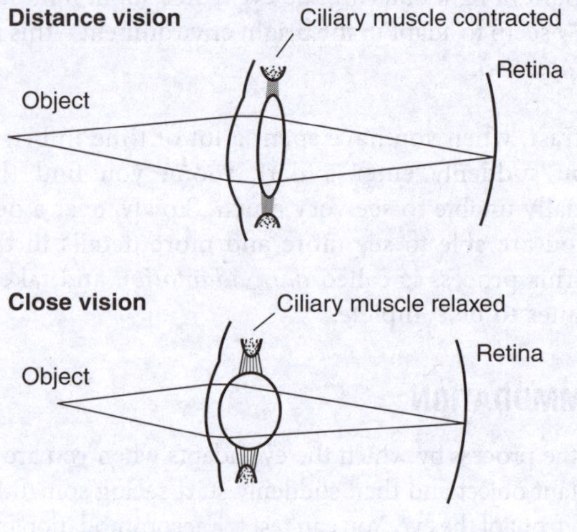

FIG. 48.7 The process of accommodation.

nasal sides of the retina cross to the opposite side of the brain at the **optic chiasma** (see the fibres that cross the 'dashed' line, which shows the midline). Thus, the **optic tract** on the right side now conveys information from the right temporal retina (right nasal field) and the left nasal retina (left temporal field), while the left optic tract conveys information from the left temporal retina and the right nasal retina.

The fibres of the optic tract synapse in a structure are called the **lateral geniculate body**. The visual pathway then continues as the **optic radiation** to the **visual cortex** which is located in the occipital lobe of the brain (areas 17–19).

It is particularly important to know what information is being carried at different points on the visual pathway, because this will determine the type of visual loss that occurs. The following text refers to visual field defects shown in Fig. 48.8. Thus:

1. When the optic nerve is completely cut, there will be complete loss of vision in that eye. Thus, if the right optic nerve is cut, there will be *complete blindness (anopia)* in the right eye.
2. If there is a lesion in the optic chiasma, the fibres from the nasal parts of the retina of both eyes will be affected. The nasal parts of the retina receive visual information from the temporal (outer) visual fields. Thus, the individual will have a loss of vision of both temporal visual fields. This condition is called *bitemporal hemianopia*, since visual loss is for half of the visual field in each eye and is restricted to the temporal fields.
3. If there is a lesion in the right optic tract, fibres from the temporal area of the retina of the right eye and the nasal area of the left eye will be affected. In this situation, there will be a loss of one-half of the visual field of each eye, restricted to

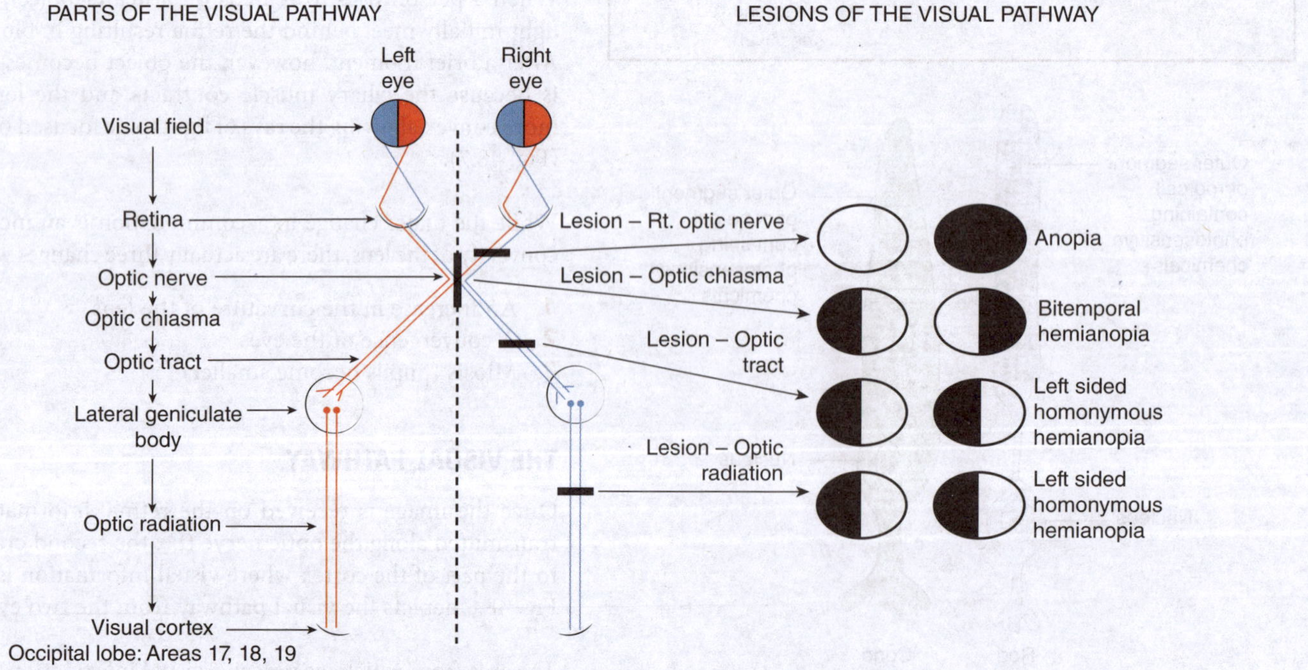

FIG. 48.8 The visual pathway.

the left side of the visual field. For this reason, the visual loss is called a *left-sided homonymous hemianopia*.

4. A lesion of the optic radiation has approximately the same visual defect as a lesion of the optic tract on the same side. There is one difference, however. The central parts of the visual field are spared – this is called *macular sparing*. This may be because the cortical representation of the macula is very large, and that lesions affecting the occipital lobe are often due to strokes. The occipital lobe receives a dual blood supply (posterior and middle cerebral artery). Thus, a block of one of the blood vessels which supply the occipital lobe will have less impact as the blood flow needs will be met by the other blood vessel supplying the occipital lobe – and the visual function (in this case, the macula) is spared.

THE EFFECTS OF AGEING ON VISION

One of the difficulties is separating the visual effects of ageing from those of chronic diseases such as diabetes and hypertension, among others, which are more common in older people. Nevertheless, certain patterns have emerged:

1. An increased corneal degeneration which may result in increased corneal fragility (the extent to which this may occur is dependent on environmental exposures and genetic factors).
2. The pupil tends to become smaller and less reactive to light compared to healthy young adults.
3. The lens hardens with age (cataract) and this makes it less able to change curvature during accommodation.
4. The decreased elasticity of the lens capsule and the hardening of the lens result in reduced accommodation and presbyopia (this is discussed further in Chapter 51).
5. There is a reduction in photoreceptors resulting in a decreased visual acuity.
6. Ageing may be associated with macular degeneration resulting in a distortion of vision and visual degeneration.

TESTING FOR VISUAL FUNCTION

Visual Fields

There are two basic tests that can be used to assess the visual field. The first is completely instrument free but assumes that the examiner has normal visual fields. This test is called the *confrontation test*. As can be seen in Fig. 48.9, the examiner and the patient sit across each other about 1 m apart. The examiner covers the left eye, while the patient covers the right

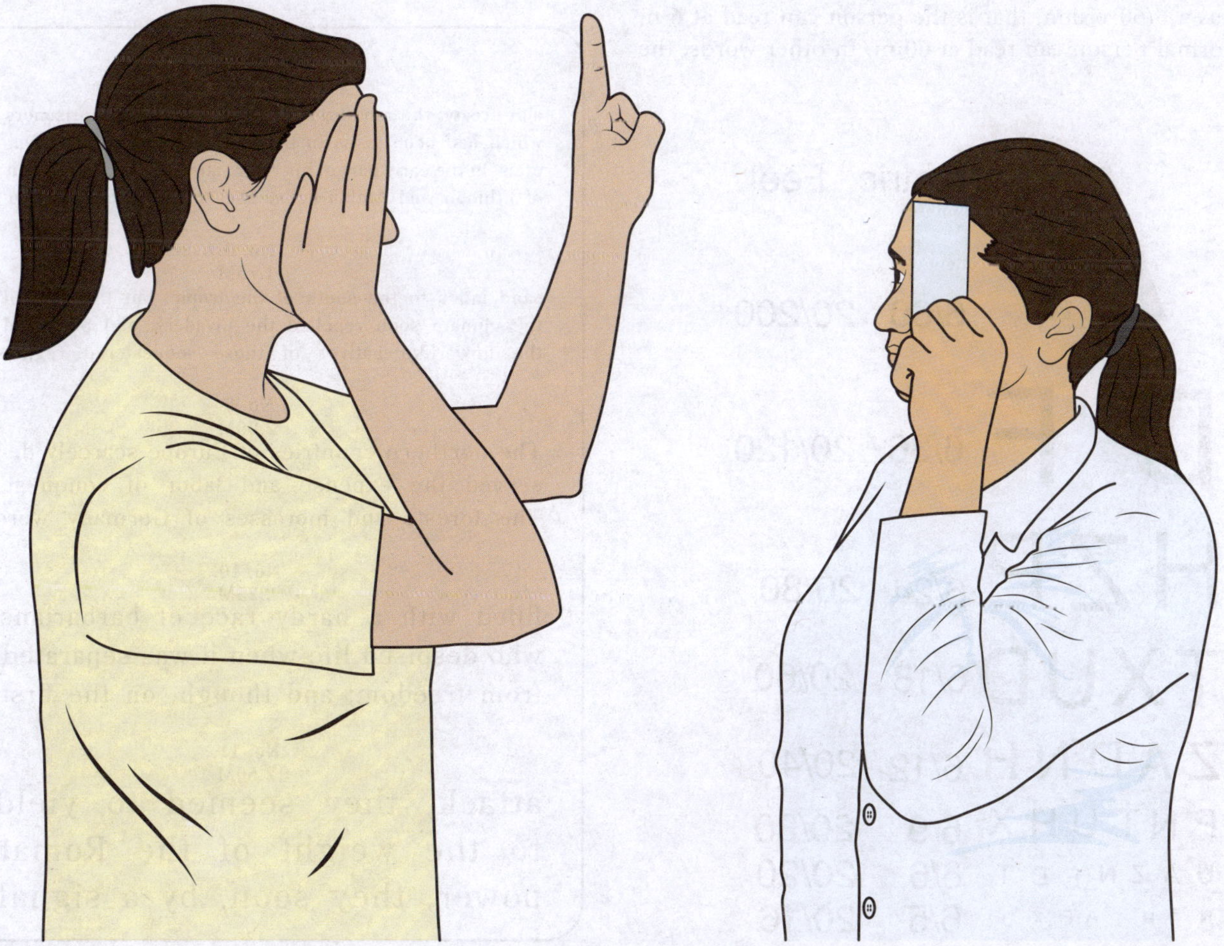

FIG. 48.9 Assessing the visual fields using the confrontation test.

eye. The examiner and the patient fix their gaze on each other's open eye. The examiner now extends the left hand with the index finger pointing out and slowly brings the finger inwards – at some point, the patient will visualize the tip of the index finger – if the patient does not have a visual defect, the patient and the examiner will visualize the tip of the index finger at approximately the same time. This process can then be repeated at different quadrants of the visual field and for both eyes.

A second way to test visual field is to use an instrument called a *perimeter*.

Visual Acuity

While there are more technical definitions, visual acuity refers to how clearly we can see an object. This is most often tested using a *Snellen's chart*. A typical Snellen's chart is depicted in Fig. 48.10. In order to use this chart, the patient is seated 6 m from the chart, covers one eye and then reads the letters line by line, starting at the topmost line. After completing a test with one eye, the other eye is tested independently.

If the person can read all the letters only up to the second last line, that is UAZNFDT, it means that the person has 6/6 vision, that is the person can read at 6 m what a normal person should read at 6 m. If, however, the person can read only the top line, that is the letter A, this means that the person has a 6/60 vision, that is the person can read at 6 m what a normal person can read at 60 m. In other words, the person has poor visual acuity. The Snellen's chart tests visual acuity at a distance.

In order to test near vision acuity, other charts such as the *Jaeger's chart* are used (Fig. 48.11). This chart contains short paragraphs of written matter at different print sizes. The individual holds that chart at a reading distance and reads the chart. A note is made of which print size the individual can read comfortably.

Light Reflexes

There are two types of light reflexes: direct and indirect (consensual). When a light is shone into an eye, the pupil constricts (direct reflex). However, if you observe the other eye, you will see that the pupil on the other side also constricts, although the light is not directly shone into it (consensual reflex). The light reflex is mediated by two different cranial nerves. Perception of the light is via the optic nerve (second cranial nerve), while the response to the light, that is constriction of the pupils, is mediated by the oculomotor nerve (third cranial nerve).

Colour Vision

Colour vision can be tested in different ways. Patients can, for instance, be asked to identify different-coloured bits of wool. A more formal test of colour vision testing was developed by

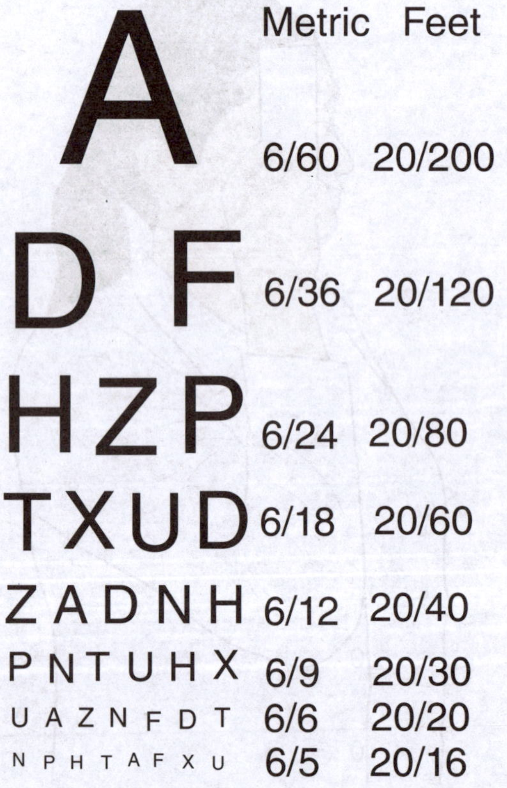

FIG. 48.10 Snellen's chart.

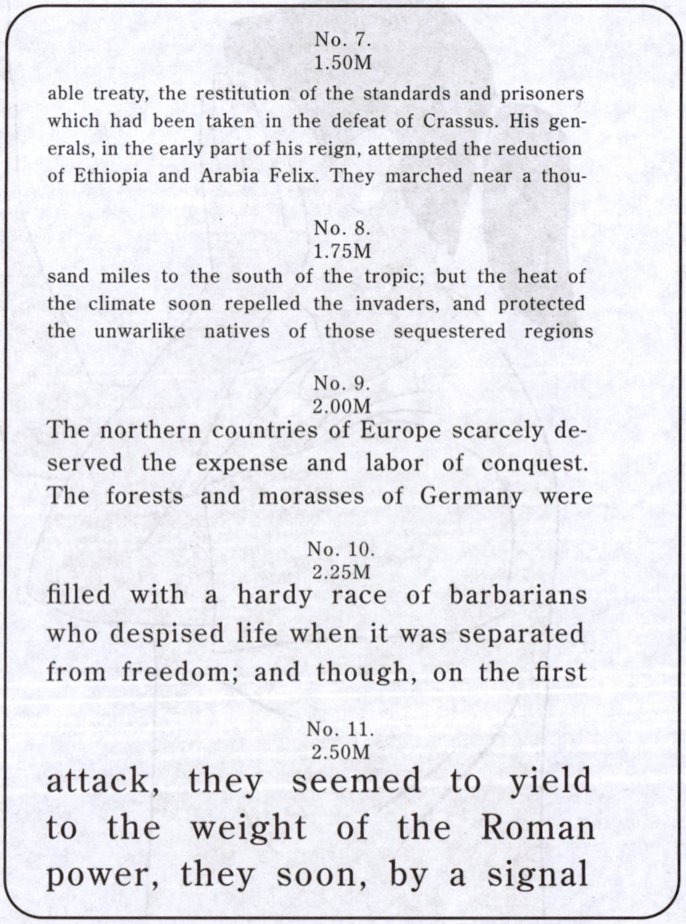

No. 7.
1.50M

able treaty, the restitution of the standards and prisoners which had been taken in the defeat of Crassus. His generals, in the early part of his reign, attempted the reduction of Ethiopia and Arabia Felix. They marched near a thou-

No. 8.
1.75M

sand miles to the south of the tropic; but the heat of the climate soon repelled the invaders, and protected the unwarlike natives of those sequestered regions

No. 9.
2.00M

The northern countries of Europe scarcely deserved the expense and labor of conquest. The forests and morasses of Germany were

No. 10.
2.25M

filled with a hardy race of barbarians who despised life when it was separated from freedom; and though, on the first

No. 11.
2.50M

attack, they seemed to yield to the weight of the Roman power, they soon, by a signal

FIG. 48.11 Jaeger's chart.

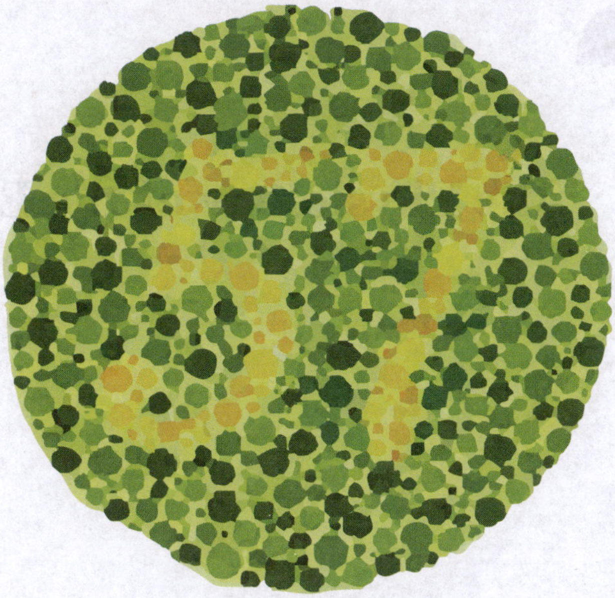

FIG. 48.12 Ishihara's charts.

Ishihara and used coloured charts called *Ishihara's charts.* Ishihara's charts consist of dots of different colours with numbers hidden in them. Patients are asked to identify the numbers. Fig. 48.12 illustrates one example of such a chart.

APPLICATIONS FOR NURSING

- Because visual defects are so common, nurses should be aware of screening tests of vision including the use of Snellen's and Jaeger's charts.
- The nurse is an integral part of the team when patients undergo surgical treatment for cataract and glaucoma. Patients are likely to be very worried about operations on their eyes. Nurses must be aware of the basic surgical procedures involved, and must be in a position to support the patient with health education and the use of their medications.
- Nurses must be familiar with the dietary requirements of special groups such as pregnant and nursing women and children. In the context of the eye, they must be able to provide nutritional advice of vitamin A–rich foods based on local customs and dietary restrictions.

SUMMARY

- Rays of light pass, in sequence, through the cornea, aqueous humour, lens and vitreous humour before reaching the retina. An image that is formed on the retina is seen clearly. The cornea and the retina provide the greatest refraction which helps focus an image on the retina.
- Rods and cones are the receptors of the retina. Rods function in dim light, while cones function in bright light and are responsible for colour vision.
- Accommodation is the process by which the eye which is focused on a distant object refocuses on a nearly object. It involves convergence of the eyeballs, constriction of the pupils and increased curvature of the lens.
- Information from the retina is transmitted via the optic nerve, part of which crosses over to the other side of the brain at the optic chiasma. The next section of the visual pathway is the optic tract which synapses at the lateral geniculate body, and then continues as the optic radiation to end in the visual cortex in the occipital lobe.
- Clinical testing of the eye, among other things, includes testing for visual fields, visual acuity, light reflexes, colour vision and movements of the eye.

CHAPTER REVIEW QUESTIONS

1. What are the extraocular muscles of the eye? State their nerve supply and indicate their function.
2. What are the differences between rods and cones?
3. Trace the visual pathway with the help of a diagram.
4. What is accommodation?

CHAPTER 49

The Physiology of the Ear

SPECIFIC LEARNING OBJECTIVES

At the end of this chapter, the student should be able to:

- Draw and label a diagram of the ear indicating the outer, middle and inner ear.
- List the functions of the middle ear.
- Describe how sound is sensed in the inner ear.
- Trace the auditory pathway.
- Describe the effects of ageing on hearing.
- Describe how hearing is tested using tuning forks and audiometry.

GLOSSARY OF TERMS

- **Audiometry:** a test which measures the ability of a person to hear sounds over a range of frequencies

The ear is the organ of hearing and balance and equilibrium (the vestibular apparatus). In this chapter, we will focus on the role of the ear in hearing. Before proceeding with the functions of the ear, it is useful to revise the characteristics of sound. Sound is described in terms of its pitch, loudness and 'timbre'. The pitch is described objectively in terms of frequency and allows us to distinguish between a low and a high sound. Timbre is the quality of the sound.

The ear allows us to distinguish all sorts of sounds, separate noise from music, appreciate the intensity of sound, determine the direction of sound and even estimate whether a sound is close by or far away.

The ear consists of three parts (Fig. 49.1):

1. External ear
2. Middle ear
3. Inner ear

THE EXTERNAL EAR

Parts of the external (outer) ear:

The external ear (Fig. 49.1) consists of two parts:

- *pinna* which is what we see and identify as the ear externally consists of elastic cartilage covered by the skin. The pinna in some ways looks like a funnel. The lower part of the external ear is the fleshy lobe or lobule of the ear.
- *external auditory canal.* This canal is about 2.5 cm in length in an adult and ends in the tympanic membrane or eardrum. The canal has sebaceous glands which secrete *cerumen* or earwax. Excess and hard earwax can reduce hearing because it interferes with the conduction of sound to the middle ear; when severe, this can result in *conduction deafness.*

Functions of the external ear:

The external ear has the following functions:

1. The pinna helps to funnel sound into the auditory canal.
2. The auditory canal helps to transmit sounds from the outside to the tympanic membrane.
3. The cerumen prevents dust particles and foreign bodies from entering the ear.
4. The direction from where the sound waves enter the external ear helps us determine the direction of the sound.

THE MIDDLE EAR

Parts of the middle ear:

1. *The tympanic membrane*: This is made up of collagen and elastic fibres. It is shaped like a shallow conical hat and appears translucent.

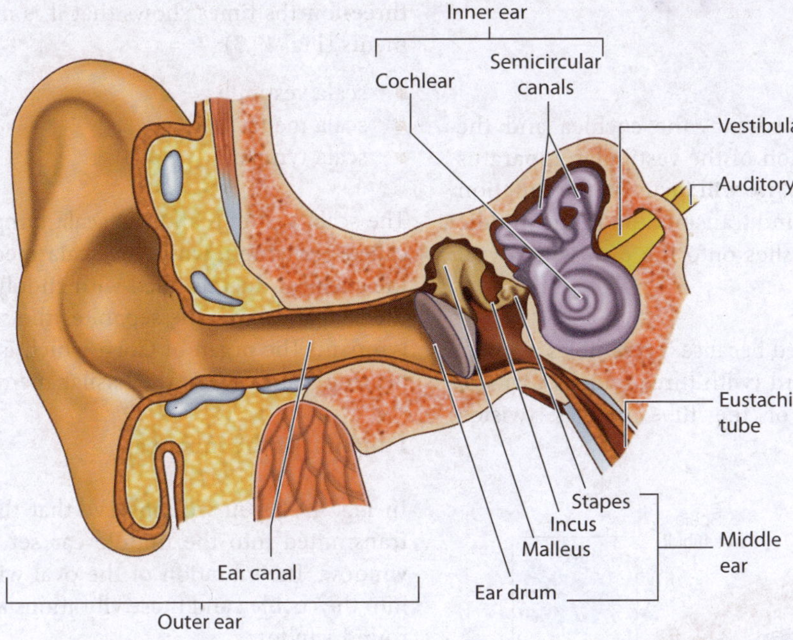

FIG. 49.1 Three parts of the ear (outer, middle and inner ear).

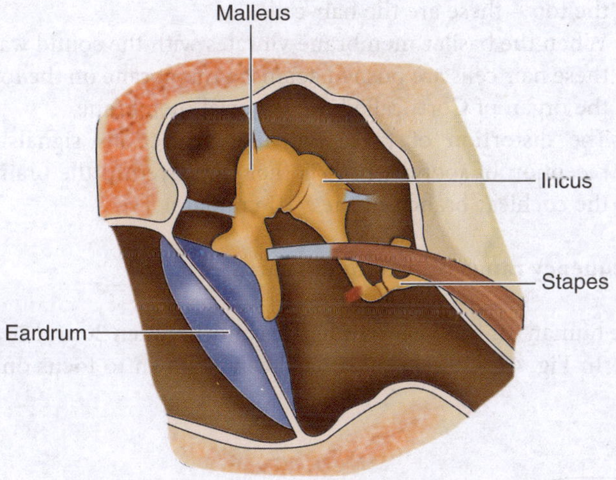

FIG. 49.2 The arrangement of the ossicles in the middle ear.

2. *Three ossicles*: These are the smallest bones in the body and, in order, from the tympanic membrane (see Fig. 49.2) are the *malleus, incus and stapes*.
3. *Two muscles*: These include *tensor tympani* which is attached to the malleus and the *stapedius* muscle which is attached to the stapes.
4. *Eustachian tube*: It connects the middle ear to the pharynx.

Functions of the middle ear:

1. The major function of the middle ear is to transmit sound waves from the external ear to the internal ear. The tympanic membrane vibrates when sound waves reach it through the auditory canal. These vibrations are then transferred to the ossicles. The malleus rests on the tympanic membrane and the footplate of the stapes rests on the oval window of the inner ear. Thus, vibrations are transferred to the inner ear.
2. The ossicles are so arranged that they act like a lever and amplify (increase) the sound waves that reach the inner ear. This process by which the normal damping (reduction) of sound waves that would occur over a distance is overcome by the lever action of the ossicles is called *impedance matching*.
3. The muscles of the middle ear help to control the movement of the ossicles. Thus, when we are exposed to a loud sound, the tensor tympani contracts – this pulls the malleus inwards, tenses the tympanic membrane and thus reduces its movement. At the same time, the stapedius muscle contracts and pulls the stapes away from the oval window, and this reduces the transmission of sound to the inner ear. The net result is to reduce the sound and decrease the damage to the ear due to loud sounds. This reflex in response to a loud sound, which attempts to reduce transmission and damage to the inner ear, is called the *attenuation reflex* or acoustic reflex.
4. The Eustachian tube helps to equalize the pressure in the middle ear to that of the atmospheric pressure. However, the connection of the middle ear to the pharynx via the Eustachian tube means that infections of the nose and throat may result in the swelling of the lining of the Eustachian tube – in these circumstances, individuals sometimes experience reduced hearing. Swallowing or yawning may open this constricted Eustachian tube with a 'pop'.

THE INNER EAR

Parts of the inner ear:

The inner ear consists of two parts – the cochlea and the vestibular apparatus. The function of the vestibular apparatus is described in Chapter 70. Here, we will focus on the function of the cochlea. As part of the sound transmission in the middle ear, the stapes vibrates, and pushes onto the oval window of the cochlea.

The cochlea (Fig. 49.3) is so called because it resembles a snail's shell derived from the Latin word (with three-fourths turns of the shell). The cross-section of the tube that is twisted three-fourths times shows that it is made up of three compartments (Fig. 49.3):

- scala vestibuli
- scala media
- scala tympani

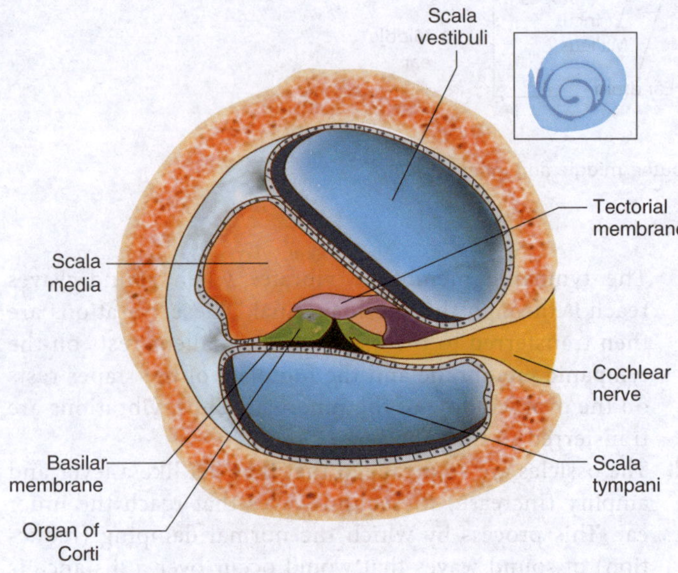

FIG. 49.3 A cross-section of the cochlea.

The scala vestibuli and the scala tympani are filled with a fluid called perilymph, while the scala media, also sometimes called the cochlear duct, is filled with endolymph. A membrane called the basilar membrane separates the scala media from the scala tympani. The organ of Corti which is the actual sense organ of hearing is located on the basilar membrane.

Function of the inner ear:

In Fig. 49.4, you will observe that the sound waves which are transmitted into the middle ear set up vibrations of the oval window. The vibration of the oval window is then transmitted into the cochlea and these vibrations are then damped out at the round window.

The organ of Corti is shown in Fig. 49.5).

- It consists of special cells which have hair-like projections on the top – these are the hair cells.
- When the basilar membrane vibrates with the sound waves, these hair cells are pushed against a membrane on the top of the organ of Corti called the tectorial membrane.
- The distortion of these hair-like projections signals the reception of sound which is then conveyed to the brain by the cochlear branch of the VIII cranial nerve.

Frequency range of the human ear:

The human ear can hear frequencies only between 20 and 20,000 Hz. In Fig. 49.6, the cochlea has been redrawn to focus on the

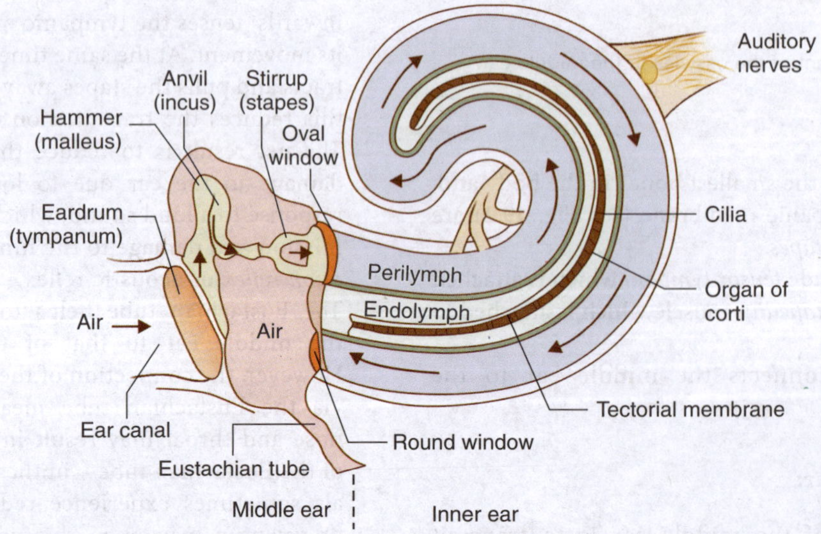

FIG. 49.4 The transmission of the sound waves in the inner ear.

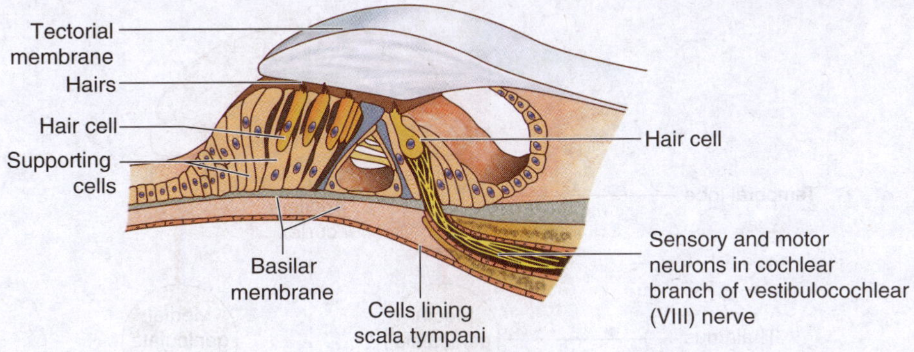

FIG. 49.5 The organ of Corti.

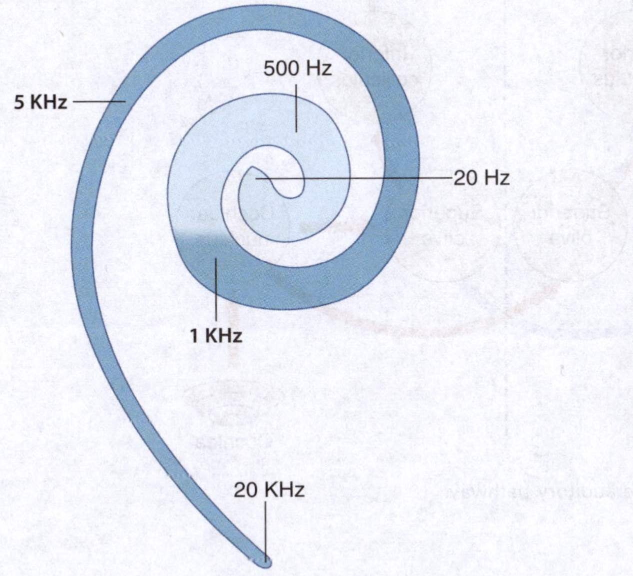

FIG. 49.6 The varying thickness of the basilar membrane in the inner ear.

basilar membrane only. Although the cochlea becomes narrower at the apex, the basilar membrane thickness is opposite, that is the basilar membrane is thinner at the base and thicker at the apex. If you have plucked the strings of a guitar or a violin or any other stringed instrument, you will have observed that the thicker strings of the instrument give a lower (more base) sound, while the thinner strings give a higher sound. Lower sounds are associated with lower frequencies of sound waves and higher sounds have a higher frequency of sound waves. When we listen to a sound, the sound is transmitted to the cochlea – if it is a more base sound, it will cause the thicker part of the basilar membrane to vibrate, while if it is a higher sound, a thinner part of the basilar membrane will vibrate. Fig. 49.6 shows that individual parts of the basilar membrane, based on their thickness, can vibrate only between 20 and 20,000 Hz. Twenty hertz is registered at the apex of the cochlea where the basilar membrane is thickest, while 20,000 Hz is registered at the base of the cochlea where the basilar membrane is thinnest. This is why the human ear hears sound only between 20 and 20,000 Hz. Many animals such as dogs and cats can hear sounds at much higher frequencies than humans.

THE AUDITORY PATHWAY

The auditory pathway which carries the signals from the organ of Corti in the cochlea to the brain involves several neurons and hence multiple synapses. The pathway is illustrated in Fig. 49.7.

- The first nerve fibres are those of the cochlea branch of the VIII cranial nerve which synapse in the cochlear nuclei in the brainstem.
- From here, some nerve fibres cross to the other side of the brain and relay first at the superior olive and then at the inferior colliculus. It is at these two areas that information is processed to allow us to localize sound (i.e. tell us where the sound is coming from).
- From the superior olive upwards information of both ears is represented bilaterally.
- There is another relay in a part of the thalamus (the sensory relay station of the brain) called the medial geniculate body. It is here that a response to the sound that we have heard begins to take place – this response may be in the form of a vocal response, that is a reply to something that we have just heard.
- Information from the thalamus is finally sent to the auditory cortex which is located in the temporal lobe.

THE EFFECTS OF AGEING ON HEARING

Hearing loss with ageing is dependent on a number of factors. Thus, prior ear infections, injury, chronic exposure to loud sounds and chronic medical conditions such as diabetes and high blood pressure, as well as certain medications, can all affect hearing.

The hearing loss with ageing typically starts with a decrease in hearing at higher frequencies and then progresses to lower frequencies along with a deterioration of the hearing threshold. Hearing loss due to ageing is often bilateral (affecting both ears) and symmetrical (equal hearing loss on both sides).

The reasons for decreased hearing with ageing (presbycusis) include:

- Degeneration of the hair cells which help to convert the sound waves into electrical signals for transmission in the

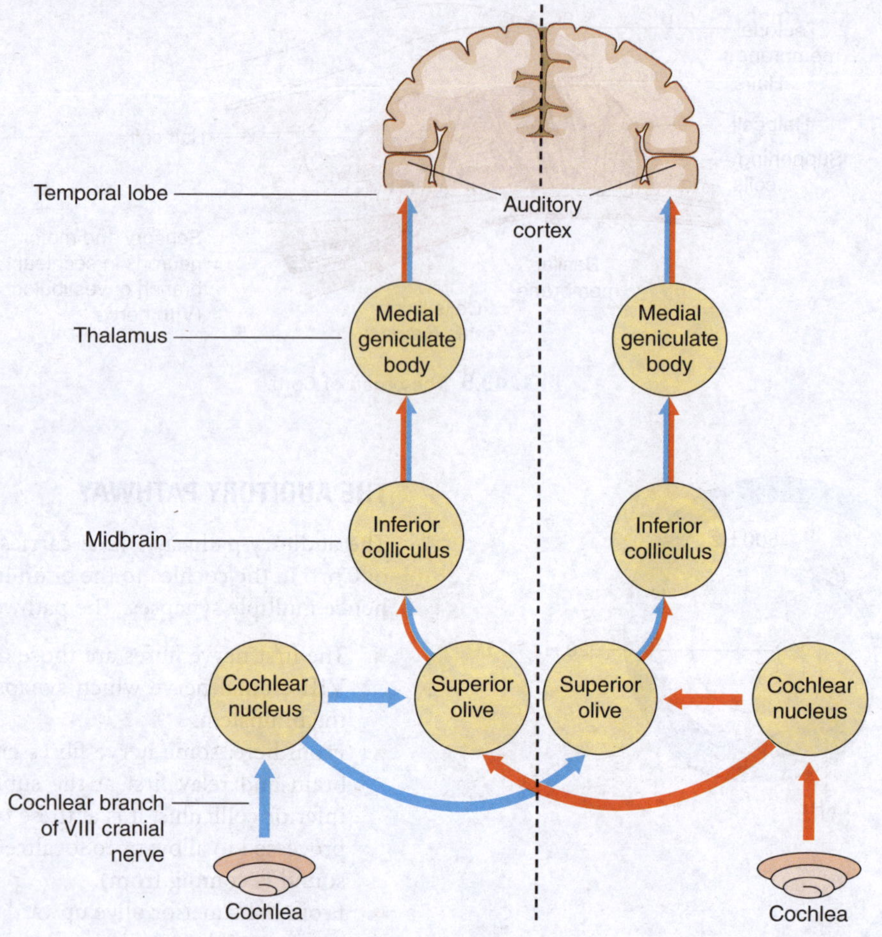

FIG. 49.7 The auditory pathway.

auditory nerve (peripheral presbycusis) (this is responsive to the use of hearing aids).

- Degeneration of the cochlear nerves that receive signals from the hair cells or degeneration of the nerves involved in the auditory pathway and in auditory processing (central presbycusis).

TESTS OF HEARING

Hearing can be tested using simple tuning fork tests. However, these tests are less sensitive than 'audiometry' which is also described in the subsequent text and which has additional advantages.

Tuning Fork Tests

Tuning fork tests of hearing are typically carried out using a tuning fork of 512 Hz. Among other reasons, this frequency is used because it is in the mid-speech frequency range and it allows for the best determination of air–bone conduction gap (details given later). Fig. 49.8 illustrates the parts of a tuning fork.

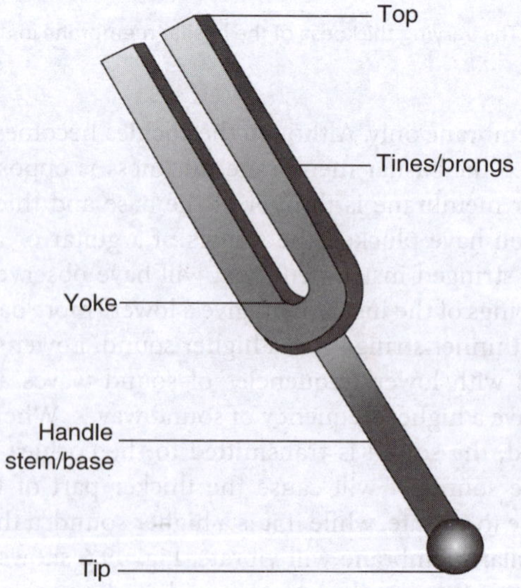

FIG. 49.8 Parts of a tuning fork.

Rinne's Test Hold the tuning fork on its side, grasp the base firmly and then strike one of the prongs against the heel (lower palm) of the hand. Now place it on the bony mastoid process behind the ear (bone conduction). When the person can no longer hear a sound, quickly transfer the tip of the tuning fork about 1–2 cm away from the opening of the auditory canal (air conduction). A person with normal hearing should be able to continue to hear a sound, since air conduction is better than bone conduction, and this normal response is called a Rinne's positive response. Both ears should be tested in this way (Fig. 49.9). If, however, bone conduction is better than air conduction, the test is a Rinne's negative test and indicates that there is a defect in the conduction of sound waves, that is there is conduction deafness.

Weber's Test In this test, the base of the vibrating tuning fork is placed in the midline of the forehead (Fig. 49.10).

The person is asked whether he or she can hear equally on both sides or whether hearing is better on one side. If in the previous example, hearing is better on the left side, there are two possibilities:

1. There may be conduction deafness on the left side. Because of conduction deafness, external sounds are masked on the affected side and the tuning fork is better heard on the affected side.
2. There may be a sensorineural deafness on the right side. Because sound cannot be processed by the brain in sensorineural deafness, the person will hear better on the affected side.

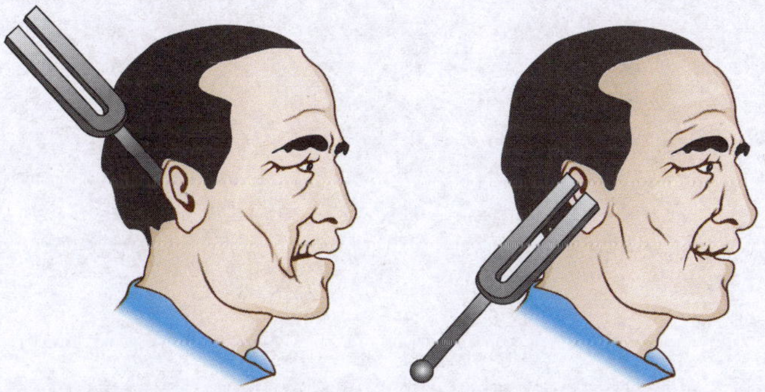

FIG. 49.9 Rinne's test.

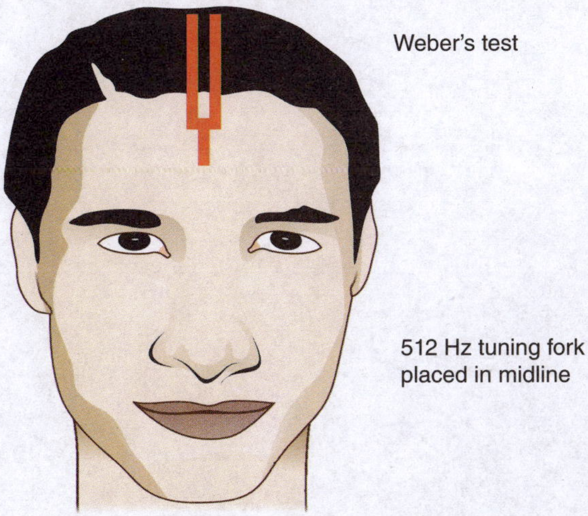

FIG. 49.10 Weber's test.

Audiometry

This is typically conducted in a soundproof room. Each ear is tested separately and subjected to sounds of a specific tone and intensity through specially designed ear phones. A tone is typically measured in hertz – sounds of lower frequency are heard as base and sounds of higher frequency appear shriller. Intensity of sound is measured in decibels. Whispering, for instance, is about 30 dB, while a food mixer is about 85 dB. The minimum intensity at which a particular frequency is heard is marked on a special chart and the completed test constitutes an audiogram. Audiometry can also be tested by applying the frequency through the auditory canal (air conduction) or through the mastoid bone (bone conduction).

Fig. 49.11 is an example of an audiogram. You will observe from this audiogram that the person can hear higher frequencies, that is 4000–8000 Hz, only at an intensity of between 70 and 80 dB, while at the lower frequencies of between 250 and 1000 Hz, the person can hear at much lower intensities of sound (i.e. ;10 dB). This is a typical picture of high-frequency deafness and illustrates one of the advantages that audiometry has over tuning fork tests – it is able to determine the exact frequencies at which there is deafness.

APPLICATIONS FOR NURSING

- In a country like India where a significant number of children are deaf because of inadequately treated otitis media, nurses may need to be a part of community screening programmes for deafness and school health education programmes that promote awareness and early treatment.
- Since nurses play an important role in the communications with patients, learning how to communicate with patients with limited hearing becomes important.

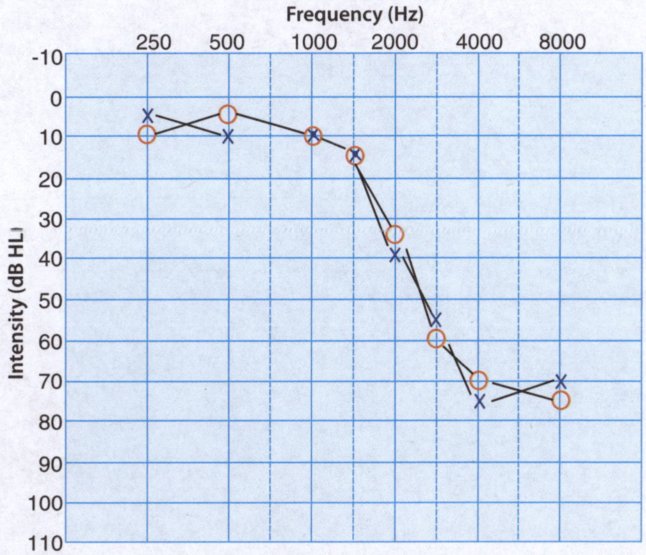

FIG. 49.11 An audiogram.

SUMMARY

- The ear is divided into an external, middle and inner ear. The external ear funnels the sounds to the tympanic membrane. The middle ear amplifies the sound and transmits to the inner ear. It also equalizes the pressure on both sides of the eardrum. The inner ear contains the sense organ, the organ of Corti, which senses the frequency and amplitude of sound waves.
- Sounds which are received in the organ of Corti are transmitted to the brain via the auditory pathway. The cochlear branch of the VIII cranial nerve is involved and the auditory cortex is located in the temporal lobe.
- Hearing can be tested using simple tuning fork tests (Rinne's and Weber's tests). Audiometry is more sensitive.

CHAPTER REVIEW QUESTIONS

1. Describe the functions of the external (outer) ear.
2. Describe the parts and functions of the middle ear.
3. Describe the organ of Corti.
4. Trace the auditory pathway with the help of a diagram.

CHAPTER 50

The Physiology of Taste and Smell

SPECIFIC LEARNING OBJECTIVES

At the end of this chapter, the student should be able to:

- List the categories of taste.
- Indicate which cranial nerves are involved in transmitting taste sensation to the brain.
- Indicate which cranial nerve is involved in olfaction.
- Describe how you would test for taste and smell at the bedside of a patient.

GLOSSARY OF TERMS

- **Olfactory:** refers to the sense of smell
- **Gustatory:** refers to the sense of taste

TASTE

The receptors for taste are the taste buds on the tongue. While we have about 10,000 taste buds at birth, these reduce slowly with age. When we chew food, small molecules of various chemicals stimulate our taste buds. However, our perception of taste is also influenced by other factors such as the smell and texture of the food.

Categories of Taste

There are five broad categories of taste. These are sour, sweet, salty, bitter and umami. Different parts of the tongue are more sensitive to different categories of taste. This is depicted in Fig. 50.1. Taste receptors are located on the surface of the tongue on small visible projections called papillae. Each papilla has many taste buds and each taste bud has between 50 and 150 taste receptor cells. Although we have only five different categories of taste, we can distinguish several thousand different tastes because of the different ways combinations of taste receptors are stimulated. Our sense of taste is closely linked to smell, and taste sensations can change in the absence of smell.

Taste Pathway

In order to perceive taste sensation, signals travel along nerves to the brain. There are three sensory nerves which carry taste sensation from the tongue. These are depicted in Fig. 50.2.

- the anterior two-thirds of the tongue is supplied by a branch of the facial (cranial nerve VII) nerve called the chorda tympani branch,
- the posterior one-third of the tongue is supplied by the glossopharyngeal nerve (cranial nerve IX)
- the posterior-most part of the tongue near the epiglottis is supplied by the vagus nerve (cranial nerve X).
- the taste area of the cerebral cortex is located in a part of the frontal cortex.

Testing for Taste

In order to test for taste, we need to test different tastes. Thus, 'sweet' is tested using a solution of sugar, 'salt' is tested using a solution of common salt, 'sour' is tested using a weak solution of citric acid and 'bitter' is tested using a weak solution of something bitter like quinine. The mouth needs to be rinsed thoroughly between each test. We test for taste sensitivity by using multiple concentrations of the 'tastant'. The lowest concentration at which we perceive the taste is the taste threshold for that taste category. Taste thresholds determine how we perceive taste. Thus, people with high thresholds for a taste sensation, say salt or sweet, may add larger quantities of salt or sugar to what they consume. Thus, taste thresholds can also determine levels of consumption of certain foods.

SMELL

The receptors for the sensation of smell are in the olfactory epithelium, located in the upper part of each nostril. Chemicals which are responsible for the smell dissolve or diffuse in the mucus that covers the receptors and then stimulate the receptors themselves. Although we do not realize it, humans are capable of detecting many thousands of different types of smells, over 75% of which we find unpleasant.

The smell receptors adapt rapidly to a new smell. This means that the receptors stop responding or reduce their response to a smell if they are exposed to it for a long period of time. This explains why get used to a new smell that at first is very strong – for example, when we enter a chemical factory.

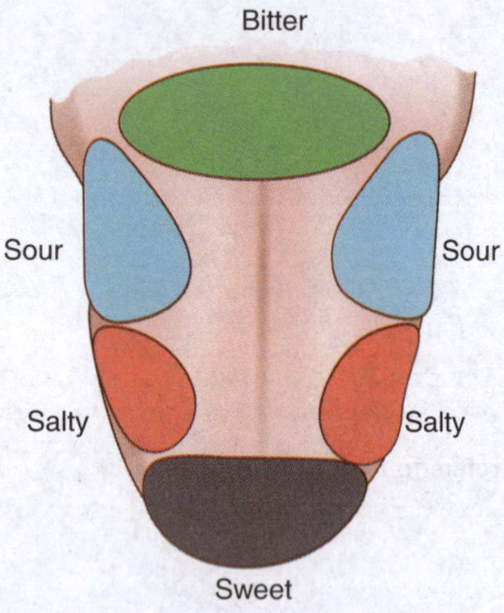

FIG. 50.1 Taste map of the tongue.

Olfactory Pathway

- The olfactory receptors are bipolar neurons (see Fig. 50.3).
- Once the olfactory receptors are stimulated, the olfactory nerve fibres (first cranial nerve) carry this information to the primary olfactory cortex after passing through a bony plate called the cribriform plate located at the roof of the nasal cavity.
- The bipolar neurons synapse in the olfactory bulb from where second neurons arise and form the olfactory tract.

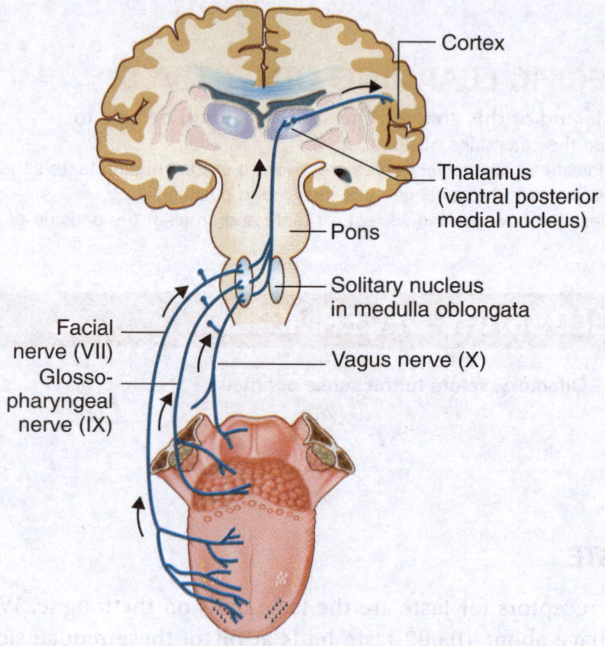

FIG. 50.2 The taste pathway.

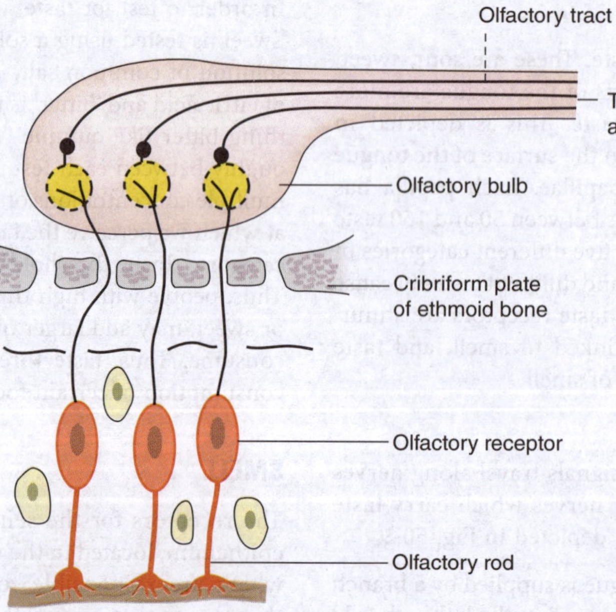

FIG. 50.3 The olfactory pathway.

- The olfactory cortex is located at the base of the frontal lobe and the medial temporal lobe.
- However, the perception of smell is the function of many parts of the brain including a part of the brain called the limbic system.

Certain animals have a highly developed sense of smell. For instance, dogs generally have a better sense of smell than humans. This is because dogs have many more receptors than humans; some species of dogs have 40 times the receptors that humans have. Dogs, like many other vertebrates, have a specialized scent organ in the roof of their mouth called the vomeronasal organ.

Testing for Smell

Basic testing for smell is done to evaluate the first cranial (olfactory) nerve. In order to test smell, pungent but very identifiable odours are presented to the patient. These are in form of solutions which are kept in bottles. The lid of the bottle is opened; the patient takes a sniff and identifies the odour. Odours could include oil of cloves, tincture of asafoetida, oil of peppermint, soaps and fruits. The odours must be something that the patient knows and can identify.

APPLICATION IN NURSING

Nurses need to be aware that lack of appetite may, apart from other causes, be due to partial or complete loss of smell and taste. In certain patient groups, such as the elderly, due care must be taken to ensure adequate oral hygiene as this can affect taste sensation.

SUMMARY

- The basic taste sensations are bitter, salt, sweet, sour and umami.
- Taste sensation is carried from the tongue by the VII, IX and X cranial nerves.
- Smell is carried to the brain by the olfactory nerve (first cranial nerve).
- Alteration in perception of smell can affect taste, and problems with both these sensations can affect appetite.
- Taste and smell can be tested using simple bedside clinical tests.

CHAPTER REVIEW QUESTIONS

1. List the different types of taste and indicate where they are best sensed on the tongue.
2. What are the cranial nerves that carry taste sensation from the tongue? From which parts of the tongue do they carry taste sensation?
3. Briefly describe the olfactory pathway.

CHAPTER 51

Application of the Physiology of Sensory Organs

SPECIFIC LEARNING OBJECTIVES

At the end of this chapter, the student should be able to:

- Briefly describe the pathogenesis and consequences of burns.
- Describe the purpose and list the types of skin grafts.
- List some causes for the loss of sensation.
- Write a short note on hyperhidrosis.
- Describe and indicate corrections for the following refractory errors: myopia, hypermetropia, astigmatism and presbyopia.
- Briefly describe the following disorders: cataract, glaucoma and vitamin A deficiency (night blindness).
- Differentiate between conduction deafness and sensorineural deafness.
- Briefly describe the use of hearing aids.
- List the disorders of taste.
- List the disorders of smell.

GLOSSARY OF TERMS

- **Anaesthesia:** complete loss of sensation
- **Hypoaesthesia:** partial loss of sensation
- **Myopia:** short-sightedness – correctable by biconcave lens
- **Hypermetropia:** long-sightedness – correctable by biconvex lens
- **Astigmatism:** deviation from the spherical curvature of the cornea resulting in distorted images as rays of light cannot be focused at a single point on the retina
- **Presbyopia:** refractory error of ageing – difficulty in accommodation – correctable by a bifocal lens
- **Presbycusis:** hearing loss associated with ageing
- **Ageusia:** loss of taste sensation
- **Anosmia:** loss of smell

In this chapter, we describe clinical conditions/disorders that affect the skin, vision, hearing, taste and smell.

APPLICATION OF PHYSIOLOGY OF SKIN

Burns

Common causes of burns include the following:

1. Scalds: due to spillage of hot fluids on the skin
2. Flames: where a person comes in direct contact with a fire
3. Contact: where a person touches a hot object
4. Electrical burns: where, for example, a person comes in contact with 'live' wires
5. Chemical burns: associated with exposure to the skin to corrosive agents such as strong acids or alkalis, among others

Burns are associated with both local and systemic (generalized effects).

Local effects:

There are three zones of injury:

- The zone that is most severely affected is the zone of coagulation – here, the damage to the tissue is so great that this tissue will be lost and cannot recover.
- Surrounding the zone of coagulation is a zone of stasis where there is reduced perfusion (blood flow) – this tissue can be saved if appropriate and prompt treatment is started.
- The outermost zone is the zone of hyperaemia where there is increased blood flow and this zone typically recovers. The extent of damage depends on the severity of the burns.

Systemic effects:

- Loss of fluid and protein from the burn area – when burns are extensive, this loss can be so severe that the blood pressure may fall (hypotension). Protein loss will need to be replaced.

- The severe inflammation that is associated with burns is the result of the production of many immune factors – some of these can cause a constriction of the bronchi and difficulty in breathing, a condition called adult respiratory distress syndrome. This problem can be increased if the person was exposed to fumes and smoke during a fire.
- The metabolic rate rises. Because the increased metabolic rate is increased, the caloric and nutrient intake of the person will also need to be raised; otherwise, there will be breakdown of tissues (catabolism) and feeding may sometimes need to be enteral (via a tube placed in the stomach) or parenteral (intravenously) – these then become important nursing issues.

Skin Grafts

Patients who have had surgery with extensive loss of skin, experienced burns or have large open wounds may need skin to cover the wound area and make healing quicker. A skin graft is the transplantation of skin to the area of the wound.

Skin grafts are usually done by taking skin from one area of a person and putting it over another area of the same person. They can be thin (split-thickness grafts) which remove only the upper layer of the skin, that is the epidermis, or thick (full-thickness) in which both the epidermis and the dermis are grafted.

Loss of Sensation and Its Consequences

The skin is an important sensory organ. There are many clinical disorders that are associated with a loss of sensation (anaesthesia) or decreased sensation (hypoaesthesia) over the skin. There are many causes for a complete or partial loss of sensation and these include, among others, the following:

- Injury or compression of a peripheral nerve
- Infections of the nerve and skin, for example leprosy
- Chronic diseases like diabetes, especially when they are uncontrolled
- Nutritional deficiencies, e.g. vitamin B_{12} – which is important to maintain the outer covering (myelin) of nerves

A loss of sensation makes the individual more prone to injury. A person with a loss of sensation over the hands she may accidentally burn themselves by picking up hot objects that they cannot feel or neglect minor injuries because they do not feel pain. If a person loses sensation over the feet, they may develop blisters and injuries which they do not feel, and hence neglect.

Neglect of injuries/blisters over an area of anaesthetic skin can result in infection, and if further neglected, this infection can spread to deeper tissues including the bone and result in deformities. Ulcers – or breaks in the skin – are a common feature of anaesthetic hands and feet and need to be treated promptly. Once the ulcers are deep and they heal by scarring, the ulcers are more likely to recur (return) because scar tissue is less strong than normal skin.

Disorders of Sweating

Sweating is required for normal regulation of body temperature. An abnormal increase in sweating is called hyperhidrosis. This may affect about 2% of the population, although only a small fraction of these people seek medical help. The most common areas affected are the axilla (armpits), hands and feet. Hyperhidrosis can cause discomfort for the individual – for instance, individuals with excessive sweating of the hands may soil papers, be unable to grip objects well and feel uncomfortable shaking hands. Patients with this condition need to be investigated to rule out any other disease that may be causing the problem – in many individuals, a cause may not be found in which case it is called primary hyperhidrosis.

Anhidrosis (absence of sweating) is a much more rare condition and when present can predispose a person to heat stroke.

DISORDERS OF VISION

Errors of Refraction

Presbyopia: In older people, usually by the time they are in their mid-forties, the lens becomes stiffer and is unable to accommodate because it cannot increase its curvature while the person is looking at near objects. The person thus sees 'blurred'. This is why older people begin to hold books or newspapers progressively further from their eyes. The condition is called *presbyopia* and can be corrected by a convex lens.

Myopia (short-sightedness): In this condition, an individual can see close objects clearly, but objects which are further away appear blurred. This is because rays of light from an object at a distance tend to fall *in front of the retina* (Fig. 51.1). The condition is corrected by using a biconcave lens which diverges the rays and thus allows them to fall on the retina where they can be seen clearly.

Hypermetropia (long-sightedness): As the name suggests, this is a condition in which the individual can see objects at a distance clearly but not those which are closer. This is because the rays of light fall *behind the retina*. The condition is corrected with a biconvex lens which helps the rays to converge and thus the rays fall directly on the retina (Fig. 51.2).

Astigmatism: When the curvature of the cornea is uneven, rays of light may fall on multiple points on the retina rather than on a single point (Fig. 51.3). The individual then experiences eye strain and headaches. This condition is corrected using a special lens called a cylindrical lens.

SOME CLINICAL CONDITIONS AFFECTING THE EYE

Vitamin A Deficiency

Nyctalopia (**night blindness**) is one of the first signs of vitamin A deficiency – this means that patients are unable to see very well in the dark. In its later stages, patients (often children) develop keratin deposits called Bitot's spots on the conjunctiva. The eyes become dry (xerophthalmia) and may be infected – in extreme situations, it can even lead to blindness. Vitamin A deficiency has been reduced due to the provision of vitamin A capsules to populations at risk. Natural dietary sources of vitamin A include orange and yellow vegetables and fruits and green leafy vegetables.

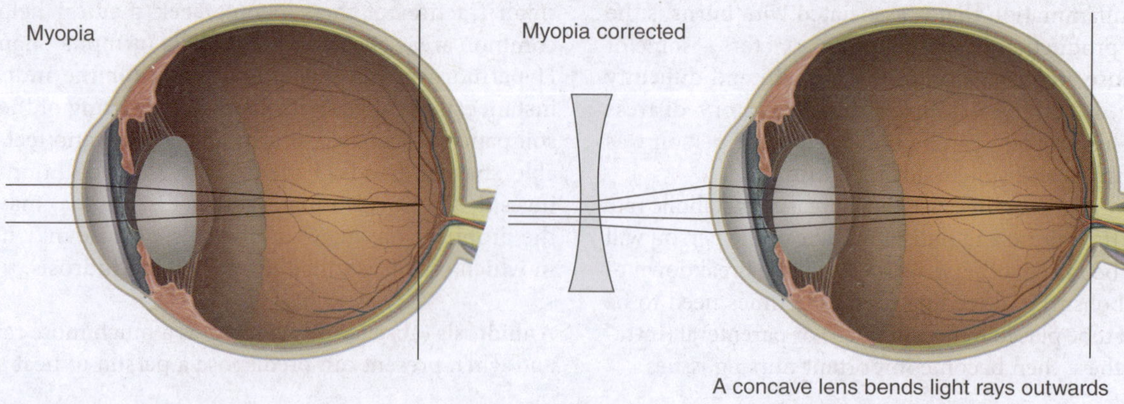

FIG. 51.1 Myopia.

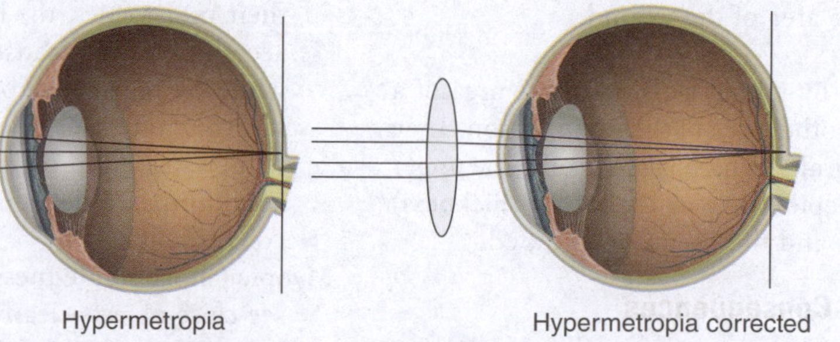

FIG. 51.2 Hypermetropia.

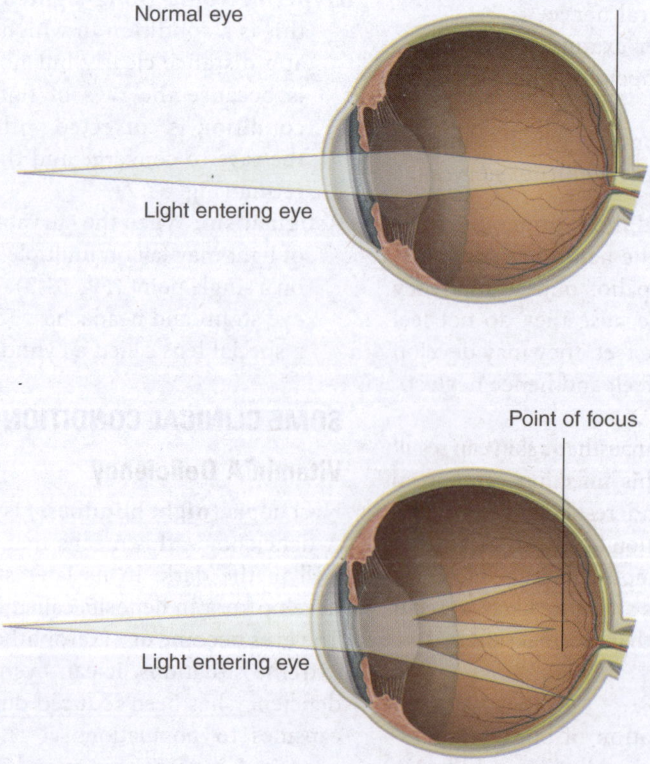

FIG. 51.3 Astigmatism.

Cataract

This is a condition in which the lens becomes cloudy and then if left untreated becomes completely opaque. As a result, light does not travel through the lens and the person loses vision. Cataract is most often associated with ageing and the development of cataract is associated with certain risk factors which include smoking, diabetes mellitus and excessive exposure to sunlight, among others. Cataract is a form of treatable blindness – the lens can be removed and replaced by a clear, artificial lens.

Glaucoma

This is a condition in which the pressure within the eye (intraocular pressure) is increased. There are many types of glaucoma, some of which require treatment by surgery. It is the second leading cause of blindness across the world after cataracts. Glaucoma may be painless and may sometimes be present for a long time without being detected. Diagnosis is based on the measurement of eye pressure using a tonometer.

DISORDERS OF HEARING

Types of Deafness

While there are a large number of causes of deafness, we can broadly classify them into two categories:

1. *Conduction deafness* occurs when there is some problem with the transmission of sound waves from the outside to the cochlea where the sense organs of hearing (organs of Corti) are located. This can happen for a variety of reasons, some of which are given as follows:
   - Impacted ear wax; here, the problem is in the outer ear and sound waves are not transmitted to the tympanic membrane.
   - Holes in the tympanic membrane (perforated eardrum) happen following untreated middle ear infections, that is otitis media. In this situation, the middle ear is involved. You might think that if there is hole in the tympanic membrane, sound would travel better to the inner ear. However, as discussed earlier, the middle ear amplifies the sound waves and this requires that the sound waves that are received by the tympanic membrane get transferred via the ossicles.
   - Fluid collection in the middle ear. This interferes with the movement of ossicles and the transfer of sound to the inner ear. Fluid can be collected in the middle ear during allergies, viral infections such as common cold or bacterial infections of the middle ear.
2. *Sensorineural deafness*, as the name implies, involves the sense organs of hearing (i.e. cochlea and organ of Corti) or the auditory pathway that carries the information from the inner ear to the brain.
   - Noise-induced hearing loss: This is due to the damage of the hair cells of the organ of Corti. Since people may be exposed to loud sounds within a certain frequency range, the damage to the hair cells may be confined to those hair cells which are activated at the loud frequencies.
   - Presbycusis: It is age-related hearing loss and is associated with the degeneration of the cochlea on both sides. By the age of 75 years, half of all individuals will have some form of age-related hearing loss.

HEARING AIDS

Although hearing aids can be very small, they actually have multiple parts which have been miniaturized (made small). A small microphone picks up the sounds from the environment, and an amplifier increases these sounds so that they can be transmitted as sound waves into the ear. Since these components require power, a hearing aid is also fitted with a battery. Hearing aids require some adjustment to use – they cannot eliminate background noise completely and this can make listening difficult.

DISORDERS OF TASTE SENSATION

Ageusia is the inability to detect any taste – this is extremely rare. In contrast, **hypogeusia** is a reduced ability to detect taste. **Dysgeusia** is a condition in which there is abnormal taste sensation, for instance, a person may feel a persistent foul, salty or metallic taste in the mouth.

Because smell and taste are closely related, it is common for people to be 'unable to taste their food' when they have a common cold. Certain medication may produce abnormal tastes in the mouth. Poor dental and mouth hygiene may also affect taste.

DISORDERS OF SMELL

Anosmia is the absence of smell, while *parosmia* is an abnormal perception of smell – here, odours which are ordinarily pleasant may be perceived as offensive. Reduced or absent smell may be due to causes in the nose or in the nervous system. A common cause of reduced sense of smell, for instance, is a common cold.

SUMMARY

- Common errors of refraction include (1) myopia (short-sightedness) corrected by a biconcave lens; (2) hypermetropia (long-sightedness) corrected by a biconvex lens; (3) presbyopia – loss of accommodation with age corrected by convex lens; and (4) astigmatism corrected by cylindrical lens.
- Vitamin A deficiency is associated with night blindness. Cataract is a clouding of the lens and glaucoma is an increased pressure in the eye.
- There are two broad categories of deafness. Conductive deafness occurs when sound waves are not adequately transmitted to the inner ear. Sensorineural deafness occurs when the inner ear or the auditory pathway is involved.

CLINICAL CASE PROBLEMS

(A) ***A 50-year-old woman complains of difficulty in reading. She has had to hold the book further and further away from her eyes to read the letters. Prior to this, she never wore spectacles.***

a. What condition is the woman likely suffering from?
b. What type of lens can be used to correct the problem?
c. Draw a diagram to show how the rays of light fall in myopia and indicate in a diagram how this can be corrected.
d. Draw a diagram to show how the rays of light fall in hypermetropia and indicate in a diagram how this can be corrected.

(B) ***A 40-year-old man is brought to the emergency department with severe burns over his back and lower limbs. Apart from other things, the doctor starts him on a course of antibiotics. His blood pressure is 80/50 mm Hg. The doctor starts him on intravenous fluids.***

a. How does intact skin protect the body from infections?
b. What is the normal blood pressure? Comment on the blood pressure of the patient.
c. Why is the doctor giving fluids and what is the likely cause of the blood pressure of the patient?

SELF-DIRECTED LEARNING

- What is heat stroke? Why does it occur?
- Apart from refractory errors, there are other disorders of vision. How does diabetes affect vision?
- How does listening to loud music over the headphones affect hearing?

WHAT YOU CAN LEARN FROM A HOSPITAL VISIT

- Check where patients with burns are treated in your hospital. What is barrier nursing for the care of burns?
- Visit the ophthalmologist – get your eyes checked. What tests are done?
- Get an audiometry chart from the hospital, and ask how this is interpreted.

8

SECTION

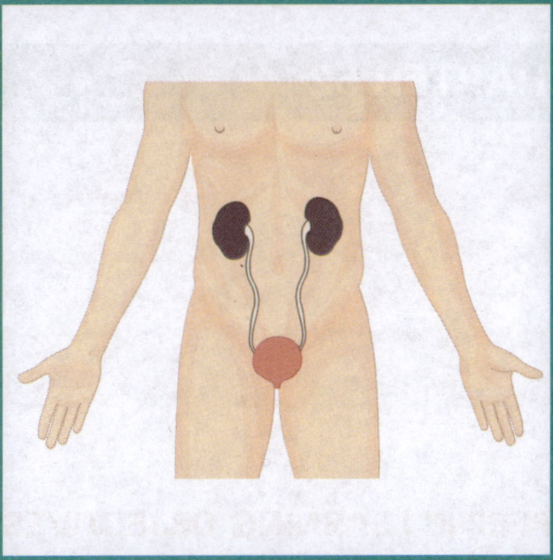

Musculo-Skeletal System

Section Outline

CHAPTER 52

Neuromuscular Junction

SPECIFIC LEARNING OBJECTIVES

At the end of this chapter, the student should be able to:

- Draw a neuromuscular junction and label its parts.
- Describe the events that occur in the neuromuscular junction.
- Briefly indicate the types of drugs that act on the neuromuscular junction.
- Write a short note on myasthenia gravis.

GLOSSARY OF TERMS

- **Neuromuscular junction:** the junction between the motor nerve and the muscle
- **End-plate potential:** the membrane potential that is developed at the neuromuscular junction following the quantal release of acetylcholine
- **Ligand-gated channel:** a channel on the membrane that is opened by the binding of a chemical

Information in nerves travels in the form of an 'impulse'. This electrical activity, also called an action potential, travels along the nerve membrane in myelinated and unmyelinated nerves.

When a motor nerve supplies a skeletal muscle fibre, the resultant junction is called the neuromuscular junction (NMJ). In this chapter, we describe the events that happen at NMJ and what can happen when NMJ is not functioning properly.

STRUCTURE OF THE NEUROMUSCULAR JUNCTION

Fig. 52.1 shows that the NMJ can be divided into three parts: the presynaptic part, the synaptic cleft and the postsynaptic part.

The *presynaptic part* of NMJ consists of an expanded nerve terminal called a synaptic knob (bouton). This nerve terminal contains the vesicles of the neurotransmitter which in NMJ is acetylcholine (ACh). These vesicles are clustered around a part of the presynaptic membrane called the active zone.

Separating the presynaptic and postsynaptic membranes is a gap called the *synaptic cleft*. This gap is about 20–30 nm wide.

The *postsynaptic membrane* is thrown into folds. This increases the surface area of the postsynaptic membrane. Located on the postsynaptic membrane are the ACh receptors. These receptors function as ligand-gated channels. A ligand is a chemical. So, in the case of the ACh receptor, the ligand is ACh. When ACh binds to its receptor on the postsynaptic membrane, the channel opens.

EVENTS THAT OCCUR AT THE NEUROMUSCULAR JUNCTION

The following is the sequence of events that occur at NMJ:

1. A nerve impulse in the form of an action potential travels down the nerve and reaches the axon terminal.
2. The axon terminal contains voltage-gated calcium (Ca) channels that open when the action potential reaches the axon terminal. Thus, Ca ions then enter the axon terminal.
3. The entry of calcium ions triggers the movement of ACh-containing vesicles towards the active zone of the presynaptic membrane.
4. By exocytosis, the vesicles fuse with the presynaptic membrane and then release their contents of the neurotransmitter into the synaptic cleft.
5. ACh released into the synaptic cleft now binds with the ACh receptors on the postsynaptic membrane. There are many different types of ACh receptors in the body. The ACh receptor on the postsynaptic membrane of NMJ is a *nicotinic* receptor.
6. The binding of ACh to its receptor results in the opening of this ligand-gated channel. The channel is freely permeable to

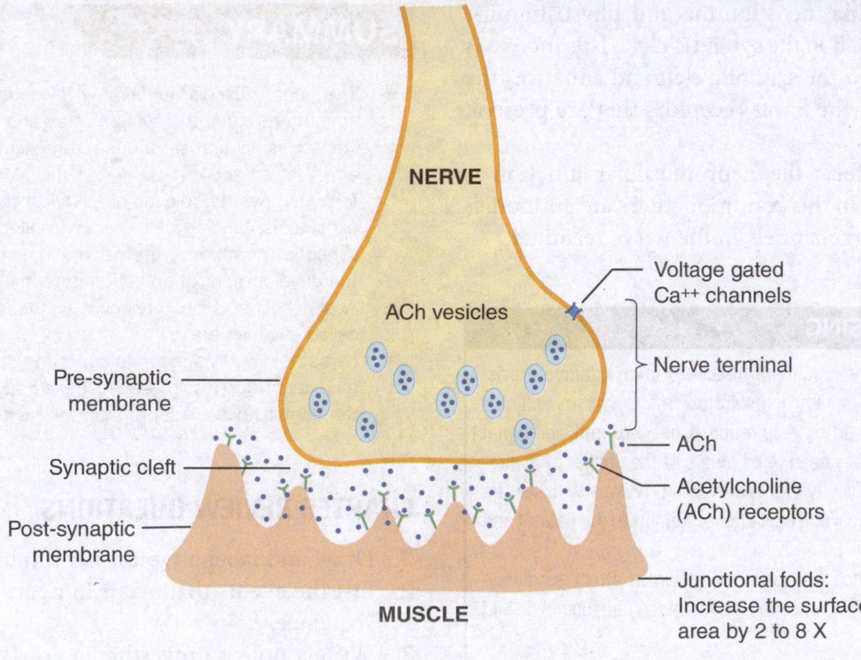

FIG. 52.1 Structure of the neuromuscular junction.

sodium and potassium. Thus, there is a change in the membrane potential from −80 mV at rest to approximately −15 mV. This potential is called the **end-plate potential**.

7. The end-plate potential now triggers a change in the membrane potential of the muscle and generates an action potential on the muscle membrane (sarcolemma) just adjacent to the postsynaptic membrane which is propagated along the muscle membrane.

The generation of the action potential on the muscle membrane is an essential step for muscle contraction to occur. The molecular basis of muscle contraction and its characteristics will be discussed in Chapter 53.

Fate of the Acetylcholine

ACh needs to be removed from the synaptic cleft so that the action of ACh is not prolonged. In the NMJ, this is done by an enzyme called cholinesterase present in the synaptic cleft which breaks down ACh into acetate and choline.

MYASTHENIA GRAVIS – A DISEASE THAT AFFECTS NEUROMUSCULAR TRANSMISSION

In this section, we describe a disease in which transmission at NMJ is severely affected.

Cause of Myasthenia Gravis

It is an 'autoimmune' disorder. Under normal circumstances, the immune or body defence system acts against 'foreign' antigens (type of protein). Thus, the body is able to withstand a range of infections whether they are viruses, bacteria or parasites. In 'autoimmune' diseases, the immune system behaves in an abnormal manner and acts against 'self' antigens, that is those which belong to the body itself. In myasthenia gravis, the body produces antibodies against the ACh receptors in NMJ and destroys them. Thus, the number of ACh receptors on the postsynaptic membrane is severely reduced and the neuromuscular transmission is affected.

ALTERATIONS IN THE STRUCTURE OF THE NEUROMUSCULAR JUNCTION

There are several changes that occur in NMJ in myasthenia gravis that reduce transmission across NMJ:

1. The synaptic cleft is widened – this means that ACh has to travel a longer distance to bind to its receptors on the postsynaptic membrane. The wider cleft also means that the volume is larger and this reduces the ACh concentration.
2. The postsynaptic membrane folds are blunted. This reduces the surface area.
3. The number of ACh receptors on the postsynaptic membrane is reduced.

Clinical Features

Because neuromuscular function is less, the muscles are not able to contract properly. Patients with the disease complain of muscle weakness and fatigue (the inability of a muscle to sustain a given amplitude of contraction). Patients may experience ptosis (drooping of the eyelids) and, when the muscles of respiration are involved, difficulty in breathing.

Treatment

Although the treatment of myasthenia gravis is complex and addresses several issues, we will discuss here only the treatment that is based on the physiology of neuromuscular transmission.

Cholinesterase inhibitors like neostigmine and physostigmine reduce the breakdown of ACh in the synaptic cleft. This increases the concentration of ACh in the synaptic cleft and enhances the chances of ACh binding to the fewer receptors that are present.

Another disease which affects the neuromuscular junction is Lambert–Eaton syndrome. In this condition, there are antibodies to the voltage-gated calcium channels in the nerve terminal.

APPLICATIONS IN NURSING

- The nurse will be required to monitor vital functions in myasthenia gravis. Of particular concern is the possibility of respiratory failure. Nurses will also be required to assist in supporting respiration if needed until additional interventions are available. They need to be aware of the danger of aspiration in patients who have difficulty with swallowing. Nurses will also be required to provide psychological and educational support to the patient and family members.
- During treatment of organophosphorus poisoning (which affects cholinesterase action), the nurse will be required to monitor vital functions and response to treatment.

SUMMARY

- The neuromuscular junction is divided into three parts: the presynaptic membrane, the synaptic cleft and the postsynaptic membrane.
- Transmission across the neuromuscular junction starts with the arrival of an action potential at the nerve terminal and involves the following events: release of acetylcholine from the nerve terminal by exocytosis, binding of the acetylcholine to its receptor on the postsynaptic membrane, the generation of an 'end-plate potential' and the development of an action potential on the muscle membrane.
- Acetylcholine is broken down in the synaptic cleft by an enzyme called cholinesterase.
- Myasthenia gravis is an autoimmune disorder which reduces neuromuscular transmission because the body produces antibodies against the acetylcholine receptors on the postsynaptic membrane.

CHAPTER REVIEW QUESTIONS

1. Draw and label a typical neuromuscular junction.
2. List the events that occur in neuromuscular transmission in sequence.
3. Write a note on myasthenia gravis.

CHAPTER 53

Physiology of Muscle Contraction

SPECIFIC LEARNING OBJECTIVES

At the end of this chapter, the student should be able to:

- Describe the structure of skeletal muscle with specific emphasis on the (1) motor unit, (2) sarcotubular system and (3) sarcomere.
- Explain the process of excitation–contraction coupling.
- List the molecular events associated with muscle contraction.
- Differentiate between isotonic and isometric muscle contractions.
- Describe the effect of increasing frequency of stimulus on muscle contraction.
- Describe briefly the different types of muscle fibres.
- Define muscle fatigue and list its causes.

GLOSSARY OF TERMS

- **Excitation–contraction coupling:** the coupling of the electrical event in muscle (action potential on the sarcolemma) with a mechanical event (contraction) via a chemical mediator (calcium ions)
- **Sarcomere:** the portion of the myofibril contained between two Z lines
- **Motor unit:** a single motor nerve fibre together with the multiple muscle fibres that it innervates
- **Quantal summation:** the increase in amplitude of muscle contraction associated with a recruitment of motor units
- **Isotonic contraction:** muscle contraction associated with muscle shortening in which work is done
- **Isometric contraction:** muscle contraction in which the length of the muscle remains unchanged and no work is done
- **Muscle fatigue:** the inability of a muscle to sustain a given amplitude of contraction

In Chapter 52, we discussed the physiology of the neuromuscular junction. During neuromuscular transmission, a motor nerve impulse, through a neurotransmitter, acetylcholine, results in the generation of an action potential on the sarcolemma (muscle membrane). In this chapter, we describe the events that occur in the skeletal muscle once the action potential reaches it. We also describe the properties of muscle contraction. Before we do that, it is important that we review the structure of the skeletal muscle, right down to its functional units.

STRUCTURE OF SKELETAL MUSCLE

Fig. 53.1 shows the anatomical organization of skeletal muscle. Each skeletal muscle is made up of many subunits. First is the muscle fasciculus which is made up of many muscle fibres. Muscle fibres are in turn made up of many myofibrils. The myofibrils appear as alternate light and dark bands because of the arrangement of the myofilaments. This is discussed later when the structure of the sarcomere is explained. A muscle fibre runs the entire length of the muscle and is usually innervated by a single nerve ending. However, a single nerve fibre can innervate multiple muscle fibres. This single nerve fibre together with the multiple muscle fibres that it supplies is called a **motor unit**. Some motor units may be small, that is a single nerve fibre supplies only a few muscle fibres, while others are large, where a single nerve fibre supplies a larger number of muscle fibres. Small motor units are typically seen in muscles which have to perform precise and intricate movements, like the muscles of the hand or those involved with movements of the eye. Larger motor units are typically seen in muscles which perform large movements as well as the muscles involved in posture.

Myofibrils are composed of actin and myosin filaments that are arranged in a precise manner. Fig. 53.2 illustrates the arrangement of these filaments in a sarcomere – the area of the myofibril between two Z lines (Z disks). The Z line is itself made up of filamentous proteins. Attached to the Z lines are the actin filaments. These are sometimes called the thin filaments. The thin filament consists of three separate components: (1) two helical strands of actin molecules, (2) the tropomyosin molecules that

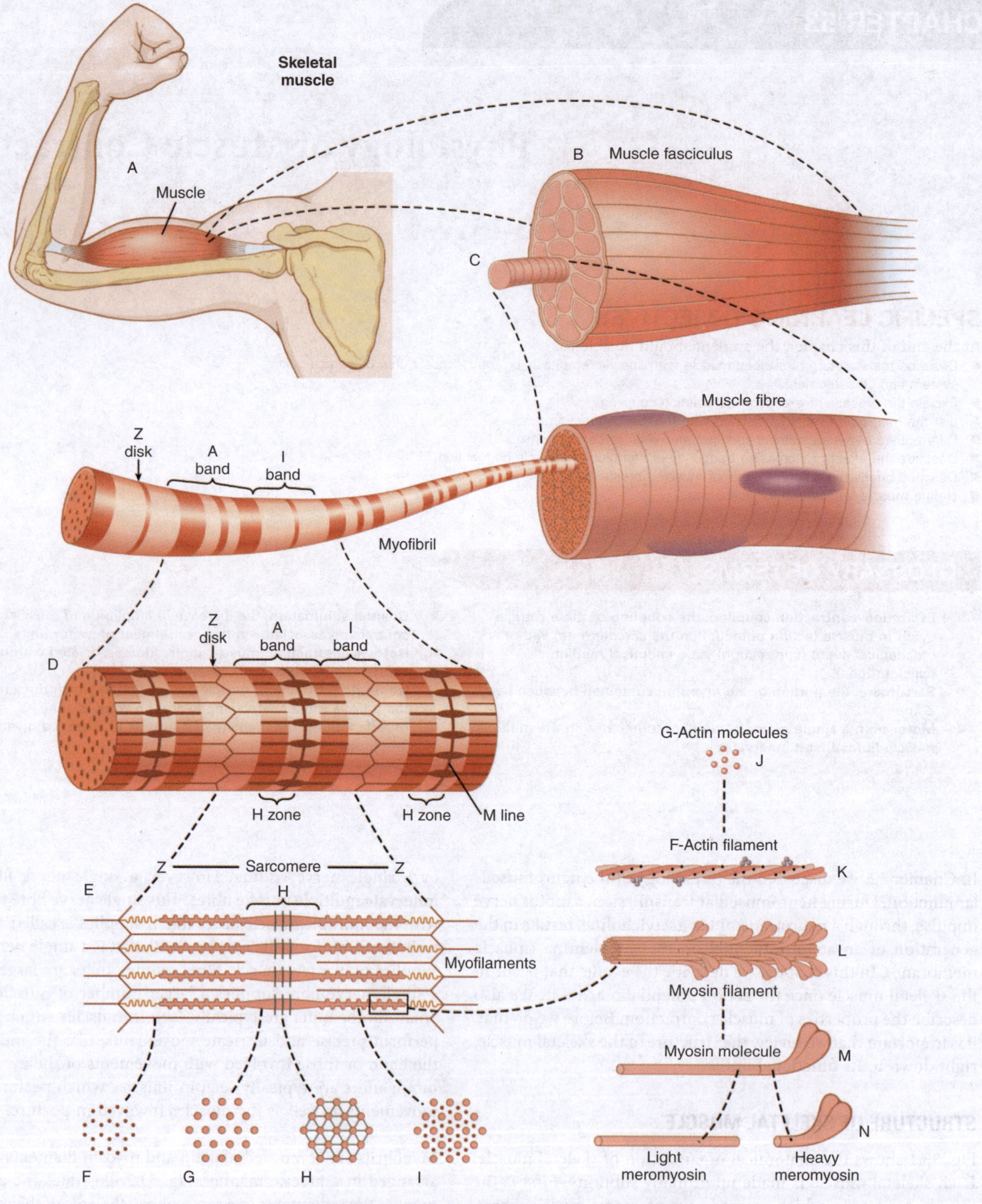

FIG. 53.1 Organization of skeletal muscle.

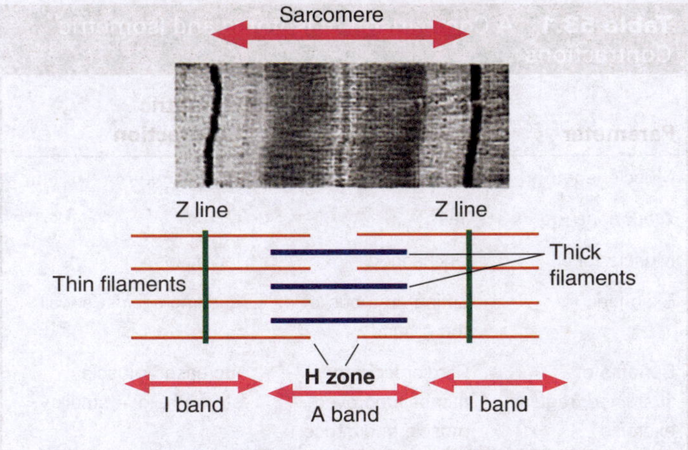

FIG. 53.2 Structure of a sarcomere.

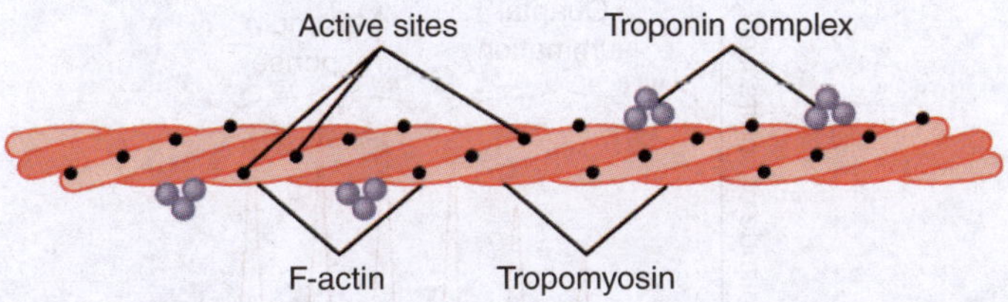

FIG. 53.3 The thin filament: troponin–tropomyosin relationship.

lie in the grooves formed by the intertwined actin strands and (3) a troponin complex that is attached to the tropomyosin molecule. This is illustrated in Fig. 53.3. The myosin filament (sometimes called the thick filament) is located in the centre of the sarcomere between the actin filaments. Each myosin filament is made up of many myosin molecules, each of which consists of a tail and two myosin heads which jut out of the myosin filament.

Actin and myosin are the contractile proteins of muscle, while tropomyosin and troponin are the regulatory proteins. Later in the chapter, we describe how muscle contraction is brought about by these proteins.

The myofibrils are surrounded by a 'sarcotubular system'. This consists of invaginations of the muscle membrane through the muscle fibre called T (transverse) tubules. T tubules are open to the exterior of the muscle fibre. The sarcoplasmic reticulum surrounds the surfaces of the myofibrils and is rich in calcium ions. Part of the sarcoplasmic reticulum is expanded as terminal cisternae which are adjacent to the T tubules.

EXCITATION–CONTRACTION COUPLING

The action potential that has been generated on the muscle membrane following neuromuscular transmission is transmitted along the sarcolemma and down the T tubules. This results in the release of calcium ions from the sarcoplasmic reticulum into the cytoplasm of the myofibrils. Calcium ions are essential to bring about contraction. This process by which an electrical event (the action potential) is coupled to a mechanical event (contraction) using a chemical mediator (calcium ions) is called excitation–contraction coupling.

MOLECULAR EVENTS OF MUSCLE CONTRACTION

The release of calcium ions into the cytoplasm starts a sequence of events which results in the contraction of the muscle:

1. Calcium ions bind to the regulatory protein – troponin C.
2. Troponin C, in turn, causes a conformational change in tropomyosin. This causes the tropomyosin to move away from the groove of the actin filament in which it is normally present.
3. This movement of tropomyosin uncovers myosin-binding sites on the actin filament.
4. The myosin head binds on to its binding site on actin, and then through an ATPase located on its head, ATP is broken down to provide the energy that causes the myosin head to bend – the so-called 'power stroke'.
5. The result of the power stroke is that the actin filament is pulled closer to the centre of the sarcomere. Thus, the thin and thick filaments slide against each other, resulting in shortening of the sarcomere.
6. Binding of a new ATP molecule to the myosin head results in dissociation of the myosin from the actin – this is the start of the process of relaxation, during which calcium ions in the cytoplasm are pumped back into the sarcoplasmic reticulum against their concentration gradient by active transport.

These molecular events of muscle contraction are shown in Fig. 53.4.

TYPES OF MUSCLE CONTRACTION

Face a wall and press against the wall using both palms of your hand. You will note that no matter how hard you push, the wall does not move; there is therefore no shortening of the muscles involved and no work can be done because work can be done only when a load is moved through a distance. This type of muscle contraction is called isometric contraction. In isometric contraction, you can feel the tension (tone) in the muscle, even though it is not shortening. We will discuss the concept of muscle tone is greater detail in a later chapter.

In contrast, if you pick a bucket of water off the floor, the load (the bucket with water) is moved through a certain distance; the muscle concerned shortens and work is done. This type of contraction is called isotonic contraction. Table 53.1 summarizes the differences between isotonic and isometric muscle contractions.

We are constantly performing isometric and isotonic contractions. Isotonic contractions include walking, running and lifting objects, while we perform isometric exercises whenever we push against stationary objects and sustain weights in a given

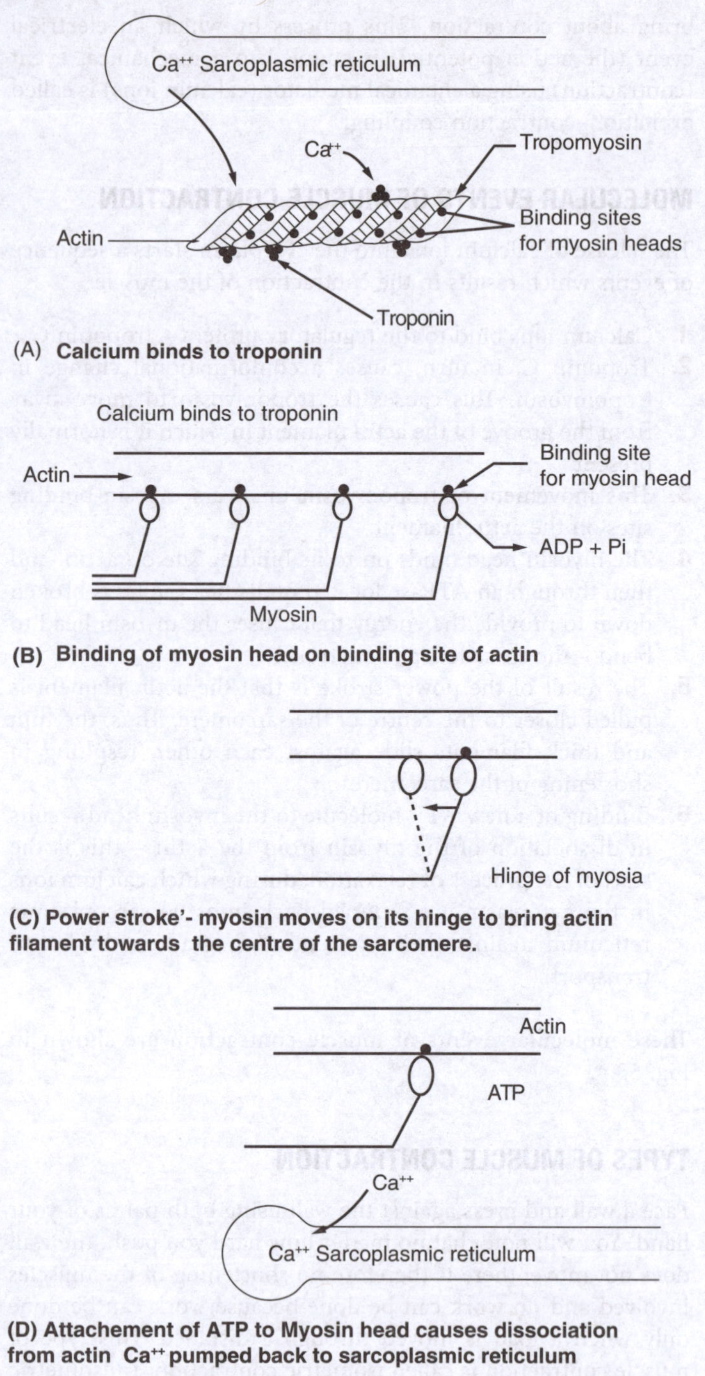

FIG. 53.4 Molecular events of muscle contraction.

Table 53.1 A Comparison of Isotonic and Isometric Contractions

Parameter	Isotonic Contraction	Isometric Contraction
Muscle length	Shortens	Unchanged
Work done	Yes	No
Muscle tone	Unchanged	Increases
Example	Lifting up a bucket off the ground	Pushing against a wall
Benefits of sustained, regular exercise	Cardiorespiratory fitness, improved muscle endurance	Increased muscle strength, joint stability

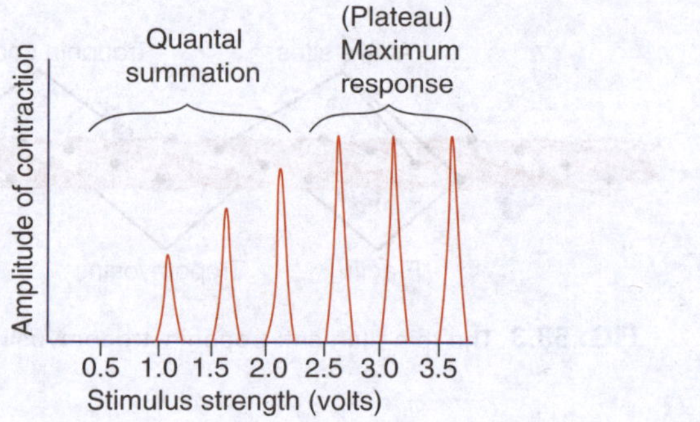

FIG. 53.5 Quantal summation.

position. People who exercise usually do a combination of such exercises. Sustained and regular isotonic exercise improves cardiorespiratory fitness and increases muscle endurance. In contrast, sustained isometric exercise increases muscle strength and enhances joint stability.

QUANTAL SUMMATION

In an experimental set-up, it is possible to directly stimulate a nerve and record a single contraction of the muscle. As the strength of stimulus increases, the force of muscle contraction also increases until it reaches a plateau (maximum after which there is no further increase). The reason this happens is that a nerve trunk is in fact made up of many nerve fibres – as the strength of stimulus increases, more and more nerve fibres within the nerve trunk get stimulated. We know that each nerve fibre supplies multiple muscle fibres (motor unit). Thus, as a nerve fibre is stimulated, the muscle fibres supplied by it will contract. As more and more nerve fibres get stimulated, more and more motor units are recruited and more muscle fibres contract, increasing the amplitude of muscle contraction. This is called quantal summation and is schematically illustrated in Fig. 53.5.

EFFECT OF INCREASING FREQUENCY OF STIMULUS

Fig. 53.6 shows the relationship of the action potential and the contractile response in skeletal muscle in response to a single stimulus. The action potential is the electrical response of the muscle. As you can see from Fig. 53.6, the action potential is very short and occurs before the contractile response. What happens if we provide a second stimulus soon after the first stimulus? What happens depends on how soon the second stimulus is provided. For much of the action potential, the nerve/muscle is 'refractory', that is it cannot respond to a second stimulus. This is discussed further in Chapter 67. However, since the contractile response of the muscle follows the action potential

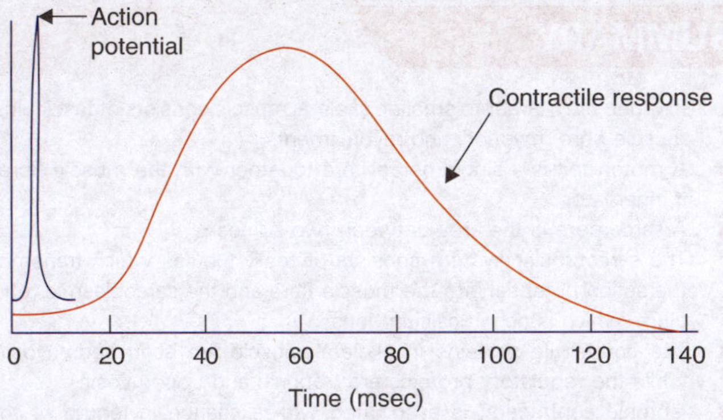

FIG. 53.6 Relationship between the action potential and the contractile response in skeletal muscle.

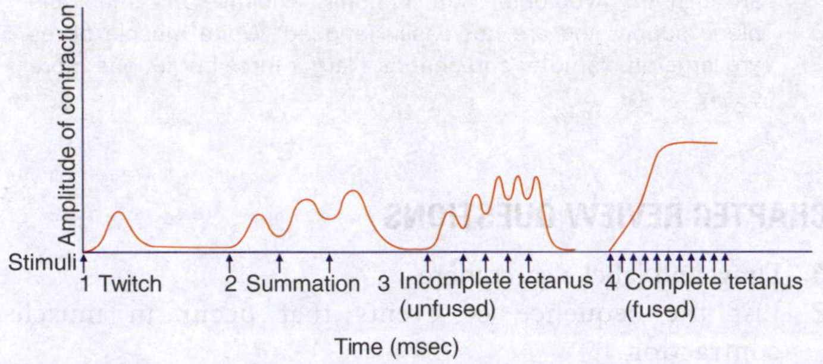

FIG. 53.7 Effect of increasing frequency of stimulus on skeletal muscle contraction.

(i.e. after the period that is refractory), this means that a second (or multiple) stimulus can be delivered at any time during the contractile response and that the muscle will respond to these stimuli.

Fig. 53.7 illustrates the effect on contraction of muscle when multiple stimuli are delivered during the relaxation phase of the preceding contraction and during the contraction phase as well. The higher responses that are seen when stimuli are delivered during the relaxation phase or soon after the relaxation phase are due to several reasons:

1. Cytosolic calcium concentration is higher because the calcium present in the previous contraction has not yet been fully pumped back into the sarcoplasmic reticulum, while more calcium has been released from the sarcoplasmic reticulum with each successive stimulus. Because more calcium is available in the cytosol, the binding of calcium to troponin C will be higher.
2. With each successive contraction, the temperature within the muscle increases and enzymatic activity in the muscle also increases.
3. Viscosity of the cytosol decreases with the increased temperature (think of ice cream that melts with increased temperature).

All these factors contribute to a greater amplitude of contraction – sometimes called the 'beneficial effect'.

If multiple stimuli are all delivered during the contraction phase, the muscle goes into a state of sustained contraction called 'tetanus'. Tetanus has the benefit that it increases the amplitude of contraction, but the disadvantage is that muscle is unable to sustain this greater amplitude for long and the muscle gets fatigued.

MUSCLE FATIGUE

If a muscle contracts continuously or repeatedly over a period of time, the amplitude of contraction gradually decreases. This inability of the muscle to sustain a given amplitude of contraction is called fatigue. Fatigue can occur because of many reasons. For instance:

1. It may be due to depletion of the neurotransmitter (acetylcholine) at the neuromuscular junction.
2. Fatigue may be in the muscle itself, because of depletion of ATP or the accumulation of metabolic products such as lactic acid.
3. Fatigue may also be subjective, in which the individual appears to be unable to perform a muscle contraction but can do so if motivated. We all know how runners appear to tire towards the end of a race, but then seem to get a second 'wind' as the crowd begins to cheer them on.

Rigor mortis *is a stiffening of the muscles after death. This occurs because of the depletion of ATP in the muscle. As we have seen earlier, ATP is required not only for contraction but also for relaxation – ATP binds to the myosin head and this causes it to disengage from the actin. In the absence of ATP after death, the myosin molecule is unable to disengage from actin and the muscle becomes stiff.*

TYPES OF MUSCLE FIBRES IN SKELETAL MUSCLE

If you observe a cross-section of the skeletal muscle under the microscope, you will notice that not all muscle fibres within a skeletal muscle are similar. There are, in fact, two broad types of skeletal muscle fibres. Red muscle fibres (type 1) are rich in myoglobin, mitochondria and oxidative enzymes, have a rich blood supply and are relatively nonfatigable. These muscle fibres can therefore 'work' longer and are of particular advantage to endurance athletes like marathon runners.

In contrast, white muscle fibres (type II) are large in diameter, but have a relatively small blood supply and fewer mitochondria. These muscle fibres can generate great force but are more easily fatigued and are of particular use to athletes like weight lifters.

The proportions of red and white muscle fibres differ in different muscles and in the same muscles of different people. The proportion of red to white muscle fibres has a strong genetic basis, but muscle fibre proportions can also be altered with training.

The differences in red and white muscle fibres are summarized in Table 53.2.

Table 53.2 Differences Between Red and White Muscle Fibres

	Red Muscle Fibres	White Muscle Fibres
Other names	Type 1, slow	Type II, fast
Size of muscle fibre	Small	Large
Capillary density	High	Low
Myoglobin	More	Less
Mitochondria	More	Less
Oxidative enzymes	More	Less
Fatigability	Less	More
Amplitude of contraction	Less	More

APPLICATIONS FOR NURSING

The nurse will encounter many conditions in which there is muscle fatigue or weakness. These include conditions such as myasthenia gravis (discussed in Chapter 52), but also conditions such as heart and kidney failure, endocrine disorders such as hypothyroidism and anaemia. In situations such as these, the nurse may play an important role in health education and working with patients on plans developed by the health team. Muscle weakness may also be a manifestation of a neurological disease and the nurse will be required to assess muscle strength and function of different muscle groups, and the response to treatment. The nurse will also be required to perform passive exercises for the patient if the patient is bedridden to maintain flexibility and muscle mass and muscle strength.

SUMMARY

- In order, from larger to smaller, skeletal muscle consists of fasciculus, muscle fibre, myofibril and myofilaments.
- A motor unit is a single nerve fibre together with the muscle fibres it innervates.
- A sarcomere is the area between two Z lines.
- The sarcotubular system consists of the T tubules which transmits the action potential into the muscle fibre and the sarcoplasmic reticulum, which is rich in calcium ions.
- The contractile proteins in skeletal muscle are actin and myosin, while the regulatory proteins are troponin and tropomyosin.
- Isotonic contraction is associated with a change in length of the muscle and work is done. Isometric contraction is not associated with any change in length of the muscle and work is not done.
- Fatigue is the inability of the muscle to sustain a given amplitude of contraction.
- There are two types of skeletal muscle fibres. Red muscle fibres are rich in myoglobin, mitochondria, oxidative enzymes and blood supply and are not easily fatigued. White muscle fibres are larger in diameter and generate larger force but fatigue more easily.

CHAPTER REVIEW QUESTIONS

1. Draw and label a sarcomere.
2. List the sequence of events that occur in muscle contraction.
3. Differentiate between isotonic and isometric muscle contraction.
4. Differentiate between red and white muscle fibres.

CHAPTER 54

Muscle Tone

SPECIFIC LEARNING OBJECTIVES

At the end of this chapter, the student should be able to:

- Define muscle tone.
- Describe how muscle tone is regulated.
- Distinguish between hypotonia and hypertonia.

GLOSSARY OF TERMS

- **Muscle tone:** a state of sustained partial contraction of a muscle at rest
- **Hypertonia:** an increase in the muscle tone
- **Hypotonia:** a decrease in the muscle tone

WHAT IS MUSCLE TONE

Muscle tone refers to the continuous and partial contraction of a muscle even in the resting state. Because of this, if a muscle is stretched passively (where another person moves, example.g. the arm or leg of a patient), there is a certain resistance to that movement.

Muscle tone can be regulated. Thus, if the body is suddenly pushed or pulled, the tension (tone) in certain muscles will be increased. This has functions: (1) it helps the body to maintain balance and (2) it ensures that skeletal muscle injury is reduced. Actually, a muscle is never completely at rest because of the resting tone. In large muscle groups, muscle tone helps to maintain the posture of the body. Muscle tone is present in all types of muscles – skeletal, smooth and cardiac.

HOW MUSCLE TONE IS REGULATED

This depends on certain stretch receptors that are present in the skeletal muscle called **muscle spindles**. When a muscle is stretched, the muscle spindle which is present in the muscle parallel to the muscle fibres is also stretched. This activates the muscle spindle which sends signals to the spinal cord – the result is that the skeletal muscle is stimulated via its motor neuron and the muscle contracts, leading to shortening. This situation can arise when the tone in the muscle is reduced. Since tone reflects partial muscle contraction (shortening), reduced tone would indicate lengthening of the skeletal muscle. When this occurs, the muscle spindle is also stretched and activated and the muscle is stimulated to contract – the result is a restoration of tone in the skeletal muscle. The spinal reflex which uses the muscle spindle is called the **stretch reflex**.

Another receptor which regulates tone is the **Golgi's tendon body**. This is located at the junction of the muscle and its tendon. Since contraction and relaxation of the skeletal muscle will stretch and shorten the tendon as well, this receptor is also capable of sensing tone in the muscle. When there is increased muscle tone, the Golgi's tendon senses this increased tone and causes the muscle attached to the tendon to relax.

Fig. 54.1 depicts these two receptors. Table 54.1 compares the two receptors.

Muscle tone is also regulated by impulses from the brain. Thus some impulses are stimulatory and increase muscle tone while some impulses are inhibitory and decrease muscle tone.

HYPOTONIA

A reduced tone in the muscle is called **hypotonia**. The neurological causes of alterations in muscle tone are described in greater detail in Chapter 70, when we deal with the regulation of the motor system.

Reduced muscle tone can be seen in a number of clinical conditions. It is sometimes evident at birth itself. Thus, children with genetic disorders like Down's syndrome (trisomy 21) exhibit

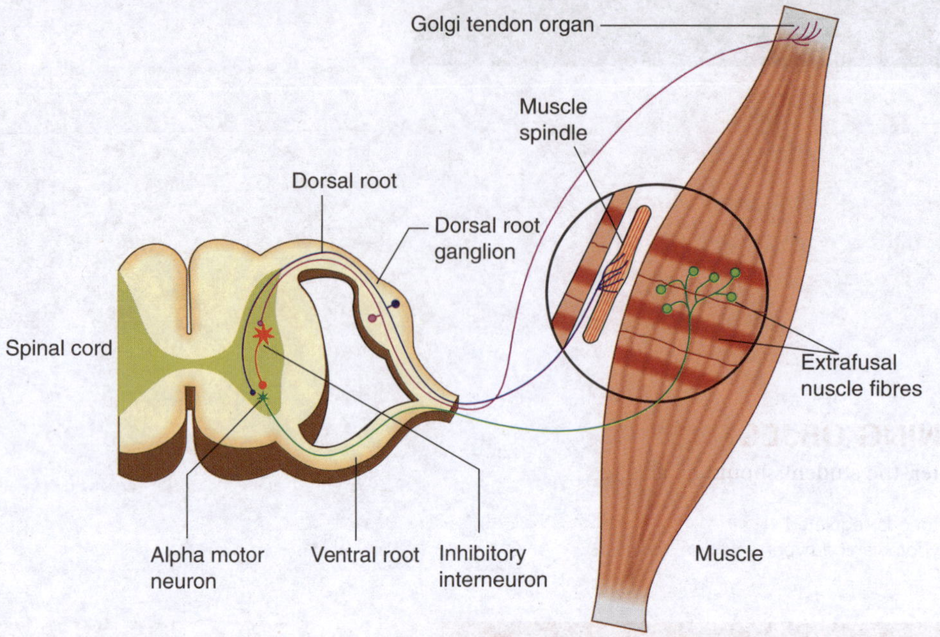

FIG. 54.1 Location of the muscle spindle and Golgi's tendon organ receptors.

Table 54.1 A Comparison on the Muscle Spindle and Golgi's Tendon Organ

	Muscle Spindle	Golgi's Tendon Organ
Location	Within skeletal muscle	In muscle tendon
Anatomical arrangement	Parallel to extrafusal muscle fibres	In series with extrafusal muscle fibres
Afferent nerves	Ia, II	Ib
Efferent nerves	γ Efferents	No efferent nerves
Stimulus	Muscle stretch	Muscle tension
Associated reflex	Stretch (myotatic) reflex	Inverse stretch reflex
Effect of the reflex	Contraction of the muscle	Relaxation of the muscle

hypotonia. In some children, the hormone thyroxine is not produced adequately right from birth – this condition, called cretinism, is also associated with hypotonia. Hypotonia can also occur in conditions which affect muscle contraction as in myasthenia gravis which was discussed in Chapter 52. When the motor nerve supplying a muscle is injured or destroyed, it results in paralysis of the muscle, and the muscle is hypotonic. This type of paralysis is called flaccid paralysis. Flaccid paralysis can result in muscle wasting in which the bulk of the muscle that is affected is reduced.

HYPERTONIA

An increased tone in muscle is called hypertonia. Hypertonia is sometimes referred to as spasticity, although the two terms are slightly different. It is most often seen in conditions affecting the areas that control motor function in the central nervous system. Muscles that are affected exhibit rigidity (increased resistance to stretch) and muscle weakness. Because spasticity coexists with muscle weakness/paralysis, this state is sometimes referred to as spastic paralysis. Reflexes such as the knee jerk (which is an example of stretch reflex) pictured in Fig. 54.2 are exaggerated and reflect the increased excitability of muscle spindles. Hypertonia may also manifest in childhood, as, for instance, in cerebral palsy. Cerebral palsy is caused by damage to the brain during foetal development or at birth or even in infancy.

APPLICATIONS IN NURSING

- The nurse may need to evaluate the muscle function including muscle tone of patients, particularly those who suffer from chronic problems.
- Since changes in muscle tone are often associated with muscle weakness, the nurse may be required to perform passive exercises for the muscles across the range of movements to ensure preservation of muscle mass and continuation of a full range of movements around a joint.
- The nurse will also need to educate the patient in consultation with the medical team on issues related to posture and active exercises (if the patient is capable of performing some movements).

SUMMARY

- Muscle tone is a state of sustained partial contraction of the muscle, even at rest.
- Receptors which sense muscle tone include muscle spindles and Golgi's tendon bodies.
- Increased tone is referred to as hypertonia and decreased muscle tone as hypotonia.

CHAPTER REVIEW QUESTIONS

1. What is muscle tone?
2. Describe the role of the (a) muscle spindle and (b) Golgi's tendon organ.
3. Write a brief note on (a) hypotonia and (b) hypertonia.

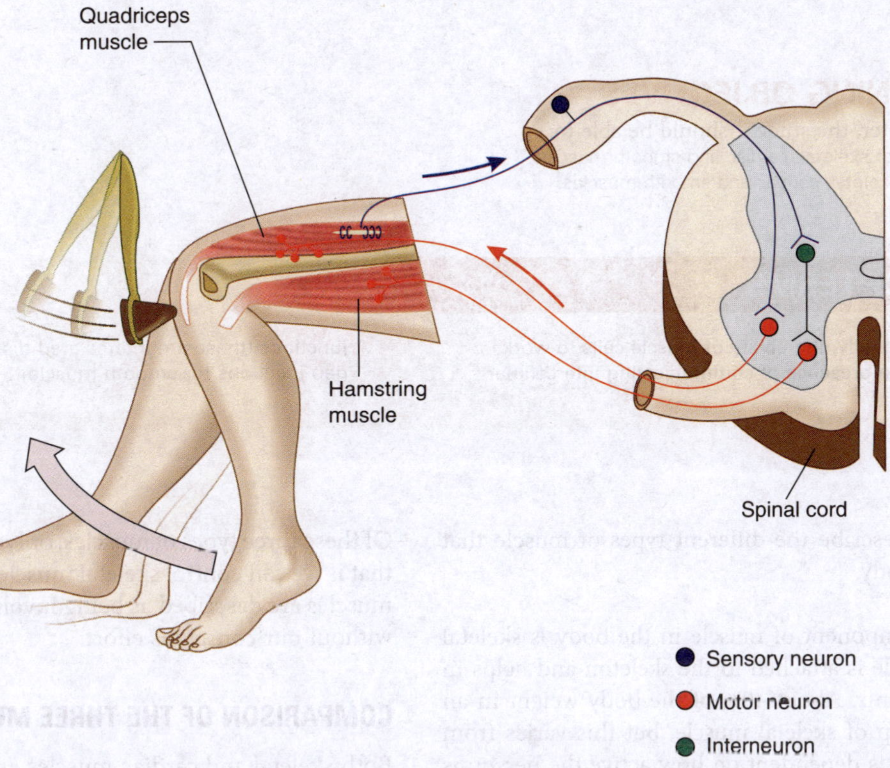

FIG. 54.2 The knee jerk reflex.

CHAPTER 55

Comparison of Skeletal, Cardiac and Smooth Muscles

SPECIFIC LEARNING OBJECTIVES

At the end of this chapter, the student should be able to:

- Describe the location of skeletal, cardiac and smooth muscles.
- Distinguish between skeletal, cardiac and smooth muscles.

GLOSSARY OF TERMS

- **Syncytium:** functionally, the ability of muscle cells to work together due to the presence of communicating intercellular junctions (these are intercalated discs for cardiac muscle and gap junctions for smooth muscle)

In this chapter, we describe the different types of muscle that exist in the human body.

By far, the largest component of muscle in the body is skeletal muscle. Skeletal muscle is attached to the skeleton and helps in movement around joints. About 40% of the body weight in an adult male is made up of skeletal muscle, but this varies from person to person and is dependent on how active the person is and on the body composition of the individual (proportion of fat to fat-free mass). Skeletal muscle mass also tends to decrease with ageing, a condition called *sarcopaenia*. In women, the percentage of skeletal muscle as a function of total body weight is less than in males because of the higher percentage of fat in women.

Smooth muscle is found surrounding the blood vessels, the digestive, respiratory and urinary tracts, and other hollow body organs. In the blood vessels, smooth muscle controls the diameter of the vessel, and hence the flow of blood as well as the pressure that is maintained within the blood vessel. In the respiratory tract, that is the trachea, bronchi and bronchioles, the smooth muscles control the diameter of the airways. In bronchial asthma, for instance, allergens may result in severe bronchial constriction. In the digestive tract, the smooth muscle is responsible for 'motility' which helps move the food through the alimentary tract at a rate that ensures optimal digestion and absorption.

Cardiac muscle is seen in the heart. The heart itself is a relatively small organ, about the size of a clenched fist, which weighs about 300 g in the adult male. Fig. 55.1 depicts the microscopic structure of the three muscle types.

Of these three types of muscles, only skeletal muscle is voluntary, that is we can control skeletal muscle action, while the other two muscles are described as being involuntary, that is they function without our conscious effort.

COMPARISON OF THE THREE MUSCLES

Both skeletal and cardiac muscles are 'striated' – that is striped. This is how the muscle appears under a microscope and is due to the specific arrangement of actin and myosin in the muscle fibre. This has been further described for skeletal muscle in Chapter 53. Smooth muscles are unstriated.

Cardiac muscle fibres are multinucleated and branched, while smooth muscle fibres are spindle shaped and small, and have a single nucleus. Cardiac muscle fibres can communicate with each other via 'intercalated discs', while smooth muscle fibres communicate via gap junctions. The result of this communication in cardiac and smooth muscles is that these two muscles can function as a 'syncytium', that is a single functional unit. This is because when one cell is stimulated, the stimulus can spread through the intercalated discs in the heart and the gap junctions in smooth muscle. The syncytium in cardiac muscle is important because it allows the entire atrium or the entire ventricle to contract as a unit – this ensures that the heart functions like an optimal pump. In the case of the intestine, the syncytium of smooth muscle allows for effective propulsion of food in the intestinal tract.

In terms of the nerve supply, skeletal muscle is innervated by motor nerves of the peripheral nervous system, while both

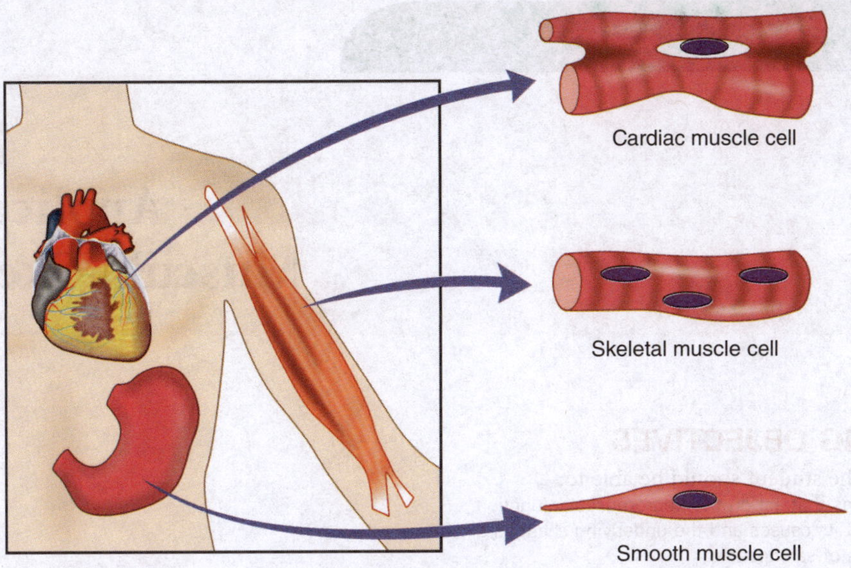

FIG. 55.1 The basic structure of skeletal, cardiac and smooth muscles.

cardiac and smooth muscles are innervated by the autonomic nervous system. The autonomic nervous system has two branches – the sympathetic nervous system and the parasympathetic nervous system. Both cardiac and smooth muscles respond to hormones, while skeletal muscle responds largely to nerves. The action of nerves/hormones in cardiac and smooth muscles can be excitation or inhibition. You will appreciate this to a greater extent when we discuss the working of the heart.

While smooth and cardiac muscles are supplied by nerves, they also have the ability to maintain their own contractile rhythm in the absence of innervation (nerves). In the heart, this means that cardiac muscle has its own intrinsic contractile rhythm. In fact, some muscle cells in the heart are specialized as pacemaker cells, which help to drive the rate of contraction of the heart. In smooth muscle, as is present in the gastrointestinal system, the intrinsic contractile rhythm helps to ensure rhythmic contractions in the interdigestive period (i.e. between meals). This is believed to help move undigested material and secretions and also prevent the overgrowth of bacteria in the intestine.

Skeletal muscle, no matter how well trained, exhibits fatigue. Fatigue is the inability of the muscle to sustain a given amplitude of muscle contraction. Thus, even a marathon runner has limits to what the muscle can perform. In contrast, cardiac muscle and smooth muscle are described as being resistant to fatigue. This is best illustrated with cardiac muscle – it is quite amazing that the heart beats once every 0.8 second for about 70 years without tiring! This amounts to about 2,759,400,000 beats in a lifetime! There are many reasons why cardiac muscle is resistant to fatigue and this is discussed in Chapter 25.

Skeletal muscle is not uniform – there are, in fact, two types of skeletal muscle fibres which make up muscle – these are the red and white muscle fibres which are discussed in greater detail in Chapter 53. Similarly, not all smooth muscles are alike. Some smooth muscles are 'single-unit', that is they can function as a single unit (syncytium); others are multiunit, that is the muscle cells can function individually – the advantage of this is that this type of smooth muscles is capable of graded responses and can also be controlled more finely.

Table 55.1 A Comparison of the Characteristics of Skeletal, Cardiac and Smooth Muscles

	Skeletal Muscle	Cardiac Muscle	Smooth Muscle
Appearance	Striated	Striated, branched fibres	Not striated, spindle shaped
Location	Attached to the skeleton	Heart	Walls of the respiratory, urinary, gastrointestinal tracts and of hollow organs
Type of contraction	Voluntary	Involuntary	Involuntary
Susceptibility to fatigue	High	Low	Low
Nerve supply	Peripheral, somatic nerves; alpha motor neurons	Autonomic: Sympathetic and parasympathetic	Autonomic: Sympathetic and parasympathetic. In GIT – enteric nervous system
Response to hormones	Small	Large	Large
Can function as a syncytium	No	Yes	Yes

Table 55.1 summarizes some of the differences between skeletal, cardiac and smooth muscles. As you get more familiar with physiological processes, other differences will emerge.

CHAPTER 56

Applications in the Musculo-Skeletal System

SPECIFIC LEARNING OBJECTIVES

At the end of this chapter, the student should be able to:

- Describe the drugs and toxins that act on the neuromuscular junction.
- Define muscular atrophy, list its causes and the underlying changes in skeletal muscle.
- Describe briefly the features of sarcopaenia.
- Describe briefly the nature of muscular dystrophies.
- Describe how muscle tone is assessed.

GLOSSARY OF TERMS

- **Muscular dystrophy:** a group of over 30 genetic disorders characterized by progressive muscle degeneration and wasting of muscles
- **Muscle atrophy:** loss of skeletal muscle due to multiple causes
- **Sarcopaenia:** an age-related, involuntary loss of skeletal muscle mass and strength
- **Cancer cachexia:** loss of muscle mass with or without adipose tissue due to cancer
- **Muscle tone:** resistance to passive stretch of a muscle

In this chapter, we describe clinical conditions that affect skeletal muscle and drugs and toxins that act on the neuromuscular junction (NMJ).

DRUGS/TOXINS ACTING AT THE NEUROMUSCULAR JUNCTION

As you can imagine, drugs which prevent neuromuscular transmission result in muscle relaxation or paralysis. Drugs and toxins that act on NMJ are often classified based on their site of action into those which act on the presynaptic membrane, those that act on the postsynaptic membrane and those that act in the synaptic cleft.

Presynaptic Membrane

Botulism is a disease caused by an organism called *Clostridium botulinum*. The disease was first described in people who ate improperly handled meat products. The toxin that is released by the organism (called botulinum toxin) prevents the release of acetylcholine (Ach) from the axon terminal. As a result, there is a failure of the neuromuscular transmission and the muscle supplied by the nerve is paralysed.

Synaptic Cleft

When Ach detaches from its receptor, it is acted upon by cholinesterase which degrades it. There are many drugs which act to prevent the action of cholinesterase and thus prevent the breakdown of Ach in the synaptic cleft – among these are drugs like neostigmine and physostigmine. We shall discuss the role of these drugs later in the chapter. Another important class of drugs/poisons which inhibit cholinesterase is 'nerve gas' and organophosphate poisons (found in pesticides and sometimes consumed by people attempting suicide).

Postsynaptic Membrane

Curare is a poison extracted from a plant that was used by native peoples in South America to create poison-tipped arrows. The poison binds to the Ach receptor and prevents the normal binding of Ach. Bungarotoxin is present in venom of the poisonous snake, the krait, and acts in a similar manner as curare.

There are also drugs that have been developed which act on the Ach receptor. An example of this is succinylcholine – which is structurally similar to Ach and therefore binds to the Ach receptor. It acts very rapidly and has a very short duration of action. It is used to relax the vocal cords for intubation (insertion of a tube into the trachea) when a patient cannot breathe and is put on a ventilator or as part of the process of inducing general anaesthesia for surgery.

The effects of the drugs and toxins acting on the neuromuscular junction are summarized in Table 56.1

Table 56.1 Drugs and Toxins Acting on the Neuromuscular Junction

Drug/Toxin	Source	Action
Presynaptic		
Tetrodotoxin	Puffer fish	• Blocks voltage-gated sodium channels • Prevents the generation of the action potential in the nerve
Conotoxin	Cone snails	• Blocks the voltage-gated calcium channels in the nerve terminal
Botulinum toxin	Bacteria – *Clostridium botulinum* – spoilt canned food	• Prevents exocytosis of acetylcholine from the nerve terminal
Synaptic		
Organophosphorus compounds	Pesticides/insecticides	• Blocks the action of cholinesterase in the synaptic cleft
Nerve gas	Artificially produced – a potential bioweapon	• Blocks the action of cholinesterase in the synaptic cleft
Neostigmine/physostigmine	Medications – artificially produced	• Blocks the action of cholinesterase in the synaptic cleft – may be used in the diagnosis/treatment of myasthenia gravis
Postsynaptic		
Curare	A vine (plant) in South America – used as a poison by natives on the arrow tips	• Blocks the nicotinic acetylcholine receptor – competitively inhibits acetylcholine
Bungaratoxin	Venom of the krait snake	• Blocks the nicotinic acetylcholine receptor – competitively inhibits acetylcholine
Succinylcholine	Artificially produced medication	• Blocks the nicotinic acetylcholine receptor – competitively inhibits acetylcholine. Artificial medications can be designed to regulate their duration and strength of action

MUSCULAR DYSTROPHY

Definition:

Muscular dystrophy is a group of over 30 genetic disorders characterized by progressive muscle degeneration and wasting of muscles.

Clinical features:

The patients typically experience muscle pain and a gradual deterioration of muscle function. This deterioration of muscle function can result in limitation of movement and, if it involves the respiratory muscle, in difficulty in breathing. Since there are different types of muscular dystrophy, the cause, clinical features and outcomes depend on the specific condition.

Examples of muscular dystrophy:

- One of the more common forms of muscular dystrophy is Duchenne's muscular dystrophy. Muscle wasting in this condition often starts by around the age of 3 years and survival may only be until the mid-twenties.
- Becker muscular dystrophy affects males more than females. Symptoms appear any time between the ages of 5 and 60, but manifest most commonly in the teenage years. The severity of the disease is variable between people.
- Myotonic dystrophy is the most common form of muscular dystrophy that occurs in adulthood. Patients have difficulty relaxing their muscles.

Cause:

In general, muscular dystrophy involves structural proteins, often on the sarcolemma, which provide stability to the muscle fibres. One of these proteins is called *dystrophin.*

DISUSE MUSCLE ATROPHY

Definition:

Muscle atrophy refers to the loss of muscle tissue (i.e. muscle wasting). Disuse muscle atrophy occurs in all situations in which the muscles are not being used.

Causes:

- Paralysis of a muscle or a group of muscles.
- Immobilization of muscles as occurs when a limb is put in a plaster cast.
- Prolonged bed rest.

Changes in the muscle:

The wasting of muscles is due to changes in the muscle, some of which can be seen microscopically and include the following:

- Shrinkage, splitting or loss of muscle fibres.
- Shift in muscle fibre type proportions, although this is dependent on the cause of muscle atrophy. Thus, with disuse, there may be a shift from red to white muscle fibres, while with fasting and ageing there may be a shift from white to slow muscle fibres.
- There are also many other molecular changes which are beyond the scope of this book.

Treatment:

Measures to counter disuse muscle atrophy include the following:

- Mechanical loading of muscles with exercise or electrical stimulation.
- Passive physiotherapy – which involves moving the limbs/muscle groups passively.
- Maintaining optimal protein nutrition to limit the loss of muscle mass.

SARCOPAENIA

Definition:

An age related, involuntary loss of skeletal muscle mass and strength

Features:

- Skeletal muscle is about 40%–60% of the total body weight.
- Muscle mass starts reducing in between 30 and 40 years of age.
- By 70–80 years of age, muscle mass reduces by about 50% of maximum adult values.

Clinical associations:

Sarcopaenia has been associated with the following clinical conditions:

- insulin resistance
- fatigue
- falls
- mortality

Preventive measures:

The rate of decline of muscle mass and function with age can be reduced by:

- regular and sustained physical activity
- exercise, especially resistance exercises – this needs to be tailored to the persons age and ability
- balanced nutrition and where appropriate, nutritional supplements

The process of sarcopaenia is shown in Fig. 56.1.

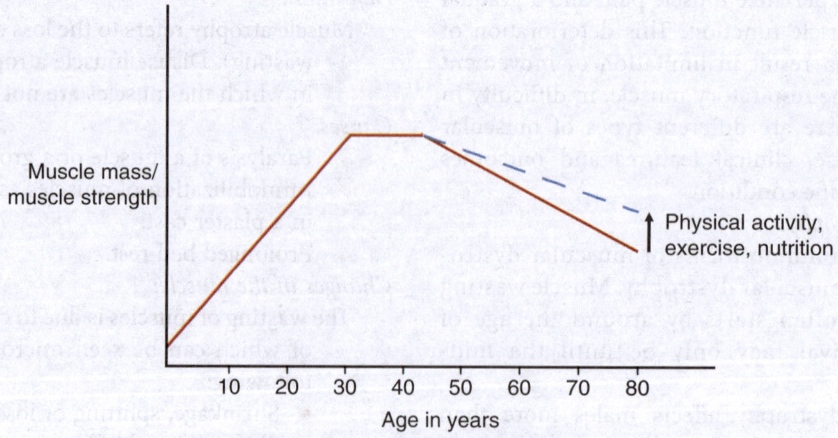

FIG. 56.1. Progression of sarcopaenia.

CACHEXIA OF CANCER

This occurs with cancer and is associated by an involuntary and progressive loss of muscle mass with or without a loss of adipose (fat) tissue. About half of cancer patients loose more than 10% of their body weight during the course of their treatment. Death may be associated with a weight loss of greater than 30%. Mortality independent of weight loss can occur due to the underlying medical condition. Nutritional supplements may only partially help because there are multiple factors involved due to the underlying cancer.

CLINICAL EVALUATION OF MUSCLE TONE

In order to evaluate muscle tone, the following steps are necessary:

1. The muscle needs to be palpated (felt) to determine the extent to which there is contraction at rest.
2. The resistance to movement at the appropriate joint needs to be checked. In children, it may be necessary to distract the child while doing this.
3. Measure the passive range of movement at slow, intermediate and fast speeds. Passive movement is one in which the movement around a joint is determined by the examiner, rather than by the patient actively using his or her muscles. This part of the examination is important because, among other things, in certain conditions, there is increased rigidity at the start of the movement.

CLINICAL CASE PROBLEMS

(A) ***A 24-year-old man complains of progressive weakness of his muscles and drooping of his eyelids as the day progresses. After clinical evaluation and other tests, he is diagnosed with myasthenia gravis (you will need to review the chapter on neuromuscular junction).***

a. What is the basis for myasthenia gravis?
b. Describe the events that occur in neuromuscular transmission.

(B) ***A 32-year-old woman had a fall. Her x-ray shows a fracture of the lower tibia. A rod is inserted to stabilize the tibia and her leg is put in a plaster cast for 8 weeks. After the cast is removed, she finds that her calf muscles in the affected leg have 'shrunk'.***

a. Why have her calf muscles shrunk in size?
b. What can be done to help her improve her muscle mass and strength?

SELF-DIRECTED LEARNING

- How can muscle strength be assessed clinically?
- What are the dangers of using anabolic steroids to increase muscle bulk?

WHAT YOU CAN LEARN FROM A HOSPITAL VISIT

Visit the physiotherapy department of the hospital and see how they advise patients with musculo-skeletal problems.

9
SECTION

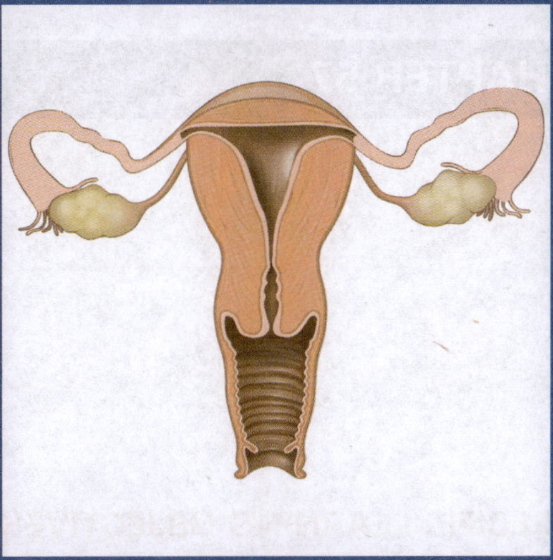

Renal System

Section Outline

CHAPTER 57

Functions of the Kidney and the Urinary System

SPECIFIC LEARNING OBJECTIVES

At the end of this chapter, the student should be able to:

- Describe the functional anatomy of the kidney.
- Draw a nephron and label its parts.
- Describe the juxtaglomerular apparatus and indicate its function.
- List the excretory and nonexcretory functions of the kidney.

GLOSSARY OF TERMS

- **Nephron:** the structural and functional unit of the kidney (while numbers vary between people, there are on average about 1 million nephrons per kidney)
- **Ultrafiltration:** filtration which allows some (smaller) molecules to pass through while retaining other (usually larger) molecules
- **Juxtaglomerular apparatus (JGA):** structure in the kidney that consists of three different cells – (1) the juxtaglomerular (JG) cells of the afferent arteriole of the glomerulus, (2) mesangial (Lacis) cells and (3) macula densa cells of the distal convoluted tubule

There are two bean-shaped kidneys located in the posterior abdomen on either side of the vertebral column. Each kidney weighs about 130 g. The cut section of the kidney (Fig. 57.1) shows two distinct zones – an outer cortex (which contains most of the glomeruli as discussed later) and an inner medulla.

The medulla contains the papillae which end in the calyx which in turn drain into the pelvis. The pelvis becomes narrow and then descends in the abdomen as the ureter. Each ureter enters the urinary bladder.

The kidneys have a very large blood supply relative to their size. Thus, the kidneys receive about 20%–25% of the cardiac output or 1000–1250 mL/min. This large blood supply is needed because the kidney has to excrete waste products from the body.

Although we have two kidneys, studies have shown that a single kidney functioning at about 75% of its capacity can perform the functions of the kidneys. This is why people who donate a kidney can function well with the remaining kidney.

THE NEPHRON

Each kidney has more than 1 million functional units called nephrons. Fig. 57.2 shows a typical nephron.

You will observe that the nephron has different parts. These are:

1. *Glomerulus* is a tuft of capillaries. This is formed by the afferent arteriole which enters the glomerulus and is drained by the efferent arteriole which exits the glomerulus. The glomerulus is the site where filtration of the plasma occurs and fluid enters the nephron. Most glomeruli are located in the cortical layer of the kidney.
2. *Bowman's capsule* is a cup-shaped structure which receives the filtrate from the glomerulus.
3. *Proximal convoluted tubule* is a site of the nephron where a lot of the solutes (salts) are reabsorbed back into the plasma. It is also the site of reabsorption of important substances like glucose.
4. *Loop of Henle* dips into the medulla. It consists of two major parts, a descending limb and an ascending limb. The ascending limb is further divided into a thin segment and a thick segment.
5. *Distal convoluted tubule* is an important site of regulation of sodium controlled by the hormone aldosterone.

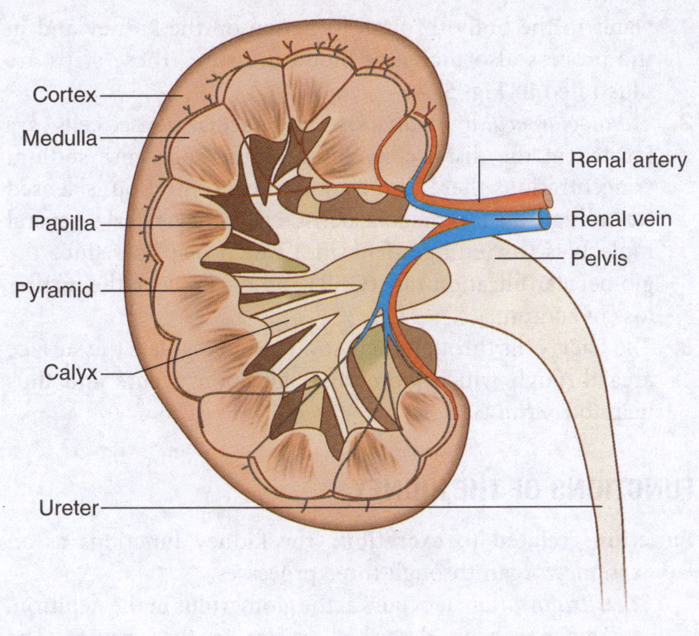

FIG. 57.1 A cut section of the kidney showing the outer cortex and inner medulla.

6. *Collecting duct* is the site of water absorption that is under the control of a hormone released from the posterior pituitary called the antidiuretic hormone.

Types of Nephrons

There are two types of nephrons in the kidney:

1. *Cortical nephrons* have their glomeruli in the cortex. They also have the following features:
   a. They comprise the majority of nephrons in the kidney (about 85%).
   b. They have short loops of Henle.
   c. They serve an important regulatory and excretory role.
2. *Juxtamedullary nephrons* have glomeruli which are at the junction of the cortex and the medulla. They also have the following features:
   a. They comprise 15% of the nephrons in the kidney.
   b. They typically have long loops of Henle.
   c. The ascending limb of the loop of Henle has a thick and thin segment.
   d. They are particularly important in concentrating urine.

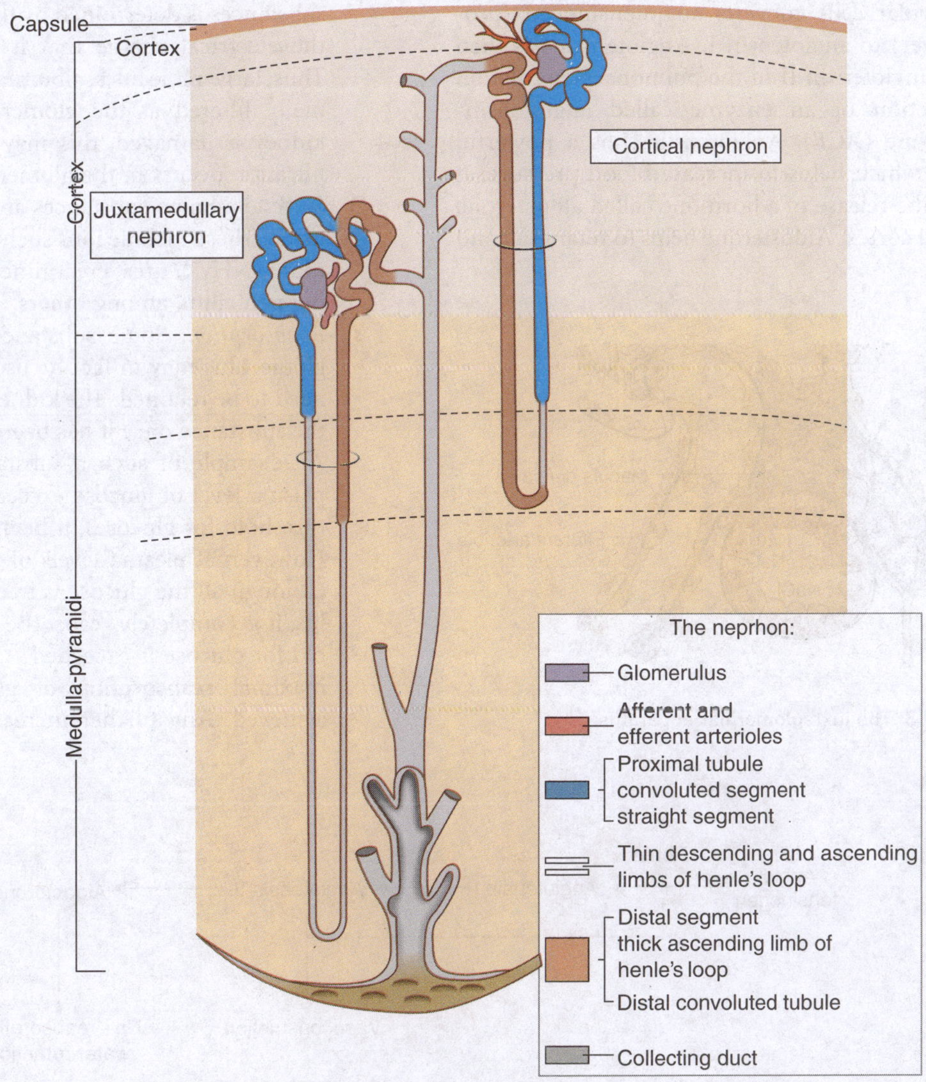

FIG. 57.2 A typical nephron.

THE JUXTAGLOMERULAR APPARATUS

If you look at the structure of the nephron, you will observe that the distal convoluted tubule lies close to the glomerulus. In Fig. 57.3, we have enlarged this section to illustrate the parts of juxtaglomerular apparatus (JGA).

Parts of the JGA

The three main cells which make up JGA are as follows:

1. The *juxtaglomerular cells* located within the wall of the afferent arteriole of the glomerulus, which secrete a substance called renin. These cells are also called *granular* cells.
2. Specialized cells of the distal convoluted tubule called the *macula densa cells* which have a special function of sensing sodium concentrations in the fluid of the distal convoluted tubule.
3. *Lacis or mesangial cells*: These cells are capable of contracting and in the process decrease the surface area of the glomerular capillaries. They thus limit filtration at the glomerulus.

Functions of the JGA

1. *Regulation of blood pressure*: The renin that is secreted by the juxtaglomerular cells converts angiotensinogen (produced in the liver) to angiotensin I. Angiotensin I is then converted into angiotensin II in the pulmonary circulation through the action of an enzyme called angiotensin-converting enzyme (ACE). Angiotensin II is a powerful vasoconstrictor which helps to increase blood pressure. It also stimulates the release of a hormone called aldosterone from the adrenal cortex. Aldosterone helps to retain salt and water in the body through its action on the kidney and in the process also increases blood pressure. These steps are illustrated in Fig. 57.4.
2. *Tubuloglomerular feedback*: The macula dense cells are located in the distal convoluted tubule and sense sodium concentrations there. If the sodium concentration is sensed to be high by the macula densa cells, they release several molecules (including adenosine) which help to reduce the glomerular filtration rate (GFR) and thus reduce the further loss of sodium.
3. The Lacis cells through their contraction regulate the surface area through which glomerular filtration occurs and thus help to *control GFR*.

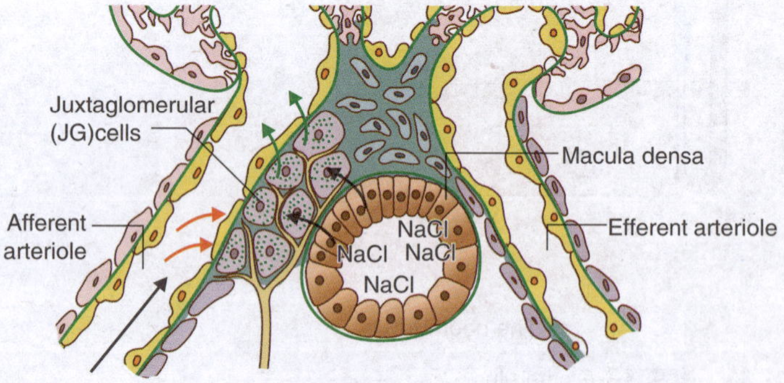

FIG. 57.3 The juxtaglomerular apparatus.

FUNCTIONS OF THE KIDNEY

Functions related to excretion: The kidney functions as an excretory organ through three processes.

1. *Ultrafiltration*: It occurs at the glomerulus in the nephron. This has been described earlier in the chapter. The process is called ultrafiltration because not everything contained in the plasma is filtered. In fact, filtration of substances is determined by the size of the molecule and the electrical charge that it possesses, among others. Thus, large molecules, albumin, for instance, are not normally filtered at the glomerulus, although when the kidney is damaged, this may occur. The rate at which filtration occurs in the glomerulus is called GFR.
2. *Secretion*: Some substances are actively secreted into the urine. These include ions such as hydrogen (H^+), ammonium (NH_4^+), urea, creatinine and various drugs including penicillin, among others.
3. *Reabsorption*: Some substances that are filtered at the glomerulus may in fact be useful for the body and may need to be retained. The kidney does this by reabsorbing the substance once it has been filtered back into plasma. An example of such a substance is glucose. Once the plasma level of glucose exceeds 170 mg/dL (the plasma threshold for glucose), it begins appearing in the urine. However, at plasma levels of glucose below 170 mg/dL although all the glucose is freely filtered at the glomerulus, it is completely reabsorbed, until the plasma threshold for glucose is exceeded – this is the point when the maximal reabsorption of glucose in the kidney is achieved. Any further increase in plasma glucose can

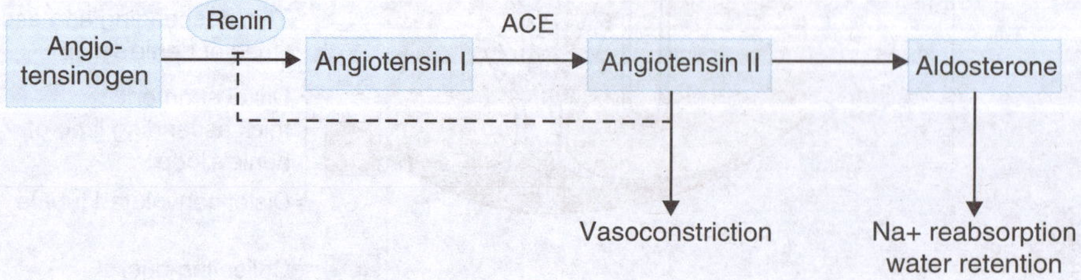

FIG. 57.4 The renin–angiotensin–aldosterone system.

therefore not be reabsorbed in the kidney after filtration and the glucose appears in the urine.

The excretion of waste products from the kidney can be regulated based on need. Thus, as examples, the hormone aldosterone regulates the excretion of sodium, while antidiuretic hormone regulates the excretion of water.

Nonexcretory functions of the kidney:

1. **Role in blood pressure regulation**: Blood pressure is regulated by many different mechanisms. The immediate regulation of blood pressure occurs through a reflex called the baroreflex. This has been discussed in Chapter 28. As discussed earlier in this chapter, however, blood pressure can also be regulated via JGA. This occurs in several ways:
   a. *Angiotensin II* is a powerful vasoconstrictor (i.e. it causes vascular smooth muscle to contract). Thus, increased levels of angiotensin II will cause blood pressure to rise.
   b. *Aldosterone* causes salt and water retention within the vascular compartment. Thus, when aldosterone levels are high, salt and water retention is more resulting in an increase in blood pressure.
2. **Endocrine role:** The kidney is a site of hormone production or of activation. Two examples of this role are given as follows:
   a. *Erythropoietin*: When there is decreased oxygen availability at the level of tissues (hypoxia), the kidney releases erythropoietin which helps to increase red blood cell production (erythropoiesis) in the bone marrow. A typical example where this may occur is at high altitudes. In this situation, oxygen concentrations in the air are low. Another situation in which this may occur is in certain chronic lung diseases in which oxygen which reaches the alveoli cannot diffuse adequately into the bloodstream resulting in a lack of oxygen at the level of the tissues. In both these circumstances, erythropoietin released by the kidney stimulates erythropoiesis to try and increase oxygen supply to the tissues.
   b. *Activation of vitamin D*: The first step of vitamin D production occurs in the skin under the influence of sunlight. A second step involves a chemical reaction called hydroxylation (addition of OH to the molecule) which occurs in the liver. However, even at this stage, the vitamin D is not active – this requires a second hydroxylation in the kidney. Once this occurs, vitamin D is active and can help maintain calcium levels in the body by increasing the absorption of calcium from the intestine.
3. **Other functions:** While the kidney's function in the excretion of waste products covers a large number of substances, these processes impact other functions of the body:
   a. *Acid–base balance*: The extracellular pH of the body is very closely regulated around a pH of about 7.4. A fall in the pH results in a condition called acidosis, while an increase in the pH results in alkalosis. The kidney plays a critical role in acid–base balance by regulating the excretion of H^+ and HCO_3^- ions.
   b. *Electrolyte balance*: The kidney plays an important role in maintaining the balance of salts such as Na^+ and K^+ in the body.

APPLICATIONS FOR NURSING

Kidney failure refers to the inability of the kidneys to function adequately. In this situation, kidney function has to be assisted by either dialysis or kidney transplantation. Because the kidneys are unable to excrete waste products adequately, these collect in the body. Two chemicals which can be tested in blood to evaluate kidney function are urea and creatinine. In addition, the individual may pass too much urine or very little. Because the kidney is involved in blood pressure regulation, the formation of RBCs through erythropoietin, bone health through the action of vitamin D and acid–base balance, all these functions can be impaired in kidney failure.

Dialysis is an artificial process in which waste products, excess salts and fluid are removed from the body. There are two broad types of dialysis; in haemodialysis, the patient is attached to a dialysis machine where the blood is filtered of harmful substances. In peritoneal dialysis, special fluids are introduced into the abdomen (the peritoneal cavity), the lining of which acts as the filtering membrane. The nurse plays an important role in monitoring vital signs during haemodialysis. In addition, patients with end-stage kidney disease on dialysis require considerable health education, counselling and support – nurses are important for all these.

SUMMARY

- The kidney receives 20%–25% of the cardiac output and is divided into the cortex and the medulla.
- The functional unit of the kidney is the nephron. The nephron consists of the glomerulus, the Bowman's capsule, the proximal convoluted tubule, the loop of Henle, the distal convoluted tubule and the collecting duct.
- The juxtaglomerular apparatus consists of the juxtaglomerular cells, the macula densa cells and Lacis cells. It has an important role in the regulation of blood pressure and the control of glomerular filtration rate.
- The kidney has important functions which include excretion of waste products, the secretion and activation of hormones (erythropoietin, vitamin D), salt and water regulation, acid–base balance and regulation of blood pressure.

CHAPTER REVIEW QUESTIONS

1. Draw a typical nephron and describe the function of each part.
2. Compare cortical and juxtamedullary nephrons.
3. List the functions of the juxtaglomerular apparatus.
4. Describe the nonexcretory functions of the kidney.

CHAPTER 58

Glomerular Filtration Rate, the Mechanism of Urine Formation, Micturition and the Regulation of Renal Function

SPECIFIC LEARNING OBJECTIVES

At the end of this chapter, the student should be able to:

- Draw and label the filtration barrier (glomerular membrane).
- Define glomerular filtration rate and list the factors that affect it.
- Describe the relationship between the loop of Henle and the vasa recta.
- Describe the counter-current multiplier and its role.
- Describe the counter-current exchanger and its role.
- Describe the mechanism of glucose reabsorption in the kidney.
- Define the term 'clearance'.
- List the key elements of urine formation in the different parts of the nephron.

GLOSSARY OF TERMS

- **Counter-current multiplier:** the mechanism by which a concentration gradient is created in the medulla of the kidney
- **Counter-current exchanger:** the mechanism by which the concentration gradient in the medulla of the kidney is maintained
- **Transport maximum for glucose:** the maximum rate of glucose reabsorption at the proximal convoluted tubule of the kidney (expressed in mg/min)
- **Starling's forces:** the hydrostatic and osmotic pressures on either side of the capillary wall which determine the movement of fluid across it
- **Micturition:** the act of voiding urine
- **Cystometrogram:** a graphical depiction of the volume–pressure relationship in the urinary bladder obtained by cystometry (this test allows the evaluation of urinary bladder capacity, the pattern of bladder contractions and the ability to voluntarily control micturition)

As mentioned in Chapter 57, there are three processes involved in the formation of urine. These are *filtration*, *secretion* and *tubular reabsorption*. Filtration occurs at the glomerular membrane, which will be described in greater detail later in the chapter. Once plasma is filtered and enters the Bowman's capsule, it may then be modified along the nephron. Thus, some substances may be secreted into the tubules, while others which were filtered at the glomerulus may be reabsorbed back into the body. The three key processes of filtration, secretion and reabsorption are illustrated in Fig. 58.1.

GLOMERULAR FILTRATION RATE

Definition

The renal plasma flow is approximately 600 mL/min, and about one-fifth (i.e. 20%) of it is filtered in all the glomeruli in the kidneys. This fraction of the renal plasma which is filtered is referred to as the *filtration fraction*. *Glomerular filtration rate* (GFR) refers to the total amount of plasma filtered in all the glomeruli of both kidneys in 1 minute. In a healthy adult, this is about 125 mL/min or 180 L/day.

Layers Involved in Glomerular Filtration

Filtration at the glomerulus is not complete for all substances – larger substances, for instance, are not filtered at all, while some smaller substances are filtered completely. In order to understand why filtration is selective, it is necessary to understand the filtration barrier across which filtration occurs (Fig. 58.2).

You will observe from the diagram that there are essentially three layers that a substance has to pass through in order for it to be filtered:

1. The glomerular endothelium: Substances can pass through this layer because the endothelial lining of the glomerular blood vessels is fenestrated, that is it has gaps. You will notice from the diagram that these gaps are not large enough to

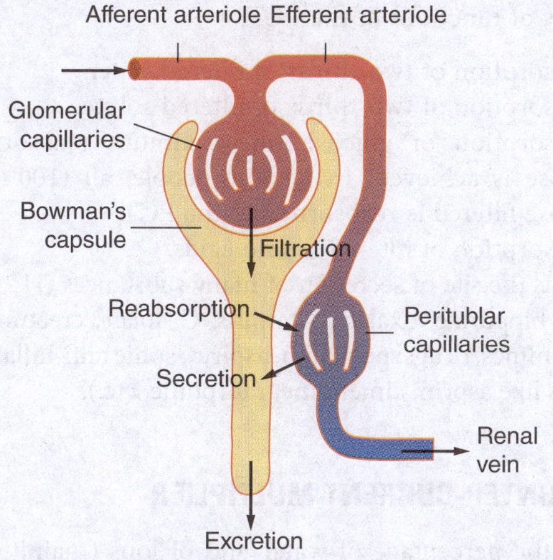

FIG. 58.1 Nephron indicating the processes of filtration, secretion, reabsorption and excretion.

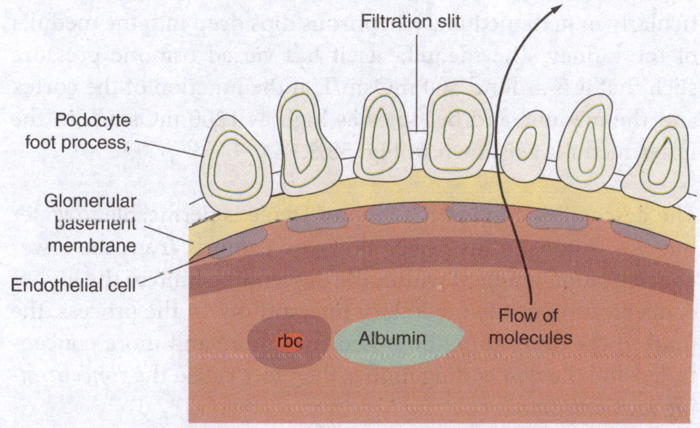

FIG. 58.2 Glomerular filtration barrier.

allow large substances such as albumin or cells to pass through but smaller molecules can pass through.

2. The glomerular basement membrane: This has small channels (even smaller than the fenestrae of the glomerular endothelium) and it is thus here that filtration becomes truly selective.
3. Bowman's capsule epithelium: The epithelial cells of the Bowman's capsule are called podocytes which have foot processes that do not completely cover the basement membrane of the glomerulus. It is through these uncovered portions called filtration slits that the filtrate finally enters the Bowman's capsule.

Factors Affecting Glomerular Filtration

Thus, the filtration barrier at the glomerulus is selective. But why should fluid move from the glomerulus to the Bowman's capsule and not in the reverse direction? In order to understand this, we need to describe the various forces that act to move fluid during filtration.

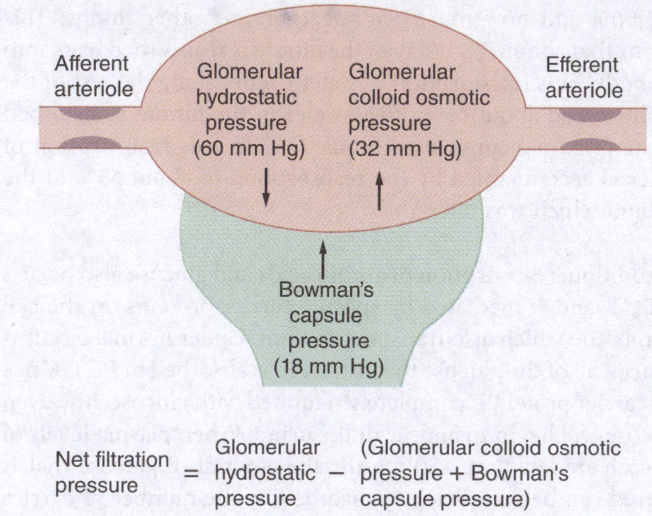

FIG. 58.3 Pressures that act to move fluid from the glomerulus into the Bowman's capsule.

You will observe from Fig. 58.3 that there are various pressures that act at the glomerulus to move fluid. Thus, the hydrostatic pressure within the glomerulus pushes fluid into the Bowman's capsule, while the hydrostatic pressure in the Bowman's capsule acts against this movement. However, the glomerular hydrostatic pressure is higher than the Bowman's capsule hydrostatic pressure so the fluid would tend to move into the Bowman's capsule. In contrast, the osmotic pressure in the glomerulus created largely by the concentration of albumin in the plasma tends to pull water back into the glomerulus (the osmotic pressure in the Bowman's capsule is close to zero, since little protein [and no albumin] is filtered in a healthy person). Thus, the net filtration pressure which drives fluid from the glomerulus into the Bowman's capsule is glomerular hydrostatic pressure minus the combined Bowman's capsule hydrostatic pressure and the glomerular osmotic pressure. These pressures which control the movement of fluid are called *Starling's forces*:

Net filtration pressure = glomerular hydrostatic pressure – (glomerular colloid osmotic pressure + Bowman's capsule hydrostatic pressure)

Filtration fraction is the percentage of the renal plasma flow that is filtered. Thus, if renal plasma flow is 600 mL and GFR is 125 mL in an adult, the filtration fraction is $125/600 \times 100$ = that is ~20%.

Filtration of molecules is dependent on:

1. Size of the molecule
2. Charge of the molecule

THE PROXIMAL CONVOLUTED TUBULE

The filtrate contained in the Bowman's capsule is a mix of salts and small molecules including amino acids and glucose. GFR of 125 mL/min translates into about 180 L/day. However, we excrete only about 1.5 L of urine/day depending on how much water we consume and how much we sweat, among other things. This means that about 178 L/day of the filtrate is reabsorbed back into the body. This reabsorption of water occurs along the rest of the nephron and about 65% of the water in the filtrate is absorbed in the proximal convoluted tubule (PCT). This reabsorption of water is accompanied by the reabsorption of about 65% of the sodium which was filtered.

In addition, reabsorption of amino acids and glucose also occurs in PCT, and is mediated by specific carrier proteins on the cell membrane which also transport sodium. Under normal circumstances, all of the glucose that is filtered is absorbed in PCT. Once the carrier protein is completely saturated with glucose, however, glucose will begin to appear in the urine. When plasma levels of glucose are less than 180 mg/dL, the amount of glucose that is filtered can be completely reabsorbed by the number of carrier proteins located on the cell membrane of the cells of PCT. When the plasma level of glucose increases beyond 180 mg/dL, however, all the carrier proteins are already saturated with filtered glucose and the glucose which cannot be bound and reabsorbed by the carrier proteins is excreted in urine. It is for this reason that we say that the *plasma threshold for glucose* is 180 mg/dL. The maximum amount of glucose that can be reabsorbed in 1 minute at PCT is called the *transport maximum for glucose* (Tm_G) and the normal value is typically about 350 mg/min, although this may vary from person to person (Fig. 58.4).

A plasma level of glucose in excess of 180 mg/dL is often seen in patients with diabetes mellitus, particularly after they have had a meal. In some individuals, however, glucose may begin to appear in the urine even at plasma levels below 180 mg/dL. In these individuals, the number of carrier proteins for glucose may be lower, and so fewer numbers of carrier proteins get saturated with glucose molecules at lower plasma concentrations of glucose. This condition is called *renal glycosuria*. This is a benign condition and does not require to be treated.

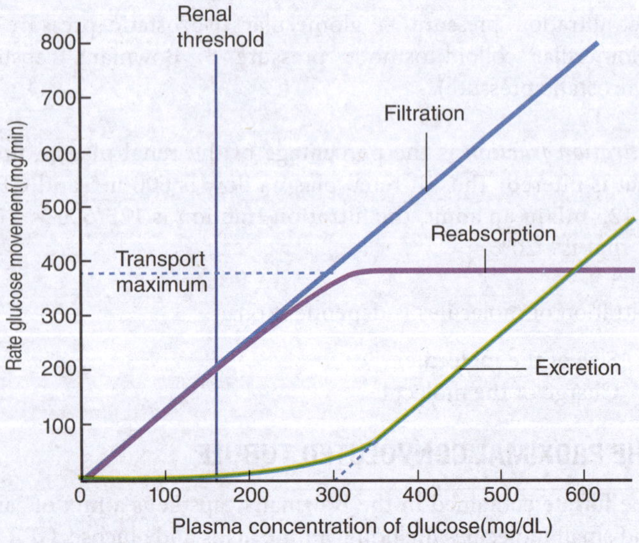

FIG. 58.4 A graph indicating the concept of transport maximum for glucose and renal plasma threshold.

Summary of functions of the PCT:

1. Reabsorption of two-thirds of filtered water.
2. Reabsorption of two-thirds of filtered solute.
3. Reabsorption of glucose till maximum reabsorption of glucose is achieved. In healthy people, all (100%) of the glucose filtered is reabsorbed in the PCT.
4. Reabsorption of filtered amino acids.
5. PCT is the site of secretion of many substances (H^+ ions, bile salts, hippurate, oxalate, vitamins: C, folate, creatinine, catecholamines, drugs: penicillin, aspirin, some anti-inflammatory drugs like asprin, cimetidine, morphine, etc.).

THE COUNTER-CURRENT MULTIPLIER

Because the percentage of water and of ions (mainly sodium) reabsorbed in PCT are almost the same, the fluid which enters the descending limb of the loop of Henle is isotonic.

The loop of Henle consists of a descending limb and an ascending limb arranged close to each other. The loop of Henle particularly in juxtamedullary nephrons dips deep into the medulla of the kidney. The medulla itself has varied osmotic pressure such that it is around 300 mOsm/L at the junction of the cortex and the medulla and becomes as high as 1200 mOsm/L in the inner medulla as shown in Fig. 58.5.

The descending limb of the loop of Henle is permeable to water but not to ions. Thus, water flows by osmosis from the lower concentration gradient within the descending limb to the higher concentration of the medullary interstitium. In the process, the fluid in the descending limb becomes more and more concentrated and the descending limb is therefore called the *concentrating segment/limb*.

The fluid then flows around the loop upwards into the ascending limb of the loop of Henle. This ascending limb is divided into two parts: a lower part called the thin ascending limb and an upper part called the thick ascending limb. The thin ascending limb is permeable to water and also to sodium and chloride which moves passively. Thus, by osmosis, water moves from the medullary interstitium to the lumen. In contrast, the thick ascending limb is impermeable to water, but contains a special transport protein on the cells which carries sodium, potassium and chloride out of the lumen into the medullary interstitium. This transport protein by increasing the ion content of the medullary interstitium thus helps to create the high medullary osmotic gradient. The second thing that happens in the think ascending limb is that the removal of salts from the lumen of the thick ascending limb and the addition of water in the thin ascending limb lower the osmolarity of the fluid in the lumen, so that the ascending limb is called the *diluting segment/limb*. The changes in the osmolarity of fluid in the nephron are illustrated in Fig. 58.6.

About 20% of the fluid that enters the nephron is reabsorbed in the loop of Henle, while the remaining 15% is reabsorbed in the

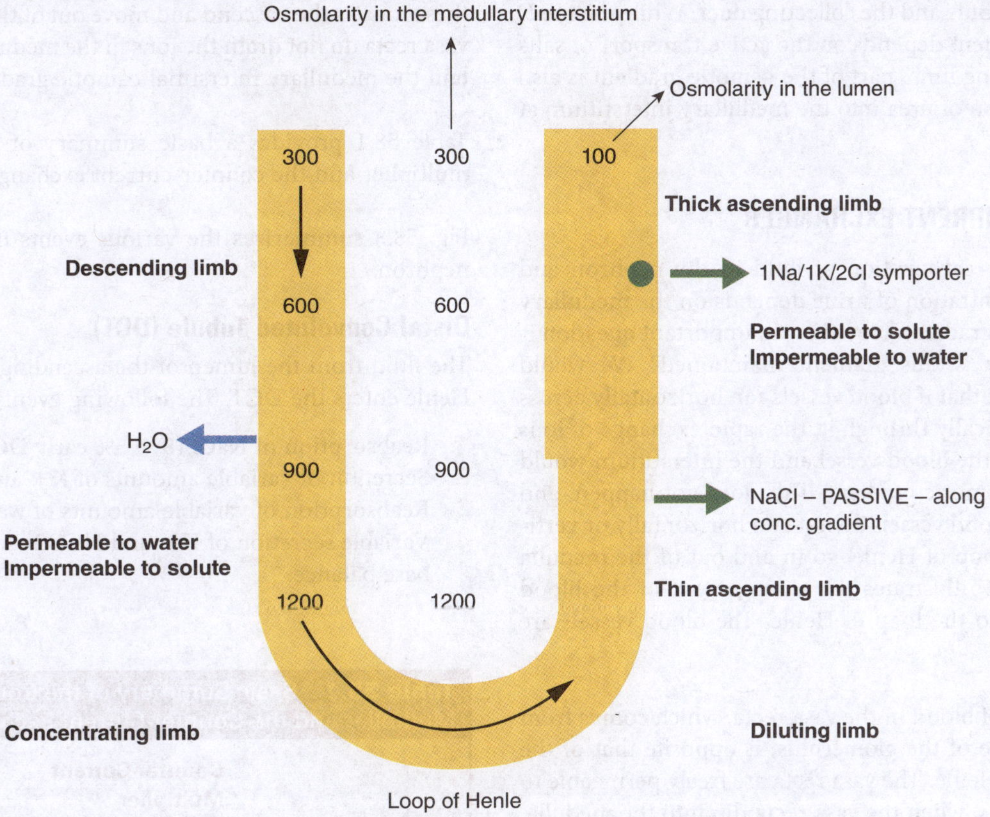

FIG. 58.5 Permeability of the loop of Henle and the medullary interstitial gradient.

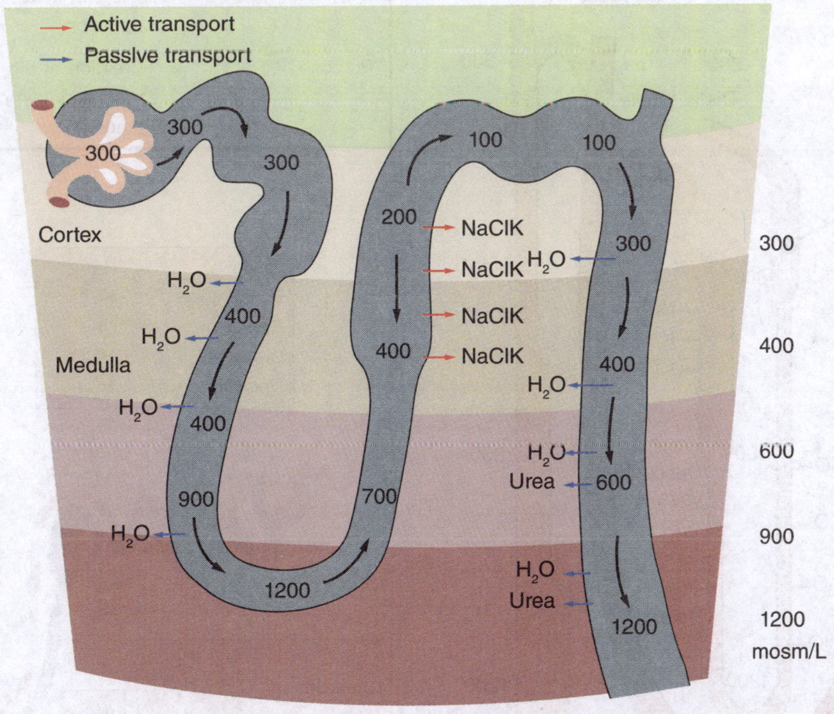

FIG. 58.6 Changes in the osmolarity in the lumen of the nephron.

distal convoluted tubule and the collecting duct. While the medullary osmotic gradient depends on the active transport of salts in the thick ascending limb, part of the osmotic gradient is also due to the absorption of urea into the medullary interstitium at the collecting duct.

THE COUNTER-CURRENT EXCHANGER

It is clear that the reabsorption of fluid in the nephron and therefore the concentration of urine depends on the medullary interstitial osmotic gradient. However, an important question is the following: how is this gradient maintained? We would expect, for instance, that if blood vessels ran horizontally across the medulla or vertically through it, the rapid exchange of ions and water between the blood vessel and the interstitium would soon destroy the osmotic gradient. This does not happen, and the reason is that blood vessels do not run horizontally or vertically but, like the loop of Henle, go in and out of the medulla as a 'loop'. Fig. 58.7 illustrates the arrangement of the blood vessels in relation to the loop of Henle. The blood vessels are called *vasa recta*.

Note that the flow of blood in the vasa recta, which comes from the efferent arteriole of the glomerulus, is opposite that of the flow in the loop of Henle. The vasa recta are freely permeable to salts and water. Thus, when the vasa recta dip into the medulla, they become progressively more concentrated with ions (which move along their concentration gradient) and then begin to lose these ions as they ascend and move out of the medulla. Thus, the vasa recta do not drain the ions in the medulla but help to maintain the medullary interstitial osmotic gradient.

Table 58.1 provides a basic summary of the counter-current multiplier and the counter-current exchanger.

Fig. 58.8 summarizes the various events that occur along the nephron.

Distal Convoluted Tubule (DCT)

The fluid from the lumen of the ascending limb of the loop of Henle enters the DCT. The following events occur in the DCT:

1. Reabsorption of NaCl (8%; 5% early DCT, 3% late DCT)
2. Secretion of variable amounts of K+ and H+
3. Reabsorption of variable amounts of water (8%–17%)
4. Variable secretion of H+ and HCO3- suggest a role in acid-base balance

Table 58.1 Basic Summary of the Counter-Current Multiplier and the Counter-Current Exchanger Systems

	Counter-Current Multiplier	Counter-Current Exchanger
Anatomical structure involved	Loop of Henle	Vasa recta
Permeability of the anatomical structure	Variable along the loop, part passive and part active transport	Freely permeable to salt and water along the entire length
Purpose	Creation of the medullary osmotic gradient	Maintenance of the medullary osmotic gradient

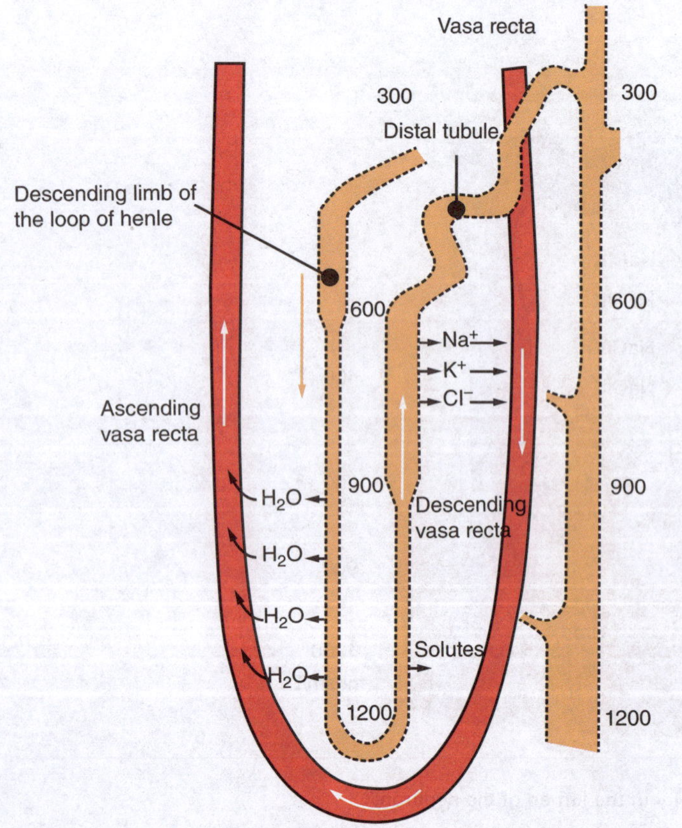

FIG. 58.7 The relationship between the loop of Henle and the vasa recta.

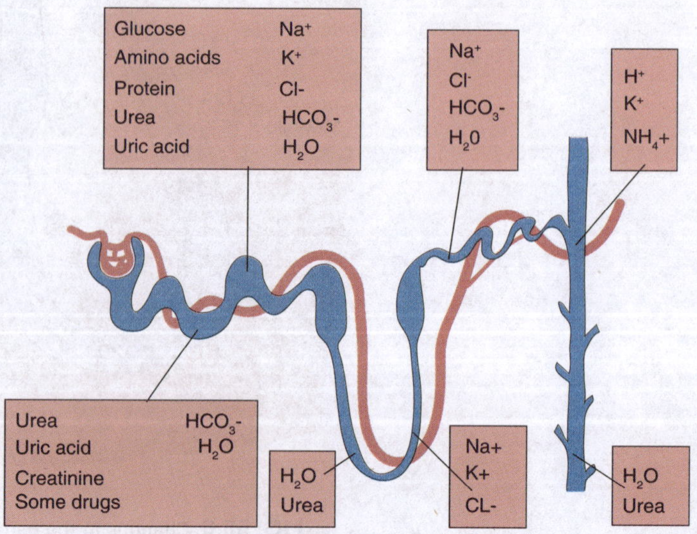

FIG. 58.8 Summary of movement of ions and molecules along the length of the nephron.

5. Two hormones are active here:
   a. Aldosterone: Na and H_20 reabsorption and K excretion
   b. ADH: water reabsorption (the major effect of ADH is in the collecting duct)

Collecting duct:

The collecting duct is the final part of the nephron. Two major events occur here:

1. Reabsorption of water occurs due to the action of the hormone vasopressin also called antidiuretic hormone (ADH). This reabsorption of water occurs through special channels called *aquaporin* channels. In the absence or reduced action of ADH, water reabsorption does not occur in the collecting duct and large quantities of poorly concentrated urine are excreted. This condition is called *diabetes insipidus* and should not be confused with diabetes mellitus discussed in Chapter 46.

   Diabetes insipidus

   Types:

   Diabetes insipidus is of two types: (1) central diabetes insipidus occurs when inadequate vasopressin (ADH) is secreted from the posterior pituitary gland and (2) nephrogenic diabetes insipidus occurs when adequate vasopressin (ADH) is secreted but the hormone is unable to act on its receptors in the kidney.

   Clinical features:

   In either condition, the person experiences *polyuria* (excess urine output) and the urine is of low specific gravity. Because of the excess loss of urine, the person also experiences increased thirst and tends to drink excessive amounts of water (*polydipsia*).

2. Reabsorption of urea into the medullary interstitium.

THE CONCEPT OF 'CLEARANCE'

As the blood flows through the glomerulus, the plasma is filtered of some molecules. Thus, for molecules that are freely filtered, the volume of plasma that enters the glomerulus will be completely cleared of that molecule. For some molecules, the plasma gets cleared of them partly by filtration and partly by secretion.

Clearance is the volume of plasma that is completely cleared of a substance. (N.B.: Clearance is a volume, NOT a quantity.)

It is beyond the scope of this book to discuss the concept of clearance further. Suffice it to say that the concept of clearance is used to measure kidney function, especially GFR and can also be used to measure renal plasma flow.

THE URINARY BLADDER

Urine that flows down the ureter from each kidney empties into the urinary bladder, located in the pelvis. The bladder is a hollow muscular organ which may have a capacity of as high as 1000 mL, although the average capacity is about half this. The muscle which makes up the bladder consists of smooth muscle cells, and the muscle of the bladder is called the detrusor muscle.

If the urinary bladder is cut in half to reveal its interior, it can be seen that it can be further divided into the following:

1. A fundus
2. A trigone (triangular area demarcated by the two ureters and the outlet from the bladder, the urethra; the prostate gland surrounds the urethra)

The parts of the urinary bladder and its nerve supply are depicted in Fig. 58.9.

There are two urethral sphincters that control the flow of urine from the bladder. The internal urethral sphincter is located at the urethral opening in the bladder, while the external urethral sphincter is located further down. The internal urethral sphincter is under the control of the autonomic nervous system, while the external urethral sphincter is under voluntary control.

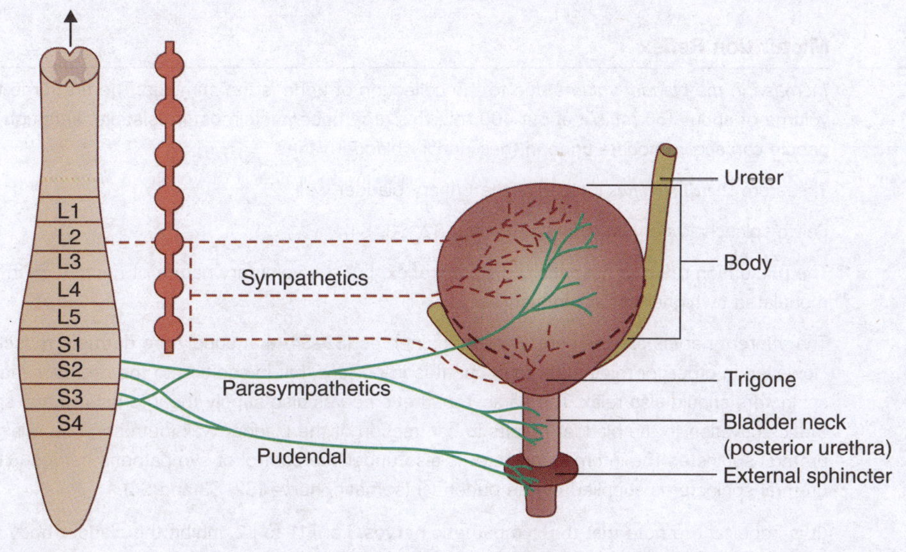

FIG. 58.9 The nerve supply of the urinary bladder.

THE MICTURITION REFLEX

The reflex which mediates the voiding (expulsion) of urine is called the micturition reflex. Like all reflexes, the micturition reflex is best understood in terms of the reflex arc. This is depicted in Table 58.2.

The micturition reflex can be studied using a test called cystometry. In this test, once the urinary bladder is emptied completely by voiding urine, the bladder is then progressively filled with water through a urethral catheter. The urinary bladder pressure is recorded at each stage of filling. This test can be done to assess urinary bladder capacity, the nature of bladder contractions and the ability to voluntarily control voiding of urine.

APPLICATIONS FOR NURSING

Diuretics are a common class of drugs used to treat patients with high blood pressure, cardiovascular disease such as heart failure and some kidney diseases. They increase the output of urine. Based on the discussion in this chapter, it is clear that in order to concentrate urine (and reduce urine output), a medullary concentration gradient is needed. If the medullary osmotic gradient is affected, urine will not be concentrated and more urine will be excreted. This is the principle of one of the classes of diuretics called 'loop diuretics'. These diuretics interfere with the reabsorption of Na^+, Cl^- and K^+ in the thick ascending loop. The reabsorption of these ions is important to develop the medullary osmotic gradient. When the reabsorption of these ions is blocked, it interferes with the creation of the medullary concentration gradient and diuresis occurs. There are other classes of diuretics that act on other parts of the nephron.

Abnormal bladder function may be seen following spinal cord injury, during infections of the urinary bladder and following some types of surgery which may affect the muscles that form the pelvic floor. Urinary incontinence or the inability to control bladder function may result in bed wetting. This increases in the elderly and affects women more than men. Nurses are integral to the care of people who suffer from urinary incontinence as they may require intermittent or indwelling urinary catheters and will need to be educated about the care of the same. Skin care is also important as also the prevention of urinary infection. Specific interventions will depend on the type and cause of urinary incontinence.

Urine output charts are typically used together with estimates of fluid intake (intake–output charts) to ensure fluid balance. Nurses need to be aware of how to measure fluid intake and output and record these accurately. They also need to be aware of common causes that can result in fluid imbalance and dehydration.

SUMMARY

- Urine is formed in the kidney through three processes – filtration, secretion and reabsorption.
- The concentration of urine in the kidney requires the creation of a medullary osmotic gradient. This is achieved by the loop of Henle through the counter-current multiplier. The two major contributors to this gradient are the ions that are absorbed in the ascending limb of the loop of Henle and urea which is absorbed in the collecting duct.
- The medullary osmotic gradient is maintained by the vasa recta through the *counter-current exchanger*.
- The bulk of sodium reabsorption occurs in the proximal convoluted tubule, with smaller contributions in the loop of Henle and the distal convoluted tubule. Reabsorption of sodium at the distal convoluted tubule is regulated by a hormone called aldosterone.
- The proximal convoluted tubule is the site of reabsorption of glucose. At plasma levels of glucose less than 180 mg/dL (the plasma threshold), all glucose is reabsorbed and glucose is not present in the urine.
- The act of passing urine is called the micturition reflex. This reflex is essentially a spinal reflex but under the modulation of the brain. The micturition reflex can be studied using cystometry.

CHAPTER REVIEW QUESTIONS

1. Describe the functions of the proximal convoluted tubule.
2. Compare the functions of the counter-current multiplier and counter-current exchanger.
3. Describe the function of ADH and its role in the concentration of urine.
4. Describe the process of micturition.

Table 58.2 Components of the Micturition Reflex

Components of the Reflex Arc	Micturition Reflex
Stimulus	*Increase in the bladder volume* due to the collection of urine is the stimulus. The first urge to void urine occurs at a volume of about 150 mL. At about 400 mL, this urge becomes almost irresistible, although the extent to which people can accommodate urine in their urinary bladder varies.
Receptors	These are *stretch receptors* located in the urinary bladder wall.
Sensory (afferent) nerves	Pelvic splanchnic nerves (parasympathetic S2, S3, S4).
Integrating centre/s	The micturition reflex is essentially a spinal reflex, but the voluntary nature of micturition indicates that it can be modulated by higher cortical influences.
Motor (efferent) nerves	The efferent nerves are the parasympathetic nerves (S2–S4) that supply the detrusor muscle of the urinary bladder. However, in order for micturition to occur, it is important that in addition to the detrusor muscle contracting, the sphincters should also relax. The parasympathetic nerves also supply the internal urethral sphincter. Thus, parasympathetic activation to the bladder results in contraction of the bladder wall (detrusor) and relaxation of the internal urethral sphincter. The internal sphincter is also under the control of sympathetic nerves (α1 receptors). The external urethral sphincter is supplied by the pudendal (somatic) nerve (S2, S3 and S4).
	(It is important to note that the sympathetic nerves, i.e. T11 to L2, inhibit the bladder body and excite the base of the bladder and urethra effectively inhibiting micturition.)

CHAPTER 59

Applications of the Renal System

SPECIFIC LEARNING OBJECTIVES

At the end of this chapter, the student should be able to:

- Describe the normal composition of urine.
- Describe the abnormal constituents of urine and their interpretation.
- List the tests in urine and blood which reflect kidney function.
- Briefly describe imaging tests specific to kidney function.
- Describe the pathophysiology of acute renal failure.
- Describe the pathophysiology of chronic renal failure.

GLOSSARY OF TERMS

- **Urine culture:** a method to grow bacteria that may be present in the urine (typically, as part of this test, antibiotics are tested for the effectiveness against the bacteria that have been grown; this is called drug sensitivity testing)
- **Biopsy:** the removal of a piece of tissue from a living person to determine the presence and nature of disease

Urine is an excretory product of the human body. Analysis of urine provides a 'window' on what is happening in the body. Thus, it is important to know what the normal composition of urine is so that we can interpret urine analysis findings.

EVALUATION OF URINE

Urinary volume: This varies from individual to individual and from day to day. It depends, for example, on the amount on water/fluids we consume, the weather and the presence of disease, among other factors. The normal urinary volume is anything between 0.6 and 2.5 L/day. At least 500 mL of urine needs to be excreted each day in order to excrete the waste products in their most concentrated form. The following terms are most often used in clinical work:

- *Anuria*: This means cessation (stoppage) of urine formation. Clinically, the term is used in adult patients for a urine output of <50 mL/day.
- *Oliguria*: A reduced excretion of urine. This is defined as a urinary output of less than 1 mL/kg/hour for infants and less than 0.5 mL/kg/hour for children and adults. This amounts to a volume of roughly less than 400 mL/day in adults. Both anuria and oliguria are seen when there is acute kidney injury. However, it may also be due to reasons outside the kidneys as, for example, severe dehydration or shock.
- *Polyuria*: Excessive excretion of urine – typically >2.5 L in an adult. This is seen in many conditions including following excessive water ingestion, uncontrolled diabetes mellitus, diabetes insipidus and some kidney diseases, among others.

Urine colour: Normal urine is clear and has a wide range in colour, from pale yellow to a deeper amber colour. The colour of the urine can change in various medical conditions. It can also change due to medications and it is important to take this history from patients. The colour of the urine can also change based on the food that we eat and the food colourings used during cooking. The following table outlines some changes in the colour of the urine and some common causes of that change:

Colour	Causes
Cloudy or milky	Urinary tract infection
Dark brown	May reflect excess bilirubin in the urine as occurs, for instance, with a viral hepatitis
Pink	Consumption of beets like beetroot, certain medications, injury to the urinary tract, urinary tract infections
Dark orange	Consumption of vitamin B complex medications, other medication like rifampicin (used to treat TB and leprosy)

Urine smell (odour): Normally urine has little odour, although it may have a smell of ammonia if contaminated. Odour of the urine may also be influenced by medications and by certain foods. A strong ammonia-like odour may be due to urinary tract infections. Sometimes, people with diabetes may report that their urine smells 'sweet' because of excess sugar that is being excreted.

Urine pH: pH is a measure of how acidic or basic a solution is. The range of pH is from 0 to 14. A pH of 7 is neutral, less than 7 is acidic and greater than 7 is basic. The urinary pH is variable based on diet, medications and the presence of disease. It can typically range from around 4.5–8, but on average in healthy people it is around 6, that is acidic. Urinary pH can be more acidic in various conditions such as acidosis, as in diabetic ketoacidosis, diarrhoea, dehydration and starvation. Urine is more basic (alkaline) in alkalosis, urinary tract infections and some forms of kidney disease.

Urine density (specific gravity): The specific gravity of normal urine is 1.000–1.030. Specific gravity can be affected by a number of conditions including excessive water intake, dehydration, diabetes insipidus and kidney disease, among others.

Normal composition of urine: Urine is typically 95% water; the remaining part of urine includes solutes, ions, urea, creatinine, uric acid, hormones and medications.

Microscopic evaluation of urine: A typical microscopic evaluation of the urine reports on a variety of things which are listed as follows:

1. *Red blood cells (RBCs)*: These are typically very few in number. RBCs can be raised when there is urinary tract inflammation, injury to the urinary tract and kidney disease. It may also be a contaminant if a woman is menstruating.
2. *White blood cells (WBCs)*: These are also typically very few in number. When the numbers are raised, they may indicate the presence of a urinary tract infection.
3. *Epithelial cells*: Again, typically few in number, they may be raised when there is inflammation, or other disease in the urinary tract.
4. *Microorganisms*: The urine in healthy individuals is typically sterile. Identification of the causative organism in urinary tract infection may require another test (urine culture). Care must be taken to collect the urine sample in a sterile container and without any contamination.
5. *Crystals*: Some of the solutes excreted in the urine form crystals. Some of these crystals are normal and some abnormal. Some crystals may also indicate the likelihood of stones in the urinary tract. Different crystals have different appearances based on their chemical composition (Fig. 59.1).
6. *Casts*: These are formed by proteins which coagulate in the urine. While some casts may be normal and are typically few in number, other casts indicate the presence of kidney disease (Fig. 59.2).

Biochemical evaluation of urine: Chemical analysis of urine includes the estimation of protein, sugars, ketone bodies, occult blood, and bile salts and pigments, among others.

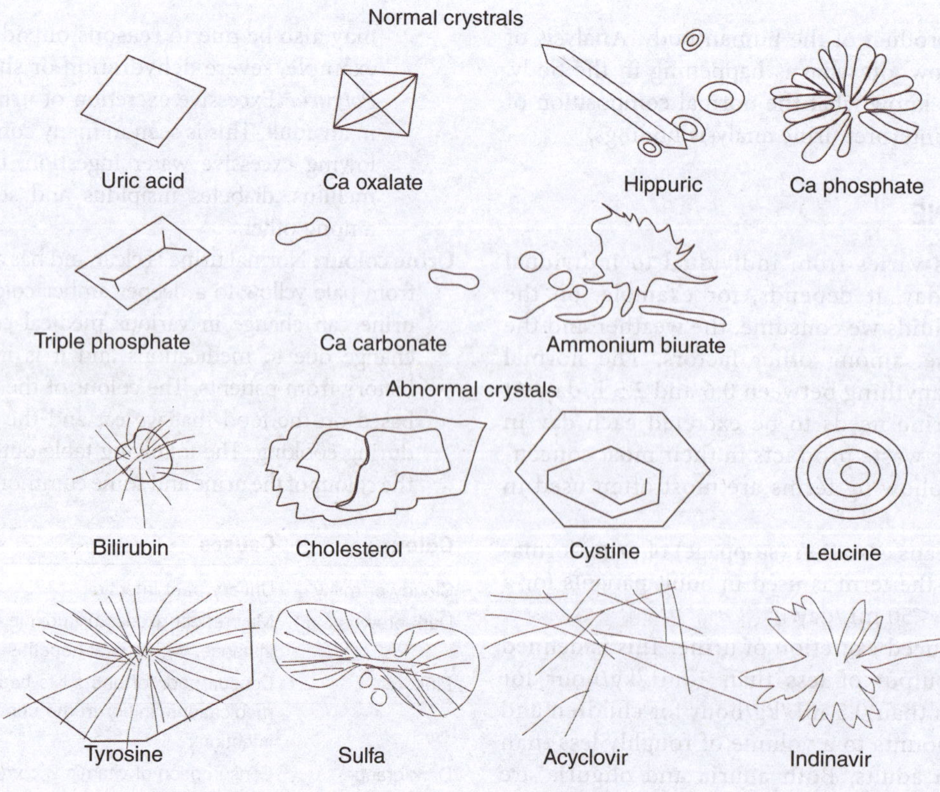

FIG. 59.1 Normal and abnormal crystals that may be found in urine.

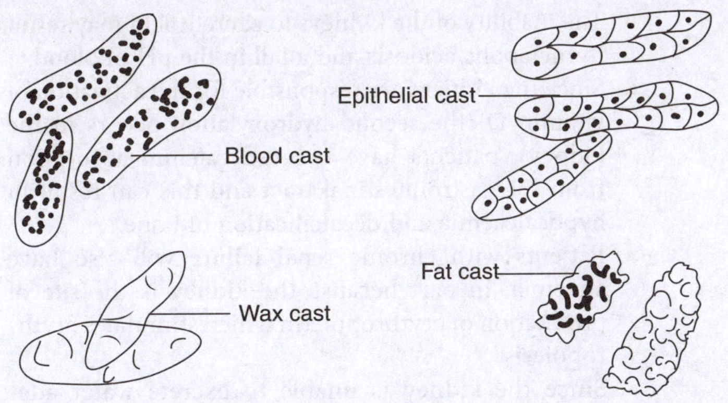

FIG. 59.2 Casts that may be found in urine.

ABNORMAL CONSTITUENTS OF URINE

In this section, we will describe some of the abnormal constituents of urine. This list is not comprehensive but is restricted to some of the more common abnormal constituents.

1. *Albumin*: Albumin is a large molecule which normally does not get filtered at the glomerulus because of its size. However, when there is damage to the glomerular membrane, albumin begins to appear in urine, a condition called albuminuria. Microalbuminuria is a disorder when small amounts of albumin leak into the urine. This condition is an indicator of early kidney involvement and may indicate future progress of the disease. Diabetics are monitored periodically for microalbuminuria as this is an indicator of renal involvement – a condition called diabetic nephropathy.
2. *Glucose*: As indicated in Chapter 58, glucose does not normally appear in urine when plasma levels of glucose are maintained below 180 mg/dL, the plasma threshold for glucose. At plasma levels above this, glucose appears in the urine and this is typically seen in diabetes mellitus. There are some situations when glucose may appear in the urine in the absence of diabetes, such as in renal glycosuria, a physiological condition, when glucose appears in the urine even when plasma concentrations of glucose are less than 180 mg/dL because the transport proteins for reabsorption of glucose in the nephron may be lower. Glucose is not the only sugar which appears in urine. Because of these reasons, a positive urine 'sugar' test is not definitive of diabetes mellitus.
3. *Ketone bodies*: These are breakdown products of fat metabolism – when fat breakdown and oxidation are excessive, ketone bodies are produced in increased quantities and may appear in urine. This is typically seen in uncontrolled diabetes mellitus leading to diabetic ketoacidosis and in prolonged starvation.
4. *Bilirubin*: This is a breakdown product of the destruction of RBCs. Bilirubin is typically taken up by the liver when it undergoes chemical modification and becomes 'conjugated'. Conjugated bilirubin is water soluble and can therefore appear in the urine which is 95% water. Bilirubin in the urine therefore indicates the presence of liver disease or of obstruction to the flow of bile once it drains out of the liver.
5. *Blood*: RBCs are too large to be filtered across the glomerular membrane. If a significant amount of blood is in the urine, the urine will change colour. However, often the blood in the urine cannot be determined without microscopy, a condition called occult blood or microscopic haematuria. Blood in the urine can indicate infections or stones in the urinary tract, cancers, kidney disease or injury.

TESTS OF KIDNEY FUNCTION

In order to evaluate kidney function, various tests can be done based on what condition is suspected:

Blood tests: The most common blood tests are the serum creatinine and blood urea nitrogen.

1. *Serum creatinine*: Creatinine is a waste product that is derived from muscle. Under normal circumstances, creatinine is filtered in the glomerulus and then excreted in the urine. The inability of the kidney to excrete waste products (including creatinine) adequately results in a rise in serum creatinine.
2. *Blood urea nitrogen*: Urea is formed from the breakdown of protein. As kidney function decreases, blood urea nitrogen rises.

Urine tests: As already described, urine analysis takes the form of microscopic examination of the urine, biochemical tests to evaluate abnormal constituents of urine and, if required, a urine culture to grow the microorganisms that may be responsible for urinary tract infection. In order to collect urine for culture, a sterile container is used and care must be taken that the collection is not contaminated. Culture reports may take up to 24–48 hours or longer – this is the duration that is required to determine the presence or absence of bacterial growth. If bacterial growth does occur, these are tested against a range of antibiotics. This informs the doctor about which antibiotics to use and which antibiotics the patient is resistant to.

Imaging of the kidney: This is required to identify kidney stones or growths, or to determine abnormal size of kidney and to confirm its position, among other things. Ordinary X-rays do not allow the kidneys to be evaluated, although they may be able to identify some types of stones in the kidney and urinary tract. Common imaging techniques that are used include ultrasonography and CT scans.

Kidney biopsy: In this test, a small amount of kidney tissues is obtained via a special needle so that the tissue can be subjected to pathological examination. The needle is inserted into the kidney most often under ultrasound guidance. Kidney biopsy is sometimes important as there are various forms of kidney disease which have different treatments and outcomes (Fig. 59.3).

ACUTE RENAL FAILURE

Clinical features:

Acute renal failure is the sudden inability of the kidney to excrete waste, concentrate urine and maintain water and

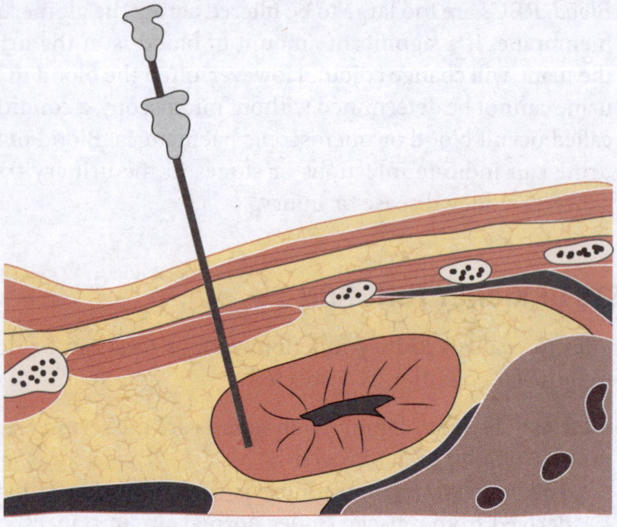

FIG. 59.3 The nature of a renal needle biopsy.

electrolyte balance. This is associated with a large fall in the glomerular filtration rate and an accumulation of nitrogenous wastes in the body. Thus, the blood urea nitrogen and serum creatinine will show a sudden rise above normal values.

Causes:

Acute renal failure can be the result of many causes. One of these is the inadequate perfusion of the kidneys resulting in renal ischaemia. The kidney normally receives between 20% and 25% of the cardiac output. Renal blood flow can be reduced during heart failure, severe hypovolaemia which accompanies dehydration due to severe vomiting, diarrhoea or inadequate fluid intake, and decreased peripheral resistance due to conditions such as sepsis (for a review of shock, and the role of sepsis, see Chapter 33). Acute renal failure may also result from direct damage to the kidneys due to toxins, overdoses of certain medications and some infections. Finally, acute obstruction to the flow of urine can result from ureteral stones, and certain growths or cancers of the urinary tract can result in a back pressure that damages the kidneys.

CHRONIC RENAL FAILURE (CHRONIC KIDNEY DISEASE)

Causes:

Chronic kidney disease is due to long-standing disease and the clinical problems that a patient faces reflect this. The most common causes of chronic renal failure include long-standing and uncontrolled diabetes mellitus, hypertension and glomerulonephritis (inflammation of the glomeruli) due to a variety of causes.

Clinical features:

In chronic renal failure, there is an irreversible loss of nephrons.

- Patients have a low glomerular filtration rate and may experience water and electrolyte imbalance.
- The inability of the kidneys to excrete acid may result in metabolic acidosis and a fall in the pH of blood.
- Since the kidneys are responsible for the activation of vitamin D (the second hydroxylation occurs in the kidney), patients have reduced calcium absorption from the gastrointestinal tract and this can result in hypocalcaemia and decalcification of bone.
- Patients with chronic renal failure will also have anaemia, in part because the kidney is the site of production of erythropoietin which stimulates erythropoiesis.
- Since the kidney is unable to excrete water adequately, water is retained in the body and this increases the load on the heart which may ultimately lead to heart failure, if left untreated. Pulmonary oedema may also occur because of the fluid overload.

APPLICATIONS FOR NURSING

The nurse has an important role prior to, during and after a kidney biopsy. As for other procedures in the hospital, the nurse must explain the procedure in simple language, while ensuring that no important information is excluded – this is necessary in order that fully informed and signed consent can be obtained. The nurse is responsible for the premedication prior to the procedure based on the doctor's written orders. During the procedure, the nurse is required to monitor vital signs and continue that monitoring as per doctor's orders following the procedure. Urine should be checked for blood (haematuria) and a fluid intake and output chart should be maintained.

Patients with chronic kidney disease require increasing care with time. Nurses will need to educate patients and family members about the need for compliance to all medications including dialysis, the need for monitoring fluid input and output, and adherence to dietary advice.

SUMMARY

- Normal urine output is between 0.6 and 2.5 L/day, is straw coloured and clear, with a pH around 6, typically with minimal odour unless concentrated and with a specific gravity of 1.000–1.030.
- Microscopic evaluation of urine includes checks for RBCs, WBCs, epithelial cells, microorganisms, crystals and casts.
- Abnormal constituents in the urine, among others, include protein, glucose, blood, and bile salts and pigments.
- Tests for evaluation of kidney function include blood tests (serum creatinine, blood urea nitrogen), microscopic and biochemical evaluation of urine, urine culture and kidney biopsy if indicated, and imaging tests of the kidney and urinary tract.
- Certain forms of acute renal failure respond well to treatment that is quickly instated.
- Chronic renal failure requires more sustained care and has many systemic effects. Chronic renal failure is associated with an irreversible loss of nephrons. Apart from excretory functions of the kidney being affected, the patients will present with features due to the nonexcretory functions of the kidney. These include bony pain and increased risk of fractures since formation of active Vit D is affected and anaemia because of reduced production of erythropoietin from the kidney.

CLINICAL CASE PROBLEMS

(A) ***A 50-year-old obese, hypertensive and diabetic woman with chronic renal failure is admitted to the hospital. She complains of extreme lethargy and tiredness. On examination, she has severe pallor. Her haemoglobin is 4 g%. She had earlier sustained a fracture of the neck of femur after sustaining a fall at home.***

a. What is the likely reason for the severe anaemia?
b. Why is she more likely to sustain fractures?
c. What other problems is this patient likely to have?
d. List the nonexcretory functions of the kidney.

(B) ***A 70-year-old man was operated for a tumour of the pituitary gland. After discharge from the hospital, he returned with the following complaints: passing large quantities of light-coloured urine and a continuous sense of feeling thirsty.***

a. What is the likely problem that the man is suffering from?
b. How is water reabsorbed in the kidney?
c. Describe the counter-current multiplier system.
d. What is the action of aldosterone in the kidney?

SELF-DIRECTED LEARNING

- What are peritoneal dialysis and haemodialysis?
- What is renal transplantation? What are the criteria for a suitable donor?

WHAT YOU CAN LEARN FROM A HOSPITAL VISIT

- Visit the dialysis unit in the hospital – see how the dialysis is done, and observe the role of the nurse.
- Pick up a laboratory biochemistry and microbiology form from the hospital – pick out all the tests that help you assess the renal and urinary system.

10

SECTION

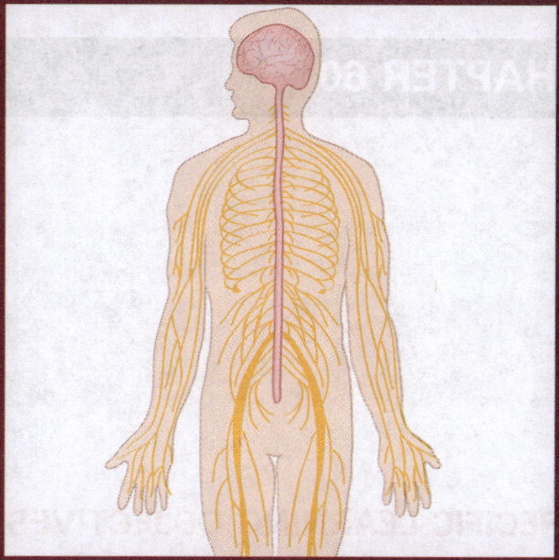

The Reproductive System

Section Outline

CHAPTER 60

The Female Reproductive System

SPECIFIC LEARNING OBJECTIVES

At the end of this chapter, the student should be able to:

- Describe with a diagram the functional anatomy of the female reproductive system.
- Define the following terms:
  - Menarche
  - Puberty
  - Menopause
- List the secondary sexual characteristics of the female which develop at puberty.
- Describe the factors which affect the onset of menarche and menopause.

GLOSSARY OF TERMS

- **Menarche:** the onset of menstruation
- **Menopause:** the complete stoppage of menstruation

The female reproductive system consists of the vagina, uterus, fallopian tubes and ovaries. The vagina joins the uterus at the cervix. Fig. 60.1 illustrates the location of these organs in the female pelvis.

INTERNAL REPRODUCTIVE ORGANS

Ovaries: These are paired organs located at the outer (lateral) parts of the pelvic cavity. Ovaries produce the eggs (ovum) at periodic intervals. They are also the site of production of various hormones which will be discussed in subsequent chapters. When the ovum is released from the ovary, it is directed into the fallopian tubes by finger-like projections of the fallopian tubes called fimbriae.

Fallopian tubes: These are muscular tubes that stretch outwards from the upper part of the uterus on either side towards the ovaries. The ovum travels down the fallopian tube and may be fertilized within the tube by a sperm. If fertilization occurs, the fertilized egg will divide multiple times to form a ball of cells called a blastocyst which can then attach itself onto the wall of the uterus. This attachment is called implantation.

Uterus: This is the major reproductive organ of the female and is pear shaped. Its major function is to accept the blastocyst and then provide a protected and nourishing environment for the development of the foetus. In the absence of pregnancy, during the reproductive age of a female, the uterus undergoes cyclical changes during the course of a menstrual cycle. This is discussed in a subsequent chapter.

Vagina: This hollow fibromuscular canal connects the outside of the body with the cervix of the uterus. The vagina accommodates the penis during sexual intercourse and also functions as the birth canal during vaginal delivery of a baby.

Cervix: This is the lower part of the uterus and is sometimes referred to as the neck of the uterus. The connection between the cervix which connects the vagina and the uterus is typically narrow but is widened considerably during childbirth to allow for the delivery of the baby. This widening of the cervical opening during childbirth is referred to as cervical dilation.

EXTERNAL FEMALE GENITALIA

In addition to the organs indicated earlier, the female reproductive system includes the external genitalia of the female which are illustrated in Fig. 60.2.

The external genitalia of the female are the vulva which comprises the following:

1. The fleshy lips around the vagina called the labia majora and labia minora. These provide a protective covering to the vagina.
2. The clitoris is highly sensitive with a rich nerve supply and is located at the front of the vulva where the labia minor meet.

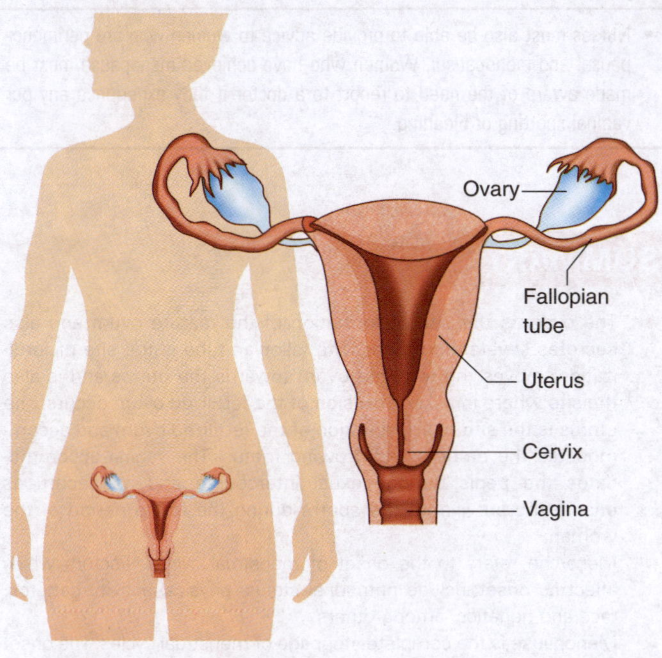

FIG. 60.1 The internal reproductive organs of the female.

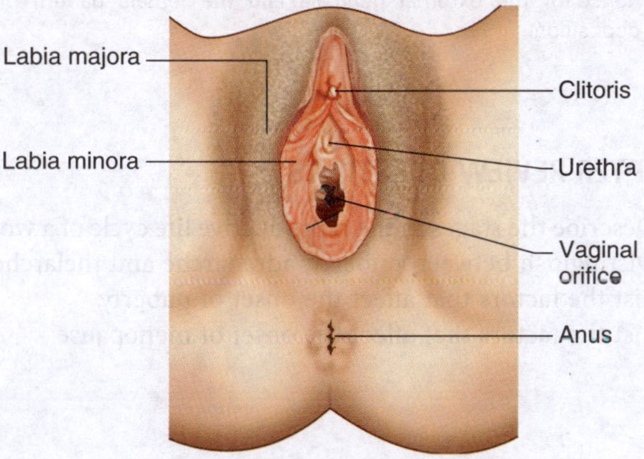

FIG. 60.2 The external genitalia of the female.

3. The opening of the vagina (introitus) is partly covered by a membrane called the hymen which may be ruptured by sexual intercourse, use of tampons or vigorous stretching exercise.
4. The urinary meatus is the opening of the urethra and is located above the vaginal orifice.
5. At puberty, coarser pubic hair begins to appear – this is one of the secondary sexual characteristics.

THE REPRODUCTIVE LIFE CYCLE

1. Premenarche is the stage of life prior to the onset of menstrual cycles.
2. Menarche is the first menstrual cycle (before menarche between 6 and 9 years, the child undergoes adrenarche – this is when the adrenal gland becomes active. As a result, the child begins to develop pubic and armpit hair, and body odour. Thelarche refers to the development of breast tissue).
3. Reproductive period refers to the age range during which a woman is capable of bearing a child. This is the phase when the woman has relatively regular menstrual cycles. While this period theoretically would be the age between the onset of menstrual cycles and its complete cessation, the most fertile years for women are the twenties, declining sharply after the age of 35 years. There is a large variation in the fertility of women.
4. Perimenopause is that period during which women move towards complete stoppage of periods. This is typically experienced in the forties, although there is a wide range. This is often divided into an early menopausal transition stage when menstrual cycles become irregular and a late menopausal transition stage when women may begin to miss menstrual cycles and the period between menstrual cycles increases.
5. Menopause is the permanent stoppage of menstrual cycles, clinically defined as the absence of menstrual cycles for 12 months. This mostly occurs in the late forties or early fifties. During this period as well as the earlier perimenopausal period, women may experience hot flushes, irregular menstrual cycles, mood swings, vaginal dryness, issues with sleeping, reduced sexual drive and fatigue, among others.
6. Postmenopausal period is the period that follows the permanent stoppage of menstrual cycles.

DETERMINANTS OF MENARCHE

Puberty is the age at which the girl is capable of sexual reproduction. Menarche is one of the events of puberty. Prior to menarche, girls may experience a height growth spurt. *Secondary sexual characteristics* are developed during puberty and these, for girls, include the following:

- Enlargement of breasts
- Growth of pubic hair
- Widening of hips
- Vulva becoming more prominent
- Fat deposition around the hips, thighs and buttocks

The age at which menarche occurs has been steadily decreasing.

Menarche is determined by a variety of factors:

1. Genetics: It is possible to predict to some extent the age of menarche of the child based on the age of onset of menarche in the mother. This suggests a genetic influence.
2. Race: There is some evidence that race may determine age of onset of menarche. Thus, in the United States, black American girls tend to have an earlier age of menarche compared to white girls.
3. Nutritional status: Undernutrition is associated with a delayed age of menarche, while improved nutritional status decreases the age at which menarche occurs.
4. Strenuous physical activity may be associated with a delay in onset of menarche.

DETERMINANTS OF MENOPAUSE

The age at which the menstrual cycles stop completely vary from woman to woman. Genetics plays a role: early age of menopause in a mother predicts an early age of menopause in the daughter.

Factors which reduce the age at which menopause occurs include the following:

- Absence of childbirth (nulliparous)
- Menstrual cycles of shorter length
- Smoking
- High intakes of fat and cholesterol

Factors which increase the age at which menopause occurs include the following:

- Giving birth to a child before the age of 25 years
- Irregular menstrual cycles

Other factors such as the age of menarche, breastfeeding, use of oral contraceptives and various other lifestyle factors have also been reported to determine the age at which menopause occurs.

Menopause is associated with an increased risk of health problems such as osteoporosis and cardiovascular disease.

APPLICATIONS FOR NURSING

- Nurses should be able to educate children and prepare them for menarche. The first menstrual cycle can be traumatic to girls who are unaware of what to expect and what to do. The fall in age at which menarche occurs means that children need to be made aware of menstrual cycles well before the average age for the population.
- Nurses must also be able to provide advice to women who are perimenopausal and menopausal. Women who have achieved menopause must be made aware of the need to report to a doctor if they experience any per vaginal spotting or bleeding.

SUMMARY

- The ovary is the site of formation of the mature ovum and also secretes several hormones. The fallopian tube is the site of fertilization, moves the fertilized ovum towards the uterus and is also the site where initial cell division of the fertilized ovum occurs. The uterus is the site of implantation of the fertilized ovum and accommodates the embryo and growing foetus. The vagina accommodates the penis during sexual intercourse and its secretions ensure the survival of the sperm during the fertile period of the woman.
- Menarche refers to the onset of menstrual cycles. Factors which affect its onset include nutritional status, physical activity patterns, race and genetics, among others.
- Menopause is the complete stoppage of menstrual cycles. The onset of menopause is influenced by genetics, nutritional status, menstrual cycle pattern and childbirth, among others.
- The secondary sexual characteristics of the female include development of breasts, growth of pubic hair, widening of hips, prominence of the external genitalia and the female pattern of fat deposition.

CHAPTER REVIEW QUESTIONS

1. Describe the stages in the reproductive life cycle of a woman.
2. Distinguish between puberty, adrenarche and thelarche.
3. List the factors that affect the onset of puberty.
4. List the factors that affect the onset of menopause.

CHAPTER 61

The Menstrual Cycle, Hormones and Oogenesis

SPECIFIC LEARNING OBJECTIVES

At the end of this chapter, the student should be able to:

- List with a diagram the phases and durations of a typical menstrual cycle.
- Describe the changes that occur during the menstrual cycle in the:
  - Ovaries
  - Uterus (endometrium)
  - Cervix
- Describe the hormonal changes that occur during a menstrual cycle.
- Define ovulation and list the tests of ovulation.
- Define the following terms:
  - Amenorrhoea
  - Menorrhagia
  - Dysmenorrhoea
- Describe the sequence of the sexual act.
- List the actions of oestrogen and progesterone.

GLOSSARY OF TERMS

- **Ovulation:** the release of the ovum (egg) from the ovaries
- **Follicular phase:** the first phase of the menstrual cycle prior to ovulation
- **Luteal phase:** the second phase of the menstrual cycle after ovulation
- **Spinnbarkeit:** the 'stretchy' property of cervical mucus around the time of ovulation
- **Endometrium:** the epithelial lining of the uterus which is shed during menstruation

The regular cycle of intermittent bleeding that occurs through the vagina in females is called the menstrual cycle. This cycle is associated with changes in the ovaries, the uterus and the cervix and these are described in detail in this chapter. Menstrual cycles vary in duration from person to person. In some individuals, menstrual cycles may also vary in duration from cycle to cycle. However, in this chapter, we will consider the events that take place in a menstrual cycle of an average duration of 28 days.

Consider Fig. 61.1. You will observe in this figure that the menstrual cycle is further divided into two broad phases.

- The first phase from the first to the fourth day is associated with menstrual bleeding.
- From the 4th to the 14th day is the follicular phase since this is the phase during which the ovarian follicles develop and a single follicle matures. This phase terminates with the release of a single ovum (egg) from the ovaries.
- Ovulation typically occurs on the 14th day.
- Following ovulation, the next 14 days, that is up to the 28th day, is the luteal phase. During this phase, hormones are produced in the ovary which would normally sustain pregnancy if fertilization (i.e. union of the sperm and the ovum) occurs. If, however, pregnancy does not occur, then this phase of the menstrual cycle is terminated at 28 days and the menstrual cycle repeats itself.

THE OVARIAN CYCLE

The female ovary contains a large number of immature or primordial follicles. At the start of the menstrual cycle, that is the beginning of the follicular phase, several of these follicles begin to enlarge. From this point, they undergo a series of changes which are depicted in Fig. 61.2.

The development of the ovum (oogenesis) in the ovary proceeds through certain stages which are listed as follows:

- Primordial follicle: This consists of the primary oocyte surrounded by a single layer of granulosa cells.

- Primary follicle:
  - Preantral follicle: The oocyte increases in size and the granulose cells proliferate to form multiple layers. The oocyte is separated from the granulosa cells by a thick layer called the *zona pellucida*.
  - Early antral follicle: The primary oocyte reaches its final size, granulosa cells differentiate to form a layer of cells called the theca and a fluid-filled space called the antrum appears within the granulosa cells.
  - Preovulatory (mature; Graafian) follicle: While many primary follicles develop to reach the antral stage, only one forms a mature follicle; the others degenerate (i.e. undergo atresia). This mature follicle is large because of the increase in the antrum and antral fluid and protrudes from the surface of the ovary.
  - Ovulation (release of the ovum): Around the 14th day of the menstrual cycle, the ovum is expelled from the follicle and released from the ovary.

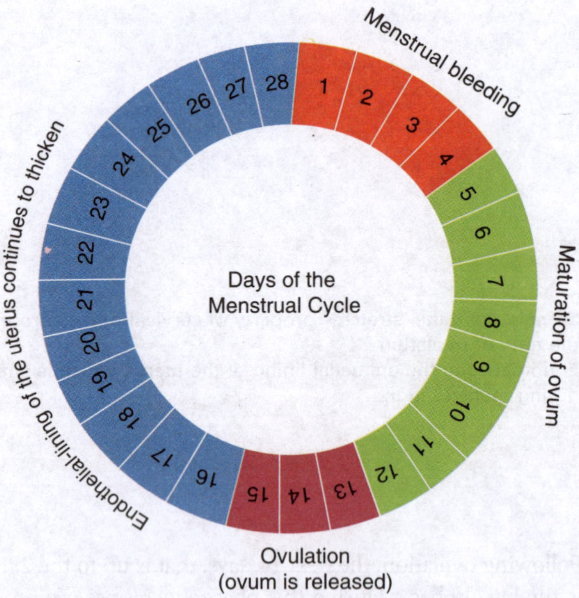

FIG. 61.1 Phases of the menstrual cycle.

  - Corpus haemorragicum: blood is present at the site originally occupied by the ovum.
  - Corpus luteum: The granulose cells and the theca cells which are left behind in the ovary enlarge in size and become filled with fatty substances. They take on a yellowish colour. The corpus luteum is important because it secretes hormones which help to maintain pregnancy. If fertilization does not occur, the corpus luteum starts degenerating.
  - Corpus albicans: The degenerated corpus luteum is replaced by fibrous tissue.

THE UTERINE CYCLE

The endometrial (epithelial) lining of the uterus also undergoes cyclical changes during the menstrual cycle. These are depicted in Fig. 61.3.

The endometrial changes in the uterus occur in three phases:

1. **Menstrual phase**: During this phase, the endometrial lining of the uterus is shed and this results in the bleeding associated with the menstrual cycle. This phase occurs if the ovum is not fertilized.
2. **Proliferative phase**: This phase follows the menstrual (bleeding) phase, and is associated with an increase in the thickness of the endometrium. The endometrial glands lengthen and there is increased vascularization (i.e. the number of arteries increases).
3. **Secretory phase**: During this phase, the endometrial glands enlarge and secrete large quantities of carbohydrate-rich fluid. The arteries become more tortuous.

The changes in the endometrium during the proliferative and secretory phases are summarized in Table 61.1.

CERVICAL AND VAGINAL CHANGES DURING THE MENSTRUAL CYCLE

The cervical and vaginal changes that occur during the menstrual cycle will be described in this section in relation to the two phases of the menstrual cycle:

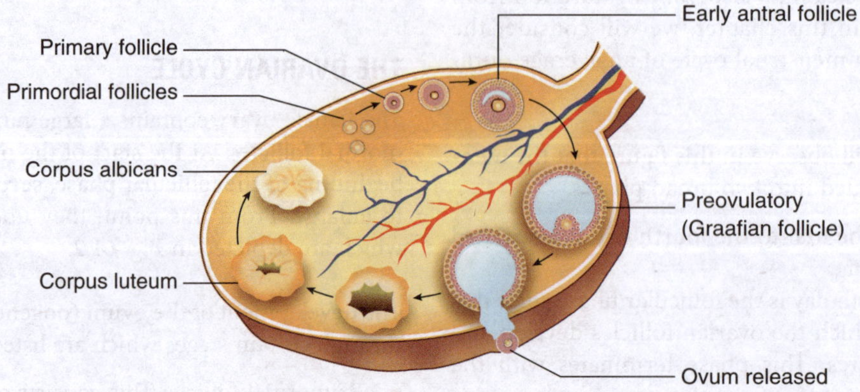

FIG. 61.2 Stages of development of the ovum (oogenesis).

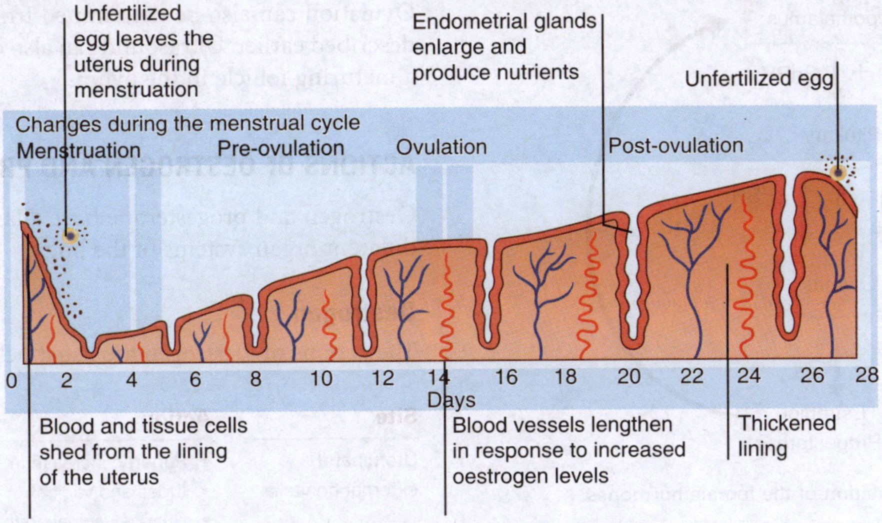

FIG. 61.3 The uterine menstrual cycle.

Table 61.1 The Endometrial Changes During the Proliferative and Secretory Phases of the Menstrual Cycle

Proliferative Phase	Secretory Phase
• Proliferation of stromal and epithelial cells • Growth of endometrial glands • New blood vessel formation into endometrium • Increased thickness of endometrium to 3–5 mm	• Endometrial glands increase in tortuosity • Cytoplasm of stromal cells: increased content of lipid and glycogen • Blood vessels increase in tortuosity • Endometrium thickness increases further to 5–6 mm

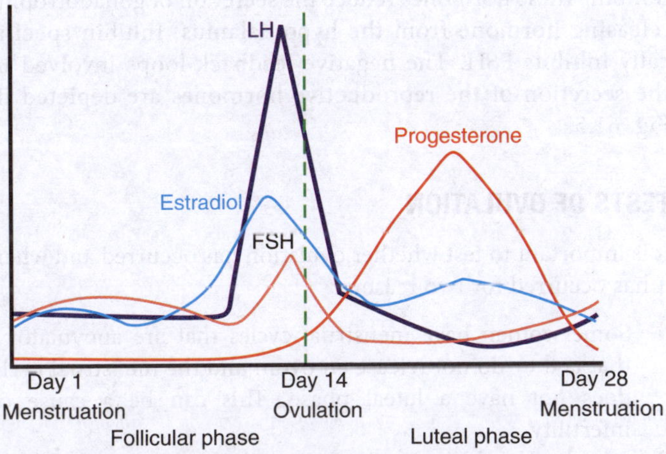

FIG. 61.4 Hormonal changes during the menstrual cycle.

1. **Follicular phase**: During this phase, the cervical secretion increases and becomes more thick and viscous. As ovulation approaches, the secretion becomes more watery, resembles 'egg-white' and can be stretched between the fingers – a phenomenon called 'spinnbarkeit'. During this phase, the vaginal cells become more keratinized (cornified).
2. **Luteal phase**: During this phase, the cervical mucus becomes thick. The vaginal epithelium also increases and a thick vaginal secretion is also secreted during this phase.

HORMONAL CHANGES DURING THE MENSTRUAL CYCLE

Fig. 61.4 represents the hormonal changes that occur during the menstrual cycle.

You will observe that:

1. During the follicular phase, there is an increased concentration of oestradiol (oestrogen) and follicle-stimulating hormone (FSH).
2. Just before ovulation on the 14th day, there is a rapid increase in luteinizing hormone (LH) – this is referred to as the 'LH surge'. The LH surge is an example of 'positive feedback'.
3. During the luteal phase, there is a pronounced increase in progesterone.

So what do these hormones do?

FSH acts to increase the proliferation of granulosa cells of developing follicles which produce oestrogen. It also increases the size of the antrum of later-stage follicles. Thus, TSH has its major effects during the follicular phase. The rising concentration of oestrogen causes FSH levels to reduce by negative feedback.

While the LH surge is primarily linked to ovulation, lower but significant levels of LH during the luteal phase help to maintain the corpus luteum for the 14 days of the luteal phase of

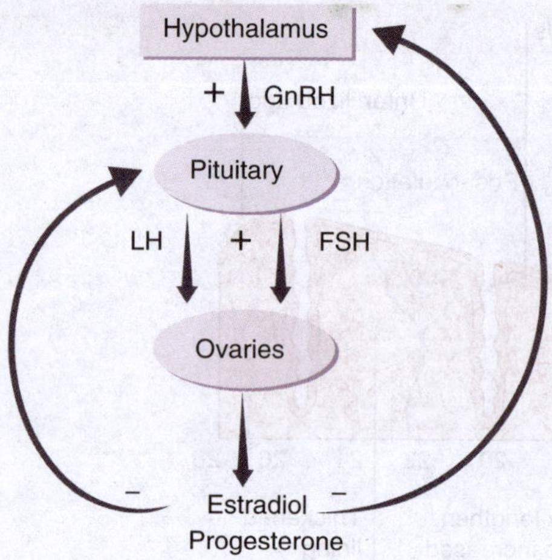

FIG. 61.5 Regulation of the female hormones.

the ovarian cycle. The corpus luteum secretes large quantities of progesterone, but also oestrogen and a hormone called inhibin. These hormones reduce the secretion of gonadotropin-releasing hormone from the hypothalamus. Inhibin specifically inhibits FSH. The negative feedback loops involved in the secretion of the reproductive hormones are depicted in Fig. 61.5.

TESTS OF OVULATION

It is important to test whether ovulation has occurred and when it has occurred for two reasons:

1. Some women have menstrual cycles that are anovulatory, that is they do not release an ovum and the menstrual cycle does not have a luteal phase. This can be a cause of infertility.
2. Couples should know that the most fertile period when a child can be conceived is around the time of ovulation. The 'fertile window' is a few days before ovulation and 1–2 days after. The fertile period is limited because the sperm has a lifespan of 3–5 days and the ovum only 1–2 days.

The different tests for ovulation include the following:

1. ***Cervical mucus test***: During the fertile window period of the menstrual cycle, the cervical mucus becomes clear and stretchy (spinnbarkeit).
2. ***Basal body temperature***: If women measure their basal body temperature, that is soon after wakening in the morning but before getting out of bed with a good thermometer, they will experience a rise in body temperature of between 0.5°C and 1°C at the time of ovulation.
3. ***Fern test***: If cervical mucus is allowed to dry on a slide and then observed under a microscope, a characteristic leaf-like pattern ('fern' appearance) is observed between about the 6th and the 22nd day of the cycle and is most prominent around ovulation. Importantly during the later luteal phase, ferning is lost and is an indicator that ovulation has occurred.

Ovulation can also be determined from the hormonal levels as described earlier. Ultrasound can also determine the presence of a maturing follicle in the ovum.

ACTIONS OF OESTROGEN AND PROGESTERONE

Oestrogen and progesterone have a large number of actions on different organ systems of the body.

Oestrogen

The actions of Oestrogen are listed below:

Site	Action
Uterus and external genitalia	• Puberty: increase in size (also ovaries, fallopian tubes and vagina) • Change vaginal epithelium from cuboidal to stratified (increase resistance to trauma/infection) • Increase size of external genitalia (labia, clitoris) • Proliferation of stroma and epithelial glands
Fallopian tubes	• Increase in glandular activity • Increase in ciliated epithelial cells • Increased activity of cilia
Breasts	• Developmental of stromal tissue • Growth of ductile system • Deposition of fat
Skeleton	• Inhibit osteoclastic activity • Stimulate bone growth
Metabolism	• Slightly positive nitrogen balance • Increased deposition of subcutaneous fat • Distribution of fat: buttocks, thighs • Slight increase in metabolic rate
Skin	• Smooth/soft texture • Increased vascularity
Water/electrolytes	• Salt and water retention
Cardiovascular	• Vascular relaxation • Cardioprotection

Progesterone

The actions of progesterone are summarized in the table below:

Site	Action

Uterus	• Secretory phase of the menstrual cycle:
	  • Glands become elongated and coiled – secrete a glycogen-rich fluid
	  • Decrease myometrial contractions

Cervix	• Cervical mucus becomes thick and viscid • Loss of 'ferning' pattern in cervical mucus
Breast	• Lobuloalveolar growth of breast
Fallopian tubes	• Increases the secretion of the mucosal lining
Immune function	• Immunomodulatory – especially T cells
Regulation of menstrual cycle	• If implantation does not occur – fall in progesterone results in sloughing of endometrium and menstrual bleeding

PENILE–VAGINAL INTERCOURSE

Sexual intercourse is preceded by sexual arousal or excitement. In the male, this leads to the penile erection (discussed later), while in the female the nipples, clitoris and vaginal walls are engorged and vaginal secretion increases. Sexual arousal is also associated with whole-body physiological responses including an increase in heart rate, respiratory rate and blood pressure.

The sexual act in the male consists of the following:

Penile erection: In this state, the penis becomes rigid and erect because the erectile tissue is filled with blood. As indicated in an earlier chapter, the erectile tissues of the penis consist of two corpora cavernosa and a corpus spongiosum.

Penile insertion into the vagina: The erect penis is inserted into the vagina which is lubricated with the increased vaginal secretion. The thrusting of the penis within the vagina and the rhythmic contraction of the muscle at the base of the penis leads to the third stage of ejaculation.

Ejaculation: This is the ejection of semen into the vagina and is associated with intense sexual pleasure, contraction of the pelvic muscles and a further increase in heart rate. This also constitutes the orgasm in the male.

In the female, the clitoris becomes especially sensitive during sexual intercourse. The nipples and clitoris have a rich nerve supply and their stimulation increases sexual arousal. Orgasm (climax) varies widely from woman to woman. It typically takes longer for a woman to achieve orgasm and this is associated with overall pleasure, a tightening of the vaginal walls and whole-body physiological responses that are similar to those of the male.

APPLICATIONS FOR NURSING

- Advice to infertile couples.
- Hygiene and reproductive advice to the adolescent girl child.

SUMMARY

- The menstrual cycle involves the ovaries, uterus and cervix. It is divided into two broad phases: the follicular phase and the luteal phase. A typical menstrual cycle is 28 days; the first 4–5 days is associated with bleeding (menstruation); ovulation occurs around the 14th day.
- The menstrual cycle is associated with cyclical variations in oestrogen, progesterone, FSH and LH. The LH surge is associated with ovulation. Progesterone increases during the luteal phase.
- The menstrual cycle is associated with changes in the ovaries, uterus and cervix. In the ovary, there is preovulatory phase during which a mature ovum develops, followed by an ovulation phase and a post-ovulatory phase aimed at maintaining pregnancy if fertilization occurs. The uterus undergoes a proliferative phase which follows menstrual bleeding and this is followed by a secretory phase.
- Tests of ovulation include examination of cervical mucus and measurement of basal body temperature and blood hormone levels.

CHAPTER REVIEW QUESTIONS

1. List the steps in oogenesis.
2. Describe the changes that are seen in the endometrium during the menstrual cycle.
3. Describe the hormonal changes in the menstrual cycle.
4. List the tests of ovulation.
5. List the actions of oestrogen and progesterone.

CHAPTER 62

Physiology of Pregnancy, Parturition and Lactation

SPECIFIC LEARNING OBJECTIVES

At the end of this chapter, the student should be able to:

- Define the following terms:
  - Fertilization
  - Implantation
- Describe the functions of the placenta.
- List the physiological changes that occur during pregnancy in the mother.
- List the tests of pregnancy.
- Define parturition and describe the process of birth.
- Define lactation and list the factors that affect lactation.
- Compare and contrast the composition of breast milk and formula/dairy milk.

GLOSSARY OF TERMS

- **Fertilization:** the union of the male and female gametes (i.e. sperm and ovum) with the exchange of nuclear material
- **Implantation:** the attachment of the fertilized ovum (actually, the blastocyst) to the lining of the uterus
- **Gestation:** the period of development in utero (i.e. inside the uterus)
- **Parturition:** process of childbirth
- **Lactation:** secretion of milk by the mammary glands (breasts)

In order for natural pregnancy to occur, the ovum needs to be fertilized by the sperm after sexual intercourse. As we have indicated in an earlier chapter, the fertile period of the women extends for a few days on either side of the ovulation. Fertilization is the union of the male and female gametes (i.e. sperm and ovum) with the exchange of nuclear material. The fertilized ovum is called a ***zygote*** (Fig. 62.1).

The ovum and sperm contain only haploid (23 chromosomes) number of chromosomes, while the diploid number of chromosomes (i.e. 23 pairs; 46 chromosomes) is seen in the zygote. The sex and biological characteristics of the new individual are therefore the result of the combined genes (on the chromosomes) of the male and female parent.

Fertilization typically occurs in the fallopian tube close to the ovary. By the time the fertilized ovum has moved down the fallopian tube to the uterus, it has divided many times and is now a ball of around 100 cells called a ***blastocyst***.

The blastocyst remains in the cavity of the uterus for about 1–3 days before it attaches to the wall of the epithelial lining of the uterus (the endometrium). The attachment of the blastocyst to the wall of the uterus is called ***implantation***. The basic structure of the blastocyst is illustrated in Fig. 62.2.

You will observe from Fig. 62.2 that the blastocyst has a cluster of cells called the inner cell mass or embryoblast which subsequently forms the embryo and goes on to develop into the foetus. A fluid-filled cavity surrounds the inner cell mass and is called the blastocoele – this will later develop into a fluid cavity that surrounds the foetus called the amniotic sac. The outer layer of cells is called the trophoblast – these cells help to attach the blastocyst to the endometrium and later form the placenta.

It is beyond the scope of this chapter to describe the details of development of the embryo and foetus. However, some broad milestones are shown in Table 62.1.

MATERNAL CHANGES DURING PREGNANCY

Pregnancy is divided into three periods called trimesters. The first trimester of pregnancy is till week 12, the second trimester is from week 13 to 27 and the third trimester is from week 28

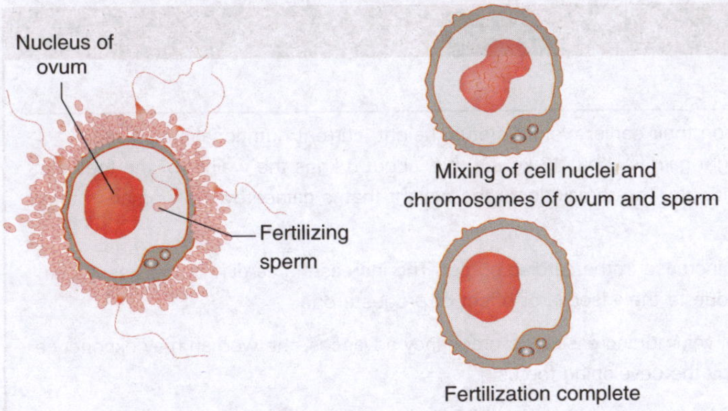

FIG. 62.1 Fertilization of the ovum by a sperm.

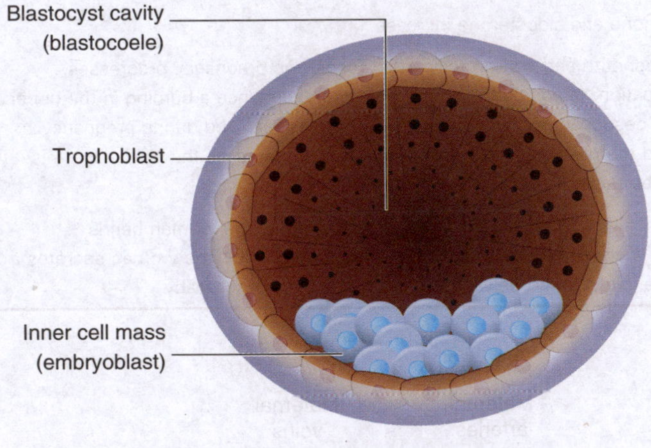

FIG. 62.2 The structure of the blastocyst.

Table 62.1 Stages of Development in Utero

In Utero Age (Weeks)	Milestone
3	This stage of development is called the blastocyst
4	Now an embryo
5	The embryonic 'heart' starts beating
6	Limb buds appear: These will form the arms and legs
8	Now a foetus: Vital organs such as kidneys, intestines, brain and liver start to function, but are still immature
9	Fingers, nose and upper lip are formed; eyes are developed but the eyelids are shut (fused)
12	Foetal heartbeat can be heard
14	Foetal kidneys start producing urine
24	Brain is growing rapidly
27	Lungs are developing but are not fully functional
34	Lungs and brain continue to develop
37	Babies delivered before 37 weeks are referred to as 'preterm' or 'premature'
40	Babies are now full term (this term is referred to for babies delivered between 39 weeks and just before 41 weeks)
42	The cut-off to define 'post-term' babies

till birth. These trimesters are associated with different development periods of the foetus and of symptoms of the mother, and are used for check-ups of the mother.

First trimester:

Among the first things that the woman notices early in pregnancy is what she feels to be a delay and then stoppage of periods. The woman will experience an enlargement of the breasts which may also be tender (painful to touch), nausea and vomiting (morning sickness), increased frequency of urination (as the growing uterus begins to press on the bladder), constipation and sometime mood swings. In the first trimester of pregnancy, the foetus is most at risk and spontaneous abortions are most likely to occur.

Second trimester:

During the second trimester of pregnancy, the woman now begins to 'show' her pregnancy – there is increasing weight gain, the abdomen enlarges, morning sickness tends to reduce and the mother experiences foetal movements.

Third trimester:

In the third trimester, the woman experiences the maximum weight gain, foetal movements increase and become stronger and the abdomen begins to droop forwards as the foetus changes its position for birth.

Table 62.2 summarizes the various changes that the mother experiences during pregnancy.

STRUCTURE AND FUNCTION OF THE PLACENTA

As the foetus grows, it is connected to the wall of the uterus through the umbilical cord (which contains two umbilical arteries and one umbilical vein) by the placenta. Fig. 62.3 illustrates the structure of the placenta and its relation to the foetus.

The maternal and foetal circulations are structurally separated from each other (see Fig. 62.3). Thus, the mother's blood and the foetal blood do not mix – this is called the placental barrier. However, substances can be transported from the mother to the foetus and from the foetal to the maternal circulation by diffusion and other transport mechanisms.

The placenta has several important functions:

1. It provides oxygen and nutrients to the foetus.
2. It removes carbon dioxide and other waste products (e.g. urea, creatinine and uric acid).
3. It is the site of formation of several hormones such as oestrogen, progesterone and human chorionic gonadotropin (hCG), among others. Progesterone is important to sustain

Table 62.2 Maternal Changes During Pregnancy

Parameter	Changes in Pregnancy
Weight gain	Women may gain a variable amount of weight based on their earlier weight status, height, current nutritional status and physical activity patterns, among others. Average weight gain is about 12 kg. Of this, about 3 kg is the weight of the foetus at term, and about 1.5–2 kg is the placenta, amniotic fluid, etc. The remainder is the weight that is gained by the woman in terms of fat, blood and extracellular fluid.
Cardiovascular system	Heart rate and stroke volume increase resulting in an increase in the cardiac output. The increase in cardiac output results in an increase in systolic BP, while diastolic BP may fall due to the vasodilator effect of progesterone.
Respiratory system	The amount that the woman breathes at rest (the tidal volume) increases. As pregnancy advances, the woman may experience some breathlessness as the diaphragm is pushed up by the developing foetus.
Blood	Although there is an increase in the red blood cell (RBC) production, the actual RBC count may decrease because plasma volume increases – so that the blood becomes more dilute.
Kidneys	Blood flow to the kidneys and glomerular filtration increases. Women may feel an increased urgency to pass urine more frequently as the growing uterus presses on the urinary bladder.
Hormonal changes	Several hormones including cortisol, thyroxine, parathormone and aldosterone increase.
Gastrointestinal tract	In early pregnancy, women experience pica (changes in appetite and craving for certain foods). As pregnancy progresses, gastrointestinal motility may decrease resulting in constipation. In addition, women may also experience a burning in the upper abdomen and chest due to reflux of gastric acid into the oesophagus. This is because hormones released during pregnancy cause the sphincter in the lower oesophagus to relax and the growing foetus exerts external pressure on the stomach – this results in the movement of acid from the stomach into the oesophagus.
Skeletal and muscular changes	As the woman starts gaining weight, her centre of gravity shifts forwards – to compensate for this, the woman bends backwards resulting in an increased curving of the spine, a condition called lordosis. Later in pregnancy, the woman secretes a hormone called relaxin which causes the ligaments in the joints of the pelvis to allow for the birth of the baby.

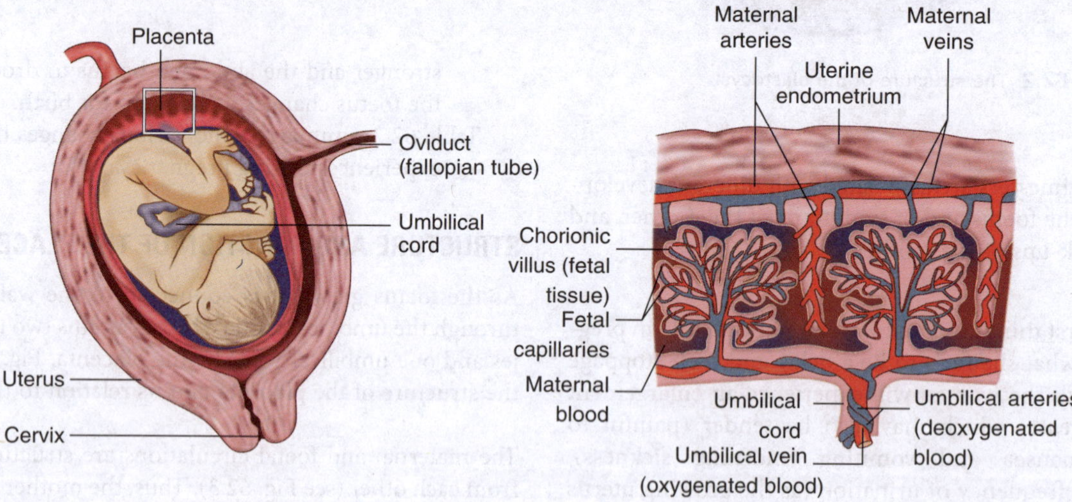

FIG. 62.3 The position and structure of the placenta.

pregnancy and low levels of progesterone are associated with spontaneous abortions. Oestrogen is important for the enlargement of the breasts and uterus, among other functions.

4. It forms a barrier against the transmission of microbes – but this is not complete and mother-to-child transmission of infections can occur. Antibodies from the body can pass to the foetus but only if they are the relatively small IgG antibodies (immunoglobulins).

TESTS OF PREGNANCY

Women typically test for pregnancy when they have been sexually active and have a delay or have missed their periods. Tests that can be done to confirm pregnancy include the following:

1. Urinary hCG: This hormone is produced by the blastocyst and later by the placenta – the urine can be tested for the presence of hCG. It reaches peak levels by 8–12 weeks.

2. Ultrasound: This can be used to visualize the foetus in the uterus and is typically done at least 4 weeks after the last menstrual cycle.

PARTURITION

Parturition Reflex

The process of childbirth is called parturition. As a woman approaches term (i.e. completion of a normal period of pregnancy), the uterus becomes more excitable. The exact way in which uterine contractions start is not clear:

1. The stretching of the uterus by the growing foetus may itself initiate uterine contractions.
2. As the foetus moves downwards, it stretches the cervix of the uterus – this initiates a release of oxytocin from the posterior pituitary gland. Oxytocin acts on the myometrium (the muscle of the uterine wall) and increases the contraction of the uterus. The contraction of the uterus pushes the foetus down some more, stretching the cervix even further, resulting in a further release of oxytocin. Thus, the uterine contractions increase in frequency and amplitude. This process is called the parturition reflex and is an example of a positive feedback loop.
3. Normally progesterone reduces uterine contractions – as the pregnancy reaches term, there is an increase in oestrogen and a decrease in progesterone.

Labour:

Labour is the common term that is used to describe the process by which the baby and placenta are delivered. It is divided into three stages:

- ***First stage***: This is the period from the onset of true (labour) uterine contractions to the full dilation of the cervix. Through the latter part of pregnancy, the woman may experience weak contractions called Braxton Hicks contractions. Labour contractions are, however, stronger, stretch the cervix and push the baby through the birth canal. This phase of labour can last quite long, often up to 8–12 hours, although it might be shorter, especially in women who have had babies before. The frequency of contractions progressively increases and the 'water might break' – that is the amniotic sac ruptures and the amniotic fluid comes out through the vagina.
- ***Second stage***: This is the period from the full dilation of the cervix to the birth of the baby.
- ***Third stage***: This is the delivery of the placenta. Because the placenta is delivered after the baby is born, it is typically referred to as the 'afterbirth'. Once the placenta is delivered, the uterus begins to contract into a hard ball-like structure – at this point, vaginal bleeding related to birth will reduce considerably and then stop. If the uterus is unable to contract adequately, it can lead to excessive bleeding called ***post-partum haemorrhage*** – if this is not treated, it can even lead to death of the mother.

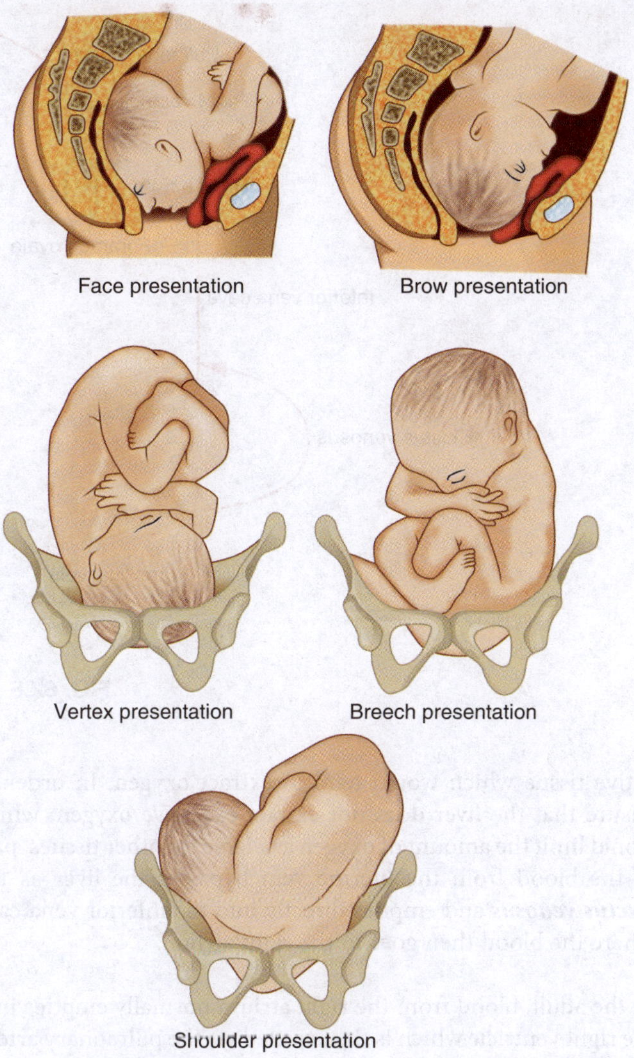

FIG. 62.4 Presentations of the baby in utero.

In most situations, the baby's head is the first to emerge. This is called the cephalic (head) presentation. Sometimes the baby's buttocks or foot may be delivered first based on how the foetus is positioned in the uterus – this is called a breech presentation. Other presentations include shoulder, arm or trunk presentations (see Fig. 62.4).

Most deliveries are vaginal. However, in the event of complications such as foetal distress or obstructed labour in which the life of the baby or mother is at risk, the baby may be delivered abdominally, by surgery called a caesarean section.

Features of the Foetal Circulation

The foetal circulation in utero differs from the adult circulation in several ways. This is depicted in Fig. 62.5.

The figure indicates that the foetal circulation derives its oxygen and nutrients from the placenta via the uterine vein. The oxygen content in the uterine vein is lower than the oxygen content of arteries in the adult. In the foetus, the liver is a metabolically

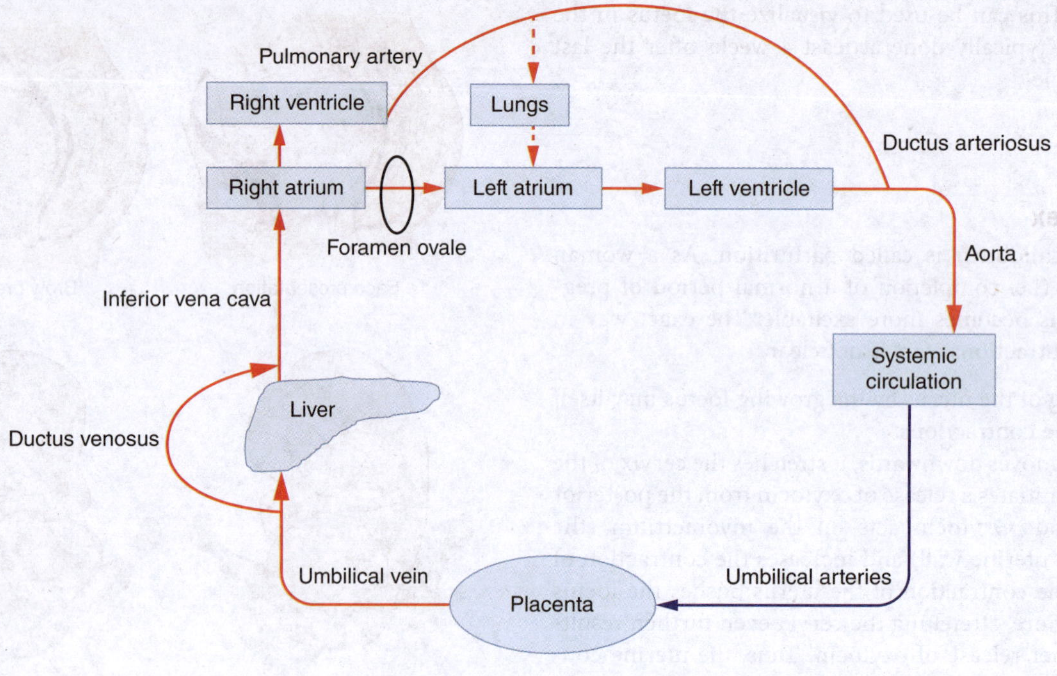

FIG. 62.5 The foetal circulation.

active tissue which would tend to extract oxygen. In order to ensure that the liver does not extract excessive oxygen, which would limit the amount of oxygen available for other tissues, part of the blood from the uterine vein bypasses the liver as the ***ductus venosus*** and empties directly into the inferior vena cava where the blood then goes to the right atrium.

In the adult, blood from the right atrium normally empties into the right ventricle which is then ejected via the pulmonary artery into the lungs. In the foetus, blood from the right atrium directly enters the left atrium through an opening in the interatrial septum called the ***foramen ovale***. Blood from the right atrium which enters the right ventricle and the pulmonary artery does not go into the lungs but is directly shunted from the pulmonary artery into the aorta via a blood vessel called the ***ductus arteriosus***. Blood in the aorta then passes through the systemic circulation supplying the foetal organs before being returned to the placenta via the umbilical arteries.

Changes in the foetal circulation at birth:

1. When the umbilical cord is clamped, this effectively shuts off the ductus venosus which is a branch of the umbilical vein.
2. When the baby takes its first breath and the lungs are oxygenated, the pulmonary circulation is opened with blood from the pulmonary artery. This blood reaches the left ventricle via the pulmonary veins.
3. The return of the increased blood to the left atrium causes the foramen ovale to shut – thus, no blood can enter directly from the right atrium to the left atrium. The left atrium now receives fully oxygenated blood from the lungs.
4. The ductus arteriosus between the pulmonary artery and the aorta closes.

LACTATION

Lactation is the secretion of milk by the mammary glands (breasts).

In the nonpregnant female, after the onset of puberty, the development of breast tissues occurs because of the monthly secretion of oestrogen during the menstrual cycle.

During pregnancy, oestrogen causes the ducts of the breast to grow and branch, while progesterone is required for the development of the lobule–alveolar system – the alveoli are the cells which actually secrete the milk. However, even with the development of breast tissue, actual secretion of milk requires another hormone called prolactin. Prolactin is secreted from the mother's anterior pituitary gland. The action of prolactin is increased by a hormone which is secreted by the placenta called human chorionic somatomammotropin (hCS).

SUMMARY OF ACTIONS OF HORMONES ON THE BREAST

- Oestrogens:
  - Development of the ductal system
    - Also, growth hormone, prolactin, glucocorticoids, and insulin
  - Deposition of fat
- Progesterone:
  - Growth of the breast lobules, with budding of alveoli
- Prolactin:
  - Milk production (lactational levels are 20 times nonpregnant levels)
  - Human chorionic somatomammotropin:
  - Probably has lactogenic properties

The first secretion of the breast is colostrum. Colostrum in humans is rich in proteins, is low in fat and has a high concentration of mother's antibodies which are good for the baby.

Milk Ejection Reflex

Even under the influence of all the hormones listed earlier, milk from the breast is not ejected unless the breast is mechanically stimulated. This occurs when the baby suckles the breast. Nerve impulses then stimulate the production of the hormone oxytocin in the hypothalamus. It is then carried to the posterior pituitary gland and released into the bloodstream. Oxytocin then acts on myoepithelial cells in the breast which contract and express the milk out of the nipple of the breast. This reflex is sometime called milk 'letdown', and since this reflex involves both nerve and hormone, it is an example of a *neuroendocrine reflex*. The milk ejection reflex is depicted in Fig. 62.6.

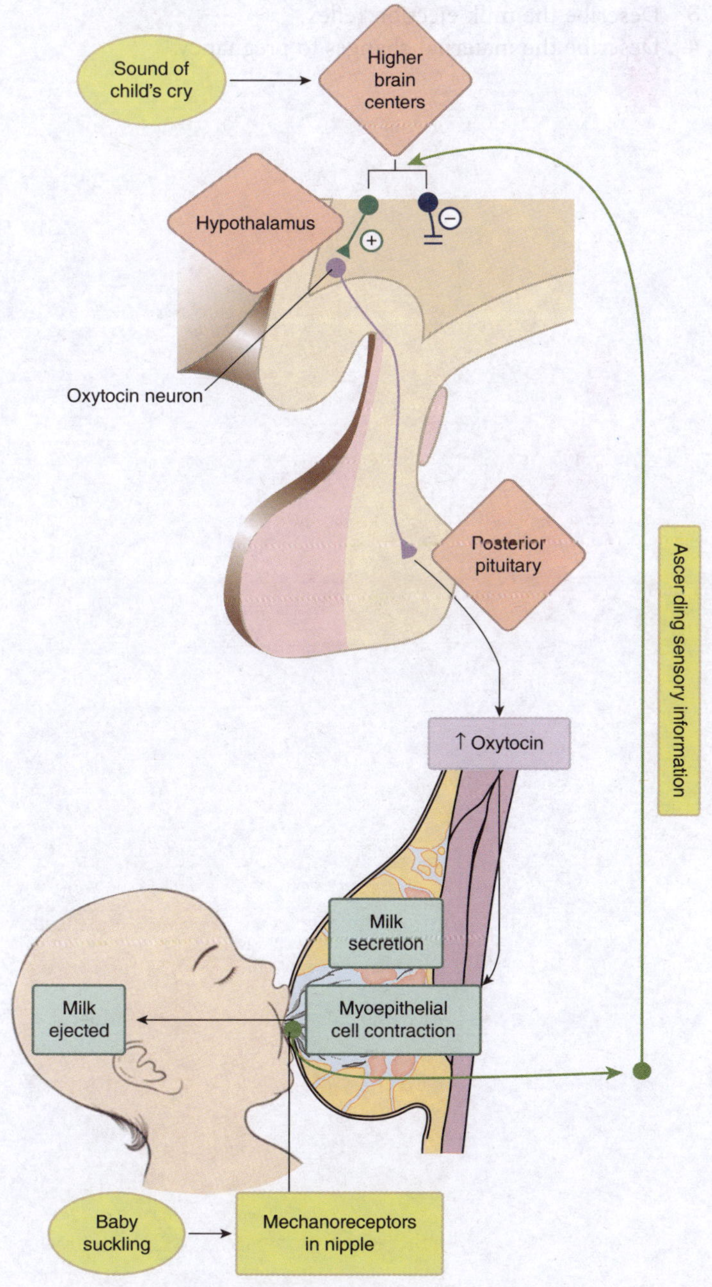

FIG. 62.6 The milk ejection reflex

Table 62.3 Comparison of Human and Cow Milk

	Human Milk	Cow's Milk
Protein (g/dL)	1.5	3.5
Casein: whey ratio	40:60	80:20
Lactose (g/dL)	7	4.5
Fat (g/dL)	3.6	3.7

Apart from suckling, the milk ejection reflex can also be stimulated by the crying of the baby and by fondling of the baby by the mother. The milk ejection reflex can be inhibited by maternal stress.

The World Health Organization recommends that for populations, babies should be exclusively breast fed for a period of 6 months.

Composition of Human Milk

Breast milk is rich in antibodies, is more digestible and also allows for mother–child bonding. Lactose is about 50% higher in human milk compared with in cow's milk, while casein (the major protein) is three times higher in cow's milk compared to in human milk (Table 62.3). The fat percentage of human and cow's milk is approximately the same. Vitamins C and D are about two to three times higher in concentration in human milk as compared to in cow's milk. While the iron content of human milk is higher than in cow's milk, sodium, phosphorus and calcium are higher in cow's milk.

Babies who are formula fed have an increased risk of diarrhoea if they belong to lower socioeconomic strata and do not observe strict hygiene in the cleaning of bottles. Babies from lower socioeconomic groups may also develop malnutrition if mothers give them diluted feeds because of the high costs of formula feeds. Babies who are formula fed also have an increased risk of childhood obesity and diabetes later in life, among other problems.

APPLICATIONS FOR NURSING

- Nurses play an important role in the care of the woman in the antenatal period (i.e. before childbirth), during labour and following delivery. In the antenatal period, the role of the nurse includes examination of the mother and growing foetus to ensure the well-being of both; advising the mother about nutrition, supplements, sanitation, hygiene and childcare; ensuring that the mother attends follow-up visits; providing information of pregnancy and childbirth; and advising the mother about the postnatal care of the child including breast-feeding and immunization.
- The nurse also plays an important role during labour. When mothers enter the hospital in labour, nurses should be able to assess the stage of labour, check for foetal heart rate, monitor vital signs of the mother and assist the woman through labour. The nurse should also evaluate whether the expectant mother has a medical history or is on medications that would cause particular concern during delivery. The nurse will also monitor the

frequency and strength of contractions and the progress of labour. Prior to delivery, the nurse cleans the genital area and conducts or assists the delivery. The nurse should be able to identify signs of foetal distress that might need other interventions.

- The nurse is critical for the care of the newborn. The status of the child is assessed using the Apgar's score. The baby is kept warm, weighed and respiratory passages cleaned or suctioned, if needed. Special needs of the child will need to be assessed by the attending paediatrician, but in the absence of a doctor, the nurse needs to assess whether the child is in distress and needs special intervention.

SUMMARY

- Following fertilization of the ovum in the fallopian tube, the zygote undergoes several cell divisions to form a blastocyst which is then attached onto the wall of the uterus. The growing embryo becomes a foetus at 8 weeks of gestation.
- The normal duration of pregnancy is 40 weeks. Babies who are delivered before 37 weeks are called premature or preterm and those who are delivered after 42 weeks are called post-term.
- The mother undergoes many changes during the period of pregnancy which affect all organ systems. The average weight gain of the mother is about 12 weeks, less than half of which is related to the growing foetus and supportive tissues.
- Parturition or childbirth is related to the stretch of the uterus and cervix and the release of a hormone called oxytocin which promotes uterine contractions.
- Lactation is the culmination of the development and sensitization of breast tissues before and during pregnancy. The milk ejection reflex is initiated by suckling of the breasts and involves the release of oxytocin. It is an example of a neuroendocrine reflex.

CHAPTER REVIEW QUESTIONS

1. Describe the functions of the placenta.
2. Describe the parturition reflex.
3. Describe the milk ejection reflex.
4. Describe the maternal changes to pregnancy.

CHAPTER 63

The Male Reproductive System and Spermatogenesis

SPECIFIC LEARNING OBJECTIVES

At the end of this chapter, the student should be able to:

- Describe the process of sex differentiation during the development of the foetus.
- Describe the functional anatomy of the male reproductive system; specifically describe the function of:
  - Vas deferens
  - Seminal vesicle
  - Prostate gland
  - List the secondary sexual characteristics of the male which develop during puberty
- List the actions of testosterone.
- List the steps of spermatogenesis with the help of a diagram.
- Define spermiogenesis.
- List the factors which affect and regulate spermatogenesis.
- List the features which are assessed during semen analysis.
- Define the following terms:
  - Oligospermia
  - Azoospermia

GLOSSARY OF TERMS

- **Puberty:** the age at which male and female adolescents achieve sexual maturity and are capable of reproduction (girls typically achieve puberty between 10 and 14 years and boys, 1–2 years later)
- **Secondary sexual characteristics:** the physical changes that occur at puberty which distinguish males from females, but which are not necessarily directly involved with reproduction
- **Spermatogenesis:** process of formation of mature spermatozoa (sperm)
- **Spermiogenesis:** a part of spermatogenesis, during which spermatids are converted to mature spermatozoa (sperm)
- **Oligospermia:** a reduction in the sperm count in the semen (although there are variations, the cut-off level accepted by many is <15 million/mL)
- **Azoospermia:** an absence of sperm in the semen

Males and females differ in their chromosomal patterns. While both males and females have 22 pairs of autosomes (i.e. nonsex chromosomes), they differ in their sex chromosomes; males have X and Y chromosomes, while females have XX sex chromosomes.

SEX DIFFERENTIATION IN UTERO

The gonads (the organ that produces the gametes) in the male are the testes, and in the female the ovaries. The seminiferous tubules in the testes (the site of production of sperm in the male) begin to form by about 6–7 weeks of gestation and testosterone, the male hormone, begins to be secreted by the testes by about 8–9 weeks. This secretion of testosterone is important because it stimulates the growth and differentiation of the Wolffian duct. The Wolffian duct forms the various parts of the reproductive system of the male including the vas deferens and the ejaculatory duct. In the developing male foetus, a substance called the Mullerian-inhibiting substance (MIS) is secreted which causes the Mullerian ducts (the precursor parts of the female reproductive system) to degenerate.

In the developing male foetus, the testes are located in the abdomen and descend into the scrotal sac through the inguinal canal. Thus, at birth, more than 97% of male babies, which are born full term, have their testes located in the scrotal sac. In the remaining male babies, and more often in babies who are born preterm, one or both testes may remain undescended and this is referred to as ***cryptorchidism***. This condition, if left untreated, is associated with infertility and increased risk of cancer of the testes.

In contrast to the development of the testes in the male foetus, the ovaries begin to develop in the female foetus by about 9 weeks of gestation. Unlike the male, the Mullerian ducts persist in the female and give rise to the fallopian tubes, the uterus and the vagina.

There are several conditions related to sex differentiation, some of which are discussed as follows:

Turner's syndrome:
In this condition, the sex chromosomal pattern is XO, that is the individual is completely or partly missing an X chromosome. People who have Turner's syndrome are typically short statured, have a webbed neck and may have a variety of cardiac and other endocrine disorders and other physical changes. In terms of their reproductive function, they typically have amenorrhoea and are infertile. They typically have a normal intelligence but may have some behavioural disorders and learning disabilities (see Fig. 63.1).

Klinefelter's syndrome:
In this condition, there is an extra X chromosome. Thus, unlike males who typically have 46 chromosomes with XY sex chromosomes, these individuals have 47 chromosomes with XXY. Symptoms in such people depend on how much testosterone they produce. They may appear taller, with less facial and body hair and less muscular development. They are typically infertile with lower or no sperm production (see Fig. 63.2).

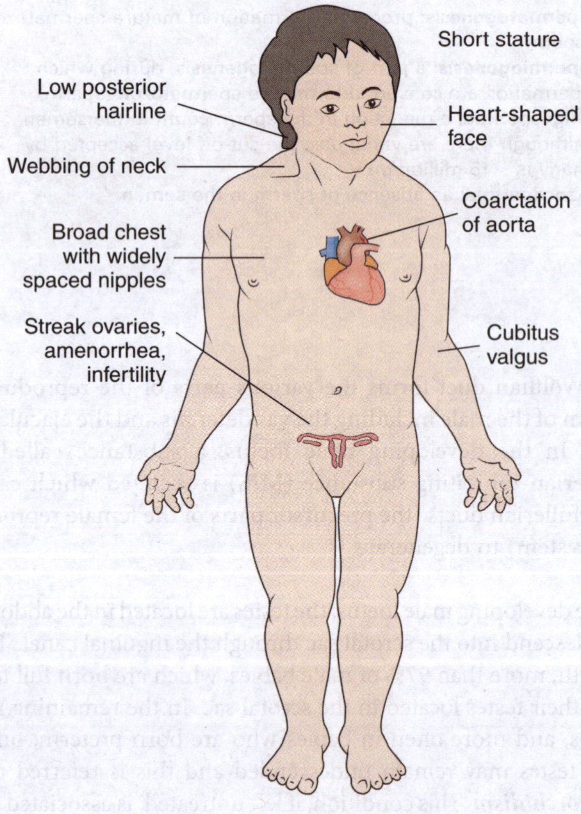

FIG. 63.1 Turner's syndrome.

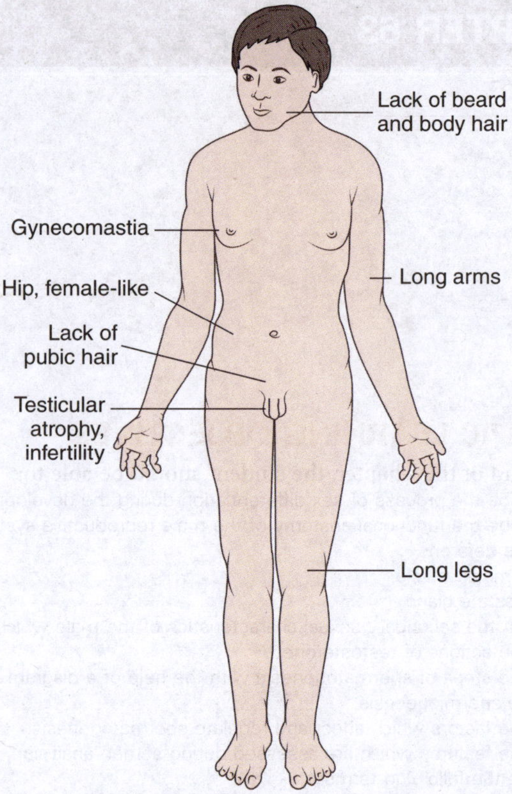

FIG. 63.2 Klinefelter's syndrome.

Hermaphroditism:
There are many variants of this condition, but typically involves a situation in which both ovaries and testes may be present.

Ambiguous genitalia:
This condition is one in which the newborn's external genitalia are not clearly identifiable as male or female and is due to a problem during foetal development.

FUNCTIONAL ANATOMY OF THE MALE REPRODUCTIVE SYSTEM

The male reproductive system consists of the following (Fig. 63.3):

1. Testes which are present in a sac-like structure called the scrotum
2. Epididymis
3. Vas deferens
4. Seminal vesicles
5. Ejaculatory duct
6. Prostate gland
7. Bulbourethral glands
8. Urethra

Testes: There are two testes located in the scrotal sac. The scrotal sac is cooler than the core body temperature and this is important for spermatogenesis (production of sperm). There are variations in the size of the testes between and within an individual, and the left testis typically hangs slightly lower than the right. Structures called seminiferous tubules are the site of spermatogenesis.

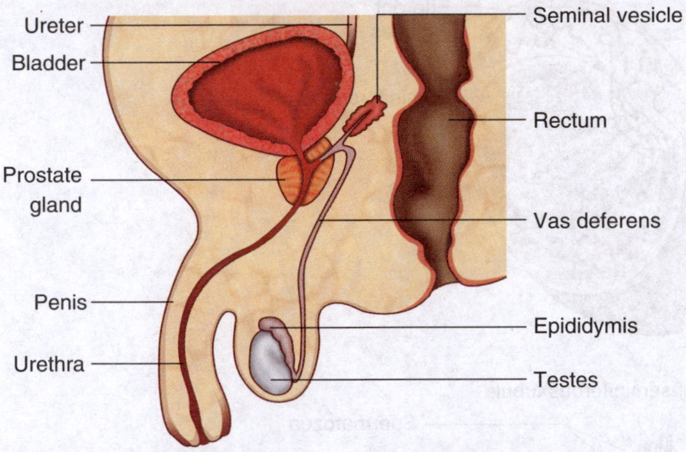

FIG. 63.3 The male reproductive system.

Epididymis: The seminiferous tubules in the testes end in the rete testis which in turn opens into the epididymis. This structure helps to store spermatozoa and allows them to mature further. Sperm also acquires the ability to move (motility) in the epididymis.

Vas deferens: This is the tubular structure that transports sperm from the testes and joins with the duct of the seminal vesicle to form the ejaculatory duct. While sperm in the vas deferens are able to move on their own, this movement is helped by the contraction of the vas deferens.

Seminal vesicle: There are two vesicles located on either side. This contributes the bulk of the volume of semen and the secretion from the seminal vesicle is rich in fructose. The fructose is an energy source for the sperm.

Prostate gland: This gland surrounds the neck of the bladder and contributes the second largest volume to semen after the seminal vesicles. The secretion of the prostate gland is slightly alkaline and helps to neutralize the acidity of the vagina. Other components help to prevent sperm from clumping together. Prostatic fluid makes sperm more motile and also increases their survival.

Bulbourethral glands: These are two small pea-shaped glands located below the prostate gland. The secretion of the bulbourethral glands to semen is relatively small – this secretion helps to lubricate the urethra and also neutralizes the acidic urine that may be present in the urethra.

TESTOSTERONE

Androgens are the group of hormones that are responsible for 'male' characteristics. The major androgen is testosterone which is secreted largely by the testes. Androgens are also secreted to a smaller extent by the adrenal glands (located above the kidneys, also called the suprarenal glands) and the ovaries in the female, although the amount of androgens in the male is many times higher than in females.

Testosterone has many actions across the life cycle of an individual:

1. During the development of the foetus, testosterone is important for the development of the male genital system.
2. After birth, and particularly at puberty, testosterone is important for the enlargement of the testis and penis, the appearance and growth of facial, pubic, axillary and chest hair in the male, the increase in muscle mass and the change in voice.
3. In adults, testosterone is important for sperm production, the male pattern of balding and libido (sexual drive).

PUBERTY AND SECONDARY SEXUAL CHARACTERISTICS IN THE MALE

Puberty is when a child's body changes into an adult body capable of reproduction. It is thus the period when children attain sexual maturity. In a male, this typically occurs around the ages of 11–12 years, although there is some variation and some boys may achieve puberty as late as 16 years.

The changes in puberty in the male typically follow a sequence: the testes enlarge followed by increase in the size of the penis. Subsequent to this is the development of pubic hair, then hair in the armpits and finally facial hair.

Puberty can be graded for both boys and girls using visual charts called the Tanner's scale.

The above-mentioned changes are typically accompanied in boys undergoing puberty by a growth spurt (i.e. an increase in height), increase in bone density and muscle growth and change in the voice.

Puberty is also associated with emotional changes; boys may experience mood swings, seek greater independence, indulge in risk-taking behaviour and develop romantic relationships, among others.

The visible physical changes that accompany puberty which are not directly involved with reproduction and which have been described earlier are called secondary sexual characteristics.

SPERMATOGENESIS

Spermatogenesis is the process by which mature sperms are formed. It takes place in a specific part of the testes called the seminiferous tubules (Fig. 63.4). The seminiferous tubules are lined by epithelial cells called Sertoli's cells. In between the Sertoli's cells are the spermatogenic cells which proceed through several steps to form sperms.

From Fig. 63.4, you will also observe cells which are adjacent to the seminiferous tubules called Leydig's cells.

STEPS IN SPERMATOGENESIS

More specifically, spermatogenesis is the process by which spermatozoa are produced from cells called spermatogonia (Fig. 63.5).

- The first step is the conversion of spermatogonia to primary spermatocytes by mitosis.

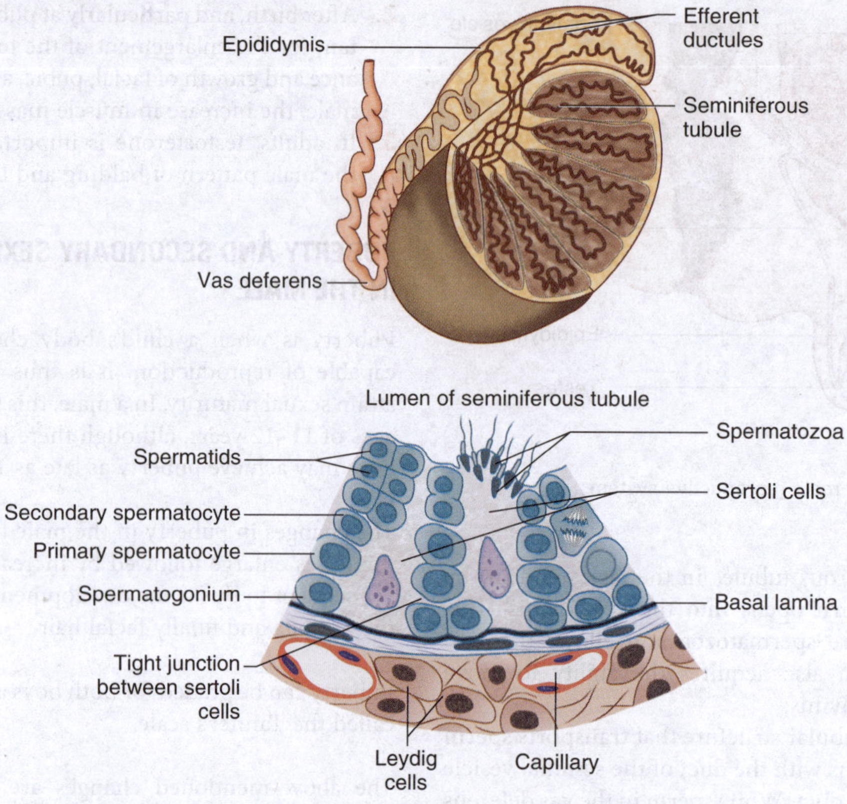

FIG. 63.4 The testis and seminiferous tubules.

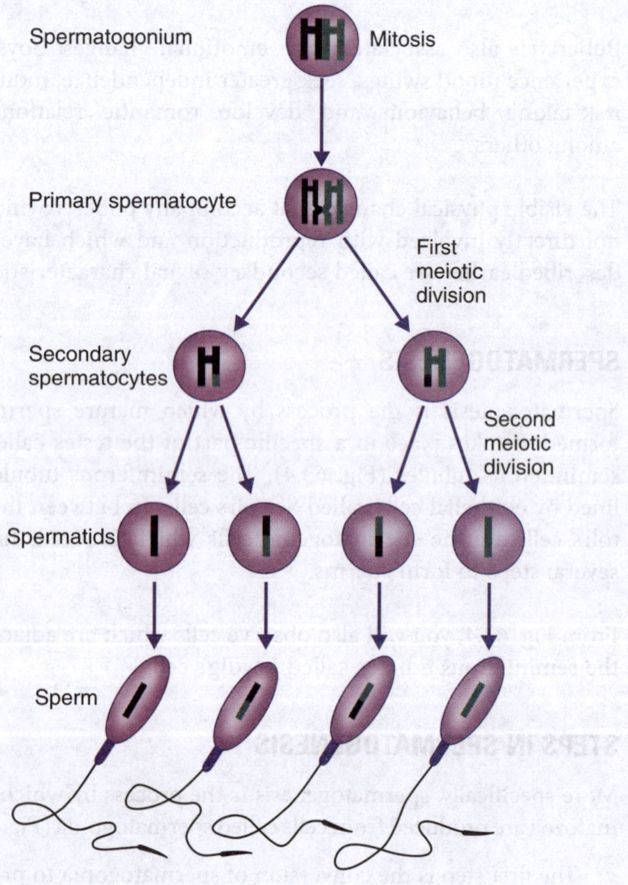

FIG. 63.5 The process of spermatogenesis.

- The primary spermatocyte then divides by meiosis to form two secondary spermatocytes.
- Each secondary spermatocyte then divides by meiosis once again to form spermatids.
- The conversion of spermatids to mature spermatozoa (sperm) is called spermiogenesis.

In mitosis, the number of chromosomes remains diploid, that is 46, while in meiosis the number of chromosomes is halved, that is haploid. This is important because when the male gamete (sperm) combines with the female gamete (ovum), the diploid number of chromosomes is restored and there is an equal contribution from the male and female gametes.

During spermiogenesis, spermatids:

- Grow a tail.
- Develop an acrosome which is a thick cap on the head of the spermatozoa and is composed mainly by the Golgi's apparatus.

The entire process of spermatogenesis including transport in the ducts takes about 3 months. The testes produce about 200–300 million sperm daily.

STRUCTURE OF THE SPERMATOZOA

Fig. 63.6 illustrates the structure of the mature spermatozoa.

- The mature spermatozoa contain a haploid number of chromosomes.

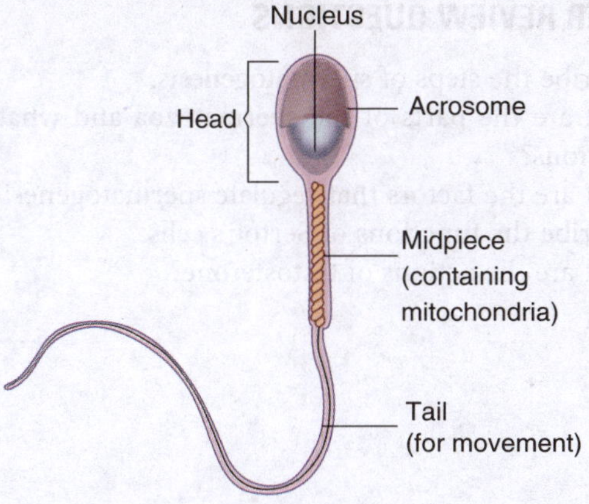

FIG. 63.6 Structure of the spermatozoa.

- The acrosome contains enzymes including hyaluronidase which can digest certain proteins and helps the sperm to enter the ovum during fertilization.
- The mid piece of the spermatozoa is rich in mitochondria which are the powerhouses of the cell – thus, energy is made available for the sperm to swim towards the ovum that is available for fertilization.
- The tail is 10 times longer than the head. The tail is important for movement. However, sperm do not become motile merely because they develop the tail – they have to be in the epididymis for about a day before they become motile and only gain full motility after ejaculation, when the sperm are ejected into the vaginal tract during intercourse.

ROLE OF THE SERTOLI'S AND LEYDIG'S CELLS

Sertoli's cells

As discussed earlier, the Sertoli's cells line the seminiferous tubules. These cells have a variety of functions:

1. They provide the structural support for spermatogenesis which takes place between them (see Fig. 63.4).
2. They are phagocytic and help remove damaged cells.
3. They provide nutrition to spermatids.
4. They secrete a number of hormones which include the following:
   a. Oestrogen
   b. Inhibin, which suppresses the production of follicle-stimulating hormone (FSH) from the pituitary gland
   c. MIS results in the regression of the Mullerian duct and the development of the male genital system in the foetus.
5. They also contribute to the blood–testis barrier. This barrier protects developing sperms from external agents and toxins.
6. Sertoli's cells have receptors for testosterone and are thus regulated by this hormone.

Leydig's cells:

Leydig's cells are present in the interstitial space between the seminiferous tubules. They secrete testosterone and also some other androgens in small quantities.

REGULATION OF SPERMATOGENESIS

Spermatogenesis is primarily regulated by hormones.

1. Testosterone which is released by the Leydig's cells diffuses into the seminiferous tubules and acts on the Sertoli's cells, which promote spermatogenesis by acting on the spermatogonia and controlling the environment around them.
2. Luteinizing hormone (LH) and FSH are hormones that are released from the anterior pituitary gland. In the male, both these hormones are essential for spermatogenesis. FSH appears to be more important for spermatogenesis at puberty.
3. Spermatogenesis is influenced by the local temperature of the scrotum which is normally lower than the core body temperature. Factors which increase the local scrotal temperature such as having hot baths, wearing tight trousers or even placing a laptop for long periods on the lap can inhibit spermatogenesis.
4. Other factors which affect spermatogenesis are poor diets deficient in certain vitamins and other micronutrients, exposure to toxins such as pesticides and dioxins, X-ray exposure, chronic alcoholism and infections that may cause orchitis (inflammation of the testes).

APPLICATIONS FOR NURSING

- Nurses need to be aware of the male causes of infertility, including the problem of erectile dysfunction in males. In this broad set of conditions, males may be unable to sustain an erection or may ejaculate prematurely (i.e. before insertive intercourse).
- Among the most common disorders of the prostate gland are benign prostatic hyperplasia (BPH) and prostatic cancer. BPH is a noncancerous enlargement of the prostate gland which is more common in older males. The enlargement can cause partial or rarely complete blockage of the urethra. People who have this condition may experience a sense of incomplete urination, dribbling and a weak urine stream, among others. Prostate cancer also occurs in older males and shares many of the symptoms of BPH.

SUMMARY

- In the developing foetus, there are two ductal systems; the Wolffian duct system is associated with the development of the male reproductive system, while the Mullerian duct system is associated with the female reproductive system.
- The male chromosomal pattern is 46,XY (i.e. 46 chromosomes of which the sex chromosomes are XY). Chromosomal abnormalities include Turner's syndrome (45,XO) and Klinefelter's syndrome (47,XXY).
- The testes are the sites of production of sperms – specifically in the seminiferous tubules. Sperm are carried sequentially in the vas deferens, ejaculatory duct and urethra.
- Apart from sperm, the volume of semen is contributed by the seminal vesicles, prostate gland and bulbourethral glands.
- Secondary sexual characteristics in the male at puberty include increased muscularity; growth of hair in the pubic and axillary regions, and later facial hair; and a change in voice.
- Testosterone has actions across the life cycle. In the developing foetus, it helps in the development of the male reproductive system, at puberty contributes to the secondary sexual characteristics and in adults to the male pattern of baldness.

- The initial steps of spermatogenesis occur in the seminiferous tubules of the testes. The stages of spermatogenesis are in sequence: spermatogonia – primary spermatocytes – secondary spermatocytes – spermatids – mature spermatozoa.
- Spermatogenesis involves both mitosis and meiosis so that the mature sperm has a haploid number (i.e. 23) of chromosome.
- Two cells which are important to the process of spermatogenesis are the Sertoli's cells and the Leydig's cells. Sertoli's cells provide structural support for spermatogenesis; contribute to the blood–testis barrier; secrete various hormones including oestrogen, inhibin and MIS; and are phagocytic. Leydig's cells secrete testosterone.
- Spermatogenesis is primarily regulated by the hormones testosterone, LH and FSH. In addition, scrotal temperature, nutritional status, exposure to certain medications and toxic chemicals and infections of the testes can affect spermatogenesis.

CHAPTER REVIEW QUESTIONS

1. Describe the steps of spermatogenesis.
2. What are the parts of the spermatozoa and what are their functions?
3. What are the factors that regulate spermatogenesis?
4. Describe the functions of Sertoli's cells.
5. What are the actions of testosterone?

CHAPTER 64

Applications in Reproductive Physiology

SPECIFIC LEARNING OBJECTIVES

At the end of this chapter, the student should be able to:

- List some common variations/disorders of the menstrual cycle.
- List the methods of contraception in the male and female.
- Outline the broad principles of antenatal care during pregnancy.
- Describe prolonged and obstructed labour.
- Describe the basic parameters of a semen analysis.
- Outline the approach to an infertile couple coming to the hospital.

GLOSSARY OF TERMS

- **Contraception:** prevention of pregnancy by interfering with ovulation, fertilization or implantation
- **Infertility:** failure to conceive by natural means in the absence of contraception
- **Sterility:** the inability to reproduce (i.e. have children)

VARIATIONS/DISORDERS OF THE MENSTRUAL CYCLE

Amenorrhoea

This refers to the absence of menstruation in women within the reproductive age group who have already started menstruating. It is important to understand that because of variations in the menstrual cycle length, women may have delayed periods. Amenorrhoea can have many causes.

During the course of a lifetime, women may experience amenorrhoea for a variety of reasons, including the following:

1. Pregnancy.
2. Breast feeding – this is referred to as lactation amenorrhoea.
3. Menopause – this occurs in older women when menstrual cycles stop all together. During the period before menopause, periods may become irregular in length and women may experience periods of amenorrhoea.

Amenorrhoea may also occur due to low birth weight, stress, hormonal abnormalities, excessive exercise and a variety of medications. It is beyond the scope of this book to discuss these in detail.

Menorrhagia

This refers to heavy menstrual bleeding. Normal blood loss is up to about 60 mL of blood during the phase of bleeding. In most cases, the cause of menorrhagia may not be determined. Causes can include hormonal imbalances during the menstrual cycle, problems with the ovaries, benign (noncancerous) tumours of the uterus called fibroids, the use of intrauterine devices for contraception, certain medications and sometimes cancers of the ovaries, uterus or cervix, among others.

Dysmenorrhoea

This refers to painful menstruation or menstrual cramps. This often occurs several hours before or just after the menstrual flow and can last for between 12 and 72 hours. Primary dysmenorrhoea occurs without any disorder of the woman's reproductive organs, while secondary dysmenorrhoea occurs when there are disorders in the woman's reproductive organs.

METHODS OF CONTRACEPTION

This section will describe in brief the methods that are available for contraception for the male and female.

Male Methods

- *The rhythm method*: This method is based on not having sexual intercourse during the period of the menstrual cycle that is most likely to be associated with fertilization (i.e. around the period of ovulation).

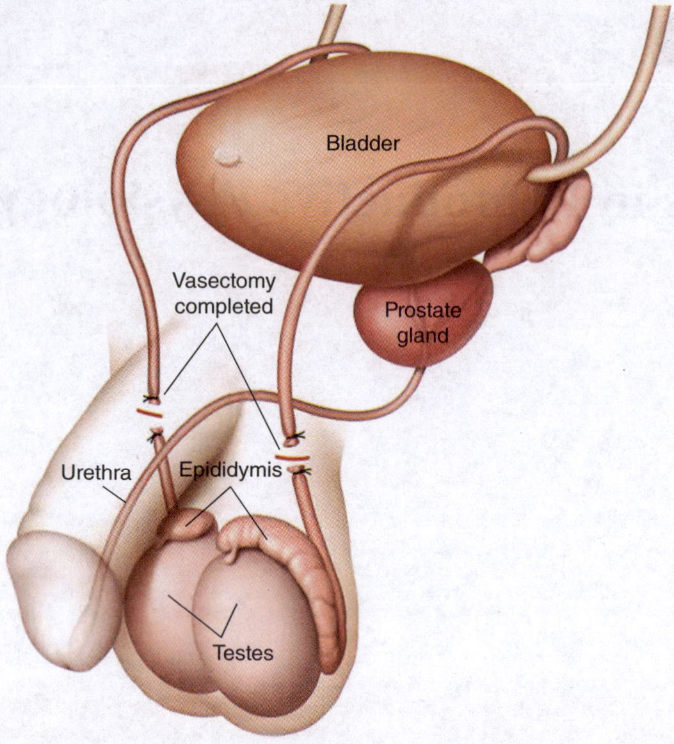

FIG. 64.1 Vasectomy.

- *Withdrawal method (coitus interruptus)*: This is the withdrawal of the penis from the vagina before ejaculation occurs. This is not very effective as it requires properly timed withdrawal.
- *Condom*: This is a barrier method which prevents the sperms that are ejaculated from being deposited in the female genital tract, thus restricting the possibility of fertilization.
- *Vasectomy*: In this operation, the vas deferens from both testes is ligated. Thus, sperm are unable to be ejaculated during sexual intercourse (see Fig. 64.1).
- *Medications:* These are available in the form of male hormonal contraceptives, both oral and by injections. They act by interfering with sperm development and production.

Female Methods

- *Diaphragm*: This is the most common barrier method used in females – this blocks the entry of sperms into the upper female genital organs and thus prevents fertilization.
- *Chemical methods*: This involves the use of various jellies, foams and creams which are spermicidal, that is they kill the sperm once they are deposited in the female genital tract.
- *Intrauterine devices*: These are devices that are placed into the uterus using a special applicator. They are most often medicated or contain copper and typically prevent implantation of the blastocyst on the uterine wall.
- *Oral contraceptive pills*: There are a variety of oral contraceptive pills – they typically contain combinations of oestrogen and progesterone and thus prevent ovulation, alter the composition of cervical mucus making it less likely for sperm to

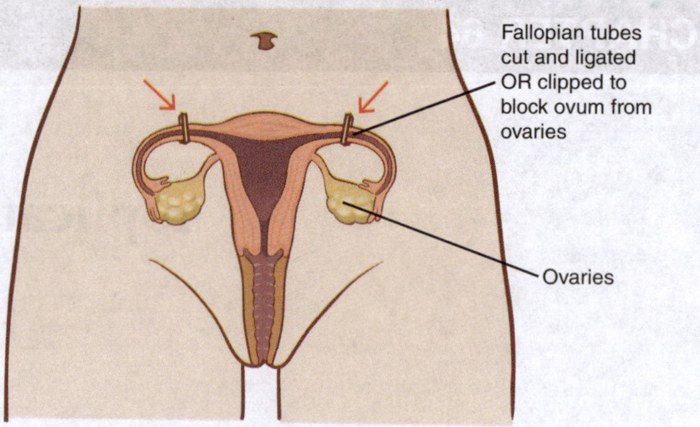

FIG. 64.2 Tubectomy.

travel up the female genital tract and also make implantation of the blastocyst less likely.

- *Tubectomy*: In this method, the fallopian tubes are ligated on both sides. This prevents the ovum from moving into the uterus – thus, fertilization does not occur. See Fig. 64.2.

ANTENATAL CARE DURING PREGNANCY

Antenatal care is the systematic monitoring and supervision of a woman during pregnancy by a health team. The aim of antenatal care is twofold:

- Ensure optimal growth and health of the foetus.
- Ensure the well-being of the mother.

Women who are pregnant are encouraged to enrol early for antenatal care, preferably within the first 12 weeks. Once enrolled, women should receive at least four visits inclusive of the registration visit. During the course of pregnancy, the woman should receive protection from tetanus, and must be provided at least 100 tablets of iron, folic acid and vitamin A (IFA).

At every visit, the patient's history must be taken and the weight, blood pressure, respiratory rate, and pallor and oedema should be assessed. The nurse should conduct an abdominal palpation for foetal growth, and auscultation of foetal heart sounds. Laboratory investigations, such as haemoglobin estimation and urine tests (for sugar and proteins), may need to be done. Additional tests include blood group, including the Rh factor, and tests to rule out syphilis, HIC and hepatitis B. These tests would need to be done with adequate counselling.

PROLONGED AND OBSTRUCTED LABOUR

There is no uniformly accepted definition of prolonged labour, although this should be considered if labour extends beyond 12 hours. There are many reasons for prolonged labour including inadequate uterine contractions.

Obstructed Labour

This refers to the inability of the foetus to descend through the birth canal because of some obstruction, despite strong uterine contractions. This may occur because of the following:

1. Issues with the mother (e.g. a small bony pelvis which is unable to accommodate the foetus) or issues with the soft tissues in the birth canal (e.g. scarring or tumours).
2. Issues with the fetus: This may be related to, among other issues, the following:
   a. Large size of the foetus
   b. Conjoined twins
   c. Presentation of the foetus, for example, breech, brow, face or shoulder

Prolonged and obstructed labour is important because it can endanger both the foetus and the mother. Thus, foetal distress and foetal death can occur if adequate medical care is not available. The mother can experience severe postpartum haemorrhage and shock, both of which are life-threatening. Prolonged pressure of the foetus on the cervix can result in damage to the tissues and later complications such as abnormal passages (fistulae) between the vagina and the urinary bladder, urethra or rectum. Prolonged and obstructed labour can be prevented by adequate antenatal care and evaluation and institutional delivery with adequately trained health personnel.

SEMEN ANALYSIS

Analysis of semen is done as part of the investigation of infertile couples.

- Semen is typically whitish, thick and translucent.
- The volume of a typical ejaculate (which is the amount released during a single ejaculation) is variable from about 1 to 7 mL.
- The number of sperms is highly variable and can go up to about 200 million/mL. A sperm count in excess of 15 million is considered normal.
- Typically, in excess of 50% of sperm should be motile if the sample is examined within 1 hour of production.

DISORDERS OF SPERM PRODUCTION

Oligospermia refers to a decrease in sperms in the semen. This can be graded based on the actual sperm count and is diagnosed when the count falls below 15 million/mL.

Azoospermia is the absence of sperms in the semen.

Decreased sperm counts may result from problems in the testes including infections, cancers, incomplete descent of the testes (cryptorchidism) and local testicular problems like hydrocele and varicocele.

Decreased sperm counts may also occur with increasing age and chromosomal abnormalities such as Klinefelter's syndrome should be excluded.

Problems in the male reproductive system in areas other than the testes, for example, vas deferens or prostate, may also result in reduced sperm counts.

APPROACH TO A COUPLE WHO CANNOT CONCEIVE

Sterility means that it is impossible for the couple to conceive and have a child. Infertility means that the couple is not sterile but are unable to conceive despite regular unprotected sexual intercourse due to some reason. It may result from problems related to the male as well as the female. Thus, in investigations of infertility, both male and female need to be assessed. Nurses need to be aware of the male causes of infertility. In many societies, women are assumed to be the cause of infertility.

- The evaluation of the infertile couple involves a detailed history of both partners. This includes an evaluation of the onset of puberty, sexual history and general medical history. Current medications and use of alcohol, substance abuse and the results of other investigations that may have been carried out need to be assessed. The sexual practice of the couple also needs to be ascertained.
- This is followed by a clinical examination of both partners.
- In the case of the male, a semen analysis is performed. In women, various tests can be done to evaluate the structure of the female reproductive system. Tests of ovulation and blood tests to evaluate endocrine function with particular reference to the reproductive hormones may be done. Genetic evaluations of both male and female partners may be done if chromosomal abnormalities are suspected in either partner, which may contribute to infertility.

Nurses need to be aware that infertility is a traumatic experience for couples and that they require emotional support during and following evaluation for infertility.

CLINICAL CASE PROBLEMS

(A) ***A young couple who have been unsuccessfully trying to have child for the last 2 years come to the clinic for evaluation. The doctor assesses both the husband and the wife and performs certain tests.***
   a. For the semen analysis of the husband, what would be considered an acceptable sperm count and motility?
   b. What tests can be performed to determine whether the woman is ovulating during her menstrual cycles?
   c. On history, the woman indicates that she has severe cramps during the bleeding phase of her menstrual cycle together with excessive bleeding. What are terms used to describe these two issues?

(B) ***A 28-year-old married woman has missed two of her 'periods'. She wants to confirm whether she is pregnant.***
   a. What are the tests that can be done to confirm pregnancy?
   b. Since this is her first pregnancy, she is apprehensive about the changes that she will undergo. Indicate what maternal changes occur during pregnancy in the following systems:
      i. Cardiovascular system
      ii. Kidney and urinary system
      iii. Respiratory system
   c. What hormones are produced by the placenta?

SELF-DIRECTED LEARNING

- Read about the following conditions that can occur in pregnancy:
  - Anaemia
  - Pre-eclampsia and eclampsia
  - Gestational diabetes
- Common causes of infertility in the male and female

WHAT YOU CAN LEARN FROM A HOSPITAL VISIT

- Visit the labour room and obtain a nurses' monitoring chart for the progress of labour.
- The health of the newborn is assessed using the APGAR score – obtain a copy of the scoring system.
- Obtain a lab form from the hospital – identify the tests that are done to assess an infertile couple.

11

SECTION

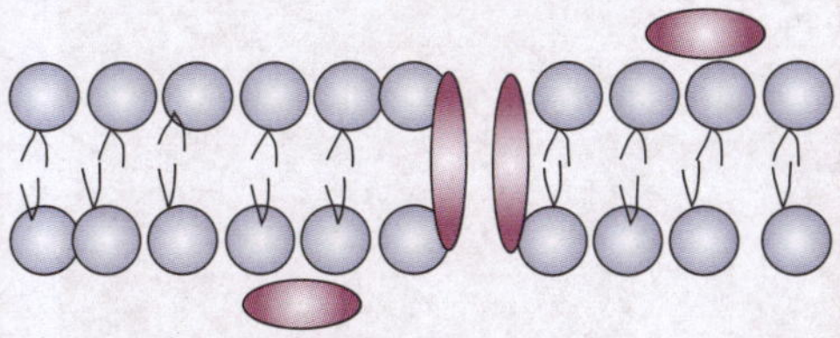

The Nervous System

Section Outline

SECTION 11

The Nervous System

CHAPTER 65

Overview of the Nervous System

SPECIFIC LEARNING OBJECTIVES

At the end of this chapter, the student should be able to:

- Categorize the different components of the nervous system.
- List the three broad divisions of the brain.
- List the lobes of the cerebrum and indicate their functions.
- Describe the functions of the following:
- Cerebellum
- Midbrain
- Pons
- Medulla
- Hypothalamus
- Identify key 'centres' in the brain and indicate their functions.
- Enumerate the different types of spinal nerves.

GLOSSARY OF TERMS

- Gyrus: ridges or folds on the surface of the brain
- Sulcus: grooves on the surface of the brain
- Brainstem: consists of the midbrain, pons and medulla (it is responsible for controlling the flow of information to and from the brain)
- Brodmann's areas: they are specific numbered areas of the brain typically associated with discrete functions (e.g. the motor speech areas = 44, 45; primary motor area = 4; primary sensory areas = 1, 2, 3)

The nervous system is divided into the central nervous system and the peripheral nervous system.

- The central nervous system consists of the brain and spinal cord.
- The peripheral nervous system consists of the autonomic nervous system and the somatic nervous system. The autonomic nervous system has two parts: the sympathetic nervous system and the parasympathetic nervous system. The somatic nervous system also has two parts: the sensory system and the motor system. This organization of the nervous system is depicted in Fig. 65.1 and each of the divisions of this system will be considered in greater detail in this chapter and in subsequent chapters.

GENERAL FEATURES OF THE BRAIN

It is beyond the scope of this book to discuss in detail the function of the different parts of the brain. However, an overview of the organization and function of the brain is provided.

The brain in an adult weighs approximately 1500 g and is protected by the bony skull. The surface of the brain is not smooth but has many folds as a result of which there are grooves called sulci (singular = sulcus) and elevations called gyri (singular = gyrus). The reason that the brain is thrown into folds is that it increases the surface area and therefore more neurons can be packed into a limited space.

The brain continues down into the vertebral column as the spinal cord. The spinal cord will be discussed in a later chapter.

The three broad divisions of the brain are as follows (these divisions are depicted in Fig. 65.2):

Forebrain: cerebrum, some subcortical structures including the thalamus and hypothalamus.

Midbrain: a small central part of the brainstem which is involved in vision, hearing and arousal, among other functions.

Hindbrain: cerebellum, pons and medulla.

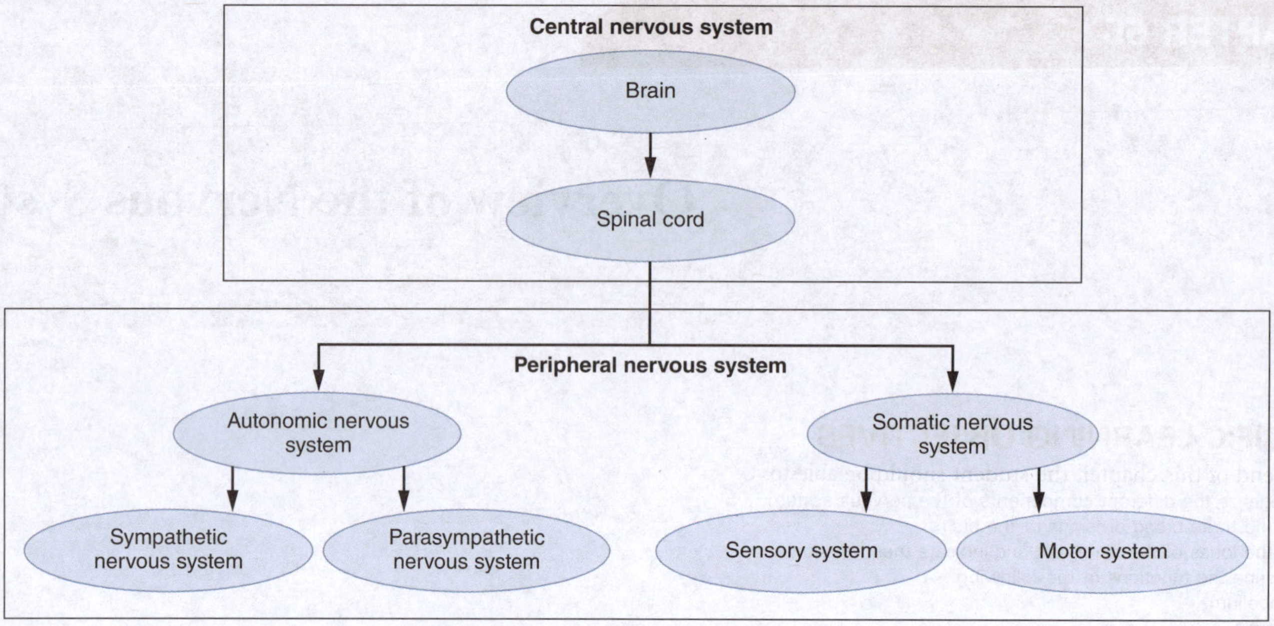

FIG. 65.1 Organization of the nervous system.

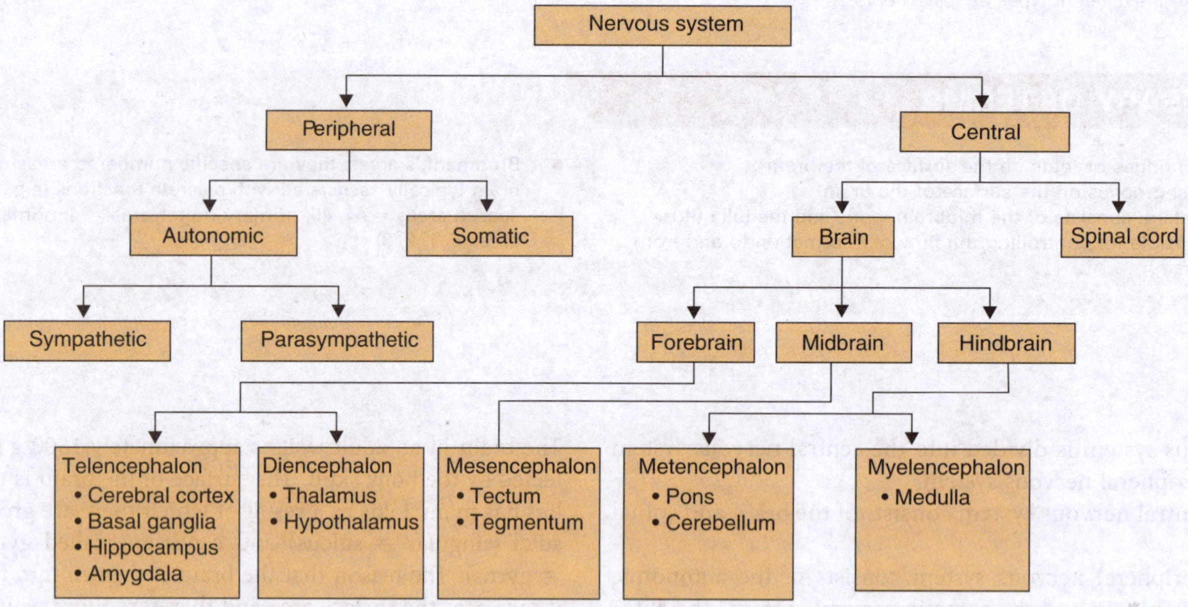

FIG. 65.2 A schematic representation of the parts of the nervous system.

Coverings of the Brain and Cerebrospinal Fluid

The brain is covered with three membranes called the meninges; these are the dura mater, the arachnoid mater and the pia mater. The space between the arachnoid mater and the pia mater is called the subarachnoid space and this space contains a fluid called the cerebrospinal fluid (CSF). The CSF:

1. Protects the brain from external trauma.
2. Provides nutrients to the brain.
3. Removes waste products from the brain.
4. Contains various molecules which can affect brain function.

THE FOREBRAIN

The cerebrum is divided into four distinct lobes called the

1. Frontal lobe
2. Parietal lobe
3. Temporal lobe
4. Occipital lobe

The cerebrum is divided into two halves, the left and right cerebral hemispheres, each with the four lobes listed previously. The two halves are joined together in the middle by the corpus callosum. This connection allows the two halves of the brain to communicate with each other. While the left and the right hemispheres of the brain look very similar, there are, in fact, some differences in the way they function.

The brainstem is further divided into the midbrain, the pons and the medulla.

THE CEREBRAL LOBES AND THEIR FUNCTION

It is important to know the functions of the different parts of the brain because these can be affected if there is damage to that part of the brain, as, for instance, with a tumour or following trauma. Fig. 65.3 indicates the four lobes of the cerebrum.

Frontal Lobe

The frontal lobe has many 'higher level' functions. These include the following:

1. Control of emotions and behaviour.
2. Intelligence and abstract thinking.
3. Speech (through a specific area called Broca's area).
4. Movement of the body: The frontal area has a part called the 'motor cortex' in which all parts of the body are represented and which is primarily responsible for body movement. This motor function of the brain is discussed in Chapter 70.

Parietal Lobe

The parietal lobe is mainly involved in processing and integrating sensory information. This involves, among other things, the following:

1. Recognition of the form (shape), texture (feel) and other sensory characteristics of common objects (this is called stereognosis).
2. Localization of where a stimulus is felt in the body (sensory localization).
3. The ability to recognize two stimuli as distinct. For instance, if we separate the points of a blunt divider in a geometry box and place them on the skin surface, we will find that we can tell the two points as being distinct from each other when they are fairly close to each other in the hands but that they need to be separated much more in order to recognize them as distinct over the back. This phenomenon is called two-point discrimination.

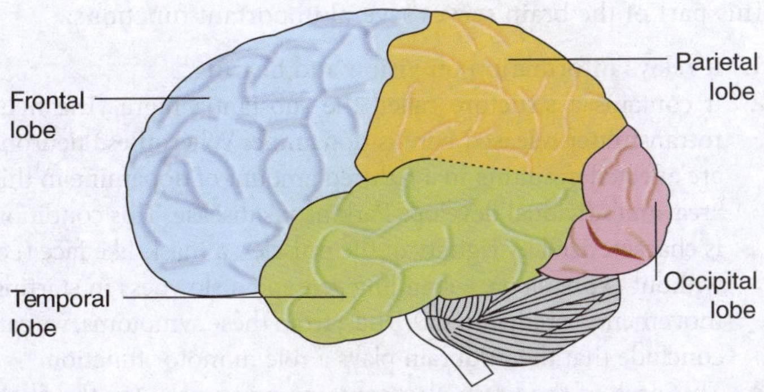

FIG. 65.3 The cerebral cortex indicating the four cerebral lobes.

Temporal Lobe

The temporal lobe has a variety of functions:

1. It is involved with auditory (sound) processing.
2. It is involved in memory through a specific area called the hippocampus.
3. It has many structures which are involved in behaviour and emotions.

Occipital Lobe

The occipital lobe is located towards the back of the head and helps process the information that we see (i.e. vision).

Sensory and motor functions of the nervous system are addressed in greater detail in Chapters 69 and 70, respectively.

HYPOTHALAMUS

The location of the hypothalamus is best appreciated in a midline section of the brain (sagittal section; Fig. 65.4) and is below the thalamus, a structure that we will refer to in Chapter 69 on sensation and its transmission to the brain. The location of the hypothalamus can, in fact, be understood from its name (hypo = beneath or below, therefore below the thalamus). The hypothalamus is made up of many neurons, the nuclei of which are arranged in clusters. The functions of the hypothalamus are carried out by these different nuclei. Most of the brain is protected from changes in the circulating levels of various chemicals in the blood by what is called the 'blood–brain barrier'. This barrier is due to modifications in blood vessels in the brain (such as 'tight junctions') which make it more difficult for harmful chemicals and germs to reach the nerve cells of the brain. Thus, while the blood–brain barrier protects the brain, it also limits the ability of the brain to 'sense' signals in the blood. In order to overcome this problem, the blood–brain barrier is broken down in certain parts of the brain so that the brain can get exposed to circulating signals in the blood and respond to them. One of the locations where this happens is the hypothalamus and we shall see later in this chapter how this is important for some functions of the hypothalamus.

1. ***Temperature regulation***: The hypothalamus has two centres which take part in temperature regulation:
   a. Heat loss centre is located in the anterior hypothalamus and responds to an increase in body temperature. Stimulation of the heat loss centre results in a loss of heat by sweating, vasodilation and panting (in animals).
   b. Heat maintenance centre is located in the posterior hypothalamus and responds to a decrease in body temperature. Stimulation of this centre results in maintenance of body temperature by shivering, vasoconstriction and increased metabolism.
2. ***Endocrine function:*** The hypothalamus has two distinct endocrine functions:
   a. It synthesizes hormones (antidiuretic hormone and oxytocin) which are then transported and released from the posterior pituitary.

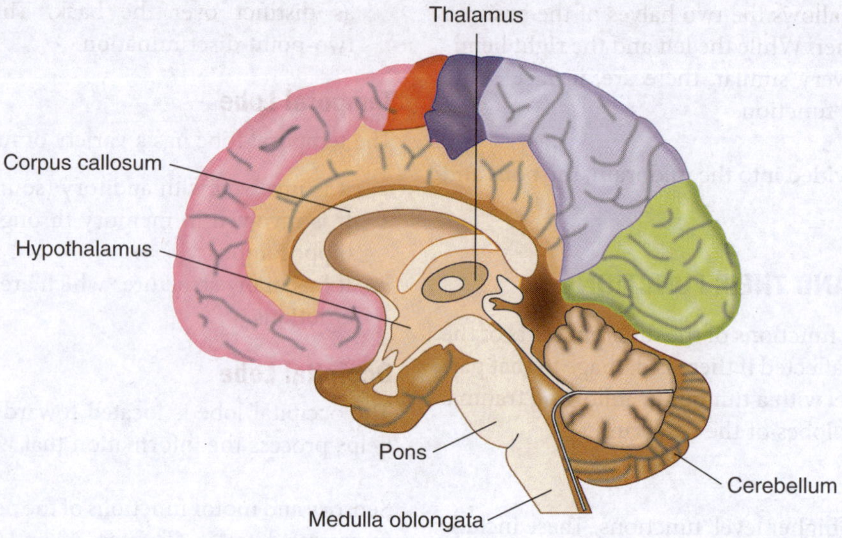

FIG. 65.4 A cut section of the brain.

b. It produces specific releasing and inhibitory factors which control the anterior pituitary gland. Among these are thyrotropin-releasing hormone (TRH), corticotropin-releasing hormone (CRH), gonadotropin-releasing hormone (GnRH), growth hormone–inhibiting hormone (GHIH) and prolactin-inhibiting factor (PIF).

3. ***Feeding and satiety:***
   a. Feeding: The lateral hypothalamus is associated with hunger and promotes feeding and is thus called the feeding centre.
   b. Satiety (a sense of fullness as occurs after eating a meal): The ventromedial hypothalamus, if stimulated, decreases the desire for food and is hence called the satiety centre.
4. ***Control of circadian rhythms***: Many of our body functions or parameters work in cycles of approximately 24 hours. These cycles are referred to as circadian rhythms (circa = around; diem = day). Our body temperature is relatively constant at 37°C, but there are small changes in body temperature throughout the day, with the temperature falling in the night and then rising in the morning to reach a peak. This pattern differs from individual to individual. There are some individuals who have an early rise in body temperature and tend to be more alert early in the morning than other individuals who have a later rise in temperature. Various biochemical and physiological parameters in our body show cyclical changes during the day. This cyclical pattern of our various activities in our body is controlled by a 'pacemaker' in the hypothalamus called the suprachiasmatic nucleus.
5. ***Control of autonomic function***: A famous physiologist named Sherrington referred to the hypothalamus as the 'head ganglion of the autonomic nervous system.' This is because the hypothalamus controls several 'automatic' activities of the body which are regulated by the autonomic nervous system (Chapter 71). Thus, the hypothalamus can influence functions of the heart (e.g. heart rate) and blood vessels (blood pressure), among others.
6. ***Control of thirst and water balance***: When a person has lost fluids, particularly water, and is in a dehydrated state, the concentration of electrolytes in fluids, particularly blood, is increased. This increase in the electrolyte concentration is sensed by the hypothalamus because the blood–brain barrier is broken down in this location. The response is a sensation of thirst as a result of which the person drinks more water. Apart from the thirst mechanism, the hypothalamus also regulates water balance by controlling the amount of urine that is excreted. This happens through the action of a hormone called antidiuretic hormone which is synthesized in the hypothalamus but released from the posterior pituitary gland.

Thalamus:

The thalamus is situated above the hypothalamus and has some specific functions:

1. it is the primary sensory relay station. All sensations with the exception of smell (olfaction) pass through the thalamus before being sent to the cortex.
2. It has connections with the basal ganglia (which are involved in the control of movement) and therefore has motor function.
3. It may be a source of some of the electrical waves that we record in an EEG (electroencephalogram).

THE MIDBRAIN

This part of the brain serves several important functions:

1. It relays information on vision and hearing.
2. It contains a structure called the substantia nigra. The neurotransmitter released here is dopamine. When these neurons are affected, resulting in a reduced amount of dopamine in this area, an individual develops Parkinson's disease. This condition is characterized by rigidity of the muscles, a mask-like face (i.e. without expression), a shuffling gait and a slowness in starting movements (bradykinesia). Thus, from these symptoms, we can conclude that the midbrain plays a role in motor function.
3. This area of the brain also contains nerve cells (in the periaqueductal grey) which help to modify pain sensation. This

explains partly why we sometimes do not feel severe pain even when we have major injuries.

4. There are nerves which originate in the brain called cranial nerves. Of the 12 cranial nerves, 2 originate in the midbrain. The cranial nerves are numbered in the Roman numerals from I to XII. Cranial nerves III (oculomotor) and IV (trochlear) originate from the midbrain and help to control the movements of the eye.

THE HINDBRAIN

The Cerebellum

The cerebellum is located beneath the cerebral hemispheres at the bottom and the back of the brain. It has many functions, some of which are given as follows:

1. Coordination of muscle function
2. Maintenance of balance and posture
3. Motor learning (this is important for learned motor activities, e.g. hitting a moving cricket ball with a bat)
4. Planning, timing and fine-tuning of movements

Pons

The pons lies between the midbrain (above) and the medulla (below). It is involved in a large number of functions:

1. It is the origin of 4 of the 12 cranial nerves. These include (1) trigeminal nerve (cranial nerve V), (2) abducens nerve (cranial nerve VI), (3) facial nerve (cranial nerve VII) and (4) vestibular–cochlear nerve (cranial nerve VIII). These cranial nerves help to control the muscles of the face during chewing, swallowing and facial expression; transmit sensations from the face and mouth; regulate specific eye movements and help with hearing and the maintenance of posture and equilibrium during movement, among others.
2. It helps control sleep and respiration and also relays information from the forebrain to the cerebellum.

Medulla

The medulla oblongata lies below the pons and continues as the spinal cord emerging out of the skull through an opening called the foramen magnum.

The medulla controls a lot of our autonomic activities, that is the automatic activities that we are normally not aware of. These include the beating of the heart, breathing, swallowing, sneezing, vomiting and coughing. The medulla also controls the blood pressure in our arteries which is important to ensure adequate flow of blood.

THE SPINAL CORD

The spinal cord is protected within the vertebral column and extends from the foramen magnum where it is continuous with the medulla of the brain to the level of the first or second lumbar vertebrae. The length of the spinal cord in an adult is variable depending on the height of the individual and the spinal cord is approximately 40–50 cm long and 1–1.5 cm in diameter. There are 31 **pairs** of spinal nerves: these include 8 cervical nerves, 12 thoracic nerves, 5 lumbar nerve, 5 sacral nerves and 1 coccygeal nerve. Below the L1 vertebra, the spinal cord breaks up into a bundle of nerves called the cauda equina. Fig. 65.5 depicts the broad arrangement of the spinal nerves and some of their functions. The list of functions is not exhaustive but the figure illustrates that damage of the spinal cord at various levels will result in the loss of specific functions.

Each spinal nerve is a mixed nerve which has sensory, motor and autonomic components. The sensory component enters the spinal cord through the dorsal root while the motor nerve originates in cell bodies located in the ventral horn of the spinal cord. These relationships are depicted in Fig. 65.6.

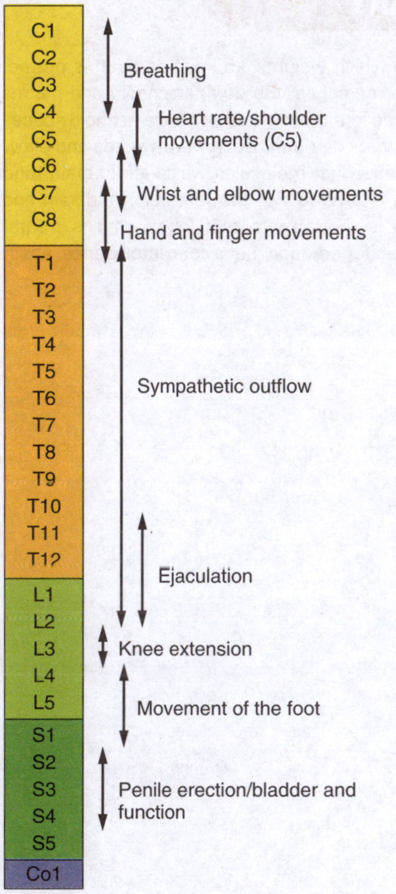

FIG. 65.5 Arrangement and broad functions of the spinal nerves.

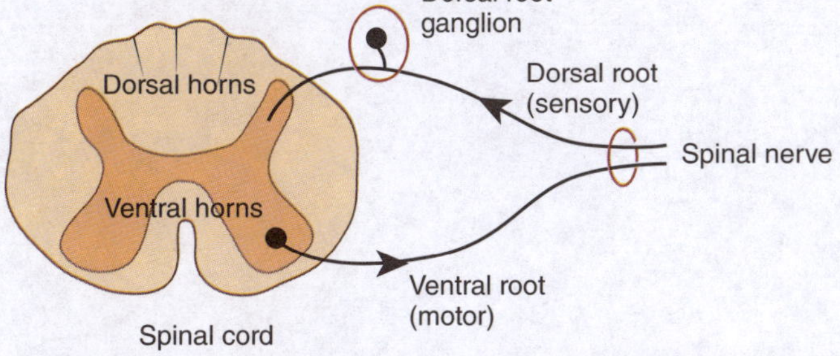

FIG. 65.6 The relationship of the spinal nerve and spinal cord.

APPLICATIONS FOR NURSING

Three common conditions affecting the brain which nurses will have to deal with are (1) strokes (in which there is a block or bleed from a cerebral blood vessel), (2) brain injury and (3) brain tumours. In each of these conditions, the level of nursing care required may be substantial depending on the nature and extent of the lesion. Apart from the intensive monitoring and care of the patient, the nurse needs to be aware that this is an extremely testing time for the patient's family who may need to deal with the patient's altered level of consciousness, the limitation of their function including the ability to comprehend and communicate and the difficulty that the medical team may have with providing clear answers with regard to prognosis and course of recovery.

SUMMARY

- The brain which weights 1.5 kg in an adult is protected by the skull and three meninges: the dura, arachnoid and pia mater. CSF which is contained in the ventricles and subarachnoid space helps to protect the brain, provide nutrition, remove wastes and allow for the circulation of messenger molecules which affect brain function.
- The brain is divided into the forebrain, midbrain and hindbrain. The cerebrum is divided into four lobes, that is frontal lobe which is responsible for emotion, behaviour, intelligence, abstract thinking and control of movement of the body and speech; parietal lobe which is responsible for processing of sensory information; occipital lobe which controls vision; and temporal lobe which is important for hearing and memory, among others.
- The two cerebral hemispheres are joined together by the corpus callosum. The left and right hemispheres control movement on the opposite sides of the body.
- The hypothalamus has many functions including the control of hormone function, emotions, feeding and satiety, body temperature, water balance, circadian rhythms and autonomic function.
- The thalamus is the main sensory relay station of the brain.
- The cerebellum is important for coordination of muscle function, equilibrium and posture and planning and fine-tuning of movements.
- The midbrain, pons and medulla comprise the brainstem and control the flow of information to and from the brain.
- There are 31 pairs of spinal nerves: 8 cervical pairs, 12 thoracic pairs, 5 lumbar pairs, 5 sacral pairs and 1 coccygeal pair.

CHAPTER REVIEW QUESTIONS

1. List the cerebral lobes and list the functions of each lobe.
2. What are the functions of the hypothalamus?
3. What are the meninges of the brain? What is the function of CSF?
4. List the types of spinal nerves.

CHAPTER 66

Physiology of the Neuron and of Supporting Cells of the Nervous System

SPECIFIC LEARNING OBJECTIVES

At the end of this chapter, the student should be able to:

- Draw and label a typical neuron.
- List the different types of neurons.
- Describe the different types of 'synapse'.
- List the supporting cells of the peripheral and central nervous system.
- Describe the functions of the supporting cells of the peripheral and central nervous system.

GLOSSARY OF TERMS

- **Myelination:** the process of the formation of a myelin sheath around nerves (this allows nerves to transmit nerve impulses faster)
- **Blood–brain barrier:** a barrier that separates the circulating blood from the extracellular fluid of the brain (it is primarily due to the endothelial lining of the blood vessels which have tight junctions, among other features; it is also partly contributed to by astrocytes which form a second layer around the endothelium)

STRUCTURE OF A NEURON

The structural and functional unit of the nervous system is a cell called the neuron. The structure of the neuron is illustrated in Fig. 66.1. The neuron consists essentially of three parts:

1. the cell body, otherwise called the soma, which contains the nucleus and a large number of cell organelles including the rough endoplasmic reticulum (called the Nissl's bodies);
2. a single axon which carries impulse away from the cell body; and
3. multiple branching dendrites which extend from the body and which receive impulses from other cells.

Nerve axons are filled with the axoplasm which transports substances from the soma to the axon terminal and from the axon terminal towards the cell body. Axons may be myelinated or unmyelinated. The myelin sheath that covers the myelinated axon is formed by the Schwann's cells. At periodic intervals, there is a break in this myelin sheet. These are the nodes of Ranvier. We will discuss the advantages of the myelin covering in Chapter 67.

TYPES OF NERVES

Nerves may be classified based on their structure, their function and their location, among others.

Thus, nerves may (among many classifications) be:

1. Based on their location:
   a. Central (confined to the brain and spinal cord)
   b. Peripheral
2. Based on their function:
   a. Motor: carrying impulses to muscle
   b. Sensory: carrying impulses from receptors in the periphery (these nerves are sometimes called *afferent* nerves)
   c. Autonomic: related to the sympathetic or parasympathetic nervous system
   d. Mixed
3. Based on their structure:
   a. Myelinated: based on size of the nerve are further classified as A, B and C
   b. Unmyelinated

SYNAPSE

Structure of a synapse:

A synapse is a junction between two nerves. However, nerves can also form junctions with muscle cells and glands. A synapse has essentially the same components as the neuromuscular junction described in Chapter 52. The main parts of a synapse are as follows:

1. The presynaptic area
2. The synaptic cleft
3. The postsynaptic membrane

The structure of a synapse is illustrated in Fig. 66.2.

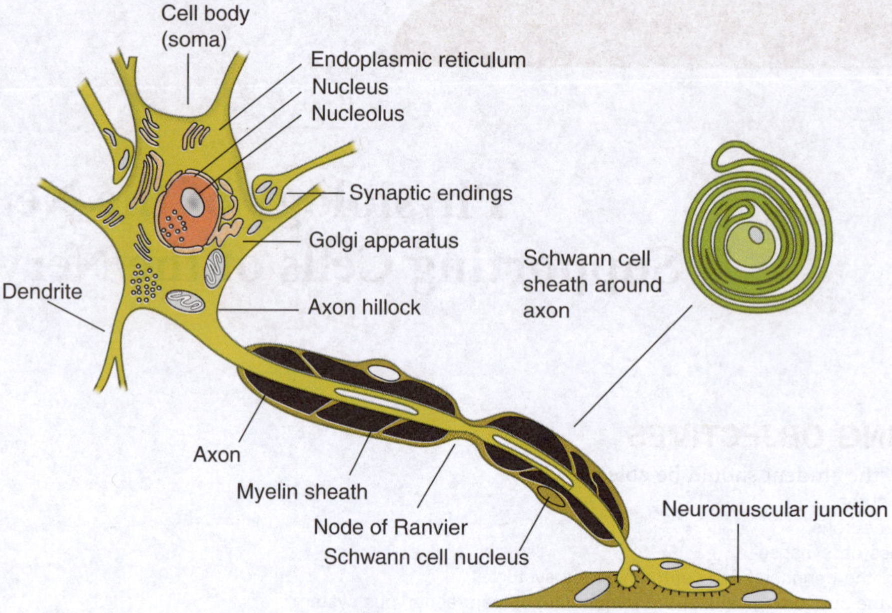

FIG. 66.1 Structure of a typical neuron.

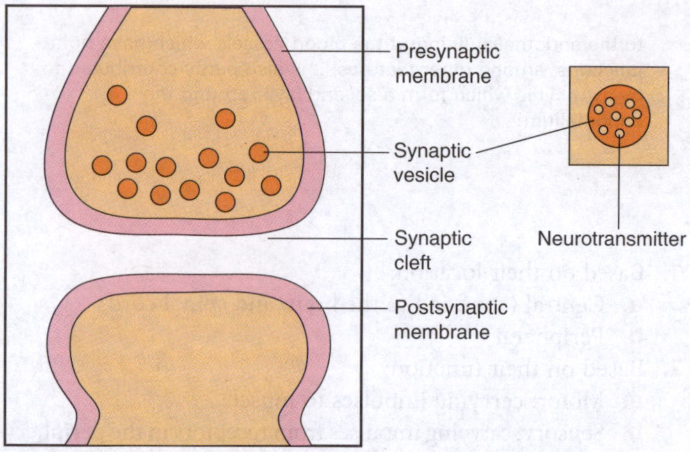

FIG. 66.2 Structure of a synapse.

Neurotransmitters – the chemical messengers of neurons:

Synapses transmit information from one cell to another using a chemical messenger called a neurotransmitter. The neurotransmitter is contained in vesicles of the axon terminal of one neuron. When released by exocytosis, the neurotransmitter enters the synaptic cleft and then binds to its receptor on the postsynaptic membrane. There are many different neurotransmitters including norepinephrine, acetylcholine, glycine and dopamine, among others.

Classification of synapses:

Based on the type of junction, that is which part of the nerves forms the synapse (axon, soma or dendrite), synapses can be classified as follows:

1. Axodendritic
2. Axosomatic
3. Axoaxonic
4. Somatodendritic
5. Dendrodendritic
6. Somatosomatic

SUPPORTING CELLS OF THE CENTRAL NERVOUS SYSTEM

The human brain has about 100 billion neurons or nerve cells. However, even more numerous than the neurons are the 'supporting' cells, which are discussed in this chapter.

The nervous system is divided into two broad parts. The central nervous system consists of the brain and the spinal cord, while the peripheral nervous system consists of structures of the nervous system other than the brain and spinal cord.

TYPES OF GLIAL CELLS

Peripheral nervous system:

The major supporting cell of the peripheral nervous system is the Schwann's cell. The Schwann's cell produces the myelin sheath of myelinated nerves. Fig. 66.3 depicts the Schwann's cell in relation to the neuron.

Although the Schwann's cell has a major role in forming the myelin sheath of the neuron, it also has other important roles. When a neuron is damaged, the Schwann's cell changes its characteristics and becomes demyelinating which is opposite that of its normal role. In this state, the Schwann's cell helps to remove the cell debris (remains/fragments) by phagocytosis and also release certain factors which help in nerve regeneration. Other Schwann's cells which are not myelinating help to maintain the nerve cells and are important in their survival.

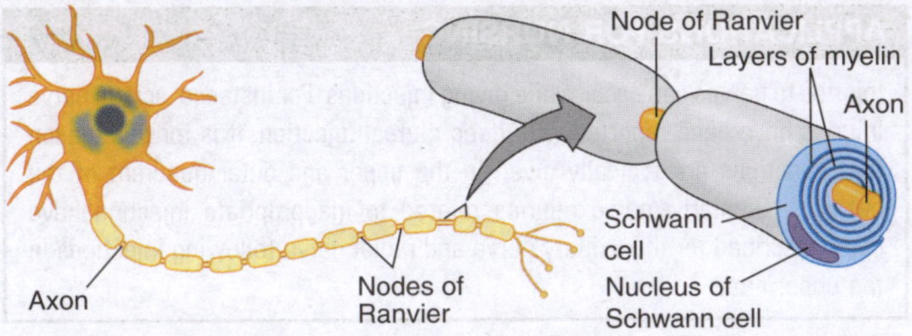

FIG. 66.3 The relationship between the Schwann's cell and the neuron.

Thus, the functions of the various types of Schwann cells can be summarized as follows:

1. Myelination
2. Promotion of nerve regeneration
3. Neuron maintenance and survival

Central nervous system:

In the central nervous system, there are several supporting cells which are called glial cells. These can be divided into two broad categories based on the size of the cell. These are indicated as follows:

1. Microglia (small cells)
2. Macroglia (larger cells):
    a. Astrocytes
    b. Oligodendrocytes

The basic structure of the various glial cells is depicted in Fig. 66.4.

In addition to the cells listed previously, ependymal cells are also considered to be glial cells. These are cells which line the ventricles of the brain and the central canal of the spinal cord which contains the cerebrospinal fluid. The major ventricles in the brain are the two lateral ventricles, the third and fourth ventricles which are depicted in Fig. 66.5.

The cerebrospinal fluid which bathes the brain helps to cushion the brain against injury or trauma, provides nutrients to the brain and removes wastes, among other functions. The ependymal cells which line the ventricles play an important role in the production and regulation of cerebrospinal fluid.

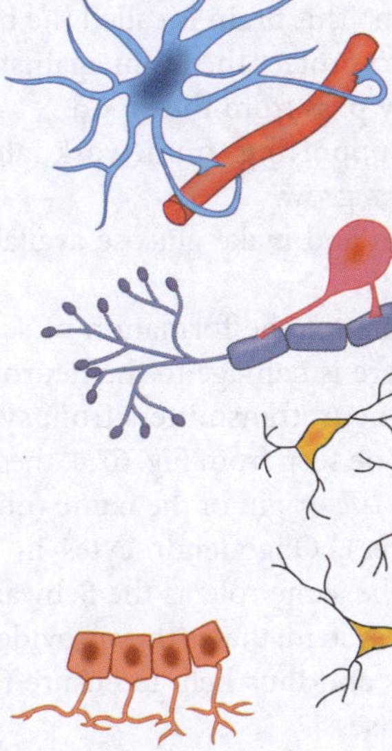

FIG. 66.4 The different glial cells of the central nervous system.

FUNCTIONS OF GLIAL CELLS

The glial cells serve several broad functions:

1. As supporting cells, they keep the neurons in place.
2. They 'insulate' neurons from one another. This is important to ensure that nerve impulses travel along defined paths.
3. They are phagocytic and help to destroy microorganisms and clear debris from damaged cells.

Each of the glial cells serves specific functions and these are outlined as follows:

Microglia: These are mobile cells (i.e. they move in the central nervous system). Their primary function is phagocytosis and they also help in the immune response to harmful substances.

Astrocytes: As the name suggests, these cells are 'star' shaped (astral = related to the stars). The astrocytes serve many functions, some of which are listed as follows:

1. Astrocytes are closely associated with blood vessels. This helps them to create, along with special features of the

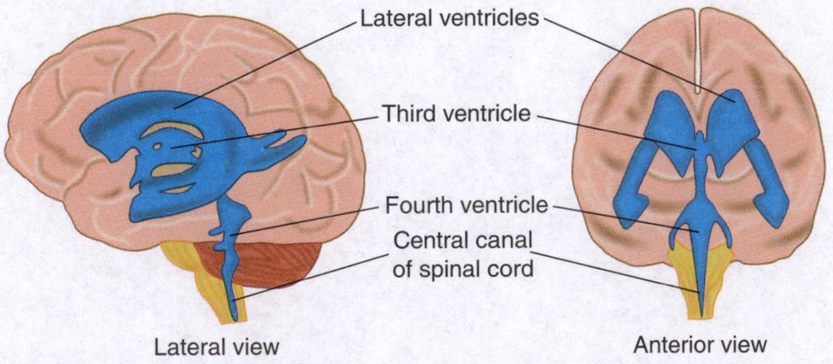

FIG. 66.5 The ventricles of the brain which contain cerebrospinal fluid.

blood vessel, a barrier between the blood in the blood vessel and the brain. This brain is called the blood–brain barrier and helps to protect the brain against toxins and infections that may pass from the blood.

2. They form the supporting framework along which developing neurons grow.
3. They store glycogen and make glucose available to adjacent neurons.
4. They are responsible for the formation of scar tissue in the brain when there is damage to the neurons.
5. They help to clear neurotransmitters from synapses.

Oligodendrocytes: As can be seen from Fig. 67.4, these cells have some branches. This is the origin of the name (oligos = few/scanty; dendron = tree). Oligodendrocytes in the central nervous system fulfil the same role as the Schwann's cells in the peripheral nervous system, that is they provide the myelin sheath for the neurons and thus help to ensure faster transmission of nerve impulses.

CLINICAL BOX

Disorders of Glial Cells

There was a time when glial cells were considered merely to be supporting cells with no major importance. In fact, a large number of clinical disorders have been associated with dysfunction of the glial cells. These include, among others, the following:

1. Alzheimer's disease: In this condition, people (usually the elderly) suffer from progressive memory loss and other intellectual deficits.
2. Psychiatric diseases: These illnesses have now been shown to be associated, in part, with altered levels of neurotransmitters in the brain. Glial cells, particularly astrocytes, play an important role in the removal of neurotransmitters from the synapse and may contribute to these illnesses.
3. Cancers of the brain: The majority of primary (arising from the brain itself) brain tumours are gliomas or tumours of glial cells. They can be further classified based on the specific glial cell from which they originate.
4. Multiple sclerosis: In this condition, neurons in the brain lose their myelin sheath either because of a destruction of the myelin by immune cells or by the inability of glial cells (oligodendrocytes) to produce myelin effectively. As a result, the patient may experience sudden loss of function due to the damage of specific nerves.

APPLICATIONS FOR NURSING

Injuries to nerves can occur while giving injections. For instance, sciatic nerve injuries have been reported with deep gluteal injection. It is for this reason that injections are typically given in the upper and outer quadrant of the buttocks. Similarly, nerve injuries related to inappropriate injection have been described for the axillary nerve and radial nerve following injections in the upper arm.

SUMMARY

- The neuron (nerve cell) is the structural and functional unit of the nervous system and consists of a cell body (soma), a single axon and multiple dendrites.
- A synapse is a junction between two nerves. It consists of three parts: a presynaptic part, the synaptic cleft and the postsynaptic membrane.
- Glial cells are important supporting cells of the nervous system. In the central nervous system, they include microglia, astrocytes, oligodendrocytes and ependymal cells.
- Broad functions of glial cells include providing support for neurons, immune function and removal of cell debris, insulation of neurons, contribution to the blood–brain barrier and regulation of neurotransmitter concentrations, among others.
- Glial cells are associated with a variety of clinical conditions including Alzheimer's disease, psychiatric illnesses, brain tumours and multiple sclerosis.

CHAPTER REVIEW QUESTIONS

1. Draw a diagram of a neuron and label its parts.
2. What are neurotransmitters? What is their function? List some common neurotransmitters.
3. What are the functions of the glial cells?

CHAPTER 67

Membrane Potentials and the Nerve Impulse

SPECIFIC LEARNING OBJECTIVES

At the end of this chapter, the student should be able to:

- Define stimulus. List different kinds of stimuli.
- Explain the meaning of resting membrane potential.
- Briefly describe the ionic basis of resting membrane in nerve.
- Differentiate between a threshold and a subthreshold stimulus.
- Define the terms depolarization and repolarization.
- Describe the characteristics of a 'local response'.
- Draw an action potential and explain its ionic basis.
- State the 'all-or-none' law.
- Distinguish between an action potential and a local response.
- Define 'refractory period'.
- Explain how an impulse travels along a nerve and list the factors that influence it.

GLOSSARY OF TERMS

- **Stimulus:** a change in the environment that elicits a response
- **Resting membrane potential:** the potential of the cell membrane at rest, that is in its quiescent or unstimulated state
- **Gibbs–Donnan effect:** the ability of nondiffusible ions to affect the distribution of the diffusible ions across a cell membrane
- **Depolarization:** the conversion of the resting membrane potential from a negative to a less negative or positive potential
- **Repolarization:** the return of the cell membrane potential back to its resting state, that is from a more positive potential to the resting membrane potential
- **Action potential:** the cell membrane potential that develops in response to a threshold or suprathreshold stimulus
- **Local response:** the cell membrane potential that develops in response to a subthreshold stimulus
- **Nerve impulse:** the propagation of the action potential along a nerve membrane
- **All-or-none law:** when threshold or suprathreshold stimuli are applied to a nerve membrane, they elicit an action potential of the same amplitude
- **Summation of local responses:** subthreshold stimuli applied together close to each other or in quick succession at the same point of the membrane result in a higher cell membrane potential (when this achieves a critical firing level, an action potential will be elicited)
- **Refractory period:** the period of the action potential during which a second stimulus elicits no response
- **Synapse:** a junction between two nerves where information is transmitted through a neurotransmitter released into the synaptic cleft
- **Saltatory conduction:** conduction of the nerve impulse from one node of Ranvier to the next node of Ranvier (this 'jumping' ensures faster conduction)

STIMULUS

A living cell is excitable, that is it has the ability to respond to a stimulus. A stimulus is a change in the environment that elicits a response and can take on different forms. For instance, a stimulus may be mechanical, thermal, chemical or electrical. Mechanical stimuli include those like touch and pressure and thermal stimuli include warmth and cold. Changes in the pH, pCO_2 and pO_2 which regulate respiration are examples of chemical stimuli. In experimental situations, physiologists prefer to use electrical stimuli because they can be controlled well in terms of strength and duration and represent the natural stimulus of many cells.

THE RESTING MEMBRANE POTENTIAL

If a tiny electrode is placed just inside a cell, it records a membrane potential. This is because the cell membrane at rest, that is in the quiescent or unstimulated state, is always negative on the inside of the cell membrane with respect to the outside (Fig. 67.1). The potential of the cell membrane at rest is called

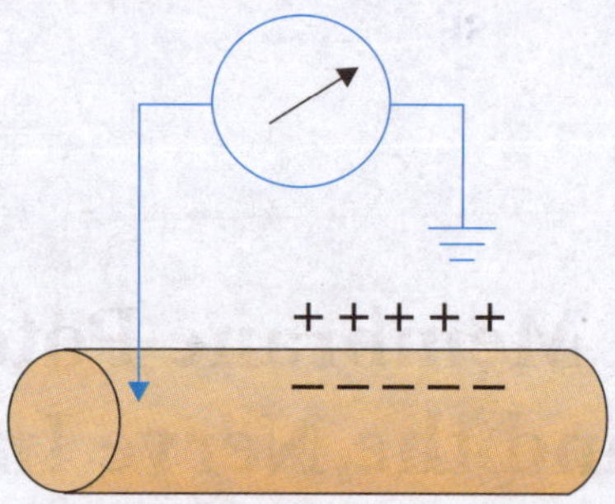

FIG. 67.1 The negative nature of resting membrane potential.

the resting membrane potential. Different cells have different resting membrane potentials.

Nernst's Potential

So, how does the resting membrane potential come about? In order to discuss this, let us take the example of the nerve cell or neuron. At rest, the nerve cell has a membrane potential of about −90 mV. The potential of a cell is always stated with respect to the inside of the cell membrane. The resting membrane potential occurs because the cell membrane has a variable permeability to different ions. Ions will tend to move along their concentration gradient. The major ions outside the cell, that is in the extracellular fluid, are Na^+ and Cl^-. The major ions inside the cell (i.e. intracellularly) are K^+ and protein anions.

If a cell membrane is permeable to one ion species only, then that ion species will tend to move along its concentration gradient, that is from high concentration to low concentration. Thus, sodium ions will tend to move from outside of the cell into the cell, while potassium ions will move from inside of the cell outwards. If we take the example of K^+ ions, while these ions move from inside the cell outwards, they leave the inside of the cell membrane relatively negative (because positive charges are leaving the inside of the cell). This movement will continue for some time, until the build-up of positive charge (electrical gradient) through the movement of potassium ions outside the cell prevents further movement of positive ions from inside the cell to the outside. The potential at which there is no net movement of the ion is called the Nernst's potential of the ion. The Nernst's potential for potassium is approximately −90 mV (because the inside of the cell membrane becomes more negative with the movement of potassium).

In contrast, if the cell membrane is permeable to only sodium, then sodium ions will move from the outside of the cell inwards, making the inside of the cell membrane more positive. Like for potassium, this movement of sodium ions will continue until the build-up of positive (sodium) ions inside the cell membrane (electrical gradient) prevents the further movement of sodium from outside. This potential at which there is no net movement of sodium ions is called the Nernst's potential of sodium. The Nernst's potential of sodium is approximately +60 mV (because the inside of the cell membrane becomes more positive with the movement of sodium ions into the cell). In a like manner, different ions have their own Nernst's potentials.

GENESIS OF THE RESTING MEMBRANE POTENTIAL

The cell membrane is permeable to many different ions, although the extent to which the cell membrane is permeable to different ions varies. For example, the nerve cell is highly permeable to potassium ions at rest, while it is less permeable to sodium ions. In fact, the permeability of the membrane to potassium is 100 times greater at rest compared to the permeability of sodium!

How does this differential permeability matter? In order to understand this, let us take each ion separately, using the example of the nerve cell. Since potassium ions are the most permeable, potassium ions move from inside to the outside of the cell and try to achieve their Nernst's potential of −90 mV. If potassium was indeed the only ion moving across the membrane, they would achieve their Nernst's potential. However, the membrane is also permeable to sodium, but much less so. So when sodium moves across the cell membrane into the cell, it changes the potential created by potassium and makes it less negative – but not by much, since its permeability is very low. Let us say that due to sodium movement, the cell membrane potential now becomes −86 mV rather than −90 mV.

There is another factor that needs to be considered with the resting membrane potential. This is the action of the Na–K-ATPase pump. This pump is present in cells throughout the body. Thus, this pump is present in nerve cells also. The Na–K-ATPase pump transports sodium and potassium against their concentration gradient. Thus, it moves sodium from the inside to the outside of the cell and potassium from the outside to the inside of the cell. However, the pump moves unequal numbers of sodium and potassium ions; three ions of sodium are moved out of the cell for every two ions of potassium that move in. Thus, the pump makes the inside of the cell membrane more negative, since it moves more positive ions out of the cell than it moves in. This contribution of the Na–K-ATPase pump is approximately −4 mV. Thus, when we add the contribution of the Na–K-ATPase pump to the movement of K^+ and Na^+ ions due to their own permeability, the cell membrane reverts back to approximately −90 mV.

Thus, in summary, the resting potential of the nerve cell is primarily due to the movement of potassium ions with a minor contribution of the movement of sodium ions and the Na–K-ATPase pump.

So, what about all the other ions that are present inside and outside cells? There are three points to consider:

1. The final potential of the resting membrane is dependent on the concentrations of each ion inside and outside the cell as well as the permeability of each ion across the cell membrane. The resting membrane potential can be calculated for each cell using these parameters in an equation called the Goldman–Hodgkin–Katz equation.
2. There are some ions which are nondiffusible. These include the large protein anions inside the cell. Nondiffusible ions affect the distribution of the diffusible ions. This is called the Gibbs–Donnan effect.
3. If the final resting membrane potential is close to the Nernst's potential of other ions, there will be minimal or no movement of these ions across the cell membrane.

WHAT HAPPENS IF A CELL IS STIMULATED?

Types of stimuli:

A neuron can be stimulated with different strengths of stimulus.

1. When a stimulus is of sufficient strength so that it elicits a biological response, it is called a '**threshold' stimulus**.
2. A stimulus which is below the threshold stimulus intensity is called a '**subthreshold stimulus**'.
3. A stimulus which is greater than the threshold stimulus is called **a 'suprathreshold stimulus**'.

When a neuron is stimulated, there is a change in the permeability of the cell membrane. Sodium ions which are outside the cell enter the cell and the cell membrane becomes less negative. If enough sodium ions enter the cell membrane, the membrane potential may even become positive. The conversion of the resting membrane potential from a negative to a less negative or positive potential is called 'depolarization'. The return of the cell membrane potential back to its resting state, that is from a more positive potential to the resting membrane potential, is called 'repolarization'. This is summarized in Fig. 67.2. Not all stimuli cause depolarization; some may result in the membrane becoming even more negative than its resting potential; this is called hyperpolarization.

Subthreshold stimuli cause small changes in the cell membrane potential. These changes are restricted to the site of the stimulus and are therefore called '**local potentials**'.

In contrast, a threshold stimulus in a neuron elicits a larger membrane potential called an 'action potential' which travels along a nerve and is termed the nerve 'impulse'.

A stimulus can be described in terms of its modality (mechanical, thermal, chemical, etc.) and its strength (subthreshold, threshold, suprathreshold). In Fig. 67.3, the threshold stimulus represents that strength of a stimulus which is associated with a biological response. All stimuli which are below this strength are called subthreshold stimuli, while all stimuli that exceed the threshold stimulus are called suprathreshold stimuli.

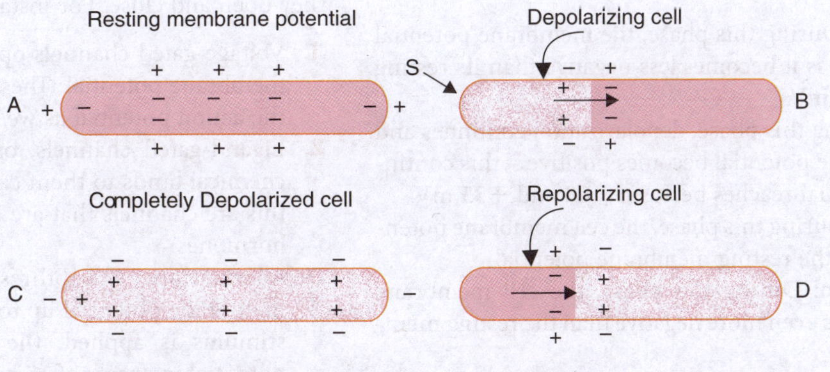

FIG. 67.2 Depolarization and repolarization in a cell.

THE LOCAL RESPONSE

Although subthreshold stimuli do not individually result in a biological response, they do cause changes in the cell membrane potential. These changes are seen at the site of the stimulus and are therefore called local responses. In Fig. 67.3, there are multiple, separate subthreshold stimuli depicted which are labelled 1s, 2s, 3s and 4s. While all of these stimuli are subthreshold, they are not of equal intensity; 4s is greater than 3s, 3s is greater than 2s and 2s is greater than 1s (4s > 3s > 2s > 1s). The change in membrane potential that occurs with these different strengths of subthreshold stimuli varies with the strength of stimulus; thus, the membrane potential change is highest with the 4s stimulus and lowest with the 1s stimulus as depicted in Fig. 67.4.

While each subthreshold stimulus does not result in a biological response, if multiple subthreshold stimuli are applied close to each other or soon after each other, their effect can add up and they can then produce a biological response – a phenomenon known as **summation**. This phenomenon will be discussed later in the chapter.

THE ACTION POTENTIAL

Fig. 67.5 illustrates changes in the membrane potential of a nerve cell as recorded during the depolarization phase of the action

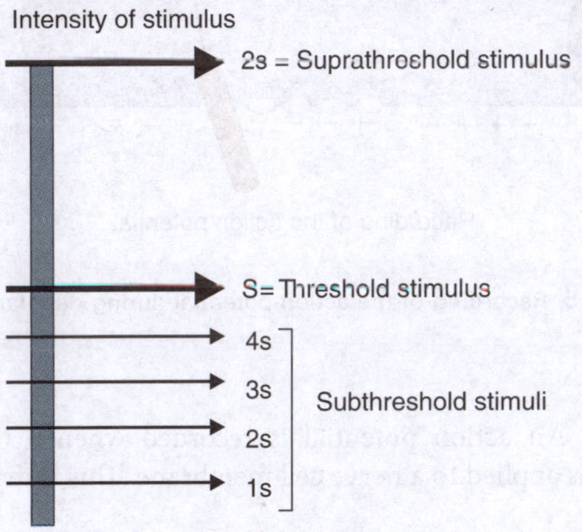

FIG. 67.3 The nature of stimulus based on the intensity of stimulus.

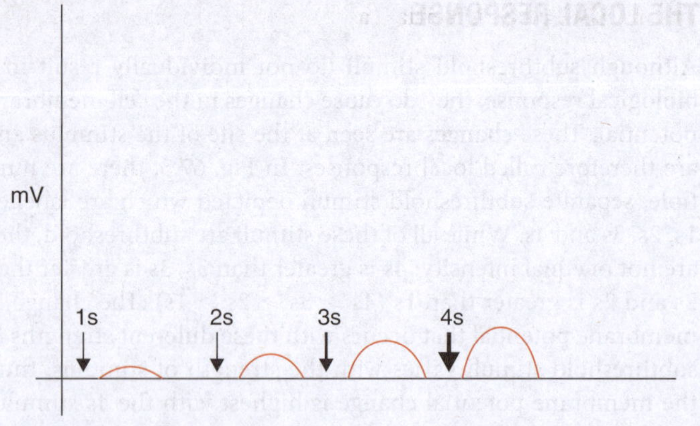

FIG. 67.4 Changes in membrane potential associated with increasing intensity of subthreshold stimulus.

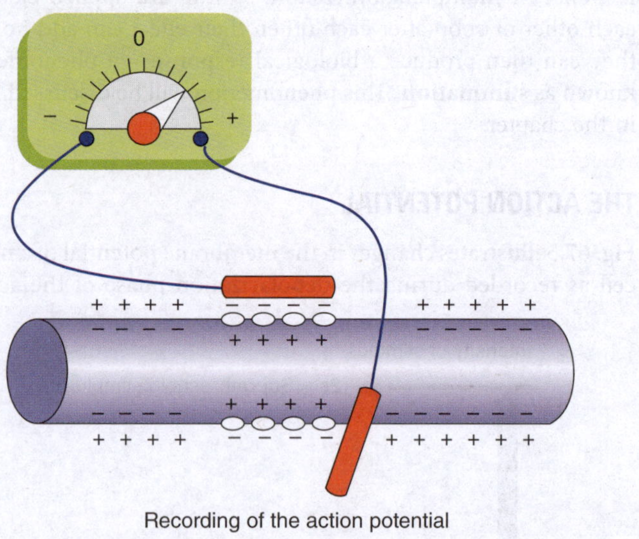

FIG. 67.5 Recording of the action potential during depolarization.

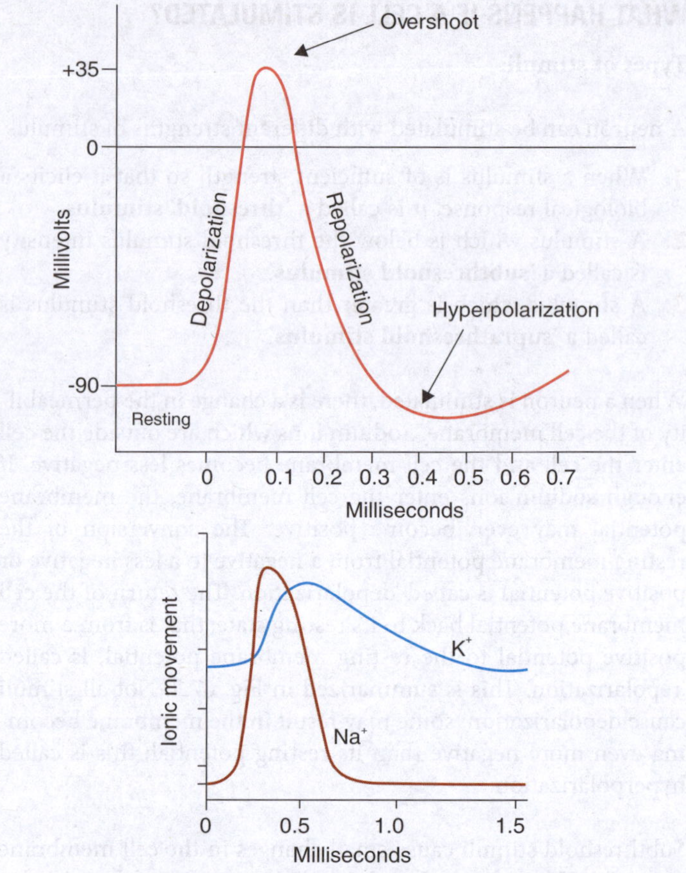

FIG. 67.6 Ionic basis of the action potential.

potential. An action potential is recorded when a threshold stimulus is applied to a nerve cell membrane. This is depicted in Fig. 67.6.

Phases of the Action Potential

Fig. 67.6, which illustrates the time course of the action potential, depicts several phases.

1. Depolarization: During this phase, the membrane potential rises rapidly, that is it becomes less negative than its resting potential of −90 mV.
2. Overshoot: During this phase, depolarization continues and the cell membrane potential becomes positive – this continues till the potential reaches between +20 and +35 mV.
3. Repolarization: During this phase, the cell membrane potential falls towards the resting membrane potential.
4. Hyperpolarization: During this phase, the cell membrane potential becomes even more negative than the resting membrane potential.
5. Return to the resting membrane potential.

Unlike the local response, the action potential is not confined to the place where the stimulus acted. The action potential in fact travels down the cell membrane. This is called propagation of the action potential (the nerve impulse) and is discussed in greater detail in the next chapter.

Major Ionic Events of the Action Potential

The action potential is the result of changes in ionic permeability of the cell membrane. Channels in the cell membrane allow for the transport of various ions including sodium and potassium (as we have discussed with regard to the resting membrane potential). Apart from the fact that different channels help transport different ions, channels can also be classified based on how they open and close. For instance:

1. Voltage-gated channels open when there is a change in the membrane potential. These are important for the genesis of the action potential as we will see later.
2. Ligand-gated channels, on the other hand, open when a chemical binds to them causing them to open. Examples of this are channels that are opened by neurotransmitters and hormones.

Depolarization: A subthreshold stimulus can change the membrane potential up to about 15 mV. When a threshold stimulus is applied, the stimulus alters the membrane potential in excess of 15 mV. This is called the critical firing level, because it is at this potential that special fast voltage-gated Na channels on the cell membrane open. The entry of sodium into the cell causes the cell membrane to become more positive – this is the phase of depolarization of the cell membrane. The cell membrane continues to rise to about 20–35 mV.

Repolarization: The reason that the membrane potential does not rise beyond 20–25 mV is related to two events. The first is that the voltage-gated Na channels begin to close after some time and the permeability of sodium reduces. The second is that the voltage-gated potassium channels begin to open; this increase in potassium permeability and the movement of positive ions from the inside of the cell to the outside results in the fall of the membrane potential to its resting state – the phase of repolarization.

Hyperpolarization: For some period of time, the cell membrane then dips below the resting membrane potential. This is called hyperpolarization. This phase is due to the continued movement of potassium out of the cell.

During all these events, the Na–K-ATPase pump continues to act and ensures that an excess of ions does not accumulate within the cell. If this were to happen, the cell would swell because of osmosis.

The major ionic movements during the action potential are summarized in Fig. 67.6.

THE ALL-OR-NONE LAW

In the previous sections, we have discussed the effect of subthreshold and threshold stimuli. However, if suprathreshold stimuli (i.e. greater than the threshold stimulus, which is just able to elicit an action potential) are applied to the nerve membrane, these potentials also elicit action potentials which are of the same amplitude as that seen with the threshold stimulus. This is the all-or-none law and is summarized in Fig. 67.7.

REFRACTORY PERIOD

Once an action potential is elicited, a subsequent stimulus can elicit a response only after a period of time. During the whole of the phase of depolarization and one-third of the phase of repolarization, a second stimulus cannot elicit a response, no matter how strong the stimulus. This phase of the action potential during which the nerve membrane is not responsive to another stimulus is called the refractory period, and because no stimulus, however, great, can elicit a response, it is further qualified as the 'absolute refractory period'.

COMPARISON OF THE LOCAL RESPONSE AND ACTION POTENTIAL

In this section, we will review the differences between the local response and the action potential. We had earlier indicated that a single subthreshold stimulus is unable to elicit a biological response by itself. However, if multiple subthreshold stimuli are delivered either in quick succession at a single point on the nerve membrane or in close proximity to each other at the same time, these subthreshold stimuli can summate, and if they achieve the critical firing level, that is the membrane potential at which the fast voltage-gated Na channels open, then they can elicit an action potential and a biological response.

When subthreshold stimuli are delivered in quick succession at the same point on the membrane, the summation that occurs is called 'temporal summation'.

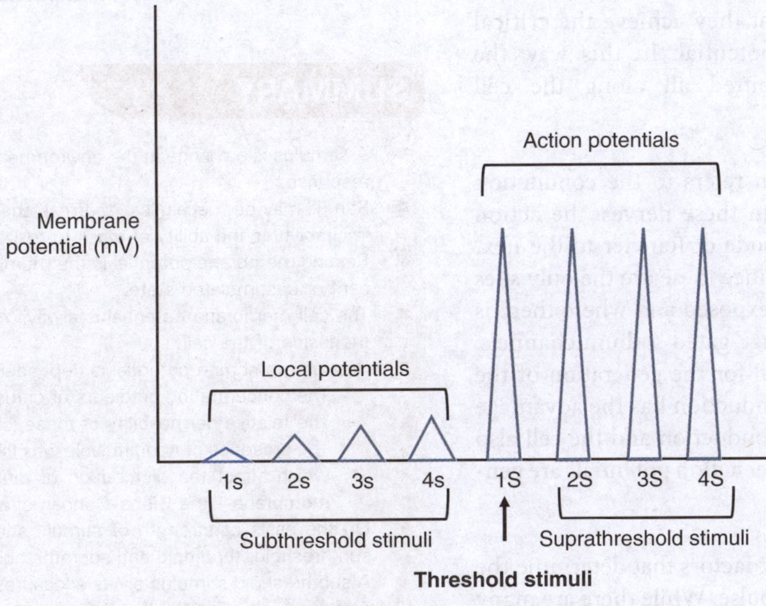

FIG. 67.7 The all or none law.

Table 67.1 Differences Between an Action Potential and a Local Response

	Action Potential	Local Response
Type of stimulus	Subthreshold	Threshold/suprathreshold
Summation	Absent	Present
Propagation along the nerve membrane	Yes	No
Obeys all-or-none law	Yes	No
Refractory period	Present	Absent

When subthreshold stimuli are delivered at the same time close to each other on the nerve membrane, the summation that occurs is called 'spatial summation'.

Table 67.1 summarizes the differences between a local response and an action potential.

TRANSMISSION (CONDUCTION) OF THE NERVE IMPULSE

The nerve impulse is an action potential which travels the length of a nerve. There are basically two types of conduction.

Unmyelinated nerves:

Simple conduction is seen in nonmyelinated nerves and is illustrated in Fig. 67.8. As can be seen in the figure, when a nerve is stimulated, an action potential is generated at the site. Thus, at the site of stimulus, the inside of the cell membrane is positively charged while the adjacent areas are negatively charged. This difference in the charges of the adjacent parts of the cell membrane results in the development of local currents. As charges flow through these local currents, adjacent areas are depolarized to the point that they achieve the critical firing level for an action potential. In this way, the action potential is transmitted all along the cell membrane.

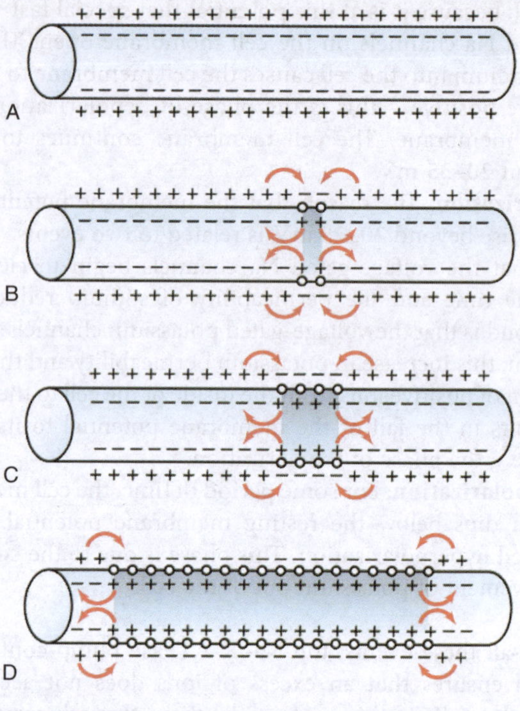

FIG. 67.8 The nature of simple conduction.

Myelinated nerves:

In contrast, saltatory conduction refers to the conduction seen in myelinated nerves. In these nerves, the action potential 'jumps' from one node of Ranvier to the next node of Ranvier (Fig. 67.9), since these are the only sites where the cell membrane is exposed and where there is a high concentration of voltage-gated sodium channels. These are, of course, essential for the generation of the action potential. Saltatory conduction has the advantage that it is faster than simple conduction and the cell also expends less energy since fewer action potentials are generated on the cell membrane.

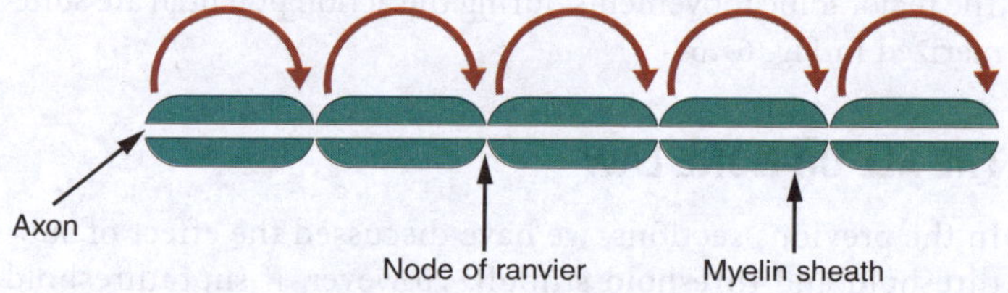

FIG. 67.9 Saltatory conduction.

Thus, myelination is one of the major factors that determine the speed of conduction of the nerve impulse. While there are many other factors, another important factor is the thickness of the axon. The greater the thickness of the axon (diameter), the faster is the conduction of the nerve impulse.

SUMMARY

- A stimulus is a change in the environment that may elicit a biological response.
- Stimuli may be mechanical, thermal, chemical or electrical.
- Excitability is the ability of a cell to respond to a stimulus.
- Resting membrane potential is the membrane potential in the quiescent or unstimulated state.
- The cell membrane potential is always represented with respect to the inside of the cell.
- Resting membrane potential is dependent on the following:
  - The concentration gradients of diffusible ions.
  - The relative permeability of these ions.
  - The presence of nondiffusible ions (like protein anions in the cell) which affect the distribution of diffusible ions across the cell membrane – the Gibbs–Donnan effect.
- On the basis of strength of stimuli, stimuli can be categorized as subthreshold, threshold and suprathreshold.
- A subthreshold stimulus elicits a local response, which is not propagated, can be summated and does not have a refractory period.

- Threshold and suprathreshold stimuli elicit an action potential, which is propagated (the nerve impulse), cannot be summated, obeys the all-or-none law and has a refractory period.
- The two main phases of the action potential are depolarization which is due to the entry of sodium into the cell through voltage-gated sodium channels and repolarization which is due to the movement of potassium out of the cell through voltage-gated channels.
- Conduction of a nerve impulse is of two types: simple conduction due to local currents in unmyelinated nerves and saltatory conduction in myelinated nerves where the action potential 'jumps' from one node of Ranvier to the next.
- Diameter of the nerve and myelination are two important factors that affect the speed of nerve conduction.

Chapter Review Questions

1. What is the resting membrane potential? Which ion contributes most to the resting membrane potential?
2. What are the phases of an action potential?
3. What are the differences between a local response and an action potential?
4. What is the All-or-None Law?

CHAPTER 68

Cerebral Lateralization and the Role of Cerebrospinal Fluid

SPECIFIC LEARNING OBJECTIVES

At the end of this chapter, the student should be able to:

- Differentiate between the left and right cerebral hemisphere.
- Describe the formation, circulation and functions of cerebrospinal fluid.

GLOSSARY OF TERMS

- **Cerebrospinal fluid (CSF):** fluid contained within the subarachnoid space of the brain and the spinal cord
- **Hydrocephalus:** an excessive accumulation of CSF in the brain
- **Cerebral lateralization:** some processes are better performed by one of the two cerebral hemispheres

The brain is covered with three membranes called the *meninges*; these are the *dura mater*, the *arachnoid mater* and the *pia mater*. The space between the arachnoid mater and the pia mater is called the subarachnoid space and this space contains a fluid called the cerebrospinal fluid (CSF). The space below the dura mater is the subdural space. It is into this space that blood may collect following a head injury. This type of collection of blood in subdural space is called a subdural haematoma.

COMPARISON OF LEFT AND RIGHT CEREBRAL HEMISPHERES

Although the left and the right cerebral hemispheres have many common features, the extent to which they perform certain functions varies. This is termed *cerebral lateralization* and implies that there are some functions in which the left cerebral hemisphere is more important ('dominant') than the right cerebral hemisphere, and vice versa. Thus, language appears to be a dominant feature of the left cerebral hemisphere regardless of whether the person is left or right handed. Table 68.1 summarizes some key differences between the left and right cerebral hemispheres.

CEREBROSPINAL FLUID

CSF is found between the arachnoid mater and the pia mater in a space called the subarachnoid space. The total volume of CSF is 150 mL.

Formation of CSF

- About 500 mL of CSF is formed each day.
- The bulk of CSF is formed by the choroid plexus, the major portion of which is present in the lateral ventricles. The choroid plexus consists of blood vessels covered by epithelial cells.

Circulation of CSF

- The circulation of CSF is summarized in Fig. 68.1.
- Most of the CSF is produced by the choroid plexus of the lateral ventricles.
- From the lateral ventricles, the CSF goes through the Foramen of Monro to the third ventricle.
- CSF then goes via the aqueduct of Sylvius to the fourth ventricle.
- CSF enters the subarachnoid space via the Foramina of Magendie and Luschka.

Composition of CSF

While some parameters such as osmotic pressure are similar in CSF and in plasma, CSF differs from blood in other important ways:

- CSF is cell-free. The appearance of cells in CSF indicates some disease process. For example, the presence of neutrophils may indicate a bacterial meningitis (inflammation of the meninges) while lymphocytes may indicate a viral meningitis.
- CSF is almost protein-free. Higher amounts of proteins may be found when there is an inflammation of the meninges. This may also result in CSF appearing turbid.
- The glucose concentration of CSF is about two-thirds that of plasma and may reduce further when there is a bacterial infection involving the meninges when the bacteria consume the glucose.

Table 68.1 Comparison of the Left and Right Cerebral Hemispheres

Left Cerebral Hemisphere	Right Cerebral Hemisphere
Controls muscle function on the right side of the body	Controls muscle function on the left side of the body
Reasoning	Emotions
Mathematics and calculations	Creative activities
Language	Music

Absorption of CSF

Since more CSF is produced every day (500 mL) than is present in the subarachnoid space (150 mL), it is clear that the major amount of CSF that is produced must be reabsorbed. This reabsorption occurs in structures called arachnoid villi through which CSF drains into the venous sinuses (Fig. 68.1).

Functions of CSF

CSF has many functions:

1. Protects the brain from external trauma.
2. Provides nutrients to the brain.
3. Removes waste products from the brain.
4. Contains various molecules which can affect brain function.
5. Acts as a buffer.

Lumbar Puncture

- Since there are changes in CSF which can help to determine disease processes occurring in the brain and meninges, a sample of CSF can be useful in helping make a diagnosis. A CSF sample is typically obtained using a procedure called a lumbar puncture.
- A needle is inserted between the third and fourth lumbar vertebrae (below the level where the spinal cord ends) into the subarachnoid space and a small sample of CSF is obtained (Fig. 68.2).

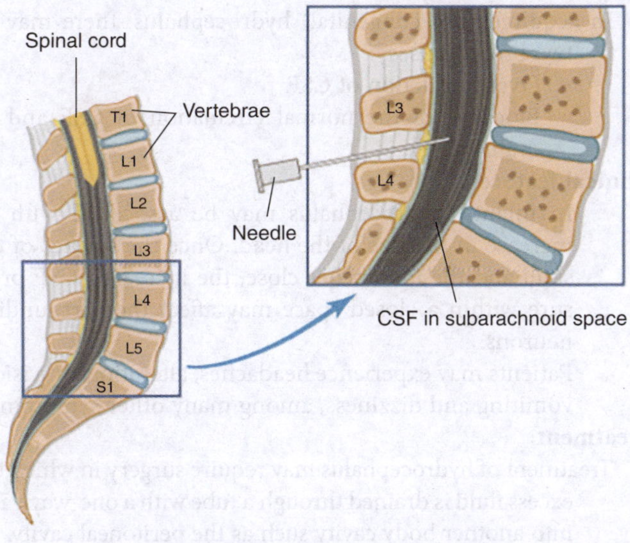

FIG. 68.2 Site of lumbar puncture.

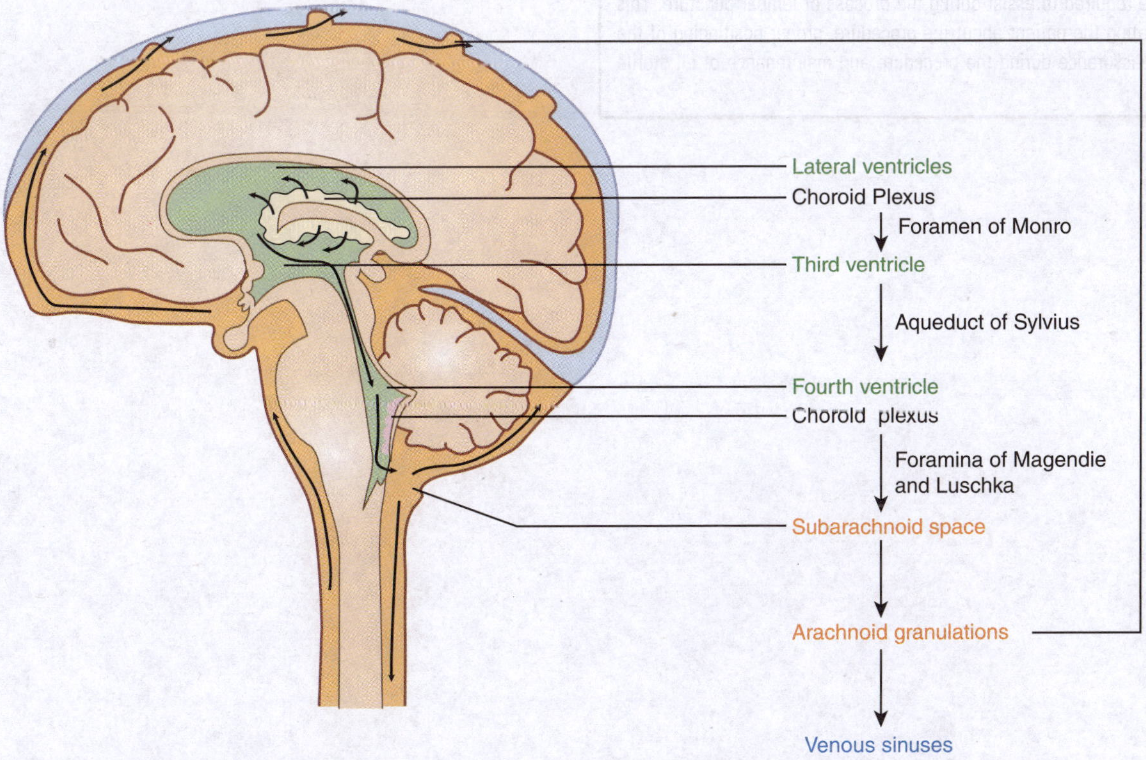

FIG. 68.1 The circulation of CSF.

- This sample can be subjected to microscopy, microbiological evaluations and biochemical assessment.

Hydrocephalus

Definition:

Hydrocephalus is an increased accumulation of CSF in the brain within the subarachnoid space.

Causes:

This may occur as a congenital condition but may also be the result of a tumour in the brain and infections in the brain, among other conditions.

In acquired (not congenital) hydrocephalus, there may be two broad causes:

- Overproduction of CSF.
- Blockage of the normal circulation of CSF and its drainage.

Clinical features:

- In infants, hydrocephalus may be associated with an increase in the size of the head. Once the sutures of the skull and the fontanelles close, the increased CSF pressure within a closed space may affect the surrounding neurons.
- Patients may experience headaches, alterations in vision, vomiting and dizziness, among many other symptoms.

Treatment:

Treatment of hydrocephalus may require surgery in which the excess fluid is drained through a tube with a one-way valve into another body cavity such as the peritoneal cavity.

APPLICATIONS FOR NURSING

Nurses will be required to assist during the process of lumbar puncture. This requires educating the patient about the procedure, proper positioning of the patient and reassurance during the procedure and maintenance of all sterile precautions.

SUMMARY

- The brain which weights 1.5 kg in an adult is protected by the skull and three meninges: the dura, arachnoid and pia mater. CSF which is contained in the ventricles and subarachnoid space helps to protect the brain, provide nutrition, remove wastes and allow for the circulation of messenger molecules which affect brain function.
- The two cerebral hemispheres are joined together by the corpus callosum. The left and right hemispheres control movement on the opposite sides of the body. The left hemisphere is dominant for language and mathematics. The right hemisphere is dominant for creative processing, music and emotions.
- CSF is produced in the choroid plexus of the ventricles and circulates in the subarachnoid space before being reabsorbed by the arachnoid villi.
- CSF is clear coloured, is almost cell- and protein-free, and has about two-thirds the concentration of glucose as plasma.
- CSF helps to protect the brain from physical injury, and is a medium for the exchange of nutrients and wastes and regulatory molecules. It also acts as a buffer.

CHAPTER REVIEW QUESTIONS

1. List the differences between the left and right cerebral hemispheres.
2. State the meningeal layers of the brain and the spaces between them.
3. What is the composition of CSF in comparison to plasma?
4. What are the functions of CSF?

CHAPTER 69

The Sensory System

SPECIFIC LEARNING OBJECTIVES

At the end of this chapter, the student should be able to:

- Classify sensory receptors.
- List the properties of receptors.
- Draw and label a diagram of a synapse.
- List the properties of synapses.
- Trace the major sensory pathways that convey information from the periphery to the brain.
- Distinguish between the different types of pain.
- Define referred pain and give some examples.
- Describe the role of the cortex in the perception of sensation.

GLOSSARY OF TERMS

- **Sensory transduction:** the conversion of a sensory stimulus into an electrical signal in the sensory nerve
- **Receptor:** a sense organ (some receptors are specific, i.e. they can sense a single type of sensory stimulus, while others are 'polymodal', i.e. they can sense multiple types of sensory stimuli)
- **Synapse**: junction between two nerves

We are surrounded with many sensations such as light, sound, smell, taste, touch, pressure and pain. In order to appreciate these various sensations, we need to first detect them. This is done by sense organs called receptors. There are many receptors in our body – some are specific for a particular stimulus, while others can detect a variety of stimuli. Sometimes, a single sensation may be detected by multiple receptors. In this chapter, we discuss how we detect these various stimuli, how information is carried about these stimuli to the brain and how our brain processes such information.

TYPES OF SENSATION

There are different types of sensation that we are exposed to, and these can be classified into the following:

- Epicritic sensations:
  - Fine sensation: touch, pressure, proprioception
- Protopathic:
  - Crude sensations such as pain and temperature

CLASSIFICATION OF RECEPTORS

There are many different ways in which sense organs or receptors are classified. They can, for instance, be classified on the basis of the stimuli they respond to, or where they are located or the properties that they possess. One simple classification of receptors is given in Table 69.1. This table classifies receptors on the basis of their location and the type of stimulus.

The location of the receptors in the skin is described in greater detail in Chapter 47.

Receptors are connected to sensory nerves. As can be seen from Table 69.1, there are a large number of stimuli that can stimulate a variety of receptors. Some of these stimuli are physical (e.g. touch and pressure), and others are chemical (e.g. taste and smell). For all types of stimuli, the information is carried in sensory nerves in the form of a nerve impulse which is electrical in nature. This conversion of a stimulus (which is variable) into an electrical signal in the nerve is called *sensory transduction*.

PROPERTIES OF RECEPTORS

1. *Receptive field*: Sensory receptors are connected to a sensory neuron. The entire area that is supplied by a single sensory neuron is called a receptive field (this may, for instance, include an area of the skin). If multiple receptors are connected to a single sensory neuron, then the receptive field

will contain all those multiple receptors. The idea of a receptive field is important because if we stimulate a single receptive field with two separate stimuli, it will be perceived as a single stimulus. In order for stimuli to be perceived as discrete (separate), they must fall on separate receptive fields (Fig. 69.1).

Table 69.1 Classification of Receptors

I. Exteroceptors: Provide Information About the External Environment	
General receptors	
Touch	Merkel's discs, Meissner's corpuscles
Pressure	Pacinian corpuscles
Pain	Free nerve endings
Temperature	Cold and warm receptors
Specialized receptors	
Vision	Rods and cones on the retina
Hearing	Hair cells in the cochlea of the inner ear
Smell	Olfactory receptors in the epithelium of the nose
Taste	Receptors of the taste buds
II. Proprioceptors: Provide Information About the Position and Posture of Body in Space	
Length of muscles	Muscle spindle in skeletal muscle
Tension in muscle	Golgi's tendon organs in the muscle tendon
Equilibrium and posture	Vestibular apparatus in the inner ear
III. Interoceptors: Provide Information About the Internal Environment of Our Body Including Visceral Organs	
Pressure in the arteries	Baroreceptors
Chemical changes	Glucoreceptors, osmoreceptors, chemoreceptors for respiration
Stretch in organs	Stretch receptors

2. *Adaptation*: If a stimulus is continually applied to a receptor, the stimulus may no longer be perceived or may be perceived to a lower extent. Thus, when we wear our clothes, we are initially aware of the cloth against our skin, but this is not so after some time. Some receptors adapt rapidly while others adapt more slowly or not at all.
3. *Intensity–sensation relationship*: As a stimulus increases in strength, more receptors may be activated, a condition that is called receptor recruitment. Our sensation of a stimulus is directly proportional to the intensity of the stimulus. In other words, the stronger the stimulus, the more we feel it.
4. *Law of projection*: When a sensory pathway is stimulated anywhere along its course, the sensation formed is referred to the location of the receptors. Thus, when a person has had an amputation (i.e. a limb has been surgically removed), he or she may continue to feel sensations on the missing part of the limb because the cut nerve is stimulated. This phenomenon is called *phantom limb*.

THE SYNAPSE

In order to transmit sensation from a receptor to the brain, the information travels across more than one nerve. This means that information from one nerve has to be transferred to another nerve. This is done through a synapse. A synapse is the junction of two nerves. In terms of structure, the synapse is similar to the neuromuscular junction (Chapter 52) except that the postsynaptic membrane is a nerve rather than a muscle. Fig. 69.2 shows a typical synapse.

There are many different types of neurotransmitters that can act at synapses. Each neuron has its own specific neurotransmitter.

Events at the Synapse

The sequence of events at the synapse is the following:

1. Arrival of the nerve impulse in the axon.
2. Movement of the vesicles containing the neurotransmitter towards the presynaptic membrane.

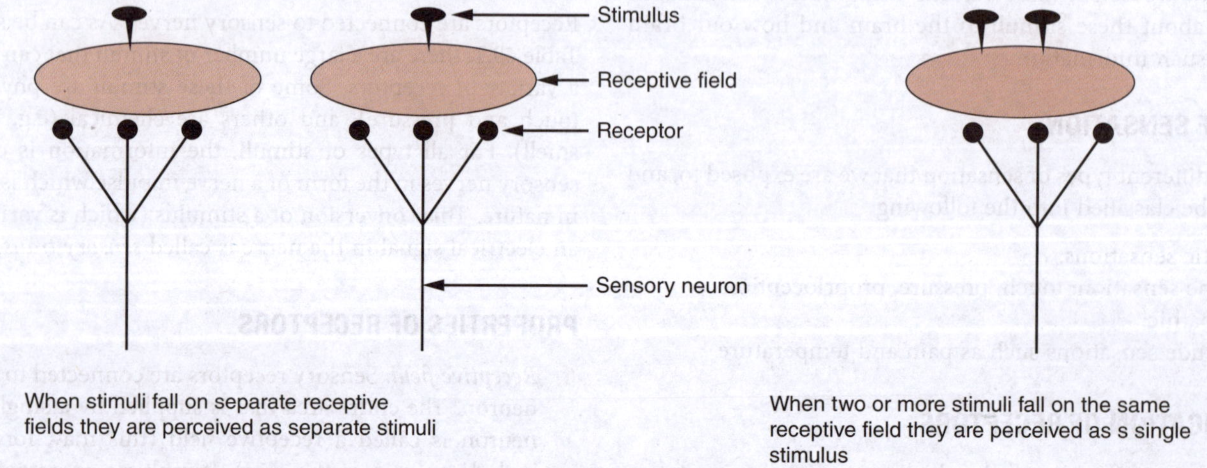

FIG. 69.1 Perception of stimuli falling on single and separate receptive fields.

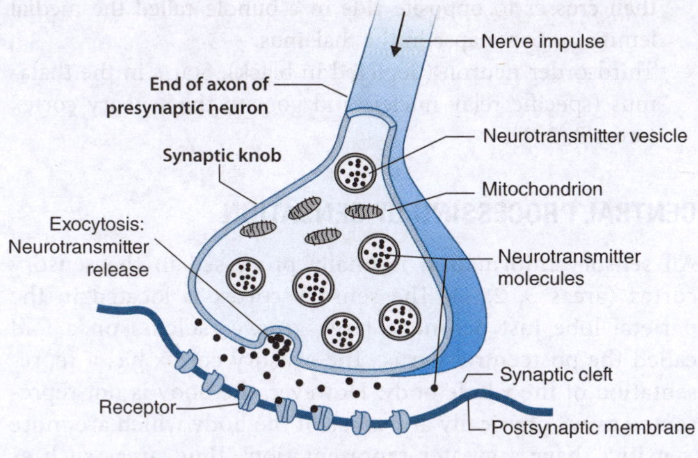

FIG. 69.2 Structure of a typical synapse.

3. Release of the neurotransmitter by exocytosis into the synaptic cleft.
4. Binding of the neurotransmitter with its receptors on the postsynaptic membrane.
5. Generation of a nerve impulse on the postsynaptic neuron.

Types of responses on the postsynaptic membrane: When a neurotransmitter binds to its receptor on the postsynaptic membrane, it causes a change in the membrane potential. This change may be either depolarizing (i.e. the membrane becomes more positive on the inside) or hyperpolarizing (i.e. the membrane becomes more negative on the inside).

- When there is depolarization, it is called an *excitatory postsynaptic potential (EPSP)*.
- When there is hyperpolarization, it is called an *inhibitory postsynaptic potential (IPSP)*.

Neurotransmitters that cause an EPSP are called excitatory neurotransmitters and include glutamate, norepinephrine and acetylcholine. Neurotransmitters that cause an IPSP are called inhibitory neurotransmitters and include glycine and GABA (Gamma-aminobutyric acid).

Some Properties of the Synapse

1. *One-way transmission*: The impulse always travels from the presynaptic neuron to the postsynaptic neuron (Bell-Magendie law). Transmission does not occur from the postsynaptic neuron to the presynaptic neuron.
2. *Synaptic fatigue*: If a presynaptic neuron is stimulated continuously, there can be a depletion of the neurotransmitter at the presynaptic nerve ending. As a result, transmission across the synapse will stop.
3. *Synaptic delay*: Because the transmission across a synapse requires several events including release of neurotransmitter, binding of neurotransmitter on its postsynaptic receptor and change in membrane potential, there is delay in transmission of the impulse. The synaptic delay because of these events is a minimum of about 0.5 ms.

SENSORY PATHWAYS

There are many paths by which different sensations are carried from different parts of the body to the brain. However, in this book, we will focus on only two major pathways. These two tracts are called the anterolateral spinothalamic tract and the dorsal columns. They carry different types of sensations and the path that they follow from the periphery to the brain is different but they have some things in common:

1. In order for sensations to travel in the sensory pathways, receptors need to be activated by specific stimuli.
2. The pathway to the brain involves three neurons; these are called first-order, second-order and third-order neurons.
3. The first-order neuron enters the spinal cord through the dorsal root of the spinal cord.
4. The pathways travel through the thalamus which is the sensory processing relay station of the brain.
5. The pathways terminate in the sensory cortex which is located in the parietal cortex and consists of Brodmann's areas 1, 2 and 3.

Note that the arrangement of the grey and white matter in the spinal cord is different to what is seen in the cerebrum. Thus, in the cerebrum, the grey matter (which comprises the nerve cell bodies) is located on the surface, while the white matter (which consists of the axons) is located deeper. In contrast, in the spinal cord, the white matter is located at the surface while the grey matter is located deeper.

The two pathways are summarized in Figs 69.3 and 69.4.

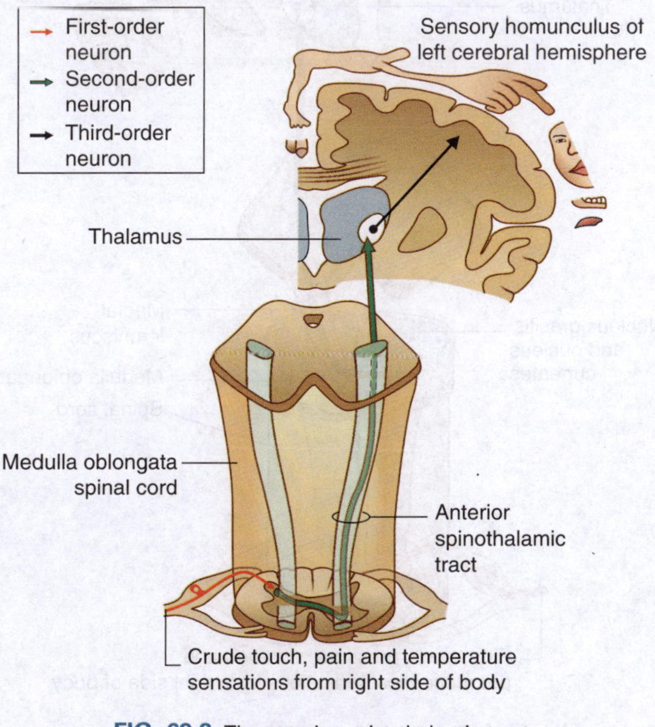

FIG. 69.3 The anterior spinothalamic tract.

Anterior Spinothalamic Tract (Fig. 69.3)

- Stimuli: Pain, temperature and crude touch.
- Receptors: Free nerve endings, thermoreceptors and touch receptors.
- First-order neuron (depicted in red in the diagram): Sensory neuron passes through the dorsal root and synapses in the dorsal horn on the same side.
- Second-order neuron (depicted in green): Starts in the dorsal horn, and then crosses the midline in the same spinal segment to the opposite side and ascends to the thalamus.
- Third-order neuron (depicted in black): Starts in the thalamus and goes to the sensory cortex (areas 3, 2, 1).

Dorsal Columns (Fig. 69.4)

- Stimuli: Fine touch, vibration, pressure and proprioception (see proprioceptors – Table 69.1).
- Receptors: Meissner's corpuscles, Merkel's discs, Pacinian corpuscles and proprioceptors.
- First-order neuron (depicted in red): Sensory neuron enters the spinal cord through the dorsal root and ascends on the same side of the spinal cord to synapse in the medulla.
- Second-order neuron (depicted in green): Starts in the medulla in specific areas (nucleus gracilis and nucleus cuneatus), and then crosses to opposite side in a bundle called the medial lemniscus to synapse in the thalamus.
- Third-order neuron (depicted in black): Starts in the thalamus (specific relay nuclei) and goes to the sensory cortex (areas 3, 2, 1).

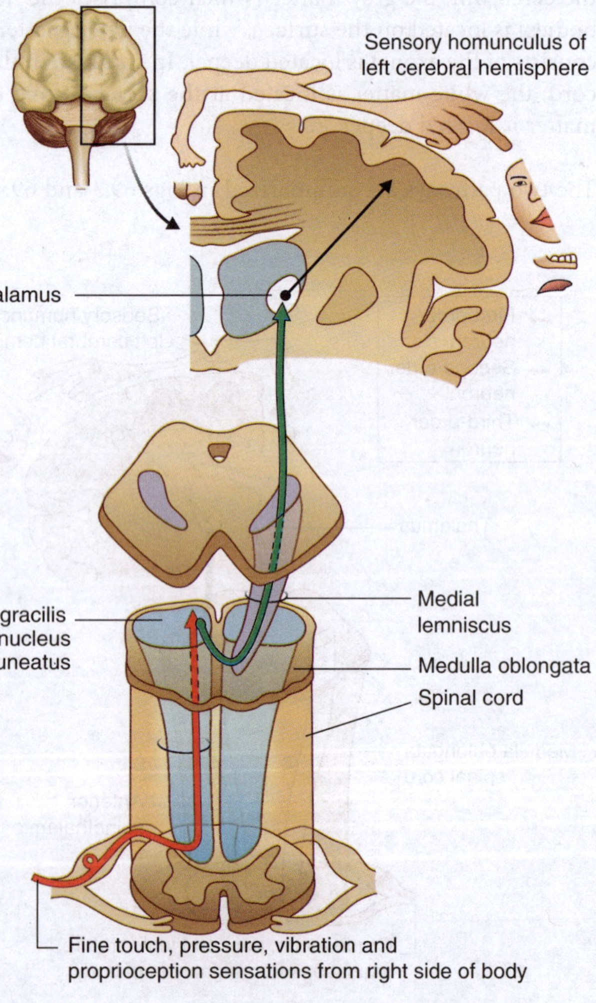

FIG. 69.4 The dorsal (or posterior) column pathway.

CENTRAL PROCESSING OF SENSATION

All sensory information is finally processed in the sensory cortex (areas 3, 2, 1). The sensory cortex is located in the parietal lobe just behind a large groove (sulcus) on a fold called the postcentral gyrus. The sensory cortex has a representation of the whole body. However, the body is not represented as we physically are: areas of the body which are more 'sensitive' have a greater representation. Thus, areas such as the lips, fingers and face where we perceive sensations better have a greater representation in the sensory cortex. The diagrammatic representation of the areas in the sensory cortex involved in sensory processing is called the sensory homunculus (Fig. 69.5).

PAIN

In this subsection, we focus on pain because it is such a common symptom that patients experience when they are ill.

Definition

Pain is an unpleasant sensory or emotional experience that is associated with actual tissue damage or potential tissue damage.

Somatic and Visceral Pain

There are different kinds of pain and patients use different words to explain what they are experiencing. Thus, in order to get a clearer understanding of what the patient is feeling, we ask

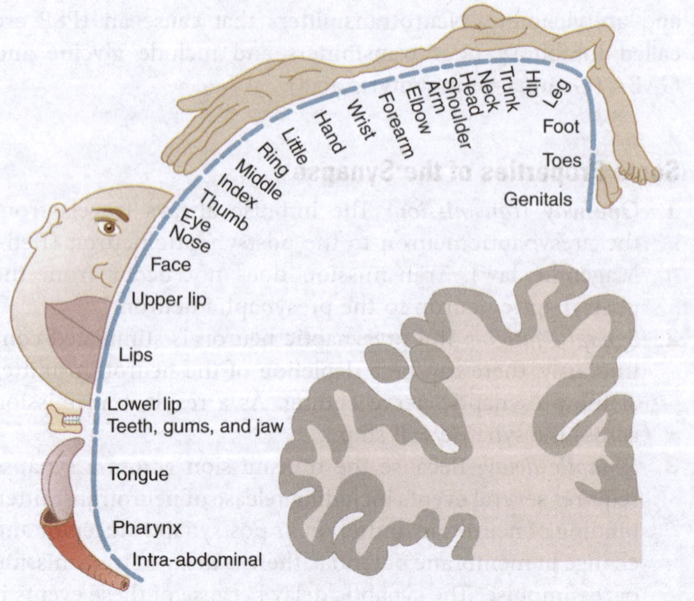

FIG. 69.5 The sensory homunculus.

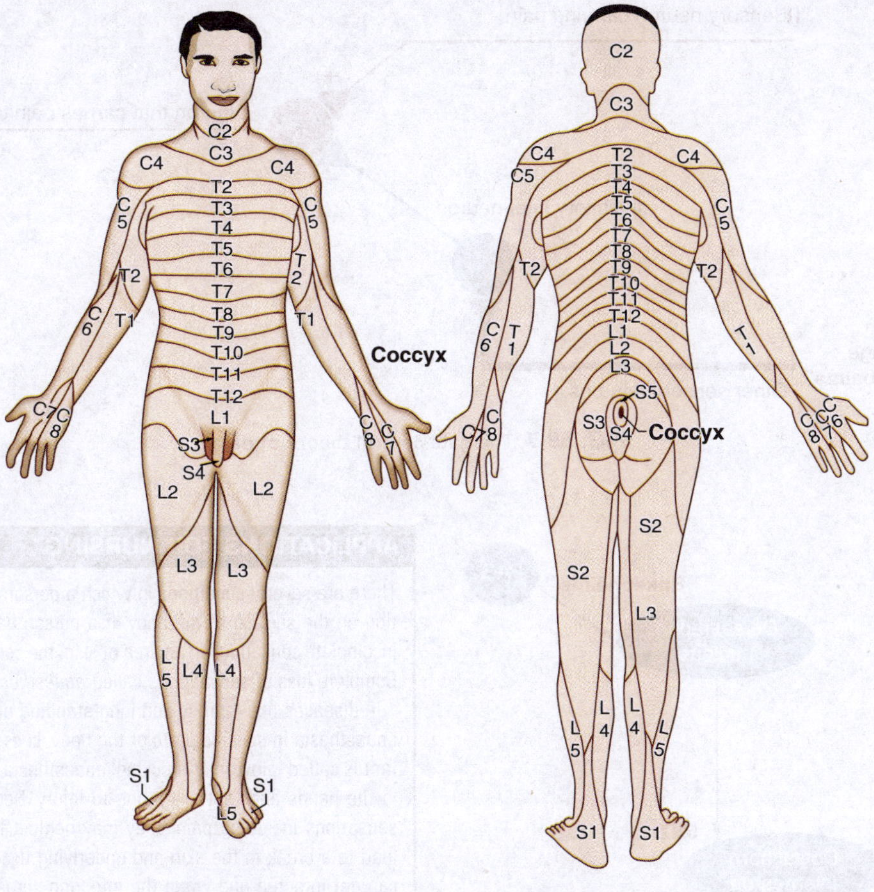

FIG. 69.6 A dermatomal map of the surface of the body.

questions about the duration of pain, its intensity and its characteristics, among others.

Pain that we experience on the surface of our body (as when we prick ourselves on something) is called superficial or *somatic pain*. This type of pain is typically well localized. The surface of the skin can be mapped in terms of the origin of the spinal nerves that supply that area of skin. This is depicted in Fig. 69.6.

A *dermatome* is an area of skin that is supplied by a single spinal nerve. In Fig. 69.6, 'C' refers to cervical spinal nerves (i.e. nerves that emerge from the spinal cord in the neck), 'T' refers to thoracic spinal nerves (nerves that emerge from the spinal cord in the thorax), 'L' refers to lumbar spinal nerves (nerves that emerge from the lower back called the lumbar region) and 'S' refers to the sacral spinal nerves that emerge from the lowest back region called the sacrum. Knowledge of dermatomes is important because they allow us to determine which part of the spinal cord is involved when sensation is lost in a localized area.

Pain that originates from the organs or viscera is most often diffuse (or poorly localized) and is called *visceral pain*.

Referred Pain

Sometimes pain is not at all felt in the region where it originates, but is felt somewhere else. This type of pain is called *referred pain*. Thus, pain from the heart is sometimes felt along the inner part of the left arm and forearm. Similarly, pain from the liver may be felt in the right shoulder and neck. One of the theories of referred pain is that the organ which is the true source of the pain and the site of the referred pain are derived from the same spinal segment. This is called the *dermatomal theory*.

Modulation of Pain

When we suffer from an injury, we are sometimes able to function in spite of the pain. We may not even experience great pain at the time of injury – the perception of pain may come later. This suggests that our bodies are capable of modulating (changing) our perception of pain. In this section, we describe briefly some ways in which our perception of pain is altered within the central nervous system.

Gate Control Theory of Pain When we have hurt ourselves by unintentionally banging into a wall, we find that massaging the area appears to relieve the pain. We also experience this when we apply a pain balm over the area that is paining. How does this work?

Fig. 69.7 is a modified diagram of the gate control theory that was proposed by Melzack and Wall in the 1960s.

They suggested that in the spinal cord, sensory nerve fibres transmit pain onwards to the brain. There are other sensory

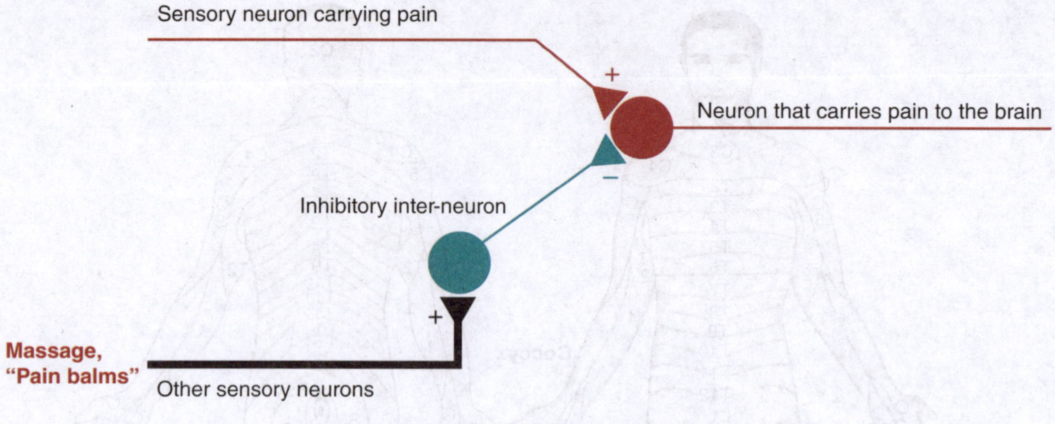

FIG. 69.7 The gate control theory of pain.

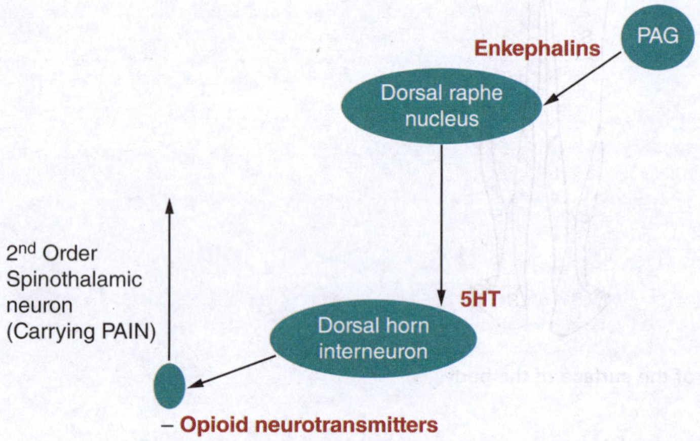

FIG. 69.8 Endogenous opioid pain control systems.

fibres which carry other sensations. When these fibres are stimulated, they stimulate an interneuron (nerve cell between two neurons) which inhibits the pain-carrying nerve fibre. This suppresses our sensation of pain. This is what happens when we massage an area or apply a balm to relieve the pain.

Central Modulation of Pain Within our central nervous system are pain-reducing substances. These are endogenous opioids and include endorphins, enkephalins and dynorphins. Apart from the gate control system at the spinal cord, there are other areas of the brain which help to modulate pain. One of these areas is called the periaqueductal grey located in the midbrain. The periaqueductal grey projects onto the dorsal raphe nucleus which has serotonin (5-HT) as its major neurotransmitter. The dorsal raphe nucleus in turn projects onto interneurons in the spinal cord which release opioid neurotransmitters and inhibit pain sensation from being transmitted to the brain (Fig. 69.8).

APPLICATIONS FOR NURSING

There are several conditions in which a person may experience loss of sensation on the surface of the body. If a person has some loss of sensation (i.e. incomplete sensation) on an area of skin, the condition is called *hypoaesthesia*. Complete loss of sensation is called *anaesthesia*.

In diseases like leprosy and long-standing diabetes, patients may develop anaesthesia in specific parts of the body. Loss of sensation in the hands and feet is called 'glove-and-stocking' anaesthesia. People with loss of sensation in the hands and feet are prone to injury. Because they are unable to feel sensations including pain, they may neglect these injuries – this can then lead to a break in the skin and underlying tissues resulting in *ulcers*. Ulcers can get infected and when the infection spreads deeper into the tissues, it can affect even bone. The result is deformity which can increase the possibility of further injury.

Nurses will be required not only to effectively clean and dress ulcers but also, more importantly, educate patients on the care of their anaesthetic hands and feet so that they minimize injury, report to the doctor early and prevent long-term deformity.

SUMMARY

- Sensations can be broadly divided into epicritic (which are fine sensations and include touch, pressure and proprioception) and protopathic (which includes crude sensations such as pain and temperature).
- Receptors (sense organs) can be divided into those that provide us information about the external environment (exteroceptors), the internal state of the body (interoceptors) and the position and posture of the body (proprioceptors).
- Receptors are associated with a receptive field, show adaptation and respond to the intensity of stimulus.
- Synapses are junctions between nerves. Transmission at the synapse can result in either inhibition in the form of an inhibitory postsynaptic potential or stimulation in the form of an excitatory postsynaptic potential.
- Transmission in synapses is one way, and shows synaptic delay and synaptic fatigue.

- Two major sensory pathways for the transmission of sensation from the periphery to the sensory cortex are the anterolateral spinothalamic tract which transmits crude touch, pain and temperature and the dorsal columns which transmit fine touch, vibration, pressure and proprioception.
- The sensory cortex is located in the postcentral gyrus – all parts of the body are represented here in the form of a 'sensory homunculus'.
- Pain is of two types – somatic and visceral. In referred pain, pain that originates in one organ is felt in some other part of the body.

CHAPTER REVIEW QUESTIONS

1. List the properties of a synapse.
2. Describe the anterolateral spinothalamic tract in terms of (a) sensations carried, (b) receptors, (c) first-, second- and third-order neurons.
3. Describe the dorsal column tract in terms of (a) sensations carried, (b) receptors, (c) first-, second- and third-order neurons.
4. What is referred pain? List some examples.

CHAPTER 70

The Motor System

SPECIFIC LEARNING OBJECTIVES

At the end of this chapter, the student should be able to:

- Define muscle tone.
- Describe the structure and functions of receptors that convey information of the 'state' of the muscles.
- Describe the location and function of the motor cortex.
- Trace and describe the function of the pyramidal tract.
- Describe the role of the basal ganglia in motor control.
- Describe the function of the vestibular apparatus.
- Describe the function of the cerebellum.

GLOSSARY OF TERMS

- **Muscle tone:** tension in the muscle that occurs even when the muscle is relaxed
- **Flaccidity:** reduced muscle tone – muscle feels soft and limp
- **Rigidity:** increased muscle tone – muscle feels firm and stiff
- **Posture:** position of the body, for example standing, sitting
- **Tremor:** involuntary, trembling movement of muscles, often seen in the hands

During the day, we perform many activities. We sit, stand, lie down, run, climb stairs, etc. While the body is undergoing various changes in position during these movements and the centre of gravity of our body is constantly shifting, there is a need for the body to continuously maintain its balance. Even if we are in a fixed position, as when we stand for a long time, there are muscles continuously acting to maintain that body position. Certain activities that we perform require us to be precise in our movements while other movements are less so. This chapter describes how we control body movements and our muscles and how we maintain posture and balance.

Even when our muscles are relaxed, we can feel a certain amount of resistance within them. This is best seen if we ask a friend to relax the muscles of his or her upper limbs. Now try and bend his or her upper limb at the elbow. The resistance that you feel in the muscle during passive stretch is called the muscle tone.

When a person moves his or her own muscle by performing some activity, it is referred to as active movement. When another person performs the movement as in the earlier example, it is called a passive movement. We can define *muscle tone* more precisely as resistance that is offered by a relaxed muscle when it is passively stretched.

Movements that we perform consciously, such as playing tennis and writing notes, are called voluntary movements, while some movements that we make are more 'automatic', for instance, withdrawal of a hand when we touch a hot object – this constitutes an involuntary movement or a reflex.

CONTROL OF MUSCLE LENGTH AND TENSION

The majority of muscles in the body receive their nerve supply from spinal motor nerves which originate in the grey matter of the spinal cord at the anterior (ventral) horn. The grey matter contains the cell bodies of neurons. The motor nerve which supplies the nerve is referred to as the alpha motor neuron. This is illustrated in Fig. 70.1.

As our muscles contract and relax, their lengths are changing; muscles shorten when they are contracting and lengthen when they are relaxing. Therefore, there must be some way in which the body senses these changes in muscle length and tension. This is in fact done by receptors present within the muscle, in the tendons of muscles and in joints.

Muscle Spindle

The change in the length of the skeletal muscle is monitored by a sense organ located within the muscle called the muscle spindle. Skeletal muscle is made up of muscle fibres which run the entire length of the muscle and are attached to bone at either end (the origin and insertion of a muscle). These muscle fibres are called *extrafusal muscle fibres*. Embedded within these extrafusal muscle fibres are the muscle spindles which are placed in the same direction as the extrafusal muscle fibres and these are called *intrafusal muscle fibres*. This arrangement of the muscle fibres is depicted in Fig. 70.2.

Within the muscle spindle are two sense organs called the nuclear chain fibres and the nuclear bag fibres. Because these fibres are arranged in the same direction as the extrafusal skeletal muscle fibres and are connected to them by connective tissue, it is clear that they are also stretched when the skeletal muscle is stretched. Similarly, when the muscle shortens during contraction, the extrafusal muscle fibres shorten and the intrafusal fibres of the muscle spindle also shorten. Thus, the muscle spindle senses the length of the muscle (Fig. 70.3).

In order to function as a sense organ, however, the muscle spindle must be able to convey information about the state of the muscle to the central nervous system. It does this through its own sensory (afferent) fibres. In addition, the muscle spindle also has its own motor neuron. This is a gamma motor neuron. The purpose of this independent motor nerve supply is so that the intrafusal muscle fibres of the muscle spindle can contract when they shorten during muscle contraction. This keeps them sensitive to the sustained or changing stretch of the extrafusal muscle fibres.

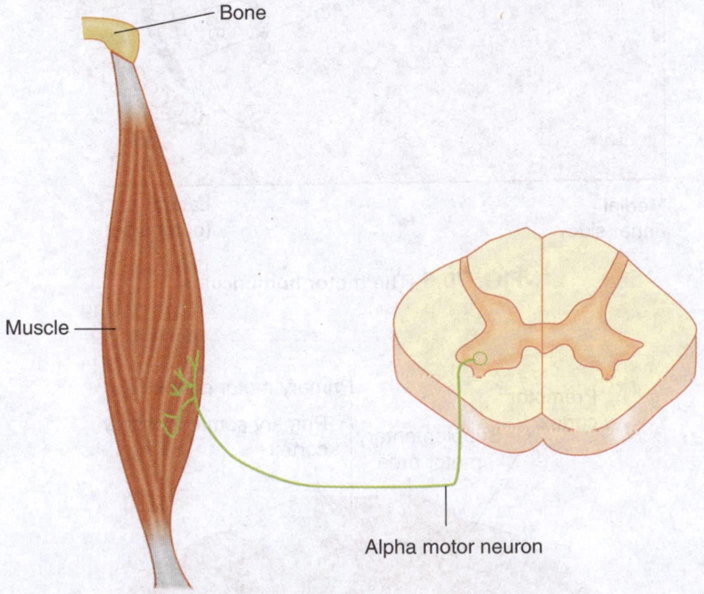

FIG. 70.1 Anatomical depiction of the alpha motor neuron supplying a skeletal muscle.

Golgi's Tendon Organ

Another receptor which is responsive to the tension of the muscle fibres is the Golgi's tendon organ. This, as the name suggests, is located on the tendon of the muscle (Fig. 70.4).

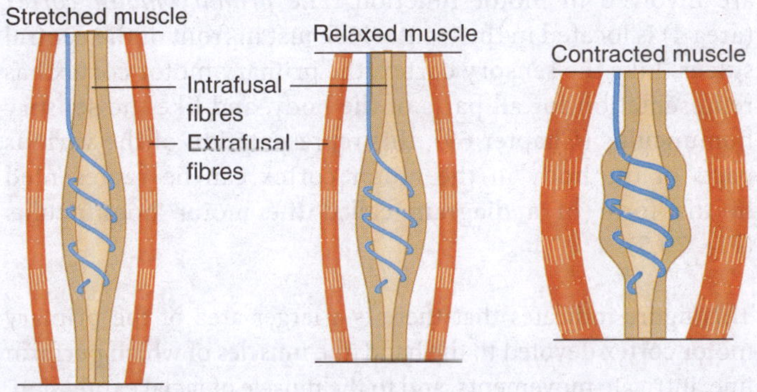

FIG. 70.3 Changes in the muscle spindle during stretch and contraction of skeletal muscle.

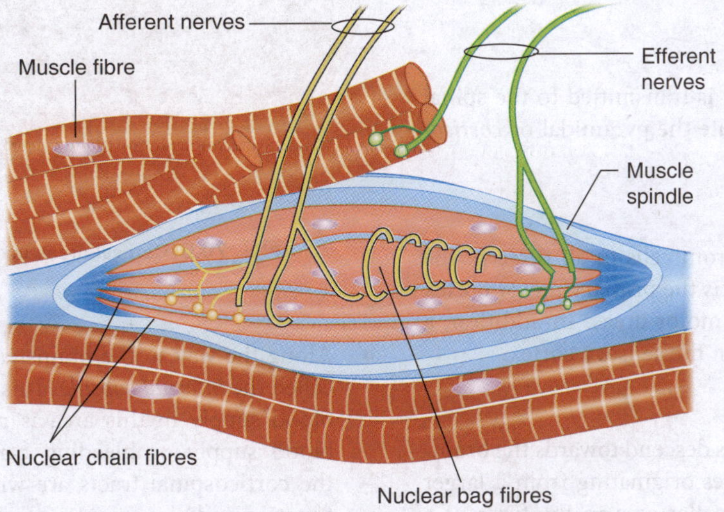

FIG. 70.2 Structure of the muscle spindle.

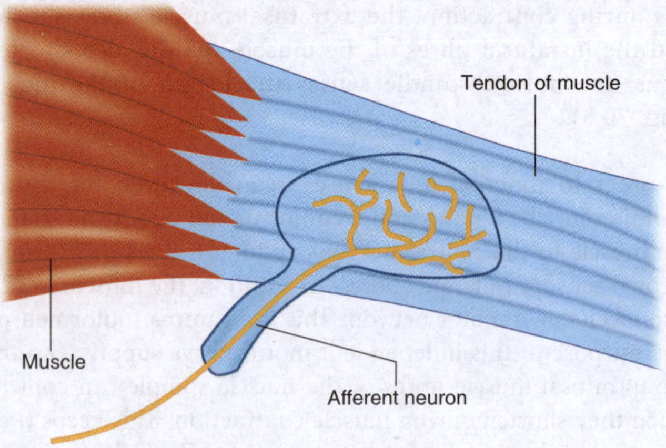

FIG. 70.4 Location of the Golgi's tendon organ.

THE MOTOR CORTEX

The part of the cerebrum which is involved in the voluntary control of muscle function and movement is the motor cortex. There are, in fact, several areas of the cerebral cortex which are involved in motor function. The *primary motor cortex* (area 4) is located in the frontal lobe just in front of the central sulcus. Like the sensory cortex, the primary motor cortex has representation for all parts of the body, and like the sensory homunculus (Chapter 69), this representation of the various parts of the body in the motor cortex can be represented in the form of a diagram called the motor homunculus (Fig. 70.5).

This figure indicates that there is a larger area of the primary motor cortex devoted to the hand, the muscles of which perform fine, intricate movements, and to the muscle of facial expression. Two additional areas that are involved in the control, planning and execution of movements are the *premotor cortex* and the *supplementary motor cortex* which lie in front of the primary motor cortex in the frontal lobe (Fig. 70.6).

THE PYRAMIDAL TRACT

Information from the motor cortex is transmitted to the spinal cord through nerves which constitute the pyramidal or *cortico-spinal tract*.

Origin

The corticospinal tract originates from cells in all three of the cortical areas described earlier, that is the primary motor cortex and premotor and supplementary motor areas. In addition, a part of the tract also originates from the sensory cortex.

Course

- On leaving the cortex, the nerves descend towards the brainstem. In the process, nerve fibres originating from a larger area are concentrated into a smaller area in the form of a fan-like structure called the corona radiata.

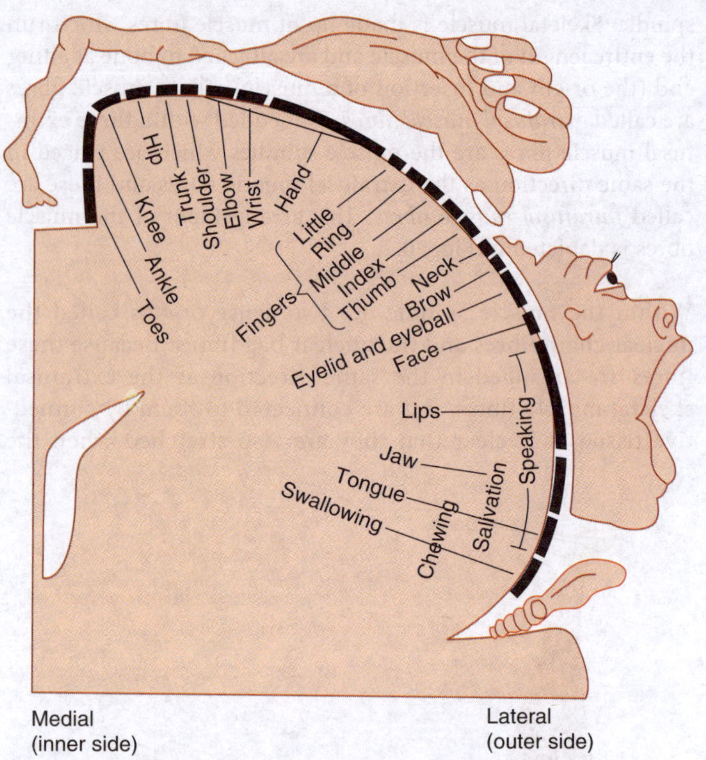

FIG. 70.5 The motor homunculus.

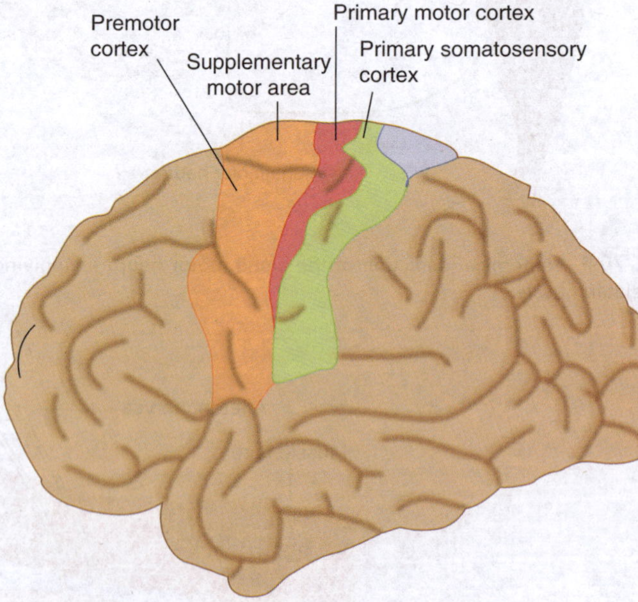

FIG. 70.6 Cortical areas involved in motor control.

- Along the way to the brainstem, they pass through an area called the *internal capsule*. This area is important because the blood supply in this area is restricted and a block in the blood supply or bleeding can result in a 'stroke'. When the corticospinal tracts are without a blood supply, motor function and movement of the body are affected – this is why people suffer from paralysis following a stroke.

- Some of the nerve fibres synapse with the cranial nerve nuclei that supply the muscles of the face. These fibres constitute the corticobulbar tract.
- In the medulla, the rest of the tract forms the *pyramids*. It is here that the majority of nerve fibres (lateral corticospinal tract) cross over to the other side and then descend into the spinal cord. Because of the crossing of fibres in the pyramids of the medulla, a lesion such as a stroke involving the internal capsule will result in paralysis of the opposite side of the body.
- In the medulla, a smaller percentage of the nerve fibres descend to the spinal cord without crossing – these form the anterior corticospinal tract.
- The corticospinal tract ends by synapsing on the anterior horn cells which give rise to the motor nerves that supply the muscles. The course of the corticospinal tract is summarized in Fig. 70.7.

Function

The corticospinal tract controls the muscles and movements of the trunk and the upper and lower limbs.

Other motor tracts:

The pyramidal tract is one of many tracts from the brain that regulates motor function. The other tracts are called the

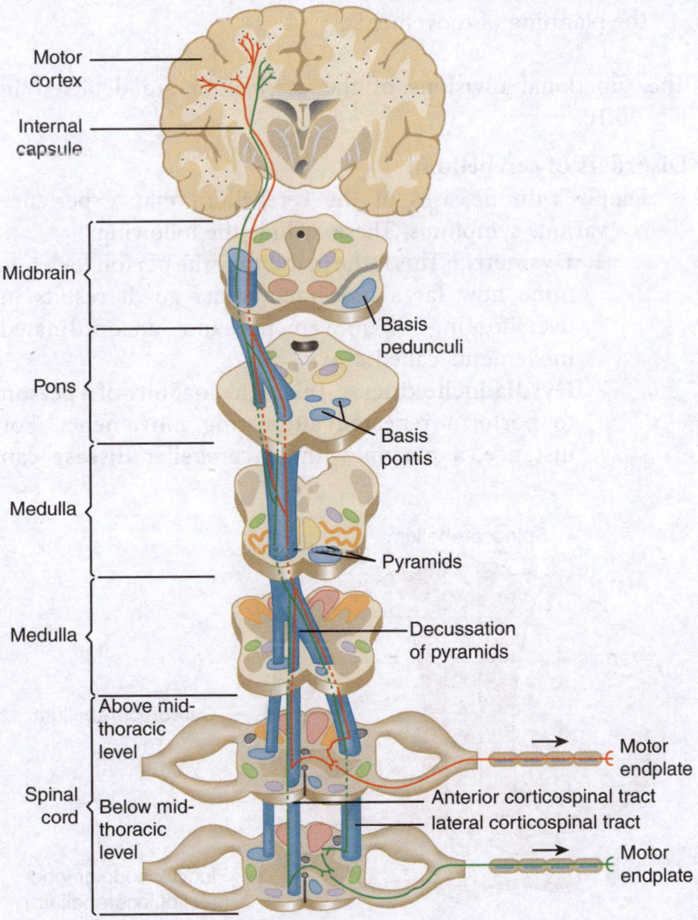

FIG. 70.7 The corticospinal tract.

extrapyramidal tracts. These include many tracts which start from subcortical structures in the brain:

1. Vestibulospinal,
2. Olivospinal,
3. Reticulospinal,
4. Rubrospinal,
5. Tectospinal tracts.

The differences between the pyramidal and extrapyramidal tracts are summarized below:

	Pyramidal System	Extrapyramidal System
Source	Motor cortex (areas 4,6,8) Sensory cortex (3,2,1) and parietal association area	Subcortical
Tracts	Corticobulbar Corticospinal • Anterior • Lateral	Reticulospinal Rubrospinal Vestibulospinal Tectospinal Olivospinal
Type of tract	Usually direct synapses to the motor neuron (in the anterior horn cell in the spinal cord)	Multisynaptic
Function	Skilled movement	Modulation of voluntary movement Maintenance of tone
Involuntary movements when affected	No	Yes

THE BASAL GANGLIA

The basal ganglia are collections of cells involved in motor control which are located in the subcortical regions of the brain (hence the name basal). The basal ganglia are involved with the control of movement and work in close association with the motor cortex and the corticospinal tract.

Parts of the basal ganglia:

There are different collections of cells (nuclei) which make up the basal ganglia and these include the:

- caudate,
- putamen (the caudate and putamen together form the striatum),
- subthalamic nuclei,
- globus pallidus
- substantia nigra.

Fig. 70.8 illustrates the location and components of the basal ganglia.

The nerve connections of the basal ganglia involve two major areas of the brain. These are the cortical areas that control movement (motor cortex) and the thalamus which receives sensory information from the body, is the major sensory relay station and is excitatory to the motor cortex.

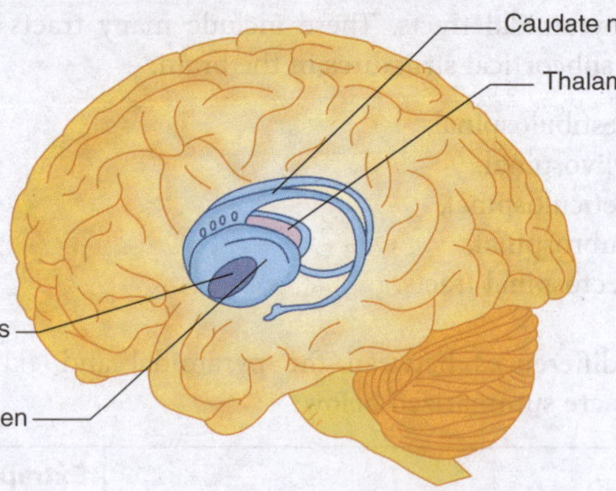

FIG. 70.8 Location of the basal ganglia.

Functions of the basal ganglia:

The basal ganglia have many functions. The more important of these are:

- Initiation of movement
- Control of muscle tone
- Control of reflex muscle activity
- Control of complex patterns of motor activity (timing/scale, etc.)
- Important in balance and posture

Disorders of the basal ganglia:

Parkinson's disease:

Cause:

Parkinson's disease is caused by the destruction of specific cells in the basal ganglia called the substantia nigra and the nigrostriatal pathway that secrete a neurotransmitter called dopamine. Although this condition most often affects people who are older, that is older than 60 years, it may also occur in younger individuals.

Clinical features:

Patients with this condition experience:

- Resting tremors.
- Rigidity.
- Their faces may tend to be expressionless, that is mask-like.
- They find it difficult to initiate body movements.
- They walk with a shuffling gait.

THE CEREBELLUM

The cerebellum is located below the occipital lobes of the brain at the base of the skull. It is divided anatomically into the anterior lobe, posterior lobe, flocculonodular lobe and the vermis as shown in Fig. 70.9.

Physiologically, the cerebellum is divided based on the functions that different parts of the cerebellum serve.

1. **Vestibulocerebellum**, otherwise called the flocculonodular lobe, has strong connections between the cerebellum and the vestibular apparatus (discussed later in this chapter). It is responsible for the control of eye movements, equilibrium and balance.

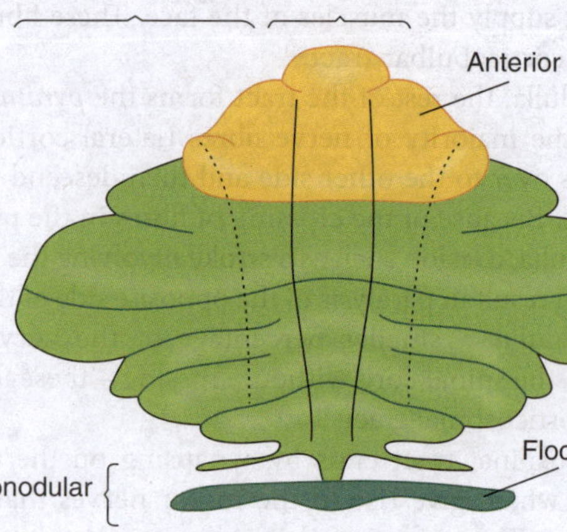

FIG. 70.9 The cerebellum and its anatomical divisions.

2. **Spinocerebellum** consists of the vermis and the adjacent portions of the cerebellar hemispheres. It receives information via the spinal cord of body position from various receptors located in the muscle (muscle spindle and Golgi's tendon receptors) and joints of the limbs and is responsible for the smoothening and coordination of movements.
3. **Cerebrocerebellum** consists of the outer (lateral) portions of the cerebellar hemispheres. This part of the cerebellum has nerve connections with the motor cortex and plays a role in the planning of movements.

The functional divisions of the cerebellum are depicted in Fig. 70.10.

Disorders of cerebellum:

People with diseases of the cerebellum may experience various symptoms. These include the following:

1. **Dysmetria**: This is the inability of the person to determine how far a movement must go. It results in overshooting of movements and uncoordinated movements called *ataxia*.
2. **Dysdiadochokinesis**: This is the inability of a person to perform repeated alternating movements. For instance, a person without cerebellar disease can

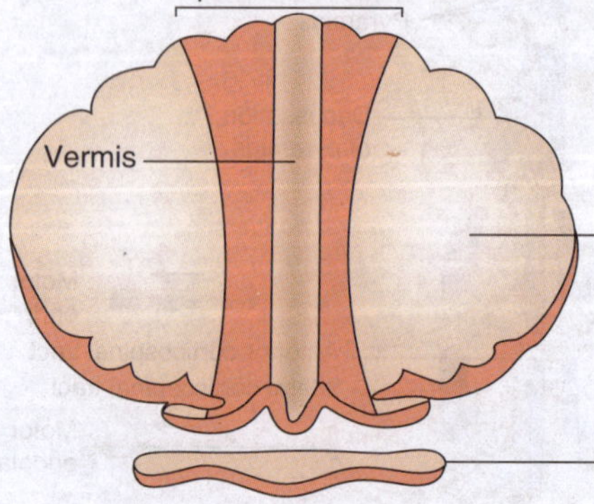

FIG. 70.10 The functional divisions of the cerebellum.

repeatedly turn the hand rapidly upwards and downwards so that the palm first faces up and then down.

3. **Tremor:** This is the trembling or shaking of the hands or limbs. With cerebellar disease, the tremor becomes more noticeable when the person performs a voluntary act as a result of which it is called an 'intention tremor'.
4. **Changes in muscle tone**: In most cases, there is reduced tone – a condition called hypotonia.

THE VESTIBULAR APPARATUS

Location and parts of the vestibular apparatus:

This is located in the inner ear (Fig. 70.11) and is responsible for the maintenance of balance and equilibrium. The vestibular apparatus is not involved with hearing and has several parts which are illustrated in greater detail in Fig. 70.12.

As can be seen from Fig. 70.12, the vestibular apparatus consists of:

- the utricle,
- saccule and
- three semicircular canals.

The three semicircular canals are placed in different directions at right angles to each other. Thus, one semicircular canal is anterior, one posterior and one horizontal. These parts of the vestibular apparatus are filled with a fluid called endolymph. Hair cells are the receptors of the vestibular apparatus – these are stimulated when there is a movement of the endolymph. The endolymph moves whenever we rotate our heads and whenever our bodies are subjected to a change in speed. When the head rotates, impulses from the vestibular apparatus are transmitted to the brain via the vestibular part of the VIII cranial nerve. This cranial nerve also carries impulses from the inner ear to the brain which allows us to perceive sound, but this is through another branch of the VIII cranial nerve called the auditory nerve. Once impulses are carried in the vestibular nerve to the brain, stabilization of the body occurs through actions on the postural muscles of the head and neck, by ensuring that eye movements are coordinated with body movements and by acting via the cerebellum.

Functions of the vestibular apparatus:

This vestibular apparatus:

- Provides the body information about rotation, head position and linear acceleration (using semicircular canals and otolith organs).
- Coordinates head and neck movement with the trunk and body through vestibulospinal reflexes.
- Stabilizes eye movements during movement through special reflexes called vestibulo-ocular reflexes.

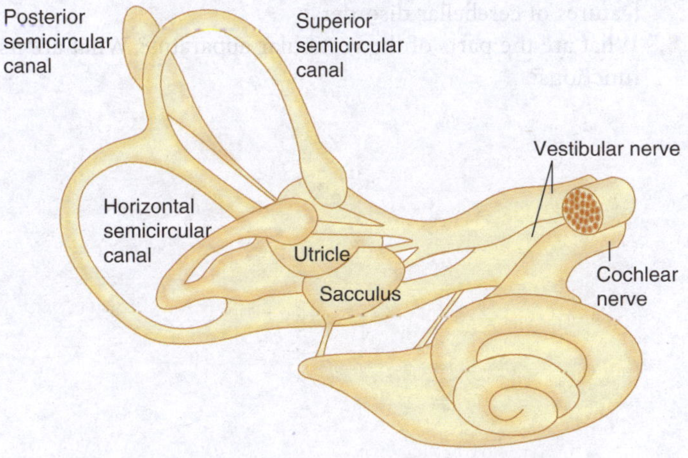

FIG. 70.12 The vestibular apparatus.

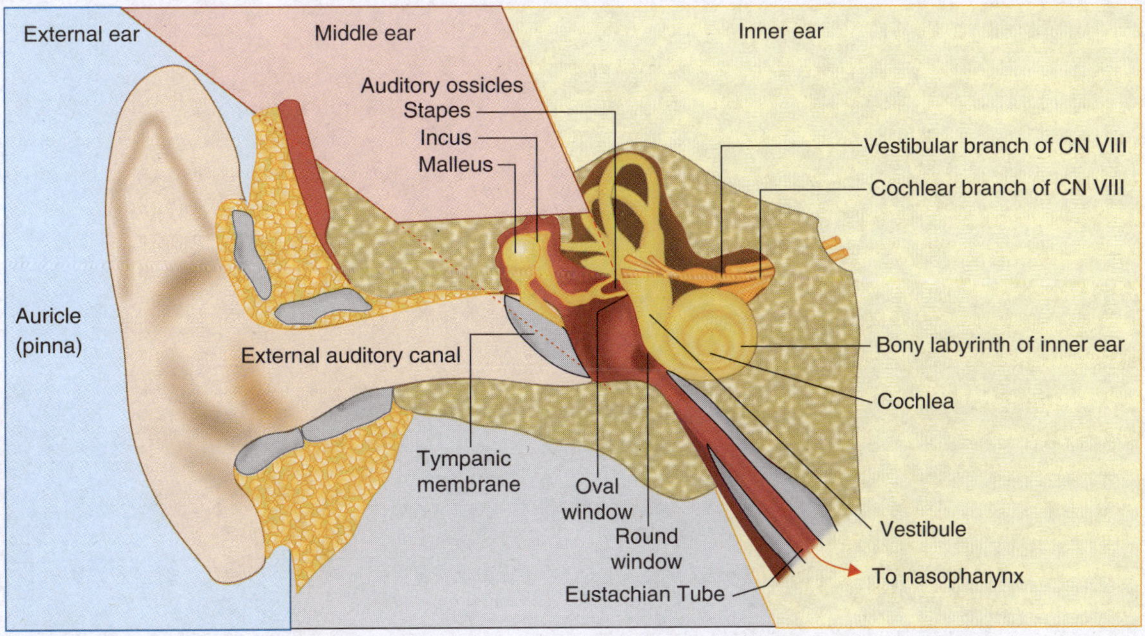

FIG. 70.11 The anatomical structure of the ear.

APPLICATIONS FOR NURSING

Patients with disorders of motor function may be ill for long periods of time. The nurse plays an important role in educating the patients and their health carers about the nature of the symptoms, the need for adherence to medication and general issues of hygiene, diet and physical activity. It is important that nurses focus not only on the patient but also on the health carers since the strain of health carers, such as family members, can be quite considerable. The nurse will need to educate carers on issues of mobility for the patient (such as walking aids) and the ways to reduce injury and falls (by assessing the home environment, etc.) if the symptoms are severe.

SUMMARY

- Muscle length and tension are controlled by sense organs in the muscle and tendons such as the muscle spindle and the Golgi's tendon organs.
- The voluntary control of muscle function in the cerebral cortex is achieved by three major areas called the primary motor cortex, the premotor area and the supplementary motor area.
- The pyramidal (corticospinal) tract transmits information from the brain to the upper and lower limbs and trunk to control movement – this tract 'crosses over' in the medulla. Damage to the tract above the medulla will therefore cause problems of movement including paralysis in the opposite side of the body (haemiplegia).
- The basal ganglia are a number of subcortical areas involved in the control of movement. Disorders of these areas result in a variety of abnormal movements. The most important of the disorders is Parkinson's disease which affects the dopaminergic nigrostriatal pathway.
- The cerebellum is involved in the control of eye movements and equilibrium, in smoothing and coordinating movements and in the planning of movements.
- The vestibular apparatus in the inner ear is responsible for the maintenance of balance and equilibrium.

Chapter Review Questions

1. Trace the pyramidal tract
2. What are parts of the basal ganglia? What are the functions of the basal ganglia?
3. What are the functions of the cerebellum? What are the features of cerebellar disorders?
4. What are the parts of the vestibular apparatus? What are its functions?

CHAPTER 71

The Autonomic Nervous System

SPECIFIC LEARNING OBJECTIVES

At the end of this chapter, the student should be able to:

- Describe the functional anatomy of the autonomic nervous system.
- List the broad actions of the sympathetic nervous system.
- List the broad actions of the parasympathetic nervous system.
- List the receptors through which autonomic nervous effects are mediated.
- List the interactions between the sympathetic nervous system and the parasympathetic nervous system.
- Describe the salient features of autonomic failure.

GLOSSARY OF TERMS

- **Craniosacral outflow:** the collection of parasympathetic nerves that emerge from the central nervous system
- **Thoracolumbar outflow:** the collection of sympathetic nerves that emerge from the central nervous system
- **Preganglionic nerves:** the motor outflow of the autonomic nervous system (both sympathetic and parasympathetic) is formed by two neurons connected in series (i.e. separated by a synapse); the first neuron which originates in the brain or spinal cord is called a preganglionic neuron
- **Postganglionic nerves:** the second neuron that originates outside the central nervous system and supplies the organs

BROAD FUNCTIONS OF THE AUTONOMIC NERVOUS SYSTEM

The autonomic nervous system is that part of the nervous system that controls the 'automatic' functions of our body. This includes a range of functions that include the secretions and motility of the gastrointestinal (GI) system, the emptying of the urinary bladder and arterial blood pressure, among others. The autonomic nervous system also controls the rate and contractility of the heart and calibre of the airways.

One of the important features of the autonomic nervous system is the speed with which it can react – often within a couple of seconds. Thus, a change in posture from lying down to standing results in a rapid fall in blood pressure which is brought back to normal through a special reflex called the baroreflex.

PARTS OF THE AUTONOMIC NERVOUS SYSTEM

The autonomic nervous system consists of two parts: the parasympathetic nervous system and the sympathetic nervous system. We will discuss these two parts of the autonomic nervous system in greater detail in this chapter. In the somatic nervous system, the somatic effector (motor nerves) arises in the central nervous system (the ventral horn of the spinal cord) and acts directly on the skeletal muscle. In contrast, the effector neuron of the autonomic nervous system arises outside the central nervous system and supplies various organs, glands and smooth muscles in the body (Fig. 71.1).

FUNCTIONAL ANATOMY OF THE AUTONOMIC NERVOUS SYSTEM

Pre- and postganglionic nerve fibres: Although the final effector neuron of the autonomic nervous system lies outside the central nervous system, it is connected to a neuron which is inside the central nervous system. The point where the two neurons meet comprises a 'ganglion'. Thus, the nerve fibre of the autonomic nervous system that emerges out of the central nervous system is called the *preganglionic nerve* fibre (because it is before the ganglion) and the nerve which is the final effector neuron is called the *postganglionic nerve* fibre because it occurs after the ganglion.

The preganglionic and postganglionic nerves are different in the parasympathetic and sympathetic nervous system.

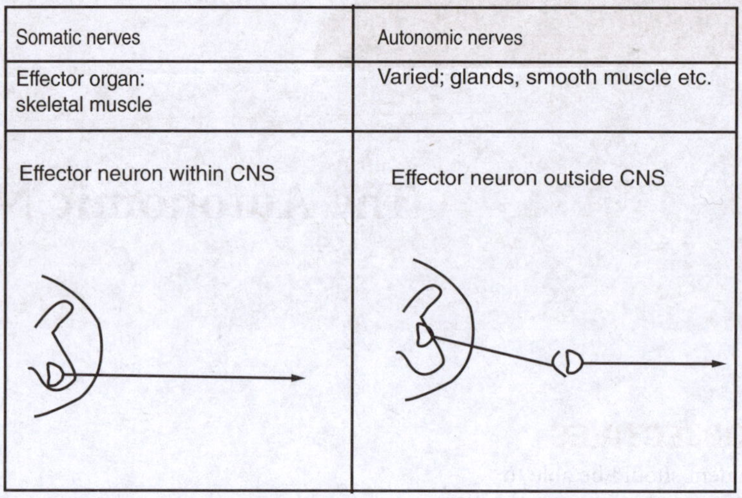

FIG. 71.1 A comparison between somatic and autonomic nerves.

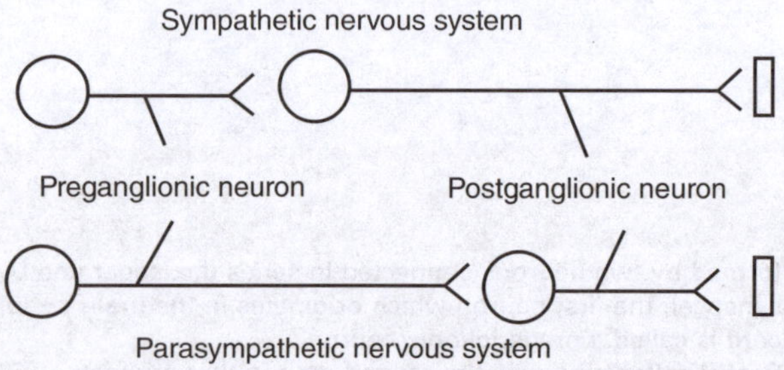

FIG. 71.2 Arrangement of preganglionic and postganglionic neurons of the sympathetic and parasympathetic nervous systems.

In the case of the sympathetic nervous system, the preganglionic neuron is relatively long while in the case of the parasympathetic nervous system, the postganglionic neuron is short. This is illustrated schematically in Fig. 71.2.

Origin of the sympathetic and parasympathetic nervous system:

- The sympathetic nerves emerge from the spinal cord from the thoracic and lumbar segments. This is therefore referred to as the *thoracolumbar outflow*. In Fig. 71.3, sympathetic nervous outflow is depicted in red.
- In contrast, the parasympathetic nerves are part of the cranial nerves as well as the spinal nerves. The cranial nerves which have parasympathetic components are the oculomotor (III), facial (VII), glossopharyngeal (IX) and vagus (X) nerves. A large part of all parasympathetic nerves is contained in the X cranial nerve, that is the vagus supplies a large part of the GI tract including the oesophagus, stomach, small intestine, parts of the large intestine, the urinary bladder and the heart and lungs, among others. In addition to the parasympathetic component of the cranial nerves, parasympathetic nerves also emerge from the sacral spinal segments. It is for this reason that the parasympathetic nerves are sometimes referred to as the *craniosacral outflow* (Fig. 71.3). In Fig.71.3, parasympathetic nerves depicted in blue emerge in the cranial nerves and from the sacral region.

Autonomic nervous function is under the influence of the central nervous system. Thus, emotions such as fright or fear or anger are associated with alterations in the body brought on by the autonomic nervous system. One of the structures that are involved in the control of the autonomic nervous system is the hypothalamus, which a famous physiologist called Sherrington referred to as the 'head ganglion' of the autonomic nervous system.

NEUROTRANSMITTERS AND RECEPTORS OF THE AUTONOMIC NERVOUS SYSTEM

Neurotransmitters:

Every nerve releases a chemical messenger called a neurotransmitter at its nerve endings. Some of these neurotransmitters are excitatory and some are inhibitory. Because the autonomic nervous systems, both sympathetic and parasympathetic, have preganglionic nerve fibres and postganglionic nerve fibres, it follows that neurotransmitters will be released from both these types of neurons. Once the neurotransmitter has been released, it acts on receptors. Fig. 71.4 summarizes the neurotransmitters and receptors of the sympathetic and parasympathetic nervous systems.

Fig. 71.4 shows that for the preganglionic neurons of both the parasympathetic nervous system and the sympathetic nervous system, acetylcholine is the neurotransmitter. In the postganglionic neurons of the sympathetic nervous system, norepinephrine is the transmitter, while in the parasympathetic nervous system, acetylcholine is the neurotransmitter.

Receptors:

Norepinephrine acts on *adrenergic receptors* of which there are different varieties – the two main types of receptors are α- and β-adrenergic receptors. These adrenergic

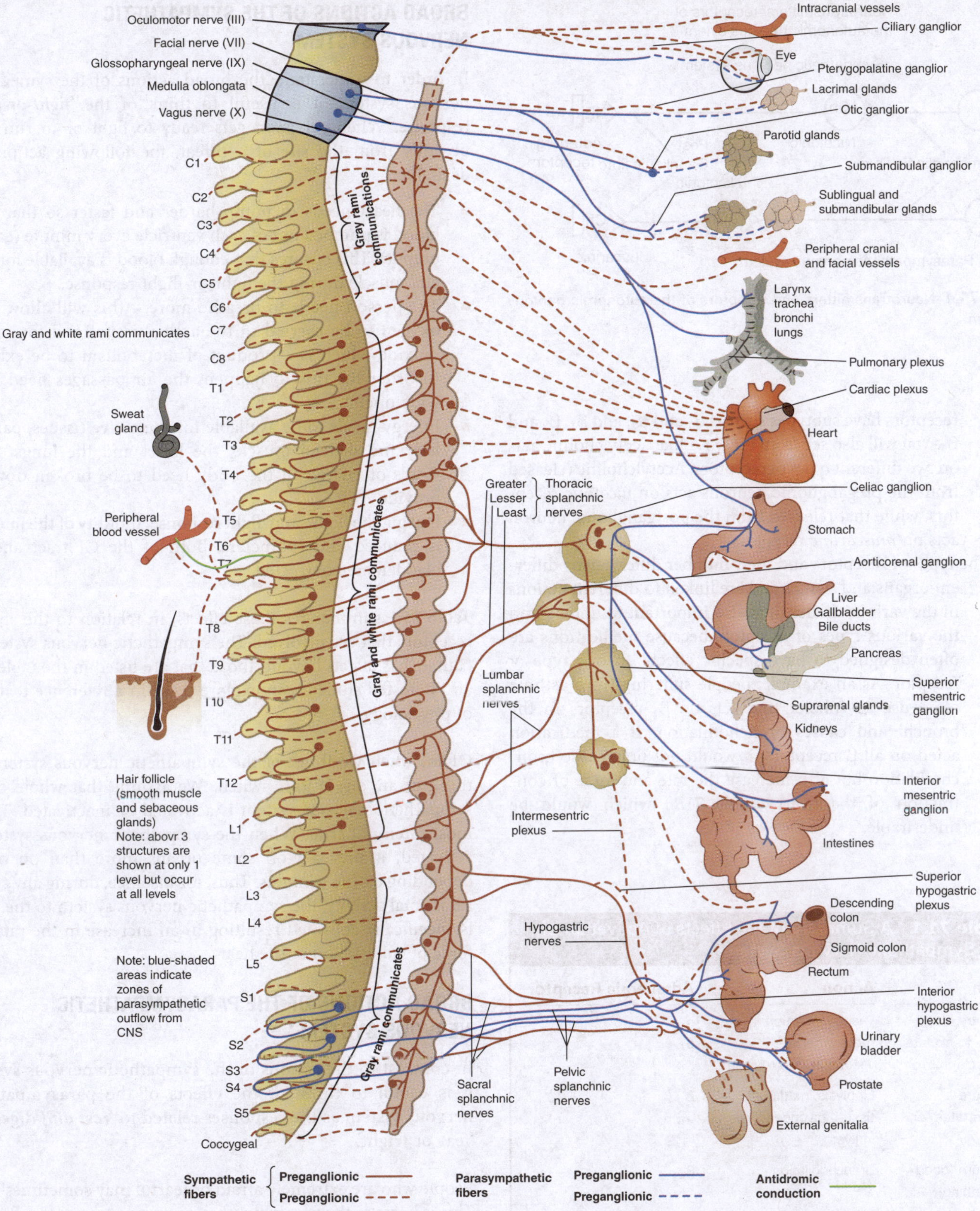

FIG. 71.3 Anatomical organization of the autonomic nervous system.

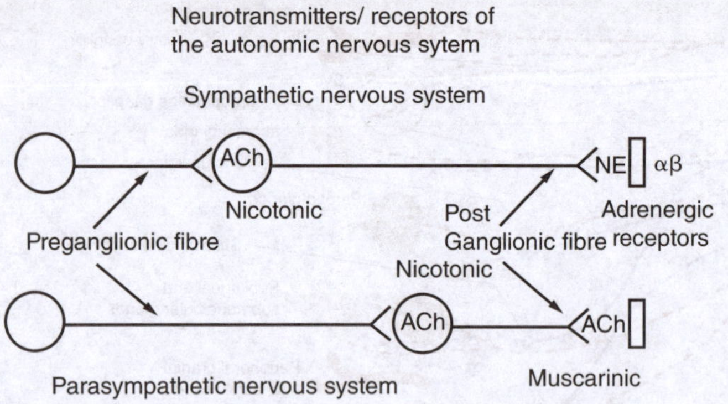

FIG. 71.4 Neurotransmitters and receptors of the autonomic nervous system.

receptors have subtypes such as α_1 and α_2, and β_1, β_2 and β_3. You will also see from Fig. 71.4 that acetylcholine acts on two different types of receptors. Acetylcholine released from the preganglionic neurons acts on *nicotinic* receptors, while that released from the postganglionic neuron acts on *muscarinic* receptors.

The types of receptors and their number differ across different organs and tissues and are linked to different actions in the various tissues. It is also important to understand the various types of receptors because medications are often designed to have specific effects on one type of receptor. As an example, people suffering from asthma often use an inhaler that acts on β_2 receptors in the bronchi and causes bronchodilation. If a medication acted on all β receptors, it would not only cause bronchodilation but also increase the rate and force of contraction of the heart (Table 71.1) which would be undesirable.

Table 71.1 A Summary of the Effects of Activation of the Sympathetic Nervous System

Aim	Action	Adrenergic Receptor
Ensure blood flow to skeletal muscle	Vasoconstriction in most organs, vasodilation in muscle	α_1 β_2
Ensure substrates for energy	Lipolysis in adipose tissue, glycogenolysis in liver	β_1, β_3 α_1, β_2
Ensure 'good' breathing	Bronchodilation	β_2
Maintain BP and perfusion	Increased heart rate and contractility of the heart	β_1
What else?	Sphincters contract Decreased GI secretion Decreased GI motility	α_1 α_2 α_1, α_2, β_2

BROAD ACTIONS OF THE SYMPATHETIC NERVOUS SYSTEM

In order to understand the broad actions of the sympathetic nervous system, it is useful to think of the ***'fight-or-flight'*** response. When a person gets ready to fight or to run away urgently from the site of a threat, the following actions are desirable:

- The heart needs to pump harder and faster so that more blood is pumped out of each ventricle every minute (cardiac output). This ensures that enough blood is available for skeletal muscle during the fight-or-flight response.
- The person needs to breathe more – this will allow more oxygen to be carried to the active tissues and for carbon dioxide which is a product of metabolism to be exhaled. In order for this to happen, the air passages need to be wide open.
- Energy needs to be available for the active tissues, particularly the skeletal muscle, the heart and the lungs. Thus, stores of energy in the body need to be broken down to provide ATP.
- During the flight-and-fight response, motility of the intestine is reduced and sphincters, both of the GI tract and the bladder, are contracted.

Table 71.1 summarizes these effects, in relation to the specific receptors that are involved. The sympathetic nervous system, of course, has effects beyond those that are listed in the table, and an interested student can explore these in a reference textbook of physiology.

Often, when we think of the sympathetic nervous system, we think of an 'on' or 'off' switch. We assume that whole of the sympathetic nervous system is activated or inactivated. This is most often not true. When the sympathetic nervous system is activated, it may act on some organs more than on others depending on the stimulus. Thus, for instance, during any stressful mental activity, the sympathetic nervous system to the heart is specifically activated resulting in an increase in the rate and force of contraction of the heart.

BROAD ACTIONS OF THE PARASYMPATHETIC NERVOUS SYSTEM

In contrast to the actions of the sympathetic nervous system, it is useful to think of the effects of the parasympathetic nervous system as the responses related to ***'rest and digest'*** or 'fear or fright'.

People who are extremely afraid or fearful may sometimes faint. This is because the parasympathetic nervous system through the vagus nerve slows the heart rate down. This reduction in the heart rate can reduce the cardiac output, that is the amount of the blood that is ejected by each ventricle every minute. This in turn reduces the blood pressure which is determined by cardiac output and total peripheral resistance. An abnormally low blood pressure can result in 'fainting'.

Another effect of the parasympathetic nervous system is that it increases intestinal motility and the contraction of bladder as well as relaxation of the sphincters. A small child who is extremely frightened may pass urine and stools as a result of these actions of the parasympathetic nervous system.

A summary of the main effects of parasympathetic nervous activation is provided as follows:

1. Sweating in palms
2. Constriction of pupils
3. Increased GI motility
4. Increased secretion from enzyme-secreting glands
5. Relaxation of sphincters
6. Widespread vasodilation
7. Decreased heart rate
8. Decreased cardiac output
9. Fall in blood pressure

RELATIONSHIP BETWEEN THE SYMPATHETIC AND PARASYMPATHETIC NERVOUS SYSTEM

A simple understanding of the relationship between the sympathetic nervous system and the parasympathetic nervous system is that when one is activated, the other is inactivated and vice versa.

Actually, the relationship is slightly more complex and examples of this are given as follows:

Dual supply – antagonistic (i.e. against each other)	Heart rate: Symp +; para –
Dual supply – antagonistic	GI peristalsis Para +; symp –
Dual supply – excitatory – different end points, because they work on different sites	Pupil Para: + constrictor Symp: + dilator
Dual supply – synergistic (i.e. having the same action)	Salivary gland secretion Symp and para +

APPLICATIONS FOR NURSING

Disorders of the autonomic nervous system are not uncommon. Chronic diseases like diabetes mellitus can result in 'autonomic failure', a condition in which autonomic nervous function is impaired or reduced. Patients with autonomic failure may suffer from bouts of light-headedness, giddiness and fainting. This is because of their inability to maintain blood pressure under certain circumstances as, for instance, during changes in posture (when people who are lying down or sitting suddenly get up). This can also happen in elderly people. People who suffer from autonomic failure may also experience other problems such as problems with sweating (too much or too little); difficulties in digestion including a loss of appetite, bloating, diarrhoea, constipation or difficulty in swallowing; urinary problems such as difficulty starting urination, loss of control of urination or incomplete emptying of the bladder; and sexual problems in men, such as difficulty in maintaining an erection or with ejaculation.

Because the autonomic nervous system controls the function of vital organs such as the heart, it is important that nurses are aware of common medications that act on the autonomic nervous system, their actions, their indications and side effects that may be associated with their use.

SUMMARY

- The autonomic nervous system consists of two branches: the sympathetic nervous system and the parasympathetic nervous system.
- The sympathetic nervous system emerges via the spinal nerves through the thoracolumbar outflow, while the parasympathetic nervous system emerges out of cranial and spinal nerves – the so-called 'craniosacral' outflow.
- Sympathetic nervous action is mediated via adrenergic receptors, while parasympathetic nervous actions are mediated via muscarinic receptors.
- Activation of the sympathetic nervous system results in 'fight-or-flight' responses, while activation of the parasympathetic nervous system results in 'fright-or-fear' responses.

CHAPTER REVIEW QUESTIONS

1. Compare the origin of the sympathetic and parasympathetic nervous systems.
2. Describe the response of the body during sympathetic activation as part of the flight or fight response.
3. Describe the broad functions of the parasympathetic nervous system.
4. What are the postganglionic neurotransmitters of sympathetic and parasympathetic nervous system? On which receptors do these neurotransmitters act?

CHAPTER 72

Higher Mental Functions

SPECIFIC LEARNING OBJECTIVES

At the end of this chapter, the student should be able to:

- List the major waves of the electroencephalogram (EEG) in terms of their amplitude and frequency.
- List the uses of EEG.
- Describe the physiology of sleep in relation to:
  - The stages of sleep
  - The difference between slow-wave and rapid eye movement (REM) sleep
- List some common disorders of sleep.
- List the areas involved with speech.
- Define aphasia and list the different types of aphasia.
- Define memory and learning.
- List the stages of memory.
- List some common disorders of memory.

GLOSSARY OF TERMS

- **EEG:** a record of the fluctuations of the electrical activity of large numbers of neurons in the brain, recorded with electrodes applied to the surface of the scalp
- **Coma:** a state of prolonged unconsciousness
- **Epilepsy:** fits or seizures triggered by abnormal electrical activity in the brain
- **Brain death:** irreversible loss of the neuronal functions of the brain (EEG shows absence of brain activity)
- **REM sleep:** rapid eye movement sleep, also called paradoxical sleep, characterized by beta waves, hypotonia, withdrawal of sympathetic tone and dreams, among other features
- **Aphasia:** a disorder of speech
- **Learning:** acquisition of new knowledge
- **Memory:** storage and retrieval of learned knowledge
- **Amnesia:** loss of memory

In the chapters before this one, we have described how the nervous system processes sensory information (sensory system), helps us to perform movements (motor system) and helps us regulate the functions of various organs in the body (autonomic nervous system). In addition to all these functions, the brain helps us to think, communicate, learn new activities and evaluate our daily experience in the light of past experiences and memories. Our bodies cannot function without rest – we all know how tired we feel and how unfocused and ineffective we can be if we do not get a good night's sleep. The brain also helps us to regulate our sleep patterns. In this chapter, we will address some of these issues.

ELECTROENCEPHALOGRAM

In Chapter 67, we described the electrical potentials developed in a single neuron. At any one point in time, millions of neurons in the brain are active. The electrical activity of the brain from moment to moment can be captured by placing electrodes on the surface of the scalp. Thus, electroencephalogram (EEG) is a record of the fluctuations of the electrical activity of large numbers of neurons in the brain, recorded with electrodes applied to the surface of the scalp.

Recording EEG

The placement of the electrodes for EEG is varied. Thus, EEG may be recorded with few or very many electrodes sometimes fitted into a tight cap that is placed on the patient's head. When many electrodes are used, it allows EEG to be picked up from different regions of the brain. This is important for some conditions which may show an alteration in electrical activity in a focal (specific, local) area of the brain.

Resting EEG is typically recorded in:

- quiet relaxed circumstances with the patient seated or lying comfortably with the eyes closed.
- Recordings are typically done for at least 30 minutes.

- In addition, EEG may be recorded during certain stimuli such as flashes of light (photic stimuli) and hyperventilation, among others. These stimuli may sometimes help to uncover abnormal electrical activity that may not be visible in a resting EEG.
- One of the common uses of EEG is during sleep studies. Larger hospitals may have a sleep laboratory where patients with disorders of sleep are studied overnight. EEG helps to study the phases of sleep during which specific problems may be seen.

Types of EEG Waves

There are four major types of EEG waves based on the amplitude and frequency of the wave. Fig. 72.1 illustrates the four different waves. You will observe from this figure that beta waves are of low amplitude (height) but have a high frequency (number of waves per second), while delta waves have a high amplitude but a low frequency.

Table 72.1 summarizes the characteristics of the different EEG waves and some of the conditions in which they are found.

Uses of EEG

EEG has many uses, some of which are listed as follows:

1. ***Evaluation of epilepsy***: Epilepsy is sometimes referred to as 'fits' or seizures. There are different types of epilepsy. *Grand mal epilepsy* is a severe form of epilepsy in which there is an abnormal burst of electrical activity which involves the whole brain. A grand mal seizure may be preceded by an 'aura' – a premonition of an impending epileptic attack. This aura may be olfactory or visual. The patient then becomes rigid before experiencing violent muscle contractions lasting from a few seconds to a few minutes. This is followed by a postictal phase in which the patient slowly recovers but may be dazed and disoriented. During grand mal seizures, all recording electrodes show bizarre bursts of electrical activity. Petit mal or focal seizure, as the name suggests, is a milder form of epilepsy which involves a group of muscles rather than the whole body. In this situation, abnormal electrical activity will be recorded in only specific electrodes.
2. ***Psychiatric disorders involving pseudoseizures***: Since seizures rely a lot on the history that a person comes with, this needs to be verified by accounts from other people who have witnessed the seizure and from EEG recordings.
3. ***Evaluation of sleep disorders:*** Sleep goes through various stages which are characterized by unique EEG wave patterns. EEG recordings allow for the study of disorders of sleep as well as of conditions that are associated with specific stages of sleep. These are discussed further in a later section of this chapter.
4. ***Assessment of coma***: Coma is a prolonged state of unconsciousness. EEG can supplement other clinical assessments to determine the stage of coma.
5. ***Determining brain death***: This has become increasingly important since certification of brain death precedes the harvesting of various organs from a donor.

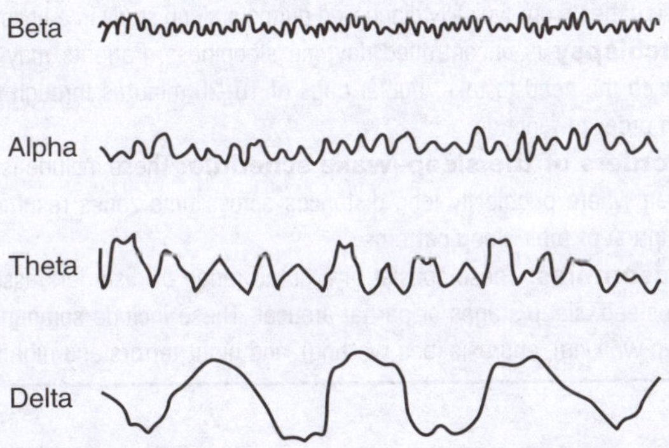

FIG. 72.1 The four normal major types of EEG waves.

Table 72.1 Characteristics of EEG Waves

Wave	Amplitude	Frequency (Hz)	Where Found
Alpha	Low	8–13	Adults who are awake and resting with the eyes open
Beta	Low	13–30	When active, alert, tense, in certain stages of sleep
Theta	Higher	4–8	In children in the parietal and frontal lobes, in certain phases of sleep
Delta	Highest	0.5–4	Deep sleep, infancy

SLEEP

Stages of Sleep

The stages of sleep are best understood in terms of a diagram as illustrated in Fig. 72.2. Let us consider an 8-hour sleep period. You will observe from Fig. 72.2 that a person shifts steadily from the awake state to deeper stages of sleep (stages 1–4).

- In stage 1, EEG shows alpha waves.
- Stage 4 is the deepest stage of sleep from which it is difficult to awaken and is characterized by delta waves on EEG.
- Having reached stage 4, the person then moves progressively up to stage 2 and then shifts into a phase called REM sleep.
- REM refers to 'rapid eye movement' and is so called because during this phase the eyes move rapidly. It is also called paradoxical sleep because during this phase EEG shows beta waves which are typically seen when a person is awake.
- The stages of sleep other than the REM phase are collectively called non-REM sleep.

Features of a sleep cycle:

1. During an 8-hour sleep period, we go through about four cycles of alternating REM and non-REM sleep.
2. As a person continues to sleep uninterrupted, he or she spends increasing times in REM sleep.

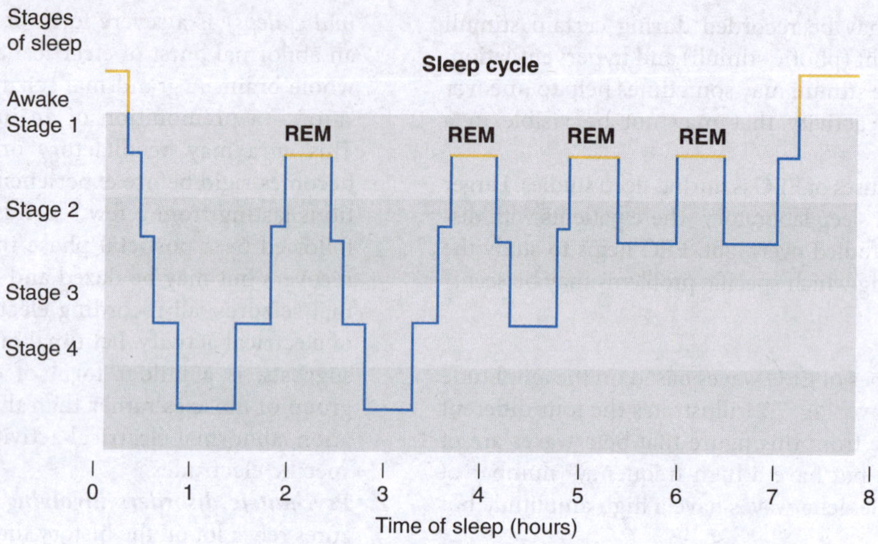

FIG. 72.2 Parts of a sleep cycle.

3. Following each REM phase, the person goes into progressively less deep sleep. Thus, while earlier on he or she may have reached stage 4, later on he or she may reach only stage 3 or stage 2.

REM Sleep

REM sleep has several characteristics. These include the following:

- Hypotonia (a reduction in muscle tone)
- Dreams (these are most likely to be recalled if a person is awakened from REM sleep than from non-REM sleep)
- Rapid eye movements
- Withdrawal of sympathetic nervous system (sympathetic nervous system has a resting tone; this means that even at rest, the sympathetic nerves are firing at a certain rate; during REM sleep, there is a reduction of sympathetic tone which means that sympathetic nerves fire less)
- Decreased thermoregulation
- Irregular heart rate/respiration
- Decreased external arousability, that is decreased ability of being woken up by external stimuli
- Increased internal arousability, that is a greater chance that a person will awaken on his or her own
- Penile erections experienced by males during this phase

Sleep Disorders

These may be broadly characterized into the following categories:

1. **Insomnias:** These are disorders of initiating and maintaining sleep. People may feel that they have had insufficient sleep and are not rested after a sleep cycle. This may be due to many causes including substance abuse, excessive drinking of alcohol, mental health conditions such as depression and anxiety and as a side effect of medications, among others.
2. **Hypersomnias:** These are disorders of excessive sleep which include conditions such as sleep apnoea syndrome and narcolepsy, among others. Obstructive sleep apnoea is a condition that is being increasingly recognized and treated. It affects males more than females and is seen in greater numbers in those who are obese and who are smokers. Patients typically experience tiredness and sleepiness during the day and inability to function optimally. During sleep, they experience periods of apnoea causing a disruption in the stages of sleep. Partners of these patients may indicate that they snore progressively louder and then seem to choke before subsiding to sleep again. These patients are typically diagnosed during a sleep study in a hospital.
   Narcolepsy is uncontrolled daytime sleepiness. Patients may experience the need to take regular naps of 10–20 minutes through the day in order to function.
3. **Disorders of the sleep–wake schedule:** These include issues of jet lag where people fly long distances across time zones resulting in a disruption of their sleep patterns.
4. **Parasomnias:** These consist of a broad range of disorders associated with sleep, sleep stages or partial arousal. These include somnambulism (sleep walking), enuresis (bed wetting), and night terrors and nightmares.

SPEECH

Speech is not merely the production of meaningful sound but involves the comprehension of other people's speech, the understanding of language and meaningful communication that allows comprehension by other people.

Fig. 72.3 indicates the pathways that are involved in the production of speech.

When we speak, we often do so in response to what we see and what we hear. This means that the production of speech must be connected to those sensory areas in the brain which process visual and auditory information. We then need to make sense of this information. Sensory information is not received in isolated packets – thus, when we see a movie, we are exposed to simultaneous visual and auditory information and this is the case for most things that we experience. We therefore need to process these multiple sensory inputs.

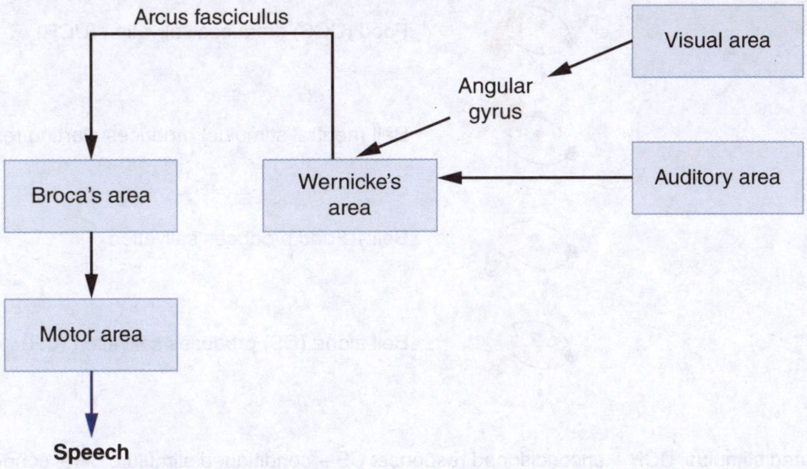

FIG. 72.3 Areas involved, and pathways in the production of speech.

Brain areas involved in speech:

In Fig. 72.3, information from the visual and auditory areas of the cerebral cortex is connected to the Wernicke's area which is sensory processing area. Information from Wernicke's area is conveyed to Broca's motor speech area. Broca's area was discovered by the French neurologist Paul Broca who noticed that a patient of his had a difficulty in speaking and would communicate only in monosyllables despite the fact that there was no apparent problem with his muscles of speech. Broca's area in turn communicates with the motor cortex from where fibres descend to synapse on the cranial nerves that supply the muscles of the mouth and tongue, among others that allow us to produce speech.

CLINICAL BOX

Aphasia

These are disturbances in the production/comprehension of spoken/written language or speech. Aphasias can occur with a problem in any area involved in the pathway for speech. Thus, if Wernicke's area is affected, the person has a sensory aphasia because he or she has a particular problem of comprehending speech. When Broca's area is affected, the person suffers from a motor aphasia. When muscles are affected that are involved in the actual production of sound, the person suffers from dysarthria – he or she comprehends speech and is clear about what he or she wants to communicate but has slurred or unclear speech because the muscles are affected.

MEMORY AND LEARNING

Learning is the process of acquiring new knowledge. Memory is the storage and retrieval of that knowledge.

Forms of Learning Learning takes on several different forms, some of which are described in this section:

- **Habituation**: This occurs when we are exposed to a repeated nonthreatening or nonpainful stimulus. Consider the bursting of crackers at Diwali – at first, we may react with alarm when a cracker is burst close by to our houses, but after some time we stop reacting. This has been studied experimentally in animal models and long-term habituation has been associated with a reduction in the branching of neurons resulting in a reduction in the number of synapses. It is important to emphasize that we habituate (or respond less) only to stimuli which are not harmful.
- **Sensitization**: Here, there is an increased response to a range of stimuli following an intense, painful stimulus. Consider a situation which may have unfortunately happened to you at school – the child behind you pricks you with a pin off and on. Later the same child pokes you with a blunt pencil. You jump up, although the object is blunt. You have been sensitized. Sensitization is associated with increased branching of the neurons and an increased release of neurotransmitter at the synapses. The process of habituation and sensitization at the level of the neuron is illustrated in Fig. 72.4.
- **Classical conditioning**: It is a form of learning that is associated with Ivan Pavlov and is also called Pavlovian conditioning. In his famous dog experiment, Pavlov demonstrated that if a bell was rung (neutral stimulus), the dog would orient itself to where the sound of the bell was coming from. He then placed a bowl of food in front of the dog (unconditioned stimulus) and the dog immediately started salivating (unconditioned response). He then started pairing the bell with the placing of the food such that the bell (neutral stimulus)

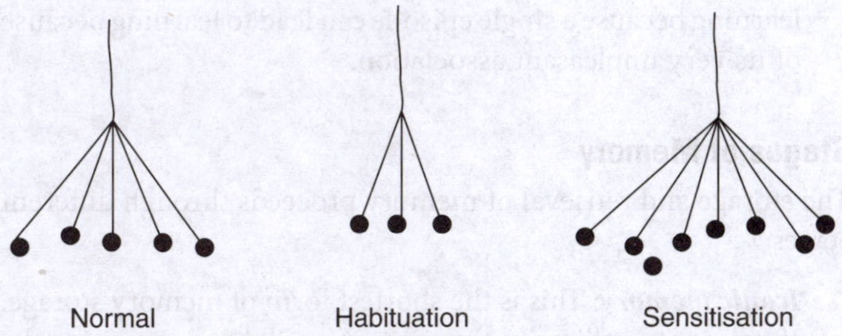

FIG. 72.4 Neuronal changes in habituation and sensitization.

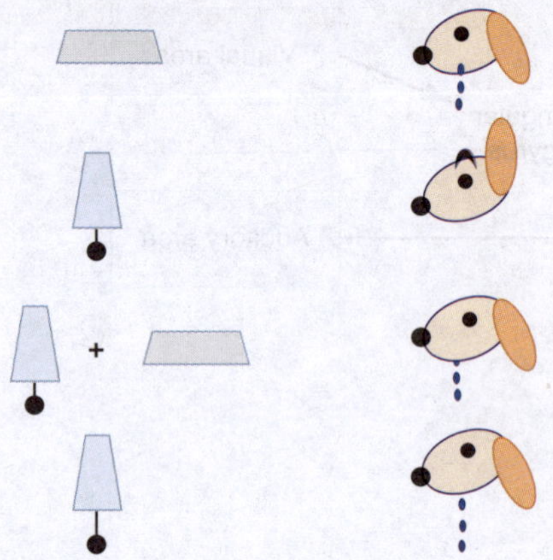

FIG. 72.5 Pavlov's experiment of classical conditioning.

always occurred before the bowl of food (unconditioned stimulus). After repeated pairing of these two stimuli, he then rang the bell and the dog started salivating, although the bowl had not been placed before it. The bell had been converted into a conditioned stimulus and the salivation into a conditioned response (Fig. 72.5).

Features of classical conditioning:

- The neutral stimulus always has to occur before the unconditioned stimulus.
- Repeated pairing of these stimuli is required before learning occurred.
- If, over time, the bell is rung but no food was provided, this form of learning is lost. This is called extinction.

- **Operant conditioning**: It is another form of learning which is also called 'trial and error' learning or Skinnerian conditioning after the man (BF Skinner) who developed this experiment. Skinner placed a rat in a special cage which had a lever. If the rat pressed the lever, a pellet of food was released for the rat to eat. When the rat was placed in the cage, it started off by exploring the cage. Over time, the rat would by chance press the lever and would receive a pellet of food. Initially the rat did not make the association between the lever and the pellet of food. But after several attempts, the rat made the association and would press the lever whenever it wanted food.
- **Food aversion conditioning**: It is a particularly powerful form of learning. If you have ever experienced a severe bout of food poisoning after eating a particular food, you will understand how you completely avoid eating that food whenever it is placed before you. This is a powerful form of learning because a single episode can lead to learning because of its very unpleasant association.

Stages of Memory

The storage and retrieval of memory proceeds through different stages:

1. ***Iconic memory***: This is the shortest form of memory storage. If you are travelling on the road, you will have experienced a situation in which you see an advertisement board – without any conscious effort, you recall the image as soon as you have passed it. This is retained for a very short period of time and has been explained on the basis of 'retinal afterimages'.
2. ***Primary memory storage*** is another form of short-term memory storage. This is improved if people find meaning in what they are trying to remember. However, this form of memory fades if new information is processed. We can all appreciate this when we are trying to learn – after a single reading, we think we have understood and remembered what we have read. However, when we read a new chapter, we begin to forget the content of what we have previously read.
3. ***Long-term memory storage*** occurs with repetition and is associated with what is called neuronal plasticity (a change in the structural and functional nature of the neurons). Although there are many parts of the brain which are involved in learning, one of the areas that is particularly involved with learning particularly of novel tasks is the hippocampus.

CLINICAL BOX

Types of Memory Loss

Amnesia refers to the loss of memory. There are many types of memory loss, some of which are described as follows:

1. **Anterograde amnesia**: In this form of amnesia, people may be able to recall past events but are unable to form new memories. For instance, they may be unable to remember a new phone number or what they have eaten in the morning or who visited them earlier in the day.
2. **Retrograde amnesia** refers to the loss of past events. If a person has had a head injury or a blow to the head (concussion) or has received electroconvulsive therapy (ECT) or has had a stroke, he or she may be unable to recall events prior to the incident.
3. **Alzheimer's disease** is a specific form of amnesia first described by Alois Alzheimer in 1907. This disease occurs in women more than in men and is associated (but not always) with ageing. There may a family history of the problem. Alzheimer's disease is characterized by more than memory loss. It is also associated with a loss of social adjustment, the inability to perform simple tasks and disturbances in sleep patterns. The problem can impose a huge burden of care on the families who require considerable emotional and social support.

APPLICATIONS FOR NURSING

Nurses may be required to educate and prepare a person for an EEG recording or for a sleep study. Since a sleep study requires admission overnight in the hospital and the patient will be connected by wires to various instruments, patients will need to be educated about the processes and will also need to be reassured. Nurses may need to educate patients with insomnia on basic sleep hygiene measures. These include, among others, the following:

- Trying to keep to a routine of going to sleep and awakening at a regular time.
- Ensuring that the bedroom is darkened and quiet and free of devices such as laptops and mobiles close at hand.
- Avoiding heavy meals, caffeine and alcohol before sleeping.
- Sticking to a routine the rest of the day, including regular exercise.

Nurses may be required to talk and counsel family members of patients who are suffering from Alzheimer's disease. It is important to recognize the distress and stress that the family undergoes when they see a loved family member in this state.

SUMMARY

- There are four types of EEG waves – alpha, beta, theta and delta. Beta waves have the highest frequency and the lowest amplitude. Delta waves have the highest amplitude and the lowest frequency.
- EEG is important in the evaluation of epilepsy and sleep disorders, in the evaluation of the stage of coma and in determining brain death.
- There are two forms of sleep – REM sleep and non-REM sleep. A normal sleep period of 8 hours has about four cycles of alternating non-REM and REM sleep.
- REM sleep is characterized by hypotonia, a withdrawal of sympathetic nervous tone, irregular heart rate, lower thermoregulation and dreams, among others.
- There are several disorders of sleep that can be categorized as insomnias, hypersomnias, disturbances of the sleep–wake cycle and parasomnias.
- Speech involves both sensory processing and motor processing involved in the production of comprehensible speech. Disorders of speech and comprehension are referred to as aphasias.
- There are several forms of learning (the acquisition of new knowledge) which include habituation, sensitization, classical and operant conditioning and food aversion conditioning, among others.
- Memory (the storage and retrieval of learned knowledge) goes through different stages including iconic memory, short-term memory and long-term memory.
- Amnesia is a loss of memory which may be anterograde (the inability to form new memories) and retrograde (inability to recall past events).
- Alzheimer's disease which most often occurs with ageing affects women more than men and is associated with loss of memory, lack of social adjustment and inability to perform simple tasks.

CHAPTER REVIEW QUESTIONS

1. What are the different waves seen in the EEG?
2. What are the features of REM sleep?
3. What is aphasia?
4. What is the difference between classical and operant conditioning?
5. What are the stages of memory?

CHAPTER 73

Functions of Cranial Nerves

SPECIFIC LEARNING OBJECTIVES

At the end of this chapter, the student should be able to describe the:

- Organization of the cranial nerves
- Functions of the cranial nerves
- Testing of the cranial nerves

GLOSSARY OF TERMS

- **Bell's palsy:** a sudden weakness in the facial muscles involving the facial nerve, and often following a viral infection (recovery is usually complete if detected early and treated)
- **Vertigo:** a sense of dizziness, 'spinning', unsteadiness, often accompanied by nausea or vomiting
- **Accommodation:** the response of the eye when it is required to suddenly focus on a nearby object after looking into the distance
- **Visual acuity:** the ability to see an object with clarity, sharpness and detail

The anatomy of the 12 pairs of cranial nerves has been described in Chapter 34 of the accompanying anatomy book. This chapter will focus on the functions of the cranial nerves and the clinical methods that are used to test them.

To re-emphasize, the 12 cranial nerves are the following:

I: olfactory nerve
II: optic nerve
III: oculomotor nerve
IV: trochlear nerve
V: trigeminal nerve
VI: abducens nerve
VII: facial nerve
VIII: vestibulocochlear nerve
IX: glossopharyngeal nerve
X: vagus nerve
XI: spinal accessory nerve
XII: hypoglossal nerve

TYPES OF CRANIAL NERVES

The cranial nerves may have sensory, motor and autonomic components. Some cranial nerves have more than one function. An understanding of these broad functions is needed if the cranial nerves are to be evaluated clinically. Table 73.1 outlines these broad functions – the coloured boxes indicate the functional category of the nerve.

Purely Sensory Cranial Nerves

Of these 12 nerves, 3 are purely sensory. They include the **olfactory nerve** which arises from the nasal epithelium and transmits sensations of smell to the brain, the **optic nerve** which arises from the retina and transmits visual information along the visual pathway to the occipital visual cortex, and the two divisions of the **VIII cranial nerve** which transmit information of body position, and linear and axial rotation of the head (vestibular division) and sound (cochlear division) and which arise out of these sense organs of the vestibular apparatus and the organ of Corti, respectively.

Purely Motor Cranial Nerves

There are four cranial nerves that have motor but not sensory function. These are cranial nerves III, IV, VI, XI and XII. Of these cranial nerves, III, IV and VI supply the extraocular muscles which are responsible for the movement of the eyes. Cranial nerve XI supplies some muscles of the neck and cranial nerve XII supplies the muscle of the tongue.

Cranial Autonomic Nerves

There are four cranial nerves that are part of the autonomic nervous system. Cranial nerve III has both parasympathetic and sympathetic nerve fibres. Cranial nerve VII supplies the salivary glands as does cranial nerve IX which specifically supplies the

Table 73.1 Broad Functional Categories of the Cranial Nerves

Cranial Nerve	Purely Sensory	Purely Motor	Sensory and Motor	Autonomic
I	X			
II	X			
III		X		X
IV		X		
V			X	
VI		X		
VII			X	X
VIII	X			
IX			X	X
X			X	X
XI		X		
XII		X		

parotid gland. The vagus nerve (cranial nerve X) constitutes more than 70% of the nerve fibres of the parasympathetic nervous system.

LOCATION OF THE NUCLEI OF THE CRANIAL NERVES

For the cranial nerves which are not purely sensory, nerve fibres originate from nuclei in the brain. Since some cranial nerves have multiple nuclei, the nerve may originate from multiple locations. Table 73.2 provides the broad area from where these cranial nerves originate. This information is important when there is a specific lesion involving a part of the brain as lesions in the brain can affect the cranial nerves. For the purely sensory nerves, the nerve fibres originate from the sense organs. Thus, for example, the optic nerve (II) originates in the retina, the olfactory nerve (I) from the olfactory nasal mucosa and the cochlear nerve (VIII) from the organ of Corti in the middle ear.

TESTING THE CRANIAL NERVES

In this section, we will briefly describe the function of each cranial nerve and the procedure for testing them.

Olfactory Nerve (Cranial Nerve I)

Function: It conveys the sensation of smell from the nasal epithelium to the brain.

Clinical features when affected:

- Loss of smell (anosmia) or altered smell (paraosmia)
- Loss of taste

Testing: Each nostril is tested in turn with the other nostril being blocked. The patient is asked to close his or her eyes and is presented with odours that he or she is familiar with such as soap and coffee powder. It is important to avoid excessively irritant smells as these can stimulate other receptors.

Optic Nerve (Cranial Nerve II)

Function: It conveys visual information from the retina to the brain via the visual pathway.

Clinical features when affected:

- Loss of vision

Testing: Vision in each eye individually is tested for several parameters. These include the following:

- Visual acuity: This tests how clearly a person can see objects.
  - For long vision, this is tested using Snellen's charts which contain letters or symbols in decreasing size with each row of letters.
  - For near vision, this is tested using Jaeger's chart which has written text in increasing smaller font size.
- Field of vision: This tests whether we can see over the entire visual field of each eye. This can be done in two ways:
  - Confrontation test: Here the field of vision is tested against the field of vision of the examiner. This assumes that the field of vision of the examiner is normal.
  - Perimetry: It uses a specific instrument – this is often computerized.
- Colour vision is tested using special charts called Ishihara's charts.
- Reflexes: These include the direct and indirect light reflexes in which light is shone into the eye and the pupil observed for pupillary constriction (direct reflex), while also observing for constriction in the opposite pupil into which the light was not directly shone (indirect reflex).

Table 73.2 Origin of the Cranial Nerves

Area of the Brain	Origin of the Cranial Nerve								
Midbrain	III	IV	V		VII	IX	X		
Pons			V	VI	VII	IX	X		
Medulla			V		VII	IX	X	XI	XII

Oculomotor (III), Trochlear (IV) and Abducens (VI) Cranial Nerves

Function: These nerves are often tested together because each of them supplies the extraocular muscles of the eye which allows the eyes to move.

The oculomotor nerve has three different functions:

- Motor: It supplies most of the extraocular muscles (levator palpebrae superioris, superior rectus, inferior rectus, medial rectus and inferior oblique).
- Parasympathetic: It supplies the sphincter pupillae (and therefore is important for the light reflex) and the ciliary muscles of the eye (important for accommodation of the eye).
- Sympathetic: Sympathetic fibres run with the oculomotor nerve to innervate the superior tarsal muscle (helps to raise the eyelid). Thus, drooping of the eyelid may be seen in conditions which affect the sympathetic fibres as in a condition called Horner's syndrome.

The abducens nerve supplies the lateral rectus extraocular muscle which moves the eye outwards in a horizontal plane.

The trochlear nerve supplies the superior oblique muscle.

Clinical features when affected:

- Problems with the movements of the eyes.
- Loss of pupillary constriction – blurred vision (cranial nerve III).

Testing: The extraocular muscles of the eye are tested one eye at a time. The patient is asked to move the eyes to follow the examiner's finger as it moves in an 'H' pattern to cover all quadrants of the visual field.

Trigeminal (Cranial Nerve V)

Function: The trigeminal nerve has both sensory and motor components. Through its sensory fibres, it supplies the face, the mucous membranes and the sinuses. The motor fibres of the nerve supply the muscles of mastication which include the masseter muscle responsible for biting and chewing.

Clinical features when affected:

- Loss of sensation in the face.

Testing:

- The sensory division of the trigeminal nerve is tested by the following:
  - Asking the patient to close his or her eyes and checking whether he or she can feel sensation over the face using a wisp of cotton.
  - Performing the corneal reflex, in which a piece of cotton is gently touched to the side of the conjunctiva which elicits a blinking response.

The motor division of the nerve is testing by asking the patient to clench his or her teeth and asking him or her to open his or her mouth against resistance.

Facial Nerve (Cranial Nerve VII)

Function: This cranial nerve has sensory, motor and autonomic functions:

- It supplies the anterior two-thirds of the tongue – when the nerve is affected, patients may experience altered taste sensation.
- It supplies the muscle of expression of the face as well as the stapedius, a small muscle in the middle ear.
- It supplies the salivary glands and helps regulate salivation.

Clinical features when affected:

- Drooping of face.
- Drooping of eyelids – inability to close eyes.
- Altered taste.

Testing:

- Taste can be tested using standard solutions that are sweet, sour, salty and bitter. The mouth must be rinsed after each test. It is preferable that 'bitter' is tested last.
- The patient can be asked to perform several actions which bring into play various muscles in the face. These actions can include asking the patient to smile, grimace and blow out of the mouth. It is also important to observe the patient while he or she is talking.

Vestibulocochlear Nerve (Cranial Nerve VIII)

Function: The two divisions of this nerve have different functions.

The vestibular division conveys information from the vestibular apparatus (utricle, saccule and three semicircular canals). The vestibular apparatus is important for balance and posture.

The cochlear division of the nerve carries auditory information from the organ of Corti, the sense organ of the inner ear.

Clinical features when affected:

- Loss of hearing.
- Difficulty in maintaining balance.

Testing: Hearing is tested using two different methods:

- Simple tuning fork tests.
- Audiometry.

Patients with vestibular nerve dysfunction may present in a clinic with vertigo – a sensation of dizziness. When patients are asked to follow an object with their eyes, they may experience nystagmus – oscillatory, jerky movements of the eye.

Glossopharyngeal and Vagus Nerve (Cranial Nerves IX and X)

These nerves are typically evaluated together.

Functions: The glossopharyngeal nerve has sensory, motor and autonomic functions.

- It carries taste sensation from the posterior one-third of the tongue and also supplies sensation to the middle ear and the Eustachian tube.
- It supplies the muscles involved in swallowing.
- It also controls the secretion of the parotid salivary gland.

The vagus nerve supplies a large number of organs and glands in the body including the heart and gastrointestinal and respiratory systems where it has a visceral sensory function and also a parasympathetic function. It also carries sensation from the larynx and the posterior-most part of the tongue. It innervates the muscles of the pharynx, larynx and soft palate.

Clinical features when affected:

- Inability to swallow.
- Hoarse voice.
- Digestive problems (X).

Testing: These nerves are tested by asking the patient to open his or her mouth and say 'ah' – the movement of the uvula is noted. The gag reflex is also performed in which a cotton bud is touched to the back of the pharynx – this typically evokes a gagging sensation.

Accessory Nerve (Cranial Nerve XI)

Function: This nerve supplies the sternocleidomastoid and trapezius muscles.

Clinical features when affected:

- Difficulty to move head and neck.

Testing: The nerve is tested by evaluating the muscles it supplies. The patient is asked to turn the head to one side and then the other against resistance – this evaluates the sternocleidomastoid muscle. The patient is then asked to shrug the shoulders against resistance – this evaluates the trapezius muscle.

Hypoglossal Nerve (Cranial Nerve XII)

Function: This nerve supplies the bulk of the muscle of the tongue which includes the following muscles: genioglossus, hyoglossus and styloglossus.

Clinical features when affected:

- Difficulty to move tongue.

Testing: The patient is asked to protrude the tongue. The tongue is examined for atrophy and deviation to one side.

APPLICATIONS FOR NURSING

While nurses may not typically be required to perform a detailed examination of the cranial nerves, it is useful for nurses to know what the nerves do and how they are tested since they may be affected in a variety of clinical disorders. One clinical problem that is not uncommon is Bell's palsy which affects the facial nerve typically on one side. The problem can be extremely distressing since it can result in facial distortions because the muscles supplied by the facial nerve are affected. Fortunately, if detected early, the condition can be treated and patients make a full recovery. These patients also need to perform certain exercises and the nurse will need to educate the patient and reinforce these instructions at subsequent visits.

SUMMARY

- There are 12 pairs of cranial nerves.
- These nerves can be classified as those which are purely sensory, are purely motor, are mixed and have autonomic function.
  - Purely sensory nerves are cranial nerves I, II and VIII.
  - Cranial nerves III, IV, VI, IX and X are motor and have no sensory function.
  - Cranial nerves III, VII, IX and X are autonomic in function.
- Most cranial nerves are tested individually but testing is sometimes clubbed when nerves share a common function.

CHAPTER REVIEW QUESTIONS

1. What are the cranial nerves that supply the extraocular muscles of the eye?
2. What is the function of the facial nerve?
3. What is the function of the vagus nerve?

CHAPTER 74

Reflexes

SPECIFIC LEARNING OBJECTIVES

At the end of this chapter, the student should be able to:

- List the components of the reflex arc with the help of a diagram.
- List the different types of reflexes.
- List the properties of reflexes.
- List the spinal reflexes and describe the components of the stretch reflex and inverse stretch reflex.
- List the major deep tendon reflexes used in clinical examination and state the spinal root values.
- List the different superficial reflexes tested during a clinical examination.

GLOSSARY OF TERMS

- **Reflex:** rapid, involuntary response to a stimulus mediated through a reflex arc
- **Deep tendon reflexes:** stretch reflexes elicited during clinical testing (the common deep tendon reflexes include biceps, triceps, brachioradialis, knee and ankle jerks)
- **Superficial reflexes:** clinical reflexes elicited by stroking the skin or mucous membrane and eliciting specific muscle contraction responses

NATURE OF REFLEXES

Reflexes are rapid, involuntary responses to a stimulus. We can think of several examples where these occur. For instance, we blink if we see something coming towards our eyes. We rapidly withdraw our hand when we touch something hot. We get startled and move away when we hear a loud sound.

Properties of Reflexes:

- Automatic
- Involuntary
- Rapid
- Stereotypical in their response – that is they tend to have predictable responses to a given stimulus
- Tend to be elicited by a specific sensory stimulus

Reflex actions can improve with training. This is, for instance, what wicketkeepers and goalkeepers undergo during training so that their response times during an actual game improve. We can also overcome certain reflexes by training. For instance, we normally withdraw from pain but people can condition themselves to withstand painful stimuli.

Types of Reflexes

Reflexes can be classified in a number of different ways:

1. ***Depending on which part of the nervous system is involved:***
   a. Somatic, for example, the spinal reflexes discussed later in the chapter.
   b. Autonomic, for example, the baroreflex which regulates blood pressure, the chemoreflex which regulates respiration, micturition reflex which regulates contraction of the urinary bladder and gastrointestinal reflexes.
2. ***Based on the number of synapses involved in the reflex:***
   a. Monosynaptic, for example, stretch reflex.
   b. Disynaptic, for example, inverse stretch reflex.
   c. Polysynaptic, for example, withdrawal reflex and crossed extensor reflex.
3. ***Based on clinical examination:***
   a. Superficial: Plantar response, abdominal reflex, cremasteric reflex and corneal reflex.
   b. Deep tendon reflexes: Biceps, brachioradialis, triceps, knee jerk and ankle jerk.

THE REFLEX ARC

This section describes the typical components of a reflex arc. In order to illustrate these components, we will consider a reflex called the withdrawal reflex. Consider a situation when you have stepped onto a sharp object such as a pin on the ground. We all know that we immediately 'withdraw' from the pin. The reflex arc is illustrated in Fig. 74.1. Later we will use these components to highlight its application to the withdrawal reflex.

SPINAL REFLEXES

There are several reflexes that are integrated at the level of the spinal cord, although they may be modulated by inputs from the brain.

In this section, we will consider four such reflexes:

1. **The stretch reflex:**
The stimulus for this reflex is stretch of the muscle. We use this reflex clinically to test the motor nervous system of a patient. The knee, ankle, biceps, triceps and supinator reflexes are examples of the stretch reflex. When a tendon hammer is struck on a tendon such as the patellar tendon at the knee, it causes the muscle attached to the tendon to stretch. This in turn stimulates the muscle spindle which sends information to the spinal cord through its sensory neurons. The sensory neuron synapses on a motor neuron in the spinal cord which when activated causes the muscle to contract, relieving the stretch. The muscle that was stimulated by stretch and which contracts is called the homonymous muscle (homo = same; since the same muscle which is stimulated is also the effector). The complete elements of the stretch reflex are depicted in Table 74.1 and Fig. 74.2.
2. **The inverse stretch reflex:**
Imagine someone tells you that they are going to place a very heavy object in your hand which you must hold in place. They ask you to stretch out your hand. In anticipation of the heavy object, you tense your muscles. The object is placed in your hand – it is much heavier than you anticipate – your muscle relaxes and the weight falls to the ground. This is an example of the inverse stretch reflex. In this reflex, the tension in the muscle increases because of the load and this is sensed by the Golgi's tendon organ. The Golgi's tendon organ sends this information to the spinal cord via its sensory nerve. In the spinal cord, the sensory nerve synapses with an interneuron (a neuron between two neurons) which inhibits the motor nerve to the homonymous (same) muscle causing it to relax. What is the purpose of this reflex? If the tension in a muscle is too high, it can damage the muscle – thus, relaxation of the muscle and the dropping of the weight help to protect the muscle from damage. The components of the inverse stretch reflex are summarized in Table 74.2 and Fig. 74.3.
3. **Withdrawal reflex and crossed extensor reflex:**
Consider the situation we considered at the start of this chapter. You are walking barefoot, and you step on a pin. You immediately withdraw your foot. This is called the withdrawal reflex – it is protective and since withdrawal involves the flexor muscles of the limb, it is also called the flexor response (see Table 74.3 and Fig. 74.4).
Even as you withdraw your foot, you need to stabilize your body position; otherwise, you will fall down. This is achieved by contracting the extensor muscles on the opposite limb making it rigid and allowing it to take the full weight of the

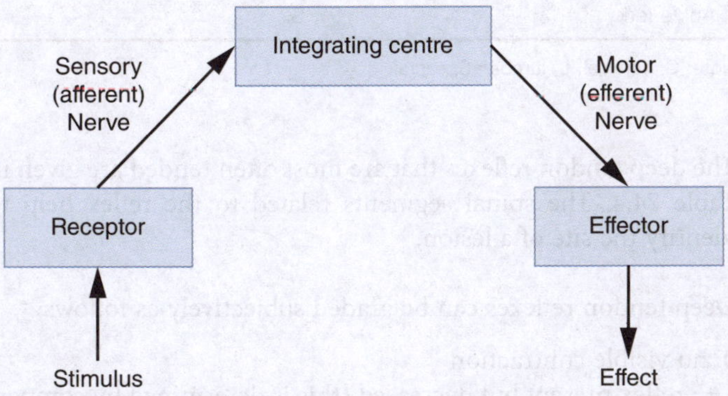

FIG. 74.1 Components of the reflex arc.

Table 74.1 The Elements of the Stretch Reflex

Part of the Reflex Arc	Myotatic (Stretch) Reflex
Stimulus	Stretch
Receptor	Muscle spindle
Sensory neuron	Sensory neurons from the muscle spindle (Ia, II nerve fibres)
Integrating centre	Spinal cord (monosynaptic for homonymous muscle)
Motor neuron	Alpha motor neuron to the muscle
Effector	Homonymous muscle
Effect	Homonymous muscle contraction

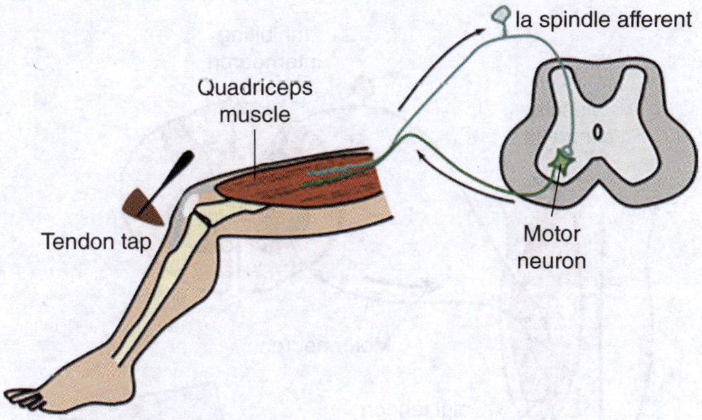

FIG. 74.2 The stretch reflex.

Table 74.2 Components of the Inverse Stretch Reflex

Part of the Reflex Arc	Inverse Myotatic (Stretch) Reflex
Stimulus	Increased tension
Receptor	Golgi's tendon organ
Sensory neuron	Sensory neurons from the Golgi's tendon organ (Ib fibres)
Integrating centre	Spinal cord (acts through an inhibitory interneuron to homonymous muscle), disynaptic
Motor neuron	Alpha motor neuron to the muscle
Effector	Homonymous muscle
Effect	Homonymous muscle relaxation (inhibition)

Table 74.3 Components of the Reflex Arc as Applied to the Withdrawal Reflex

Part of the Reflex Arc	Withdrawal Reflex
Stimulus	Pain
Receptor	Pain receptors (nociceptors)
Sensory neuron	Pain afferents
Integrating centre	Spinal cord
Motor neuron	Alpha motor neuron supplying the muscle
Effector	Flexor muscles of the limb
Effect	Withdrawal of the limb

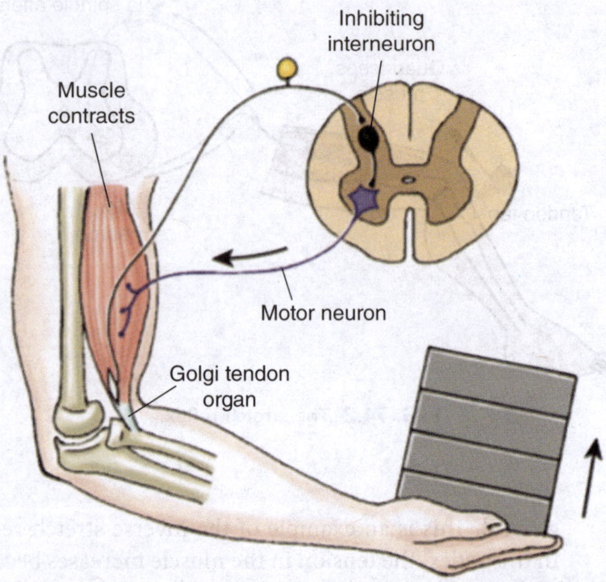

FIG. 74.3 The inverse stretch (Golgi's tendon organ) reflex.

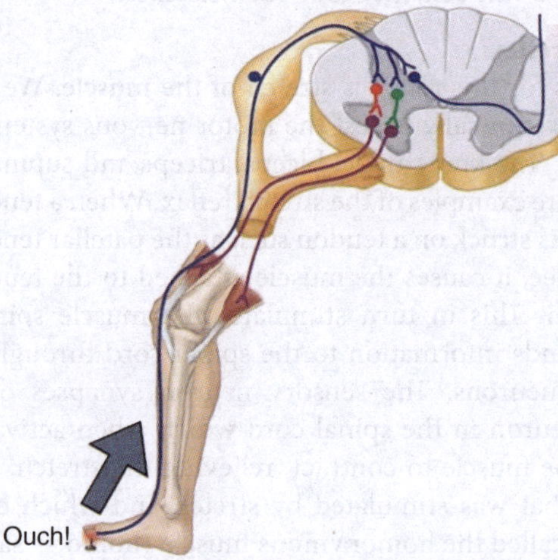

FIG. 74.4 The withdrawal reflex.

body. Since the extensor muscles contract on the opposite limb, this is referred to as the crossed extensor reflex.

REFLEXES IN CLINICAL TESTING OF PATIENTS

Deep Tendon Reflexes

The principles of testing deep tendon reflexes are as follows:

- The patient should be relaxed and should be instructed to keep the muscle 'loose'.
- The muscle should be in a neutral position, that is, neither stretched nor contracted.
- The muscle should be exposed so that contraction of the muscle can be seen, even if movement around a joint is not visible.
- The tendon of the muscle should be clearly identified and struck once, firmly.
- Observe for movement at the joint and of the muscle.

Table 74.4 Spinal Segments Associated with Clinically Tested Deep Tendon Reflexes

Reflex	Spinal Segment
Triceps	C6, C7
Biceps	C5, C6
Supinator	C5, C6
Knee jerk	L2, L3, L4
Ankle jerk	S1, S2

Note: C, cervical; L, lumbar; S, sacral.

The deep tendon reflexes that are most often tended are given in Table 74.4. The spinal segments related to the reflex help to identify the site of a lesion.

Deep tendon reflexes can be graded subjectively as follows:

0: no visible contraction

1+: reflex present but decreased (this is determined by comparing the reflex with that at the other side)

2+: normal reflex
3+: hyperreflexia (exaggerated reflexes)
4+: clonus – repetitive shortening of the muscle after a single stimulation

Superficial Reflexes

Superficial reflexes are elicited by stimulating the skin/mucous membrane by stroking the surface. The response is the contraction of specific muscles associated with the reflex. Examples of superficial reflexes are listed as follows together with the spinal segment/nerve involved:

- Corneal/conjunctival reflex (V and VII cranial nerves)
- Palatal reflex (IX and X cranial nerves)
- Abdominal reflex (T7 to T12)
- Cremasteric reflex (L1 and L2)
- Anal reflex (S3 and S4)

Superficial reflexes are polysynaptic in nature and require processing in the brain. These reflexes are lost if the sensory afferents from the skin, the motor efferents to the specific muscles and integrating areas are damaged.

SUMMARY

- Reflexes are spontaneous, almost instantaneous, stereotypical responses to specific stimuli.
- Reflexes can be classified variously as somatic and autonomic; superficial and deep; monosynaptic, disynaptic or polysynaptic.
- The components of a reflex arc include the stimulus, receptor, afferent (sensory) nerve, integrating centre, efferent (motor) nerve, effector and effect.
- Clinical testing involves deep and superficial reflexes. Deep reflexes are stretch reflexes and include biceps, triceps, brachioradialis, knee and ankle jerks. Superficial reflexes produce muscle contraction by stroking the skin or mucous membrane in specific locations of the body. All these reflexes are linked to specific spinal segments or cranial nerves.

CHAPTER REVIEW QUESTIONS

1. List the components of a reflex arc in correct sequence.
2. Describe the stretch reflex.
3. Describe the inverse stretch reflex.
4. Describe the withdrawal reflex.

CHAPTER 75

Applications of the Nervous System

SPECIFIC LEARNING OBJECTIVES

At the end of this chapter, the student should be able to:

- List the common types of nerve injury.
- Explain the term 'Wallerian degeneration'.
- List the common causes of peripheral neuropathy.
- Differentiate between an upper motor and a lower motor neuron lesion.
- Outline the salient features of:
  - Stroke and haemiplegia
  - Parkinsonism
  - Types of amnesia
  - Transection of the spinal cord
  - Brown-Séquard's syndrome
  - Mental health disorders
- Outline the physiological basis of fever and chills.

GLOSSARY OF TERMS

- **Paralysis:** the inability to move a part of the body (this may be complete or partial)
- **Haemiplegia:** paralysis of one side of the body
- **Hyperreflexia:** excessive or greater than normal reflexes
- **Amnesia:** loss of memory (this may be partial or complete)

The nervous system may be affected by many conditions and due to a variety of causes. For example, disorders of the nervous system may occur due to injury, tumours, nutritional deficiencies, exposure to toxins and chronic cardiovascular or metabolic diseases, among others. In this chapter, we will be discussing a few of these conditions. This chapter is not complete – the field of neurology is very vast!

WALLERIAN DEGENERATION

This was first described by a physiologist called Augustus Waller. This is seen when an axon is cut. There are changes both proximal (before) to the lesion and distally (after the lesion) (Fig. 75.1). Changes distal to the lesion include the formation of 'ovoids' as Schwann cells begin to fragment the myelin sheath and an invasion of the area by white blood cells. The removal of the cell debris by white blood cells is critical if regeneration of a peripheral nerve is to take place. Proximally, in the cell body, there is a shift in the nucleus to the periphery and a break-up of the rough endoplasmic reticulum (chromatolysis). This occurs as the endoplasmic reticulum reorganizes itself to produce new proteins required for nerve regeneration.

PERIPHERAL NEUROPATHIES

These conditions involve the degeneration or abnormal functioning of the peripheral nerves, that is, those outside the central nervous system.

Causes of peripheral neuropathies:

- Nerve injuries due to trauma (these may be of varying grades, which are discussed later).
- Systemic diseases like diabetes mellitus, particularly when the disease has been present for a long time and when blood sugars are not controlled well.
- Nutritional deficiencies such as vitamin B_{12} deficiency. It has become increasingly clear that these deficiencies are more widespread than we initially thought. Issues with nutritional neuropathies may not only be due to an inadequate diet but also because of inadequate absorption when the diet seems adequate.

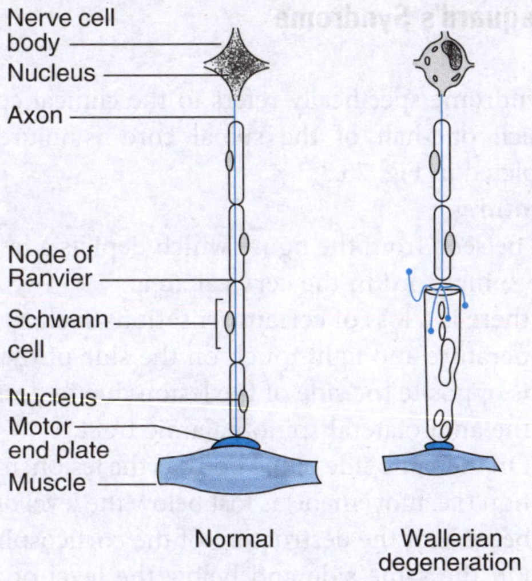

FIG. 75.1 Wallerian degeneration.

- Infections like leprosy – which can cause localized or widespread nerve damage based on the subtype of the disease.
- Disruptions to the blood supply of nerves occur with vasculitis and arteriosclerosis.
- As a side effect of some drugs.
- Exposure to toxins in the environment. This can include exposure to mercury, lead and arsenic and can even involve chronic exposure to some pesticides.

Clinical Features of Peripheral Neuropathy

The clinical features of a neuropathy depend on the type of nerve/s involved and the extent of the damage.

- If sensory nerves are involved, patients may experience numbness (loss of sensation), tingling and some abnormal sensations.
- If motor nerves are involved, patients will experience weakness or paralysis of the affected muscles.
- If autonomic nerves are involved, patients will experience disturbances of bowel movements or emptying of the bladder or a sense of giddiness, and even fainting.

TYPES OF NERVE INJURIES

There are different ways in which the extent of a nerve injury can be graded. The following classification is one such method:

1. The least severe type of injury is called a ***neurapraxia***. In this form of injury, the nerve is intact but transmission of the nerve impulse at the site of injury is affected. This type of injury can occur due to prolonged pressure on the nerve or because of blunt injury. Recovery is typically complete but may take several weeks.
2. The next level of injury is ***axonotmesis***. In this form of injury, the axon of the nerve is damaged.
3. The most severe form of nerve injury is ***neurotmesis***. In this form of injury, the nerve is completely disrupted along with the surrounding tissue. The prognosis or recovery for this type of injury is the worst and requires surgery.

UPPER AND LOWER MOTOR NEURON LESIONS

Fig. 75.2 illustrates what we mean by upper and lower motor neurons.

Upper motor neurons are located within the central nervous system and emerge from the motor cortex of the cerebrum. In contrast, the lower motor neuron is the final neuron that supplies a muscle. Lower motor neurons may be contained within cranial nerves, as, for instance, the facial nerve (cranial nerve VII), which control the muscles of expression in the face. They are also contained within spinal nerves. The type of clinical features that are seen is very different when these two neurons (i.e. upper motor neuron vs lower motor neuron) are affected. Table 75.1 summarizes the differences between an upper and a lower motor neuron lesion.

STROKE AND HAEMIPLEGIA

A stroke occurs when the blood flow to a part of the brain is reduced. This may happen if a blood vessel in the brain is blocked

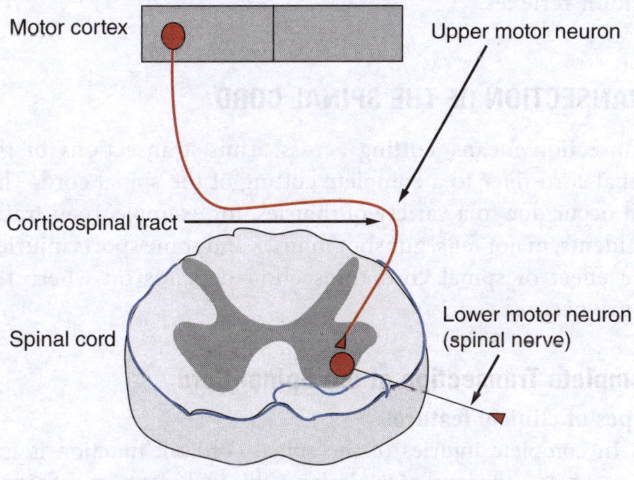

FIG. 75.2 Anatomical location of upper and lower motor neurons.

Table 75.1 A Comparison of Upper and Lower Motor Neuron Lesions

	Upper Motor Neuron Lesion	Lower Motor Neuron Lesion
Muscles involved	Group of muscles	May involve a single muscle
Tone of the muscle	Increased (hypertonia)	Decreased (hypotonia)
Bulk (mass) of the muscle	Maintained	Decreased (muscle atrophy)
Tendon reflexes (e.g. the knee jerk)	Increased (hyperreflexia)	Decreased
Example	Lesion in the corticospinal tract as, for instance, after a stroke	Injury to a peripheral motor nerve

(ischaemic stroke) or if it bleeds (haemorrhagic stroke). The symptoms associated with a stroke depend on the location of the blood vessel that is affected and the extent to which blood flow to the specific area of the brain is reduced.

The major risk factor for a stroke is high blood pressure, but there are other risk factors and these include smoking, diabetes mellitus, obesity and high blood cholesterol levels, among others.

When a stroke involves the upper corticospinal tract (Chapter 70; above the decussation of the pyramidal tract in the medulla), it may be associated with haemiplegia (haemi = half; plegia = paralysis) on the opposite side of the body to where the lesion is. This is because the nerve fibres of the corticospinal tract cross over to the opposite side of the body only at the medulla. Strokes resulting in haemiplegia most often occur because of a lesion of the corticospinal tract at the level of the internal capsule. The muscle paralysis that occurs with lesions in the corticospinal tract is of the upper motor neuron type, that is, there is increased tone and increased tendon reflexes.

TRANSECTION OF THE SPINAL CORD

Transection means 'cutting across'. Thus, transections of the spinal cord refer to a complete cutting of the spinal cord. This can occur due to a variety of injuries, for example, road traffic accidents, major falls, gunshot injuries and some sports injuries. The effect of spinal cord transection depends on where the injury occurs.

Complete Transection of the Spinal Cord

Types of clinical features:

In complete injuries of the spinal cord, all function is lost below the level of the lesion – this includes a loss of sensation as well as muscle paralysis. Dysfunction of the gastrointestinal tract, the bladder and sexual function depends on the level of the lesion. Lesions of the spinal cord at the cervical level (neck) may result in paralysis of all four limbs, a condition called ***quadriplegia*** or tetraplegia. When the lesion occurs in the lower back (lumbar area), paralysis may occur in the lower limbs, a condition called ***paraplegia***.

Spinal shock:

Complete spinal injury goes through several stages and this is sometimes referred to as ***spinal shock***:

1. In the first stage which lasts for about a day, all reflexes below the level of the lesion are lost.
2. In the next two stages, some but not all reflexes begin to appear.
3. In the final stage, there is increase in muscle tone (spasticity) and deep tendon reflexes related to the spinal cord below the level of the lesions are exaggerated or increased.

Brown-Séquard's Syndrome

Cause:

This syndrome specifically refers to the clinical condition in which one-half of the spinal cord is injured. This is depicted in Fig. 75.3.

Clinical features:

As can be seen from the figure which depicts a lesion of half the spinal cord in the cervical area:

- there is a loss of certain sensations such as pain, temperature and light touch on the side of the body that is opposite the side of the lesion due to destruction of the anterolateral spinothalamic tract.
- On the same side of the body as the lesion, motor function (i.e. movement) is lost below the level of the lesion because of the destruction of the corticospinal tract.
- On the same side and below the level of the lesion, certain sensations such as vibration, position and deep touch are lost because of the destruction of the dorsal columns. The important issue is why this type of distribution of motor and sensory loss occurs.

Explanation for the clinical features:

As can be seen from Fig. 75.4, the anterior horn cells of the motor neurons innervated by the corticospinal tract remain on one side of the spinal cord once they cross at the medullary pyramids. Thus, motor function will be affected on the side of the lesion because it disrupts the corticospinal tracts on that side. The dorsal columns which convey the sensations of vibration, position and deep touch also run on one side of the spinal cord until they cross as the second-order neuron. Thus, sensations of vibration, position and deep touch will also be lost on the same side of the lesion. In contrast, the spinothalamic tract crosses in the spinal cord at the level where the nerve enters the spinal cord through the dorsal root and

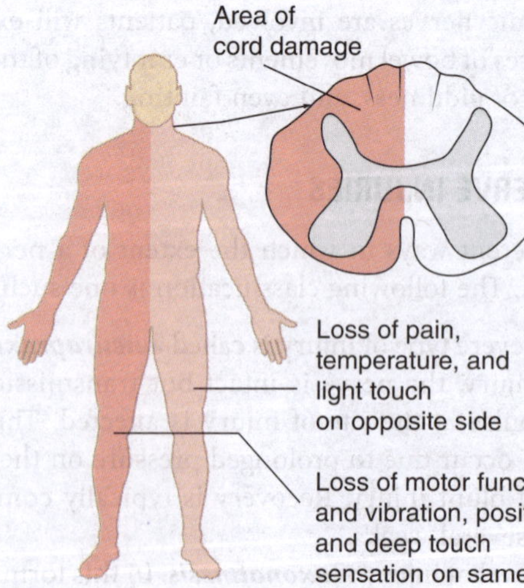

FIG. 75.3 The nature of effects seen in Brown-Séquard's syndrome (hemisection of the spinal).

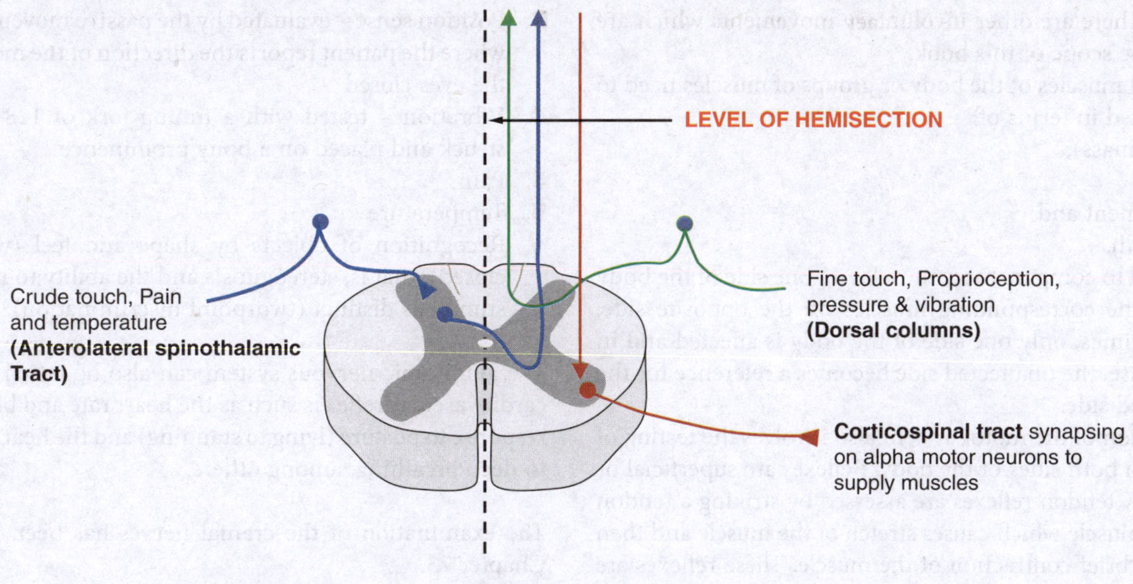

FIG. 75.4 Sensory and motor tracts involved with hemisection of the spinal cord.

then ascends on the opposite side of the spinal cord. Thus, sensations that are carried by the spinothalamic tract, such as pain and temperature, are lost on the opposite side of the body, below the level of the lesion.

AMNESIA

Amnesia is a partial or complete loss of memory which may be related to a variety of causes.

There are two broad categories of amnesia:

1. ***Anterograde amnesia*** is the inability to create new memories. Thus, a person may be able to remember events which have happened a long time ago but will be unable to remember things that have happened more recently. This type of amnesia occurs when there is damage to a part of the brain called the hippocampus and is seen when there is injury or trauma to this region.
2. ***Retrograde amnesia*** is that type of memory loss in which events cannot be recalled which have occurred prior to the onset of memory loss. In some patients, the memory loss can be of events that have occurred several years prior to the event, while in others this may be restricted to events just prior to the onset of amnesia.

Alzheimer's Disease

This was first described in 1907 in a 55-year-old woman by Prof. Alois Alzheimer. It typically affects people who are elderly, although it may sometimes occur earlier in life, such as middle age. There is often a family history of memory loss and females are affected more than males. Alzheimer's disease is more than memory loss, and includes difficulties with social adjustment and disturbances in sleep patterns. Patients with this condition may ultimately be unable to perform simple tasks related to personal care and hygiene.

EXAMINATION OF THE NERVOUS SYSTEM

- Prior to examining the nervous system of a patient, it is important to obtain a detailed clinical history. The history will inform the doctor about the likely problem even before a formal examination takes place. This section is a brief overview of the clinical examination of the nervous system in terms of principles and is not meant to replace more detailed books of the clinical examination of a patient.
- The first step in the examination is to evaluate the general appearance and behaviour of the patient.
- Important issues to assess are whether the patient is aware of his or her surroundings – the place he or she is visiting, the location of his or her home, and the date and time of day. Simple tests of memory can include recall of the patient's date of birth, names of family members, his or her phone number. It is also important to determine whether the patient is able to follow the flow of conversation, understand questions and provide appropriate responses to them. While the patient responds to questions, it is important to assess whether he or she has specific problems of articulating words. The emotional state of the patient can also be gauged as the clinical history and examination progress.

The Motor System

- The gait (walking) of the subject needs to be evaluated. Simple things like whether the patient can walk at all or in a straight line and whether the patient has a recognizable disorder of walking (e.g. haemiplegia and Parkinson's disease) are important.
- During the examination, it is also important to record whether there are any involuntary movements such as

tremors. There are other involuntary movements which are beyond the scope of this book.

- Individual muscles of the body or groups of muscles need to be evaluated in terms of:
  - bulk (mass),
  - tone,
  - movement and
  - strength.

  It is useful to compare these muscles on one side of the body with the corresponding muscles on the opposite side. Sometimes, only one side of the body is affected and in this case, the unaffected side becomes a reference for the affected side.
- Examination of the motor system also involves the testing of reflexes on both sides of the body. Reflexes are superficial or deep. XXX tendon reflexes are assessed by striking a tendon of major muscle which causes stretch of the muscle and then leads to a brief contraction of the muscle. These reflexes are referred to as the *monosynaptic stretch reflex* (because the reflex has a single synapse and because it is initiated by a stretch of the muscle) or *tendon reflex*. Reflexes are tested on both sides of the body and the face. In the upper limb, the reflexes include the triceps, biceps and supinator reflexes, while the lower limb reflexes include the knee jerk and the ankle jerk. The jaw jerk is a reflex of the face. Each of these reflexes is conducted in a specific position and for the upper and lower limb reflexes reflect a given spinal segment from where the motor nerves emerge. These spinal segments are indicated in Table 75.2.

  Superficial reflexes are tested by stroking the skin in specific locations and observing the contraction of muscles that are stimulated. Among these are the abdominal reflexes, the cremasteric reflex and the planter reflex.

The Sensory System

The major sensations of the body can be tested at the bedside of the patient. Testing is typically done in specific areas of the surface of the body called dermatomes. Each dermatome represents a specific spinal segment from where the sensory nerve emerges. As for the motor system, sensation is tested on both sides of the body. The sensations that are tested include the following:

1. Touch
2. Pressure
3. Position sense – evaluated by the passive movement of joints, where the patient reports the direction of the movement with the eyes closed
4. Vibration – tested with a tuning fork of 128 Hz which is struck and placed on a bony prominence
5. Pain
6. Temperature
7. Recognition of objects by shape and feel (with the eyes closed), that is, stereognosis and the ability to recognize two stimuli as distinct (two-point discrimination)

Table 75.2 Spinal Segments Associated with Clinically Tested Reflexes

Reflex	Spinal Segment
Triceps	C6, C7
Biceps	C5, C6
Supinator	C5, C6
Knee jerk	L2, L3, L4
Ankle jerk	S1, S2

Note: C, cervical; L, lumbar; S, sacral.

The autonomic nervous system can also be tested using simple cardiovascular reflexes such as the heart rate and blood pressure response to posture (lying to standing) and the heart rate changes to deep breathing, among others.

The examination of the cranial nerves has been dealt with in Chapter 73.

MENTAL HEALTH DISORDERS

An early understanding of mental health disorders was based on the description of behaviour in patients who had suffered lesions in a certain part of the brain. For instance, in one situation, a man called Phineas Gage suffered an injury while working on a railway line where an iron rod pierced his brain just behind his eyes and destroyed a part of his prefrontal lobe. Although he survived, his behaviour changed considerably after the accident. He became obstinate and would curse people with foul language while before the incident he was a very courteous man.

Behaviour in the human brain is influenced by a set of structures called the limbic system. Earlier, the idea of the limbic system was very simple and involved few structures (Fig. 75.5). An early model of the limbic system, for instance, involved just four structures and is called the Papez's circuit.

We now understand that the functional limbic system involves a large number of structures in the brain which are interconnected with each other. These structures are involved in memory and learning, reward and punishment, attention and motivation and emotion.

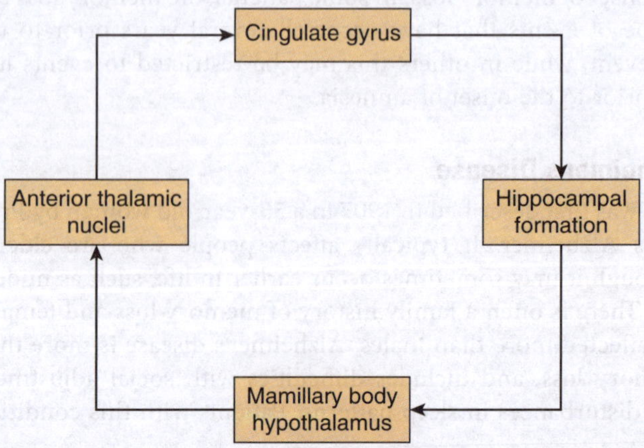

FIG. 75.5 The Papez's circuit.

As part of the expanded limbic system, the amygdala plays a role in modulating behaviour based on sensory input, playing a role in the autonomic responses associated with behaviour such as an increase in heart rate, sweating, through its connections with the hypothalamus, and in sexual behaviour.

In recent years, the role of altered neurotransmitter levels in the brain as a cause of certain mental health disorders has been increasingly recognized. Alterations in serotonin and other neurotransmitters, for example, norepinephrine and dopamine, have been reported with certain mental disorders, including major depression, obsessive compulsive disorder, phobias, post-traumatic stress disorder and generalized anxiety disorder. Medications are now used in psychiatry to tackle the chemical imbalance that may be found in these disorders.

The basis of mental health disorders is multifactorial involving genetics, early life experiences, parenting, critical incidents, etc., and it is beyond the scope of this chapter to discuss this in detail. What has been presented is the idea that behaviour can be linked with dysfunction of structures in the brain and with the neurotransmitters involved.

FEVER AND CHILLS

The hypothalamus plays an important role in temperature regulation and maintains core body temperature at a constant level of about 37°C. A rise in temperature above this level is called fever (pyrexia). An infection accounts for about three-fourths of the fevers in hospitals. The fever is the result of exogenous pyrogens (fever-causing chemicals) that are from infective organisms as well as endogenous pyrogens due to the immune response of the body to the infection.

During fever, the body may reset the core body temperature to a higher level. When this happens, the person feels cold and experiences chills, and the temperature rises.

APPLICATIONS FOR NURSING

Disorders of the nervous system are profoundly disturbing for both the patient and the family members. A nurse has an important duty of communicating with the patient and family so that they understand the nature of the disease, the medications that are prescribed and the additional therapies that may be required. In patients who are bedridden, the nurse becomes extremely important in the daily care of the patient and in teaching family members how they can prevent pressure ulcers in the patient. Patients may be unable to take care of their personal hygiene and this is also an important issue of nursing care. It may be that the patient requires physiotherapy or gradual mobilization – these are again areas where the nurse can play an important role.

SUMMARY

- Peripheral neuropathies can result from a variety of causes including trauma, nutritional deficiencies (e.g. vitamin B_{12}), infections like leprosy, metabolic diseases like diabetes mellitus, exposure to toxins and as a result of side effects of drugs, among others.
- Injuries to nerves are varied in grade and include neurapraxia (least injury), axonotmesis and neurotmesis (greatest injury).
- Upper motor neuron lesions refer to those lesions which occur above the level of the peripheral motor nerve, while lower motor neuron lesions involve the peripheral motor nerve which supplies a muscle and is typically associated with muscle wasting, hypotonia and reduced tone and reflexes.
- Haemiplegia or paralysis of one-half of the body is often associated with a stroke that involves the upper corticospinal tract, that is, above the level of the medulla where the tract crosses over to the opposite side.
- Brown-Séquard's syndrome is a condition which is associated with a transection of one-half of the spinal cord, in which there is a loss of vibration, pressure and position sense as well as paralysis of the muscles below and on the same side of the lesion and a loss of pain and temperature on the opposite side, below the level of the lesion.
- Amnesia is a loss of memory and is of two broad types: anterograde and retrograde. Alzheimer's disease is associated with memory loss, in addition to other issues including difficulties in socialization, sleep disorders and the ability to perform simple tasks, among others.

CHAPTER REVIEW QUESTIONS

1. List some common causes of peripheral neuropathy.
2. What is haemiplegia? What are its causes?
3. What is Brown Séquard's syndrome? What are its features?
4. What is Alzheimer's disease?

CLINICAL CASES

(A) ***A 70-year-old woman with uncontrolled hypertension is brought into the hospital with disorientation, slurring of speech and weakness on one side of the body.***
   a. Which tract is likely to be involved?
   b. Trace the tract from its origin.
   c. Is the weakness likely to be upper motor neuron or lower motor neuron type?
   d. What is weakness of one-half of the body called?

(B) ***A 40-year-old labourer has a fall at a building site onto a sharp object. He has an injury to his back. On examination, he has a loss of muscle function in the right leg and a loss of fine touch, pressure, vibration and joint sense in the same leg. However, he has a loss of temperature and pain sensation in the left leg.***
   a. What type of spinal cord injury is he likely to have sustained?
   b. Explain the loss of fine touch, pressure, vibration and joint sense in the right leg.
   c. Explain the loss of muscle function in the right leg.
   d. Explain the loss of pain and temperature in the left leg.

SELF-DIRECTED LEARNING

- Find out about the common medications used for mental health conditions. What neurotransmitters do they act against?
- What are the common ways in which memory is tested?
- What is depression? What are its causes and physiological basis?

WHAT YOU CAN LEARN FROM A HOSPITAL VISIT

- Visit the ward in the hospital. What are the issues that a nurse faces in the care of a patient with stroke?
- Look at the patient's chart. What is the neurological examination that has been performed on the patient?
- If the patient is unconscious, how is the level of unconsciousness determined?

SECTION 1

Workbook: General Physiology – Basic Concepts

SPECIFIC LEARNING OBJECTIVES

At the end of this chapter, the student should be able to:

Chapter 1

- Describe the levels of organization of the human body.
- Define a hormone.
- Differentiate between the terms endocrine, paracrine and autocrine.
- Differentiate broadly between endocrine and nervous regulation.
- Describe the concept of negative feedback with examples.

Chapter 2

- Draw a diagram of the cell membrane and label its parts.
- List the functions of the proteins in the cell membrane.
- List the different types of transport across the cell membrane with examples.
- Distinguish between active and passive transport.
- Distinguish between simple and facilitated diffusion.

Chapter 3

- List the factors which affect total body water.
- List the factors that contribute to the intake and output of water on a daily basis.
- Describe the components of total body water.
- Distinguish between intracellular fluid and extracellular fluid.

Chapter 4

- Outline the composition of the fluid in the different body compartments.
- Describe the methods by which fluid intake occurs.
- Describe the ways in which fluid is lost from the body.
- List the key electrolytes in the body.
- Describe how fluid balance is maintained in the body.
- Describe how electrolyte concentrations are in the body regulated.

Chapter 5

- List the functions of cell division.
- Describe the phases of mitosis.
- Describe the process of meiosis.
- Distinguish between mitosis and meiosis.
- Describe the phases of the cell cycle.

Chapter 6

- Outline the various processes of cell death and tissue injury.
- Describe the location of adult stem cells and their role in tissue repair.
- List various growth factors and describe their function.
- Describe the stages of wound healing.

Chapter 7

- Describe a simple application of the use of cell membrane transport in relation to diffusion, osmosis and active transport.
- Describe the importance of input–output chart.
- List features of dehydration.
- List common intravenous fluids used in clinical medicine.
- Apply the learning in Section 1 to the understanding of simple clinical problems.

GLOSSARY OF TERMS

Chapter 1

- **Endocrine:** related to hormones
- **Hormone:** a chemical messenger secreted by ductless glands in small quantities which acts at a distance from the site of its secretion
- **Paracrine:** when a chemical messenger secreted by a cell acts on neighbouring cells
- **Autocrine:** when a cell secretes a chemical messenger which acts on itself (the same cell)
- **Neurotransmitter:** a chemical messenger released from nerve endings
- **Negative feedback:** when a stimulus acts to reverse (reduce) its own activity
- **Positive feedback:** when a stimulus acts to enhance (increase) its own activity

Chapter 2

- **Passive transport:** transport of substances across the cell membrane along their concentration gradient, without the use of energy
- **Active transport:** transport of substances across a cell membrane against their concentration gradient, requiring the use of energy
- **Vesicular transport:** transport of substances into and out of the cell in the form of cell inclusions called vesicles (common examples are exocytosis and endocytosis)

- **Simple diffusion:** movement of molecules from an area of high concentration to an area of low concentration
- **Osmosis:** movement of water molecules from an area of low solute concentration to an area of high solute concentration

Chapter 3

- **Intracellular fluid:** fluid present inside the cell
- **Extracellular fluid:** fluid present outside cells
- **Transcellular fluid:** fluid contained in spaces in the body; fluid includes cerebrospinal fluid (CSF), pleural fluid, peritoneal fluid, intraocular fluid and pericardial fluid
- **Insensible water loss:** water loss from the body without us being aware of it
- **Homeostasis:** constancy of the internal environment

Chapter 4

- **Dehydration:** the excessive loss of body water
- **Plasma osmolarity:** normal 280–300 mOsm/L, it is a reflection of the hydration of the body and is dependent on the concentration of substances in the plasma such as sodium, chloride, glucose and urea
- **Natriuresis:** process of sodium excretion in the urine

Chapter 5

- **Cell cycle:** the period between one cell division and another cell division
- **Chromosome:** a long deoxyribonucleic acid (DNA) molecule that contains genetic information (in humans, chromosomes are in pairs, one from the father and one from the mother; this pairing is referred to as homologous chromosomes)
- **Chromatids:** the DNA replication of a chromosome forming an identical DNA molecule results in two 'sister chromatids' joined together by a 'centromere'
- **Mitosis:** a form of cell division in which the number of chromosomes in the two daughter cells is the same as in the parent cell
- **Meiosis:** a form of cell division in which the chromosomes in the four daughter cells are halved as compared to in the parent cell
- **Diploid:** two copies of each chromosome (in humans, 23 *pairs* of chromosomes, i.e. 46 chromosomes)
- **Haploid:** a single copy of each chromosome (in humans, 23 chromosomes)

Chapter 6

- **Apoptosis:** programmed cell death (it is called programmed because it is genetically determined)
- **Necrosis:** cell death due to injury or loss of blood supply (unlike apoptosis, the causes of cell death are external to the cell)
- **Growth factors:** proteins which stimulate cell growth, differentiation and tissue healing

Chapter 7

- **Input–output chart:** a recording of all the fluid intake (oral and intravenous) and fluid loss (urine, stools, fluid loss via drainage tubes) in a day
- **Intravenous:** via a vein
- **Enteral:** via the gastrointestinal tract

MULTIPLE CHOICE QUESTIONS

Chapter 1:

1. Which of the following organelles is the site of protein synthesis?
   a. Mitochondria
   b. Ribosomes
   c. Golgi's bodies
   d. Lysosomes
2. Which of the following are features of hormones?
   a. Produced by ductless glands
   b. Produced in large quantities
   c. Act on many receptors
   d. Released by nerves
3. When a cell produces a substance which acts on neighbouring cells, it is called:
   a. Autocrine
   b. Neurocrine
   c. Paracrine
   d. Neuroendocrine
4. An example of positive feedback is:
   a. Control of blood pressure
   b. Process of birth
   c. Control of hormone levels
   d. Control of body temperature
5. The aim of negative feedback is:
   a. To maintain homeostasis
   b. To amplify a response
   c. To accelerate a response
   d. To anticipate a response

Chapter 2:

1. The cell membrane has:
   a. A protein bilayer
   b. A phospholipid bilayer
   c. A cholesterol bilayer
   d. A carbohydrate bilayer
2. Movement of oxygen across a cell membrane is an example of:
   a. Active transport
   b. Facilitated diffusion
   c. Simple diffusion
   d. Endocytosis
3. Na-K ATPase is an example of:
   a. Facilitated diffusion
   b. Simple diffusion
   c. Primary active transport
   d. Secondary active transport
4. Movement of glucose with sodium in the intestine is an example of:
   a. Simple diffusion
   b. Facilitated diffusion
   c. Primary active transport
   d. Secondary active transport

5. Entry of glucose into muscle using GLUT4 is an example of:
   a. Simple diffusion
   b. Facilitated diffusion
   c. Primary active transport
   d. Secondary active transport

Chapter 3:

1. In which of the following is total body water the highest?
   a. Adult males
   b. Adult females
   c. Elderly
   d. Dehydration
2. Which of the following body water compartments has the highest volume?
   a. Extracellular
   b. Intracellular
   c. Interstitial fluid
   d. Transcellular
3. Pleural fluid is an example of:
   a. Interstitial fluid
   b. Intracellular fluid
   c. Intravascular fluid
   d. Transcellular fluid
4. A sample of fluid has a high concentration of potassium, phosphates and proteins. Which of the following fluid compartments is the sample like to be from?
   a. Intracellular
   b. Interstitial
   c. Transcellular
   d. Plasma
5. Which of the following indicators can be used to measure total body water?
   a. Deuterated water
   b. Inulin
   c. Labelled albumin
   d. ^{51} Cr-labelled red cells

Chapter 4:

1. What is the average insensible water loss on a pleasant day (not too hot)?
   a. 100 mL
   b. 500 mL
   c. 1 L
   d. 2 L
2. Increase in sodium concentration of plasma is called:
   a. Hypernatraemia
   b. Hyponatraemia
   c. Hyperkalaemia
   d. Hypokalaemia
3. Which of the following may be associated with hypokalaemia?
   a. Increased potassium intake
   b. Addison's disease
   c. Insulin deficiency
   d. Some diuretics
4. Which of the following results in the greatest loss of body water normally?
   a. Sweating
   b. Loss in faeces
   c. Loss in urine
   d. Loss in breath
5. During dehydration, which of the following helps to restore body water back to normal?
   a. Increased urine output
   b. Decreased water intake
   c. Release of antidiuretic hormone
   d. Increased sweating

Chapter 5:

1. During prophase of mitosis, two identical copies of chromosomes are held together by a:
   a. Centrosome
   b. Centromere
   c. Mitotic spindle
   d. Nuclear membrane
2. During which of the following phases do the sister chromatids align themselves in the centre of the mitotic spindle?
   a. Prophase
   b. Anaphase
   c. Metaphase
   d. Telophase
3. In which of the following cells does meiosis occur?
   a. Neurons
   b. Nephrons
   c. Epithelial cells
   d. Gametes
4. Which of the following occurs in meiosis?
   a. Single cell division
   b. Two daughter cells produced
   c. Haploid chromosomes in daughter cells
   d. Promotes genetic stability
5. In which of the following phases of the cell cycle does cell growth occur?
   a. G1
   b. S
   c. G2
   d. G0

Chapter 6:

1. Which of the following is associated with programmed cell death?
   a. Apoptosis
   b. Necrosis
   c. Ischaemia
   d. Fibrosis
2. Which of the following cells shows the slowest regeneration?
   a. Red blood cells
   b. Skin
   c. Endometrium
   d. Neurons

3. Which of the following steps occurs first during wound repair?
   a. Inflammation
   b. Haemostasis
   c. Proliferation
   d. Remodelling
4. Which of the following factors was described by the famous woman scientist – Rita Levi Montalcini?
   a. Fibroblast growth factor
   b. Platelet-derived growth factor
   c. Nerve growth factor
   d. Vascular endothelial growth factor
5. Which of the following types of soft tissue injury are likely to be caused by a sharp object?
   a. Abrasions
   b. Contusions
   c. Crush injury
   d. Lacerations

SHORT ANSWER QUESTIONS (FOR RAPID REVIEW)

1. Define homeostasis.

___

___

2. List three differences between neural (nervous) and hormonal regulation.
   i.
   ii.
   iii.
3. Given one example of each of the following:
   a. Negative feedback: ___

   ___
   b. Positive feedback: ___

   ___
4. Give two differences between negative and positive feedback.
   i.
   ii.
5. Label the structures illustrating the cell membrane in the following figure:

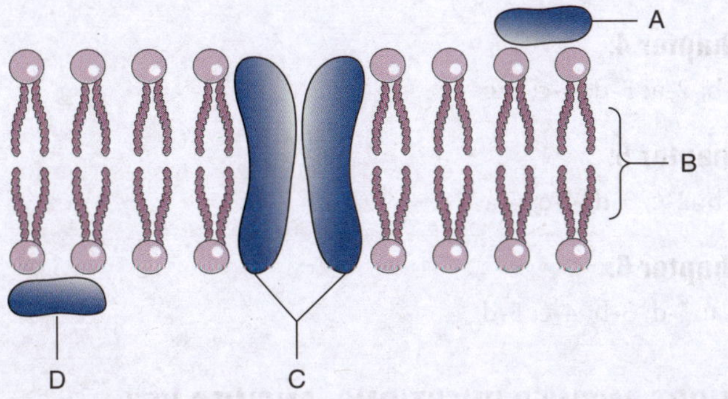

6. List four functions of cell membrane proteins.
   i.
   ii.
   iii.
   iv.
7. In the following diagram, indicate the different transport processes across the cell membrane labelled from A to H.

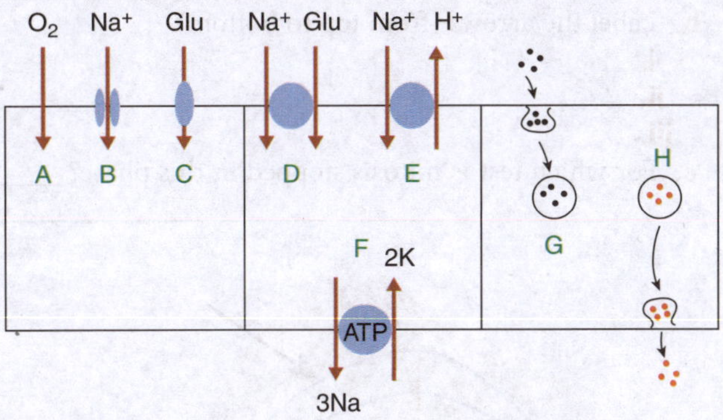

A)
B)
C)
D)
E)
F)
G)
H)
8. Give three differences between simple and facilitated diffusion.
   i.
   ii.
   iii.
9. Indicate whether the following statements are true or false about body water compartments:
   a. Body water is 70% of body weight in adult males.
   b. Intracellular water is greater than extracellular water.
   c. Synovial fluid is an example of transcellular fluid.
   d. Deuterated water is used to measure blood volume.
   e. Deuterated water is used to measure intracellular water.
10. Which of the following statements are true and false for extracellular fluid:
    a. Potassium concentration is higher than intracellular fluid.
    b. Sodium concentration is higher than intracellular fluid.
    c. Chloride concentration is higher than intracellular fluid.
    d. It is 50% of total body water.
11. List two causes of hyponatraemia.
    i.
    ii.
12. List two causes of hyperkalaemia.
    i.
    ii.
13. List three ways in which fluid is lost from the body.
    i.
    ii.
    iii.
14. List the five phases of mitosis in order.
    i.
    ii.
    iii.
    iv.
    v.

15. In the following figure:
   a. Identify the phase of mitosis: ____________
   ____
   b. Label the arrows (from top to bottom).
      i.
      ii.
      iii.
   c. For which test is mitosis stopped in this phase? ____________
   ____

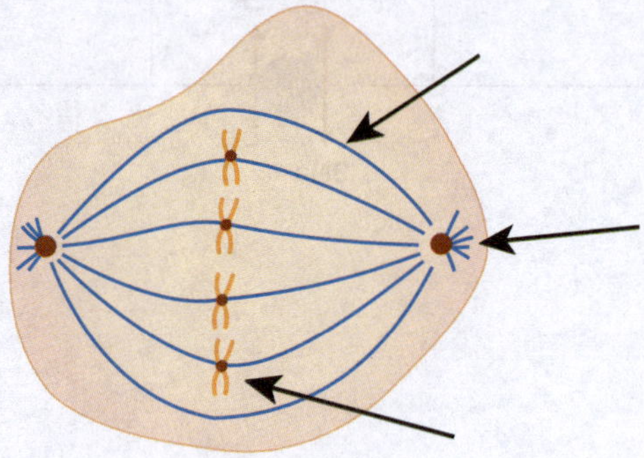

16. List three differences between mitosis and meiosis.
   i.
   ii.
   iii.
17. Indicate the function of each of the following stages of interphase:
   a. G1:
   b. G0: ____________
   ____
   c. S: ____________
   ____
   d. G2: ____________
   ____
18. Give two features that distinguish apoptosis from necrosis.
   i.
   ii.
19. List the phases of wound healing in order.
   i.
   ii.
   iii.
   iv.
20. List four factors that affect wound healing.
   i.
   ii.
   iii.
   iv.
21. List two growth factors.
   i.
   ii.

SHORT ESSAY QUESTIONS

1. List the characteristics of hormones with examples.
2. List the various body water compartments and their relative contribution to total body water.
3. Discuss physiological and pathological factors that affect total body water.
4. Indicate the principle used to measure total body water. List the features of an ideal indicator giving an example.
5. Differentiate between intracellular and extracellular fluid.
6. Differentiate with an example positive and negative feedback.
7. Differentiate between active and passive transport across the cell membrane by giving examples.
8. Distinguish between simple and facilitated diffusion.
9. Describe the different types of vesicular transport by giving examples.
10. Write a short note on the regulation of electrolytes.
11. Distinguish between mitosis and meiosis.
12. Discuss the significance of mitosis and meiosis.
13. Discuss the various mechanisms of cell death.
14. Discuss the stages of wound repair and factors which affect this.

LONG ESSAY QUESTIONS

1. Describe the structure of the cell membrane with a diagram and list the types of transport across the cell membrane.
2. Discuss the functions of the cell membrane and its components.
3. Discuss the importance of cell division in clinical medicine.
4. Describe the phases of mitosis.
5. Describe the phases of meiosis.
6. Discuss the factors which regulate water balance in terms of water intake and water loss.

MULTIPLE CHOICE QUESTIONS ANSWERS

Chapter 1:
1-b; 2-a; 3-c; 4-b; 5-a

Chapter 2:
1-b; 2-c; 3-c; 4-d; 5-b

Chapter 3:
1-a; 2-b; 3-d; 4-a; 5-a

Chapter 4:
1-b; 2-a; 3-d; 4-c; 5-c

Chapter 5:
1-b; 2-c; 3-d; 4-c; 5-a

Chapter 6:
1-a; 2-d; 3-b; 4-c; 5-d

SHORT ANSWER QUESTIONS: ANSWER KEY

1. Maintenance of constancy of the internal environment.
2. See Chapter 1, Table 1.2.
3. (a) Regulation of hormone secretion, for example, thyroxine, control of blood pressure, body temperature; (b) clotting, parturition reflex.

4. See Chapter 1, Table 1.3.
5. (A) Peripheral (extrinsic) protein, (B) phospholipid bilayer, (C) integral (transmembrane) protein, (D) peripheral (intrinsic) protein.
6. See Chapter 2, Table 2.1.
   i. Receptor
   ii. Antigen
   iii. Transport protein (carrier/pore/pump)
   iv. Structural
7. (A) Simple diffusion of a lipid-soluble molecule; (B) simple diffusion of a water-soluble molecule through a channel; (C) facilitated diffusion using a carrier protein; (D) cotransport: SYMPORT – two substances in the same direction; (E) cotransport: ANTIPORT – two substances in opposite directions; (F) primary active transport; (G) vesicular transport – endocytosis; (H) vesicular transport – exocytosis.
8. See Chapter 2, Table 2.3.
9. a. False
   b. True
   c. True
   d. False
   e. False
10. a. False
   b. True
   c. True
   d. False
11. See Chapter 4, Table 4.1.
12. See Chapter 4, Table 4.2.
13. See Chapter 3, Table 3.1.
14. i. Prophase
   ii. Prometaphase
   iii. Metaphase
   iv. Anaphase
   v. Telophase
15. a. Metaphase
   b. i. Mitotic spindle
      ii. Centrosome
      iii. Sister chromatids on the equatorial plate
   c. Karyotyping
16. See Chapter 5, Table 5.1.
17. See Chapter 5, Fig. 5.8.
18. a. CAUSE: Apoptosis – programmed cell death; necrosis – injury or ischaemia.
   b. Apoptosis – no inflammation unlike necrosis in which inflammation is present.
19. i. Haemostasis
   ii. Inflammation
   iii. Proliferation
   iv. Remodelling
20. See Chapter 6 for extended list.
21. i. Nerve growth factor
   ii. Platelet-derived growth factor

SECTION 2

Workbook: Respiratory System

SPECIFIC LEARNING OBJECTIVES

At the end of this chapter, the student should be able to:

Chapter 8

- List the functions of the respiratory system.
- Describe the constituents and functions of the different zones of the respiratory system.
- Describe the tracheobronchial tree.
- Describe the characteristics of the pulmonary circulation.

Chapter 9

- List the muscles that are involved in inspiration and expiration.
- Define the following terms: respiratory minute volume, dead space, alveolar ventilation, maximal voluntary ventilation and breathing reserve.
- Describe the changes in pressures (intrapleural, alveolar, transpulmonary) that occur during inspiration and expiration.
- Describe the concept of compliance and list the factors that affect it.
- List the functions of surfactant.

Chapter 10

- Describe the basic gas laws as applied to the respiratory system.
- Describe the composition of atmospheric, alveolar and expired air.
- Describe the process by which gas diffuses across the respiratory membrane.
- Describe the concept of ventilation–perfusion ratio.
- Describe the regional distribution of air and blood flow in the lungs.

Chapter 11

- Describe the ways in which oxygen is transported in the blood.
- Draw and explain the oxygen–haemoglobin dissociation curve.
- Describe the ways in which carbon dioxide is transported in the blood.

Chapter 12

- Describe the chemical respiration of respiration in terms of the following:
  - Anatomical sites involved
  - Stimuli that trigger chemical control of respiration
  - Effects of simple manoeuvres on the chemical control of respiration
- Describe the neural control of respiration in terms of the following:
  - Anatomical sites involved
  - Function of each of the anatomical sites
  - Reflexes concerning respiration
- Describe the cough reflex.

Chapter 13

- List the causes of different types of hypoxia.
- Differentiate between the different types of hypoxia.
- Distinguish between central and peripheral cyanosis.
- Describe the different types of dyspnoea.
- Describe the different types of periodic breathing.

Chapter 14

- Draw a normal spirogram and label the various volumes and capacities.
- Describe the timed vital capacity with the help of a diagram.
- Describe the use of peak expiratory flow rate.
- Differentiate between restrictive and obstructive lung diseases.
- Describe the use of spirometry in clinical practice and list the criteria for an acceptable test.

Chapter 15

- Describe the pulmonary responses to acute exercise.
- Explain the regulation of respiration during acute exercise.
- Describe the effect of chronic exercise on lung function.
- Describe the pulmonary changes with exercise in:
  - High altitude
  - Cold environment

Chapter 16

- Describe the changes that occur in the foetal respiratory system in utero.
- Describe the changes that occur in the respiratory system during infancy.
- Describe the changes that occur in the respiratory system in ageing.

Chapter 17

- Describe the respiratory changes in high altitude in native highlanders and those who ascend to high altitudes.

- List the clinical features of respiratory distress in children and adults.
- Describe the modalities and principles of oxygen therapy.
- Describe the physiological principles of ventilatory support.
- List the aims and describe the process of nebulization.
- Describe the role of tracheostomy in clinical medicine.

GLOSSARY OF TERMS

Chapter 8

- **Pulmonary oedema:** a condition in which there is excess fluid in the lung parenchyma and the air sacs
- **Pulmonary embolism:** blockage of a blood vessel in the pulmonary circulation, usually due to a clot
- **Dyspnoea:** uncomfortable breathing as experienced by the patient

Chapter 9

- **Dead space:** that part of the respiratory system which does not take part in gas exchange
- **Vital capacity:** the volume of exhaled air during a maximal expiration following a maximal inspiration
- **Residual volume:** the volume of air left in the lungs after a maximal expiration
- **Dyspnoea:** a subjective experience of discomfort during breathing
- **Hyaline membrane disease:** difficulty in breathing in the newborn often due to a deficiency of surfactant related to prematurity

Chapter 10

- **Perfusion:** delivery of blood to a capillary bed
- **Ventilation–perfusion ratio:** applied either to the whole lung or to a part of the lung (in the case of the latter, it is the ratio of alveolar ventilation in that part of the lung to the capillary blood flow in the same part)
- **Partial pressure of a gas:** in a mixture of gases, each gas is described in terms of its own partial pressure which is the hypothetical pressure of that gas if it alone occupied the volume of the mixture

Chapter 11

- **Bohr's effect:** haemoglobin's oxygen binding affinity is inversely related to the concentration of carbon dioxide; thus, as carbon dioxide concentration increases, the oxygen affinity decreases
- **Haldane's effect:** oxygenation of blood in the lungs displaces carbon dioxide from haemoglobin

Chapter 12

- **Apnoea:** temporary stoppage of breathing
- **Tachypnoea:** increased rate of respiration
- **Hyperpnoea:** increase in the depth of breathing

Chapter 13

- **Hypoxia:** a reduction in oxygen at the tissue level
- **Cyanosis:** a bluish discolouration of the skin and mucous membranes due to an elevation in deoxyhaemoglobin
- **Dyspnoea:** a subjective feeling of difficulty of breathing
- **Periodic breathing:** abnormal pattern of breathing in which normal or increased depth of breathing alternates with periods of reduced breathing or apnoea

Chapter 14

- **FEV_1:** the amount of air forcefully expired in 1 second after a maximal inspiration
- **FVC:** the amount of air that can be completely expired after a maximal inspiration
- **PEFR:** the maximal expiratory flow that is achieved when expiring maximally and as rapidly as possibly following a maximal inspiration

Chapter 15

- **Physical activity:** any bodily movement produced by the contraction of skeletal muscle that increases energy expenditure above a basal level
- **Exercise:** structured physical activity aimed at achieving some end point, for example, increased fitness
- **Oxygen debt:** the extra oxygen consumed following strenuous activity to break down accumulated lactic acid and replenish energy stores
- **VO_2 max:** the maximum amount of oxygen that the body can use during intense exercise – typically determined by increasing the intensity of exercise until this is achieved
- **Tachypnoea:** rapid breathing
- **Hyperpnoea:** abnormal rapid or deep breathing

Chapter 16

- **Surfactant:** a surface tension–reducing agent produced by the alveolar type II cells in the lung (surfactant reduces the work of breathing and ensures that alveoli are kept dry and open)
- **Dendritic cell:** an immune cell found in tissues that is capable of phagocytosis and also helps in presenting antigens to other immune cells
- **Senescence:** a state in which cells age and are unable to divide
- **Natural killer cells:** a lymphocyte that binds to tumour cells and viruses and helps to destroy them

Chapter 17

- **Aspiration:** accidental inhalation of fluid or food into the trachea and lungs which may result in pneumonia
- **Mechanical ventilation:** process by which a person breathes with the help of an external device called a ventilator
- **Nebulization:** the conversion of a liquid medication into a fine spray which can then be inhaled directly into the lungs
- **Tracheostomy:** a surgical procedure which involves the insertion of a tube directly into the trachea and which is then used for spontaneous breathing or mechanical ventilation

MULTIPLE CHOICE QUESTIONS

Chapter 8:

1. How many divisions are there between the trachea and alveoli?
   a. 6
   b. 17
   c. 23
   d. 30
2. What defines the conducting zone of the tracheobronchial tree?
   a. Contains alveoli
   b. Removes water vapour from the air
   c. Decreases the temperature of the air
   d. Does not take part in gas exchange
3. Which of the following is a feature of the pulmonary circulation?
   a. Has greater volume than systemic circulation
   b. Arterial pressure is 120/80 mm Hg
   c. Blood flow is equal in all parts of the lung
   d. Hypoxia induced vasoconstriction
4. Which type of antibody is present in secretions of the respiratory airways?
   a. Ig A
   b. Ig D
   c. Ig G
   d. Ig M

Chapter 9:

1. Which of the following muscles is most active during quiet inspiration?
   a. External intercostals
   b. Internal intercostals
   c. Diaphragm
   d. Anterior abdominal muscles
2. Which of the following muscles is used only during forced inspiration?
   a. Diaphragm
   b. Sternocleidomastoid
   c. Internal intercostals
   d. Anterior abdominal muscles
3. Which of the following is true of pressures in the lungs?
   a. Alveolar pressure increases to +1 cm H20 during inspiration
   b. Transpulmonary and alveolar pressure are the same
   c. Intrapleural pressures are always negative
   d. During inspiration, atmospheric pressure is less than alveolar pressure
4. Which of the following is true of surfactant?
   a. Produced by type I alveolar cells
   b. Reduces surface tension in the alveoli
   c. Made up mainly of cholesterol
   d. Increases the work of breathing
5. Neonatal distress syndrome due to surfactant deficiency is most likely to be seen in a baby born at:
   a. 30 weeks
   b. 34 weeks
   c. 36 weeks
   d. 40 weeks

Chapter 10:

1. Which of the following is true of atmospheric air?
   a. % of nitrogen is 70%
   b. % of oxygen is ~21%
   c. Amount of water vapour is fixed
   d. Carbon dioxide is 4%
2. Which of the following is true of alveolar air compared to atmospheric air?
   a. % of nitrogen is unchanged
   b. There is more oxygen
   c. There is less carbon dioxide
   d. There is more water vapour
3. Compared to atmospheric air, expired air has:
   a. Less oxygen content
   b. More nitrogen
   c. Less carbon dioxide
   d. Less water vapour
4. Gases need to diffuse through the respiratory membrane. Which of the following statements is true?
   a. Oxygen diffuses from blood to the alveoli
   b. Carbon dioxide diffuses from alveoli to the blood
   c. Pressure gradient for oxygen is less than carbon dioxide
   d. Carbon dioxide is more soluble than oxygen
5. The ventilation of the lungs is unequal. Which of the following areas of the lung has the greatest ventilation?
   a. Apex of lung
   b. Mid zone – left lung
   c. Mid zone – right lung
   d. Base of lung

Chapter 11:

1. Most of the oxygen in blood is carried by haemoglobin as oxyhaemoglobin. What quantity of oxygen is carried per gm of haemoglobin?
   a. 0.34 mL
   b. 1.34 mL
   c. 13.4 mL
   d. 134 mL
2. By which methods is most of the carbon dioxide carried in blood?
   a. Dissolved
   b. As carboxyhaemoglobin
   c. As carbaminohaemoglobin
   d. As bicarbonate
3. Haemoglobin is almost fully saturated with oxygen at the following arterial partial pressures:
   a. 60–100 mmHg
   b. 40–80 mmHg
   c. 20–60 mmHg
   d. 0–40 mmHg
4. A shift in the oxygen-haemoglobin dissociation curve to the right occurs with:
   a. Decreased temperature
   b. Increased pH

c. Increased PCO_2
d. Decreased 2,3 DBG

5. Which of the following is associated with a shift in the oxygen-haemoglobin dissociation curve to the left?
a. Increased PCO_2
b. Increased 2,3, DBG
c. Increased temperature
d. HbF

Chapter 12:

1. To which of the following arterial stimuli do the peripheral chemoreceptors (carotid and aortic bodies) respond to?
a. Reduced PO_2
b. Increased PCO_2
c. Reduced pH
d. All of the above

2. Which of the following cranial nerves carries impulse from the carotid bodies?
a. Trigeminal
b. Facial
c. Glossopharyngeal
d. Vagus

3. Which of the following are medullary neural respiratory centres?
a. Dorsal respiratory group
b. Ventral respiratory group
c. Pre-Botzinger complex
d. All of the above

4. Which neural centre in the pons inhibits the apneustic centre?
a. Dorsal respiratory group
b. Ventral respiratory group
c. Pneumotaxic centre
d. Botzinger complex

5. In which of the following phases of the cough reflex is the glottis (vocal cords) closed?
a. Inspiratory phase
b. Compressive phase
c. Expulsive phase
d. Expiratory phase

Chapter 13:

1. At high altitude, what type of hypoxia is likely to develop?
a. Hypoxic
b. Anaemic
c. Stagnant
d. Histotoxic

2. A patient has heart failure. Which type of hypoxia is he likely to develop?
a. Hypoxic
b. Anaemic
c. Stagnant
d. Cytotoxic

3. Which type of hypoxia responds best with oxygen therapy?
a. Hypoxic
b. Anaemic
c. Stagnant
d. Histotoxic

4. Cyanosis is due to an increase in:
a. Carbaminohaemoglobin
b. Carboxyhaemoglobin
c. Deoxyhaemoglobin
d. HbS

5. Dyspnoea is defined as:
a. Rapid breathing
b. Increase in rate and depth of breathing
c. A transient stoppage of breathing
d. A difficulty in breathing

Chapter 14:

1. Tidal volume during quiet breathing in an adult is:
a. 150 mL
b. 500 mL
c. 1000 mL
d. 1500 mL

2. When a person breathes in maximally and then breathes out maximally, the volume of air is:
a. Inspiratory reserve volume
b. Expiratory reserve volume
c. Functional residual capacity
d. Vital capacity

3. The volume of air that remains in the lungs after a forceful expiration is called:
a. Functional residual capacity
b. Expiratory reserve volume
c. Residual volume
d. Expiratory capacity

4. A person with a first attack of bronchial asthma (acute obstructive lung disease) will have:
a. Decreased FVC
b. Decreased residual volume
c. Decreased FEV1/FVC
d. Decreased functional residual capacity

5. A person with severe kyphosis (restrictive lung disease) will have:
a. Reduced FVC
b. Reduced FEV1/FVC
c. Decreased residual volume
d. Decreased peak expiratory flow rate

Chapter 15:

1. During exercise there is an increase in breathing. Which of the following parameters shows the greatest percentage increase?
a. Respiratory rate
b. Tidal volume
c. Residual volume
d. Total minute ventilation

2. Oxygen debt is seen as the increase in oxygen consumption:
a. During the early part of exercise
b. During the maintenance of exercise
c. At the end of exercise
d. After exercise – during recovery

Chapter 16:

1. Which of the following is the final phase of development of the respiratory system in utero?
   a. Alveolar
   b. Embryonic
   c. Canalicular
   d. Terminal sac
2. Which of the following cells secretes surfactant?
   a. Alveolar type I cell
   b. Alveolar type II cell
   c. Mucous cells
   d. J cells
3. With the babies first cry, which of the following changes causes blood to flow in the lungs?
   a. Vasodilation of pulmonary blood vessels
   b. Closure of ductus venosus
   c. Closure of ductus arteriosus
   d. Clamping of umbilical cord
4. Till what age do the alveoli continue to grow and mature?
   a. 1 year
   b. 5 years
   c. 8 years
   d. Till young adulthood
5. Which of the following changes in the respiratory system are seen with ageing?
   a. Development of alveoli
   b. Development of pulmonary capillaries
   c. Decreased mucociliary function
   d. Increased size of airways

SHORT ANSWER QUESTIONS (FOR RAPID REVIEW)

1. The two broad zones of the respiratory system are:
   a.
   b.
2. List four functions of the respiratory system.
   a.
   b.
   c.
   d.
3. List four features of the pulmonary circulation.
   a.
   b.
   c.
   d.
4. Write two features each of the following:
   a. Pulmonary embolism: ______
   b. Pulmonary hypertension: ______
5. List the muscles of inspiration.
   a.
   b.
   c.
6. List the muscles of expiration.
   a.
   b.
7. Define each of the following terms and give their normal values.
   a. Tidal volume: ______
   b. Respiratory rate: ______
   c. Respiratory minute volume: ______
   d. Dead space: ______
   e. Alveolar ventilation: ______
8. Indicate the pleural pressure and alveolar pressure in cm H_2O during inspiration and expiration in the following table.

	Inspiration	Expiration
Pleural pressure	a. ______	b. ______
Alveolar pressure	c. ______	d. ______

9. Match items in column A with those in column B.

Column A	Column B
1. Maximal voluntary ventilation	a. The change in lung volume per unit change in transpulmonary pressure
2. Compliance	b. Difficulty and discomfort in breathing
3. Breathing reserve	c. Amount of ventilation that can theoretically be achieved with maximal hyperventilation in 1 min
4. Transpulmonary pressure	d. The difference between maximal voluntary ventilation and respiratory minute volume
5. Dyspnoea	e. The difference between alveolar and pleural pressure

10. List two factors that affect lung compliance.
    a.
    b.
11. With regard to surfactant, answer the following:
    a. The major component of surfactant is ______.
    b. Surfactant is produced by ______ cells.

c. Five functions of surfactant are:
  i.
  ii.
  iii.
  iv.
  v.

12. A deficiency of surfactant in premature infants gives rise to a condition called ______________________________.

13. The six layers of the respiratory membrane are:
  a.
  b.
  c.
  d.
  e.
  f.

14. Indicate whether the following statements are true or false:
  a. The average ventilation–perfusion ratio of the lungs in 0.8.
  b. Blood flow in the lungs is more in the apex of the lungs.
  c. Ventilation is relatively more in the apex of the lungs.
  d. Ventilation–perfusion ratio varies in different parts of the lungs.
  e. Alveolar air has lower nitrogen concentration than atmospheric air.
  f. Carbon dioxide concentration in alveolar air is lower than atmospheric air.
  g. Alveolar air is less humidified than atmospheric air.
  h. Oxygen in alveolar air is lower than in atmospheric air.

15. Two ways in which oxygen is carried in blood in order of importance are:
  a.
  b.

16. Three ways in which carbon dioxide is carried in blood in order of importance are:
  a.
  b.
  c.

17. In relation to the following diagram which represents the oxygen–haemoglobin dissociation curve, answer the following:

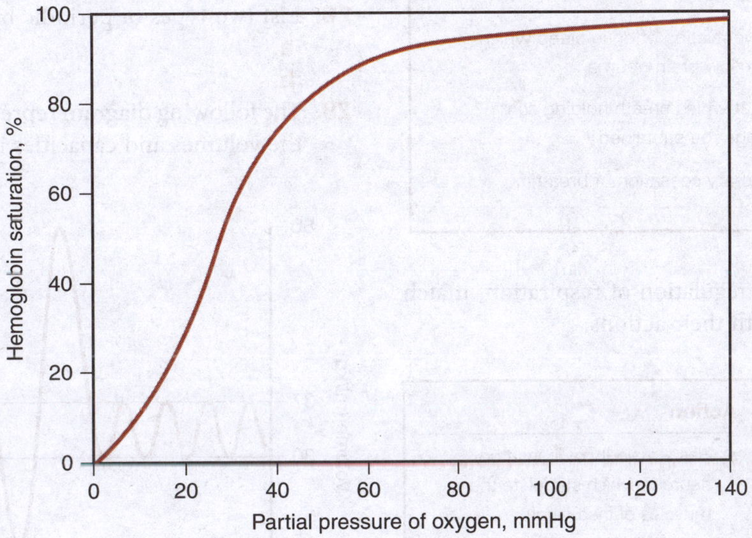

First, draw a horizontal line that corresponds to 50% haemoglobin saturation – drop a vertical line down to *X*-axis where your horizontal line meets the curve.

In BLUE, indicate a shift to the left; in RED, indicate a shift to the right.

  a) The arterial partial pressure of oxygen at 50% saturation is called ______________; its normal value is ______________.
  b) List three conditions that cause a shift to the right.
    i.
    ii.
    iii.
  c) A shift to the right due to an increased PCO_2 which is associated with decreased affinity of oxygen to haemoglobin and increased dissociation and release of oxygen is called ______________.
  d) Which type of haemoglobin will cause a shift to the left? ______________

18. Exchange of bicarbonate and chloride between RBC and plasma which allows for carriage of carbon dioxide is called ______________.

19. Binding of oxygen to haemoglobin in the lungs releases carbon dioxide from haemoglobin, a phenomenon called ____.

20. List the types of chemoreceptors involved in the regulation of respiration and their location.

i.

ii.

21. List three chemical stimuli in the blood that can stimulate ventilation.

i.

ii.

iii.

22. Match items in column A with those in column B.

Column A	Column B
1. Apnoea	a) An increase in the partial pressure of CO_2 in blood
2. Break-point	b) Increased ventilation which allows the body to expel a greater amount of CO_2
3. Hypercapnia	c) Initiation of expiration when lungs are inflated
4. CO_2 washout	d) Hypoventilation often in sleep which may follow brain trauma
5. Ondine's curse	e) Time at which breath holding can no longer be sustained
6. Hering–Breuer inflation reflex	f) Temporary cessation of breathing

23. With regard to the neural regulation of respiration, match the centres in the brain with their actions.

Centres	Action
1. UPPER PONS: pneumotaxic centre	a) Has a majority of inspiratory neurons which stimulate the muscles of inspiration
2. LOWER PONS: apneustic centre	b) Has mixed inspiratory and expiratory neurons
3. MEDULLA: dorsal respiratory group	c) Stimulates the dorsal respiratory group neurons
4. MEDULLA: ventral respiratory group	d) Inhibits the apneustic centre

24. Define hypoxia. ____

25. In the following table, column A lists the various types of hypoxia, column B lists the mechanisms of hypoxia and column C lists specific causes of hypoxia. Match the types of hypoxia in column A with their mechanisms in column B and specific cause in column C.

Type of Hypoxia	Mechanism	Cause
Hypoxic hypoxia	1. Reduced blood flow resulting in low tissue perfusion	a) Cyanide poisoning
Anaemic hypoxia	2. Inadequate oxygenation of the blood in the lungs	b) Heart failure
Stagnant hypoxia	3. Inability to utilize the oxygen delivered to the tissues	c) High altitude
Histotoxic hypoxia	4. Lowered/abnormal haemoglobin or RBC count	d) Severe iron deficiency

26. Define cyanosis and list the two types of cyanosis.

i)

ii)

27. List three types of dyspnoea.

a.

b.

c.

28. List two types of periodic breathing.

a.

b.

29. The following diagram represents a normal spirogram. Label the volumes and capacities indicated by the letters A–H.

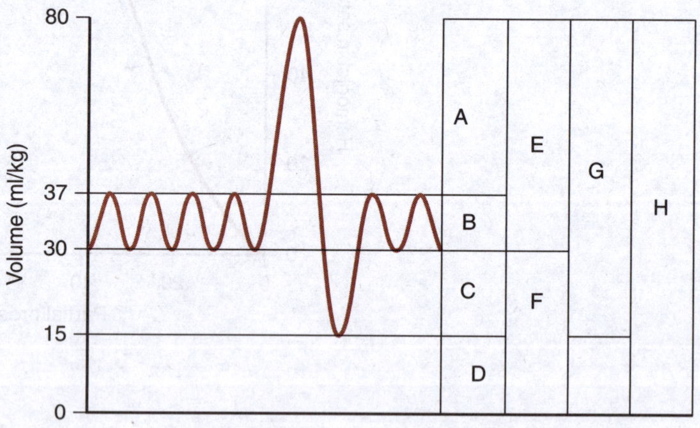

A) E)

B) F)

C) G)

D) H)

30. With regard to timed vital capacity, complete the following statements:

a) The normal FEV_1/FVC is ______________ %.

b) In obstructive lung disease, FEV_1/FVC is ______________.

c) In restrictive lung disease, FEV_1/FVC may be normal but ______________________________ is reduced.

d) Bronchial asthma is an example of ______________ ______________ disease.

e) Severe kyphosis may lead to ______________ ______________ disease.

31. Define oxygen debt and explain its cause. ______________

32. Define maximal aerobic capacity (VO_2 max). ______________

33. List three factors which affect VO_2 max.

a.
b.
c.

34. List the phases of development of the respiratory system in utero.

a.
b.
c.
d.

35. List three mechanisms by which the pulmonary circulation is bypassed in utero.

a.
b.
c.

36. List the changes that occur in the respiratory system at birth.

a.
b.
c.

37. List three changes that occur in the respiratory system with ageing.

a.
b.
c.

38. List three reasons why elderly are more prone to respiratory infections.

a.
b.
c.

39. List three features that are seen in the respiratory system of native highlanders.

a.
b.
c.

40. List three changes which occur when people move from sea level to high altitude above 2500 m.

a.
b.
c.

41. Give four features of acute respiratory distress in infants.

a.
b.
c.
d.

42. List four ways in which oxygen can be delivered to a patient in hospital.

a.
b.
c.
d.

43. What is nebulization? ______________

44. What is tracheostomy? ______________

SHORT ESSAY QUESTIONS

1. List the muscles that are involved in inspiration and expiration.
2. Draw and label a typical spirogram.
3. Describe the changes in pressures (intrapleural, alveolar, transpulmonary) that occur during inspiration and expiration.
4. Define lung compliance and list the factors that affect it.
5. List the functions of surfactant.
6. Draw a diagram of the respiratory membrane and list the factors which affect the diffusion of a gas through it.
7. What is ventilation–perfusion ratio? Explain the differences in this ratio in different parts of the lung.
8. Describe the transport of oxygen in blood.
9. Draw and explain the oxygen–haemoglobin dissociation curve.
10. Discuss the factors that cause a shift in the oxygen–haemoglobin dissociation curve.
11. Draw a diagram indicating the chloride shift and discuss its importance.
12. Describe the cough reflex.
13. Define cyanosis. Differentiate between central and peripheral cyanosis.
14. Define dyspnoea. List the types and indicate some common causes.
15. What is vital capacity? List the factors which affect it.
16. What is timed vital capacity? How is it used to differentiate between obstructive and restrictive lung disease?
17. Discuss the respiratory responses to acute exercise.
18. What is oxygen debt? Explain its basis.
19. Describe the physiological changes that occur at high altitude.
20. Describe the features of acute respiratory distress.
21. Discuss the use of oxygen therapy in a clinical setting.
22. Discuss the principles of mechanical ventilation.
23. Describe the purpose and nursing care of a tracheostomy.

LONG ESSAY QUESTIONS

1. Describe the functions of the respiratory system.
2. Describe the mechanics of respiration.
3. Describe the transport of carbon dioxide in blood.
4. Describe the chemical regulation of respiration.
5. Describe the neural regulation of respiration.
6. List the different types of hypoxia. Indicate their causes and differences.
7. Describe the various lung function tests and their application.
8. Describe the respiratory changes that occur in utero and at birth.
9. Describe the respiratory changes that occur with ageing.

MULTIPLE CHOICE QUESTIONS ANSWERS

Chapter 8:

1-c; 2-d; 3-d; 4-a

Chapter 9:

1-c; 2-b; 3-c; 4-b; 5-a

Chapter 10:

1-b; 2-d; 3-a; 4-d; 5-d

Chapter 11:

1-b; 2-d; 3-a; 4-c; 5-d

Chapter 12:

1-d; 2-c; 3-d; 4-c; 5-b

Chapter 13:

1-a; 2-c; 3-a; 4-c; 5-d

Chapter 14:

1-b; 2-d; 3-c; 4-c; 5-a

Chapter 15:

1-d; 2-d

Chapter 16:

1-a; 2-b; 3-a; 4-c; 5-c

SHORT ANSWER QUESTIONS: ANSWER KEY

1. (a) Conducting zone, (b) respiratory zone.
2. (a) Gas exchange, (b) speech, (c) protection, (d) endocrine and metabolic function.
3. (a) Cardiac output is 5 L/minute (same as the systemic circulation); (b) pressures are one-fifth those of systemic circulation pressures; (c) blood flow varies in different parts of the lung; (d) shows hypoxic vasoconstriction.
4. (a and b) – see Chapter 8.
5. (a) Diaphragm, (b) external intercostals, (c) sternocleidomastoid and scalene neck muscles.
6. (a) Internal intercostals, (b) anterior abdominal muscles in forced expiration.
7. Please see Chapter 9 for definitions. Normal values: (a) 500 mL; (b) 12–16 breaths/minute; (c) tidal volume × respiratory rate (0.5 L × 12 = 6 L/minute); (d) 150 mL; (e) (tidal volume − dead space) × respiratory rate, that is, 500 − 150, that is, 350 × 12 = 4200 mL.
8. (a) −7.5, (b) −5, (c) −1, (d) +1.
9. 1 – c; 2 – a; 3 – d; 4 – e; 5 – b.
10. See Chapter 9.
11. (a) Dipalmitoyl-diphosphatidyl choline; (b) type II alveolar cells; (c) (i) reduces surface tension, (ii) prevents alveoli from collapsing, (iii) improved compliance, (iv) decreases the work of breathing, (v) keeps lungs dry.
12. Neonatal respiratory distress syndrome (hyaline membrane disease).
13. (a) The fluid and surfactant layer that lines the alveolus, (b) the alveolar epithelium, (c) the epithelial basement membrane, (d) the interstitial space, (e) the capillary basement membrane, (f) the capillary endothelium.
14. (a) True, (b) false, (c) true, (d) true, (e) true, (f) false, (g) false, (h) true.
15. (a) Combined with haemoglobin – 98%; and (b) dissolved – 2%.
16. (a) As bicarbonate – 70%; (b) combined with haemoglobin – 23%; (c) dissolved – 7%.
17. (a) P50, 27 mmHg; (b) (i) increased temperature, (ii) increased PCO_2, (iii) decreased pH; (c) Bohr's effect; (d) foetal haemoglobin (HbF).
18. Chloride shift.
19. Haldane's effect.
20. (i) Peripheral – carotid and aortic bodies; (ii) central – chemosensitive zone of the medulla.
21. Increased PCO_2, decreased PO_2, decreased pH (increased H^+).
22. 1, f; 2, e; 3, a; 4, b; 5, d; 6, c.
23. 1, d; 2, c; 3, a; 4, b.
24. See Chapter 13.
25. Hypoxic hypoxia – 2, c; anaemic hypoxia – 4, d; stagnant hypoxia – 1, b; histotoxic hypoxia – 3, a.
26. See Chapter 13.
27. See Chapter 13.
28. See Chapter 13.
29. (A) Inspiratory reserve volume, (B) tidal volume, (C) expiratory reserve volume, (D) residual volume, (E) inspiratory capacity, (F) functional residual capacity, (G) vital capacity, (H) total lung capacity.
30. (a) ≥80%, (b) less than 80%, (c) FVC, (d) obstructive lung disease, (e) restrictive lung disease.
31. See Chapter 15.
32. See Chapter 15.
33. Gender, age, level of physical fitness.
34. Embryonic, pseudoglandular, canalicular, terminal sac, alveolar.
35. Foramen ovale shunts blood from the right atrium to the left atrium; ductus arteriosus shunts blood from the pulmonary artery to the aorta; hypoxic environment promotes pulmonary vasoconstriction.
36. Babies cry – inspiratory gasp – removes hypoxic environment – pulmonary vasodilation; closure of foramen ovale; closure of the ductus arteriosus.
37. See Chapter 16.
38. See Chapter 16.

39–44. See Chapter 17.

Workbook: Digestive System

SPECIFIC LEARNING OBJECTIVES

At the end of this chapter, the student should be able to:

Chapter 18

- Describe with the help of a diagram the parts of the gastro-intestinal (GI) system.
- List the broad functions of the GI system.
- Describe the cross-section of the gut.
- Describe the neural control of GI function.
- Describe the circulation of digestive system.

Chapter 19

- Describe the source, composition, functions and regulation of salivary secretion.
- Describe the source, composition, functions and regulation of gastric juice secretion.
- Describe the source, composition, functions and regulation of pancreatic juice secretion.
- Describe the source, composition, functions and regulation of biliary secretion.
- Describe the source, composition and functions of small intestinal secretions.

Chapter 20

- Describe the functional anatomy of the hepatobiliary system.
- Describe the functions of the liver.
- List the factors which regulate the secretion of bile.
- List the tests that can be used to evaluate liver function.

Chapter 21

- Describe the phases and process of deglutition.
- List the factors which affect gastric emptying.
- Describe the movements of the small and large intestine.
- Describe the defaecation reflex.

Chapter 22

- List the end products of digestion for the major food groups.
- List the features of the gastrointestinal tract that favour the absorption of nutrients.
- List the nutrients that are absorbed in each segment of the alimentary tract.
- Describe the role of the large intestine.
- Describe the basis of malabsorption syndromes.

Chapter 23

- Describe the pathways by which glucose is utilized in the cells.
- Describe how glucose is stored and how it can be mobilized for use.
- Describe how amino acids are utilized.
- Describe how fatty acids are metabolized and how fat is stored.

Chapter 24

- Describe the pathophysiology of gastro-oesophageal reflux disease (GERD).
- List the mechanism of action of drugs used for acid peptic disease based on the physiology of gastric acid secretion.
- Enumerate and interpret liver function tests.
- Describe the causes and consequences of malabsorption syndrome.
- Describe the pathophysiology and broad causes of constipation.
- Describe the pathophysiology of diarrhoea.
- Describe the pathophysiology of irritable bowel disease.

GLOSSARY OF TERMS

Chapter 18

- **Digestion:** the process by which the food that we eat is converted into simpler substances that can be used by the body
- **Absorption:** the process by which the products of digestion are taken up from the lumen of the gut into the blood vessels and lymphatics so that they can be used by the body
- **Motility:** the movement of the gut resulting in the passage of the contents of the gut
- **Portal circulation:** two capillary beds in series

Chapter 19

- **Digestion:** the mechanical, enzymatic and chemical breakdown of food such that it can be absorbed into the body
- **Absorption:** the process by which the end products of digestion pass from the lumen of the intestine into the bloodstream or the lymphatic vessels in the intestinal wall

Chapter 20

- **Hepatitis:** an inflammation of the liver (the most common types are hepatitis A, B and C)

- **Cholecystitis:** an inflammation of the gallbladder
- **Cholestasis:** decrease in bile flow due to either decreased secretion or blockage of flow

Chapter 21

- **Peristalsis:** contraction and relaxation of the gastrointestinal wall which propels food forwards
- **Law of the gut:** the direction of peristalsis is from oral (mouth) to aboral (anal) end

Chapter 22

- **Macronutrient:** a substance required in large amounts in the diet (e.g. fat, protein and carbohydrate)
- **Micronutrient:** a substance required by the body in small amounts (e.g. minerals and vitamins) which is required for growth and development
- **Villi:** folding of the small intestine into finger-like processes which are critical for the absorption of nutrients
- **Fermentation:** the digestion of carbohydrates by bacteria and gas

Chapter 23

- **Glycolysis:** the breakdown of glucose by specific enzymes resulting in pyruvate or lactate and energy (ATP)
- **Glycogenesis:** the formation of glycogen from glucose
- **Glycogenolysis:** the breakdown of glycogen to glucose
- **Gluconeogenesis:** the formation of glucose from noncarbohydrate sources
- **Lipogenesis:** the formation of fat
- **Lipolysis:** the breakdown of fats into fatty acids and glycerol
- **Ketogenesis:** the formation of ketones following breakdown of fats

Chapter 24

- **Gastro-oesophageal reflux disease (GERD):** a condition in which acid enters the oesophagus through the lower oesophageal sphincter resulting in various symptoms and, if chronic, oesophageal injury
- **Ulcer:** in the context of the digestive tract, a discontinuity of the mucosa
- **Malabsorption:** diseases in which there is an inability to absorb nutrients, minerals and vitamins from the digestive tract
- **Steatorrhoea:** increased excretion of fat in the stools (stools are typically bulky, fatty and foul smelling)
- **Constipation:** infrequent stools (<3 per week), difficult stool passage or both
- **Diarrhoea:** the passage of three or more loose/watery stools per day

MULTIPLE CHOICE QUESTIONS

Chapter 18:

1. The nerves that are present between the inner circular and outer longitudinal muscle layers are:
   a. Parasympathetic nerves
   b. Sympathetic nerves
   c. Meissner's plexus
   d. Auerbach's plexus
2. The nerves that are located in submucosa which control the intestinal secretions are:
   a. Auerbach's plexus
   b. Meissner's plexus
   c. Parasympathetic nerves
   d. Sympathetic nerves
3. Nerves which inhibit gastrointestinal motility are:
   a. Auerbach's plexus
   b. Meissner's plexus
   c. Sympathetic nerves
   d. Parasympathetic nerves
4. Which of the following is true of the hepatic blood flow?
   a. It receives about 10% of the cardiac output at rest
   b. It contains 25% of the total blood volume
   c. Three-fourths of its blood flow is from the portal vein
   d. One-half of its blood flow is from the hepatic artery
5. The sphincter between the stomach and the duodenum is:
   a. Lower oesophageal sphincter
   b. Pyloric sphincter
   c. Gastro-ileal sphincter
   d. Gastro-duodenal sphincter

Chapter 19:

1. The major digestive enzyme produced by the salivary glands is:
   a. Amylase
   b. Protease
   c. Lipase
   d. Pepsin
2. The cell which produces HCl in the stomach is:
   a. Enterochromaffin-like cell
   b. G cell
   c. Parietal cell
   d. Chief cell
3. The hormone which produces a watery, bicarbonate-rich pancreatic secretion is:
   a. Gastrin
   b. Cholecystokinin
   c. Secretin
   d. Somatostatin
4. The hormone which contracts the gallbladder to release bile is:
   a. Cholecystokinin
   b. Secretin
   c. Motilin
   d. Somatostatin
5. The enzymes that convert lactose/maltose/sucrose to monosaccharides are called:
   a. Amylase
   b. Enterokinase
   c. Trypsin
   d. Disaccharidases

Chapter 20:

1. Which of the following cells of the liver are phagocytic?
   a. Dendritic cells
   b. Kupffer's cells

c. Epithelial cells
d. Endothelial cells

2. Which plasma protein that maintains plasma osmotic pressure is synthesized in the liver?
   a. Albumin
   b. Globulin
   c. Fibrinogen
   d. Immunoglobulin
3. What is the function of the gallbladder?
   a. It synthesizes bile
   b. It conjugates bilirubin
   c. It stores albumin
   d. It concentrates bile
4. Which vitamin K-dependent clotting factor is produced in the liver?
   a. I
   b. II
   c. III
   d. IV
5. Which of the following is dependent on bile?
   a. Absorption of vitamins A, D, E and K
   b. Synthesis of clotting factors
   c. Gluconeogenesis
   d. Formation of cholesterol

Chapter 21:

1. Which of the following events is responsible for deglutition apnoea?
   a. Movement back of the tongue
   b. Movement of soft palate upwards
   c. Closure of vocal cords
   d. Primary peristalsis
2. Which of the following events helps the stomach to accommodate food?
   a. Peristalsis
   b. Segmentation contractions
   c. Contraction of the pyloric sphincter
   d. Receptive relaxation
3. Which of the following is an example of motility in the small intestine?
   a. Segmentation contractions
   b. Haustral movements
   c. Mass movement
   d. Receptive relaxation
4. Which of the following is an example of motility in the large intestine?
   a. Mass movement
   b. Peristalsis
   c. Segmentation contractions
   d. Receptive relaxation
5. Which of the following nerves controls the external sphincter of the anus?
   a. Sympathetic nerves
   b. Parasympathetic nerves
   c. Meissner's plexus
   d. Pudendal nerve

Chapter 22:

1. The major enzyme responsible for the digestion of starch is:
   a. Amylase
   b. Sucrase
   c. Trypsin
   d. Enterokinase
2. Lactase breaks down lactose to form:
   a. Glucose + glucose
   b. Glucose + galactose
   c. Glucose + fructose
   d. Maltose + glucose
3. Which of the following is the enzyme which breaks down proteins in the stomach?
   a. Trypsin
   b. Chymotrypsin
   c. Pepsin
   d. Peptidases
4. In which part of the gastrointestinal tract are disaccharidases secreted?
   a. Stomach
   b. Liver
   c. Pancreas
   d. Small intestine
5. Which of the following nutrients are absorbed into the lymphatic system?
   a. Amino acids
   b. Peptides
   c. Fats
   d. Monosaccharides

Chapter 23:

1. In the liver, conversion of glucose into its storage form occurs through:
   a. Gluconeogenesis
   b. Pentose phosphate pathway
   c. Glycogenesis
   d. Glycolysis
2. The major storage form of fats is:
   a. Cholesterol
   b. Fatty acids
   c. Phospholipids
   d. Triglycerides
3. Excess production of ketone bodies as occurs with starvation or uncontrolled Type I diabetes is called:
   a. Lipolysis
   b. Gluconeogenesis
   c. Ketoacidosis
   d. Beta oxidation

SHORT ANSWER QUESTIONS (FOR RAPID REVIEW)

1. List five functions of the digestive system.
   a.
   b.
   c.
   d.
   e.

2. Label the structures listed in the following diagram which illustrates the cross-section of the gut.

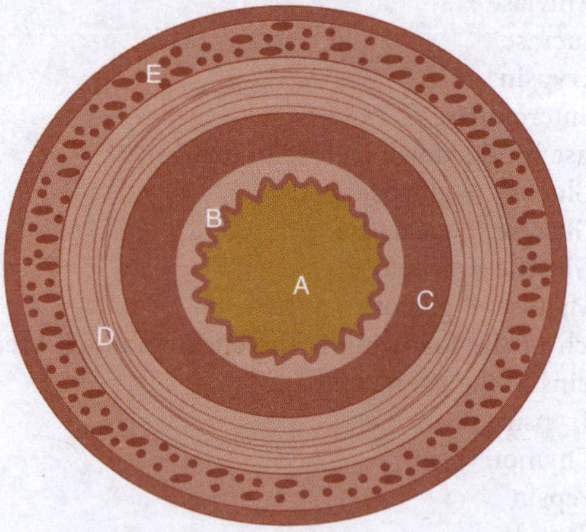

3. Match column A (type of enteric nerve plexus) with column B (location) and column C (function).

Column A: Nerve Plexus	Column B: Location	Column C: Function
1. Auerbach's	a. Between circular and longitudinal muscle layers	i. Controls secretion
2. Meissner's	b. Submucosa	ii. Controls motility

4. Indicate whether the following statements are true or false:
   a) The hepatomesenteric circulation is a portal circulation.
   b) A portal circulation has two capillary beds in parallel.
   c) Intestinal blood flow increases with food ingestion.
   d) Blood flow to the liver is more from the hepatic artery than the portal vein.

5. Match the location (column A) with the enzyme (column B).

Column A: Location	Column B: Enzyme
1. Salivary gland	A. Maltase
2. Stomach	B. Bile
3. Pancreas	C. Pepsinogen
4. Liver/gallbladder	D. Amylase
5. Small intestine	E. Lipase

6. List four functions of saliva.
   a.
   b.
   c.
   d.

7. List three constituents of gastric juice.
   a.
   b.
   c.

8. List three functions of HCl produced by the stomach.
   a.
   b.
   c.

9. Both gastric and pancreatic secretion occurs in three phases. Indicate in the following table, the percentage contribution of each phase. As an example, the cephalic phase of gastric secretion is filled.

	Gastric Secretion	Pancreatic Secretion
Cephalic phase	30%	
Gastric phase		
Intestinal phase		

10. Three receptors on the parietal cell of the stomach are:
    a.
    b.
    c.

11. Three ways in which the gastric mucosa is protected from injury are:
    a.
    b.
    c.

12. Fill in the functions of the pancreatic enzymes that have been listed in the following table:

Name of Pancreatic Enzyme	Function of Enzyme
Amylase	
Lipase	
Cholesterol esterase	
Phospholipase	
Trypsinogen	
Chymotrypsinogen	
Procarboxypeptidases	
Ribonuclease/deoxyribonuclease	

13. Indicate whether the following statements are true or false:
    a. Hepatic bile is more concentrated than gallbladder bile.
    b. Ninety-five per cent of bile salts are reabsorbed by the enterohepatic circulation.
    c. Bile does not contain enzymes.
    d. Bile salts emulsify fats.

14. List two functions of the gallbladder.
    a.
    b.

15. List five functions of the liver.
    a.
    b.
    c.
    d.
    e.

16. List three proteins which are synthesized in the liver.

a.

b.

c.

17. The liver has many metabolic functions. Briefly describe these functions under the headings given as follows:

a. Carbohydrate metabolism: ____________

____

____

____

b. Fat metabolism: ____________

____

____

c. Protein metabolism:

____

____

____

18. State the law of the gut.

____

____

19. List the three phases of deglutition.

a.

b.

c.

20. List three things that happen in the second phase of deglutition that ensure that the bolus of food enters the oesophagus.

a.

b.

c.

21. Match column A with column B.

Column A	Column B
1. Achalasia cardia	A) A relaxed lower oesophageal sphincter
2. Receptive relaxation	B) A tight lower oesophageal sphincter
3. Gastro-oesophageal reflux disease	C) Relaxation of the stomach to accommodate food from the oesophagus

22. Rearrange the factors affecting gastric emptying time so that they are placed in the correct columns.

Increased Gastric Emptying	Decreased Gastric Emptying
Solids	Liquids
High-carbohydrate food	High-fat food
Old age	Increased food volume

23. Observe the diagram which depicts two types of motility seen in the small intestine and answer the questions that follow.

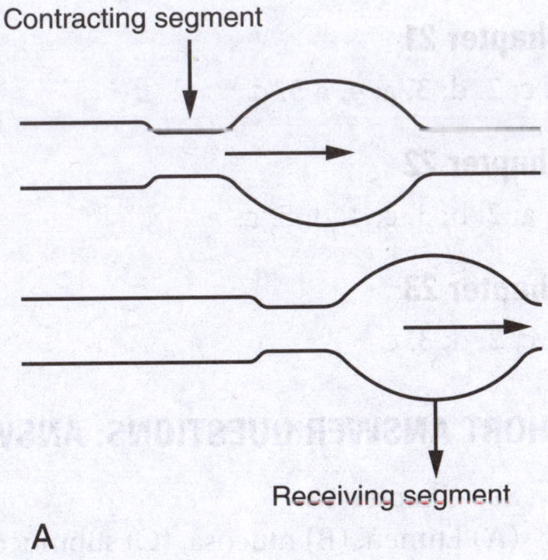

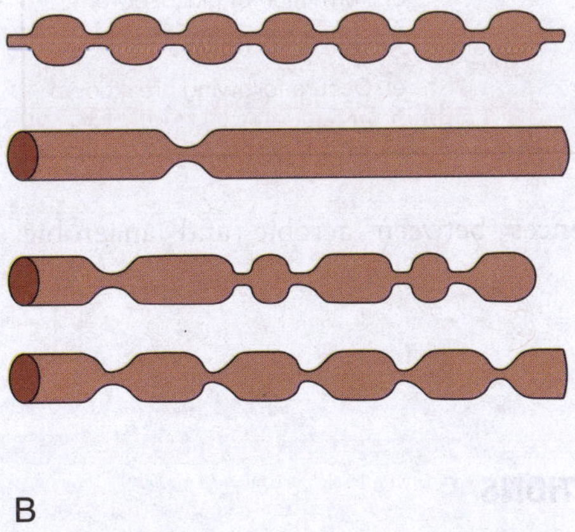

a) Indicate the types of intestinal movements labelled as A and B.

A)

B)

b) List three factors which affect the movement 'A'.

i.

ii.

iii.

c) What is the function of the movements labelled:

A:

B:

24. List two reflexes of the digestive tract.

a.

b.

25. Fill in the following table to indicate the enzymes that are involved in the digestion of carbohydrate, fat and protein.

	Carbohydrate	Protein	Fat
Salivary gland			
Stomach			
Pancreas			
Small intestine			

26. List three ways in which the absorptive surface of the small intestine is increased.

a.

b.

c.

27. List two functions of the large intestine.

a.

b.

28. Match column A with column B.

Column A	Column B
1. Glycolysis	a) Formation of glucose from glycogen
2. Gluconeogenesis	b) Formation of fat
3. Ketogenesis	c) Breakdown of glucose into lactate/pyruvate
4. Glycogenolysis	d) Formation of glucose from noncarbohydrate sources
5. Lipogenesis	e) Occurs following breakdown of fats

29. List three differences between aerobic and anaerobic glycolysis.

a.

b.

c.

SHORT ESSAY QUESTIONS

1. Describe the broad functions of the gastrointestinal system.
2. With a labelled diagram, indicate the location of the enteric nerve plexuses and describe their function.
3. Describe the composition and functions of saliva.
4. Describe the composition and functions of small intestinal secretions.
5. Describe the composition, function and regulation of biliary secretion.
6. Discuss the functions and regulation of gastric acid.
7. Describe the phases of deglutition (swallowing).
8. Describe the process of gastric emptying. List the factors which affect gastric emptying.
9. Describe the movements of the small intestine.
10. Describe the defaecation reflex.
11. Describe the process of carbohydrate digestion in the GIT.
12. Describe the process of protein digestion in the GIT.
13. Describe the process of fat digestion in the GIT.
14. List the sites and process of absorption of carbohydrates, fats and proteins.

LONG ESSAY QUESTIONS

1. Describe the composition, function and regulation of gastric juice.
2. Describe the composition, function and regulation of pancreatic exocrine secretion.
3. Describe the functions of the liver.
4. Describe the process of digestion and absorption of carbohydrates.
5. Describe the process of digestion and absorption of proteins.
6. Describe the process of digestion and absorption of fats.

MULTIPLE CHOICE QUESTIONS

Chapter 18

1. d; 2. b; 3. c; 4. c; 5. b

Chapter 19

1. a; 2. c; 3. c; 4. a; 5. d

Chapter 20

1. b; 2. a; 3. d; 4. b; 5. a

Chapter 21

1. c; 2. d; 3. a; 4. a 5. d

Chapter 22

1. a; 2. b; 3. c; 4. d; 5. c

Chapter 23

1. c; 2. d; 3. c

SHORT ANSWER QUESTIONS: ANSWER KEY

1. See Chapter 18.
2. (A) Lumen, (B) mucosa, (C) submucosa, (D) circular muscle layer, (E) longitudinal muscle layer.
3. 1 – a, ii; 2 – b, i.
4. (a) True; (b) false (capillary beds in series); (c) true; (d) false (three-fourths portal vein, one-fourth hepatic artery).
5. 1, D; 2, C; 3, E; 4, B; 5, A.
6. See Chapter 19.
7. See Chapter 19.
8. See Chapter 19.

9. Gastric – 30%, 60%, 10%; Pancreatic – 20%, 10%, 70%.
10. See Chapter 19.
11. See Chapter 19.
12. See Table 19.1.
13. (a) False, (b) true, (c) true, (d) true.
14. See Chapter 20.
15. See Chapter 20.
16. See Chapter 20.
17. See Chapter 20.
18. See Chapter 21.
19. See Chapter 21.
20. See Chapter 21.
21. 1, B; 2, C; 3, A.
22. Increased gastric emptying – liquids, high-carbohydrate food, increased food volume; decreased gastric emptying – old age, solids, high-fat food.
23. (a) A, peristalsis; B, segmentation. (b and c) See Chapter 21.
24. See Chapter 21.
25.

	Carbohydrate	Protein	Fat
Salivary gland	Amylase		
Stomach	Pepsin	Lipase	
Pancreas	Amylase	Trypsin	Lipase
	Chymotrypsin	Colipase	
Small intestine	Disaccharidases (lactase, maltase, sucrase)	Peptidases	lipase

26. See Chapter 22.
27. See Chapter 22.
28. 1, c; 2, d; 3, e; 4, a; 5, b.
29. See Chapter 23.

SECTION 4

Workbook: Circulatory and Lymphatic System

SPECIFIC LEARNING OBJECTIVES

At the end of this chapter, the student should be able to:

Chapter 25

- Describe the organization of the circulatory system and differentiate between the pulmonary and systemic circulations.
- Describe the different blood vessels that make up the circulatory system.
- Describe the functional organization of the heart
- Describe the cells in the heart.
- List the special features of cardiac muscle.

Chapter 26

- List the pacemaker areas of the heart.
- Draw a diagram of the conducting system of the heart and describe the sequence of events.
- Explain the functions of the conducting system of the heart.
- List the leads of a 12-lead ECG.
- Draw a typical ECG and label its parts.
- List the uses of ECG with specific focus on (1) arrhythmias and (2) myocardial ischaemia and infarction.

Chapter 27

- List the phases of the cardiac cycle in sequence.
- Describe the volume, pressure and valvular changes that occur during the cardiac cycle.
- Describe the relationship between the waves of ECG in relation to the cardiac cycle.
- Describe the heart sounds and their relationship with the phases of the cardiac cycle.
- Describe the waves of the jugular venous pulse and outline its importance.
- Define cardiac output and list its determinants.
- Define venous return and list its determinants.

Chapter 28

- Describe the basic relationship between pressure, flow and resistance.
- List the determinants of flow as given by Poiseuille's law.
- Distinguish between laminar and turbulent flow.
- Describe the pressure pattern along the circulatory tree.
- Describe the features of the microcirculation.
- Draw and label the arterial pulse pressure curve.
- Describe the determinants of arterial blood pressure.
- Describe the variations in blood pressure.
- Describe the regulation of blood pressure by the baroreflex.
- Describe the longer-term control of blood pressure.
- Describe the nature of the 'pulse' and its variations.

Chapter 29

- Describe the distribution of blood in the major organs in absolute terms and as a percentage of the cardiac output.
- Describe the salient features of the following circulations:
  - Coronary
  - Cerebral
  - Renal
  - Cutaneous
  - Skeletal muscle
- Describe the concept of autoregulation of blood flow.

Chapter 30

- Describe and explain the cardiovascular responses to exercise with specific reference to:
  - Cardiac responses
  - Blood pressure responses
  - Responses in regional blood flow
  - Regulation of cardiovascular function during exercise
- Differentiate between the cardiovascular responses to isometric and isotonic exercises.
- Describe cardiovascular homeostasis to change in posture.
- Describe and explain the basis of syncope.

Chapter 31

- Describe the cardiac changes that occur with ageing.
- Describe vascular changes with ageing.
- Describe alterations in regional blood flow that occur with ageing.
- Describe alterations in cardiovascular regulation with ageing.

Chapter 32

- List the factors that influence the flow of fluid between the interstitial space and the vascular compartment.
- Describe the basic organization of the lymphatic system.
- Discuss the functions of the lymphatic system.
- Describe the factors that affect lymph flow.
- Define lymphoedema and list its common causes.
- Differentiate between peripheral oedema and lymphoedema.

Chapter 33

- List the criteria for measuring blood pressure appropriately.
- Describe the principles of cardiopulmonary resuscitation.
- Define shock.
- List the causes of shock.
- Describe the pathophysiology of shock.
- Define heart failure and list the types of heart failure.
- Describe the basis of the clinical features of left and right heart failure.

GLOSSARY OF TERMS

Chapter 25

- **Autorhythmicity:** the ability to generate its own rhythm
- **Fatigue:** the inability to sustain a given amplitude of contraction (therefore, nonfatigability refers to the absence of fatigue)
- **Excitability:** the ability of a cell to respond to a stimulus
- **Syncytium:** many cells functioning as a single unit
- **Refractory period:** that time period when a cell does not respond to a stimulus

Chapter 26

- **Pacemaker (P) cells:** cells which generate their own electrical rhythm (seen in the SA and AV nodes in the heart)
- **Nodal delay:** delay in transmission of the cardiac impulse that occurs at the AV node
- **Chronotropy:** relating to heart rate
- **Tachycardia:** increase (tachy = XX beats per minute
- **Bradycardia:** decrease (brady = slow) in heart rate below 60 beats/minute

Chapter 27

- **Cardiac cycle:** the repeated electrical and mechanical events of the heart
- **Systole:** contraction
- **Diastole:** relaxation
- **Isovolumetric:** having the same volume
- **Cardiac output:** volume ejected per ventricle per minute (resting value XX L/minute)
- **Stroke volume:** volume ejected per ventricle per contraction
- **Venous return:** the rate at which blood is returned to the heart

Chapter 28

- **Blood pressure:** (unless otherwise specified refers to systemic arterial blood pressure) the lateral pressure exerted by the blood on the walls of the artery
- **Systolic blood pressure:** the highest pressure in the artery during systole (normal 120 mmHg)
- **Diastolic blood pressure:** the lowest pressure in the artery during diastole (normal 80 mmHg)
- **Pulse pressure:** the difference between the systolic and the diastolic pressure (normal 40 mmHg)
- **Mean blood pressure:** calculated as diastolic blood pressure + one-third pulse pressure

Chapter 29

- **Autoregulation:** the maintenance of blood flow at fairly constant levels despite changes in perfusion pressure
- **Portal circulation:** two capillary beds in series (normally an arteriole leads to a capillary bed which then empties into a venule which drains into larger veins to be returned to the heart; in a portal circulation, the venous drainage of the first capillary bed then supplies a second capillary bed)

Chapter 30

- **Exercise:** structured physical activity with the aim of achieving some end point, for example, fitness, better health and optimal performance
- **Isometric exercise:** exercise which does not involve the shortening of muscle – typically geared towards building up strength
- **Isotonic exercise:** exercise which involves shortening of muscle and the performance of work (this may involve small muscle groups or whole-body exercise, e.g. running and jogging)
- **Syncope:** a transient loss of consciousness due to a sudden fall in blood pressure and a reduction in cerebral blood flow
- **Postural hypotension:** a fall of greater than 20 mmHg systolic or 10 mmHg diastolic blood pressure during a change in posture from lying to standing within a 3-minute period

Chapter 31

- **Demographic transition:** a shift in population composition from younger individuals to older individuals
- **Epidemiological transition:** a shift in disease patterns from largely infectious diseases to a greater prevalence of noncommunicable diseases associated with ageing
- **Chronological age:** the age of the individual as calculated from the date and year of birth
- **Ventricular hypertrophy:** enlargement of the walls of the ventricle due to an increase in the size of the cardiac muscle cells (cardiomyocytes)
- **Aerobic capacity:** the maximum amount of oxygen that can be consumed during maximal exercise (this is largely a function of the heart and lungs and is sometimes referred to as cardiorespiratory fitness)
- **Autonomic failure:** a reduction in sympathetic or parasympathetic nervous activity or both, resulting in functional deficits

Chapter 32

- **Lymphoedema:** the accumulation of fluid in the tissues due to impaired lymphatic drainage
- **Starling's forces:** the pressures that operate to determine fluid shifts across two compartments and include the osmotic and hydrostatic pressures in each compartment (the osmotic pressure retains the fluid within a compartment while the hydrostatic pressure pushes fluid out of the compartment)

Chapter 33

- **Cardiopulmonary resuscitation:** repetitive chest compression and artificial respiration (often mouth-to-mouth) to maintain circulation and breathing

- **Shock:** a reduced perfusion of tissues associated with reduced blood pressure
- **Cardiac failure:** an inadequate pumping of the heart which is unable to meet the needs of the body

MULTIPLE CHOICE QUESTIONS

Chapter 25:

1. One of the reasons for the nonfatigability of cardiac muscle is:
   a. Short refractory period
   b. Large amount of mitochondria
   c. Autorhythmicity
   d. Large muscle fibres
2. The property that explains why the whole ventricular muscle contracts together is:
   a. Conductivity
   b. Autorhythmicity
   c. Long refractory period
   d. Syncytium
3. The elastic blood vessels of the circulatory system are:
   a. Large arteries
   b. Veins
   c. Capillaries
   d. Arterioles
4. The resistance vessels of the circulatory system are:
   a. Large arteries
   b. Veins
   c. Capillaries
   d. Arterioles
5. The pacemaker cells in the heart are located in:
   a. Atrial muscle
   b. SA node
   c. Bundle of His
   d. Ventricular muscle

Chapter 26:

1. The correct sequence in the transmission of the cardiac impulse is:
   a. AV node – SA node – bundle of His – Purkinje's fibres
   b. SA node – bundle of His – AV node – Purkinje's fibres
   c. SA node – AV node – bundle of His – Purkinje's fibres
   d. AV node – bundle of His – SA node – Purkinje's fibres
2. Nodal delay which allows the atria to complete contraction before the ventricles start to contract occurs at:
   a. SA node
   b. AV node
   c. Bundle of His
   d. Ventricle
3. Which of the following ECG leads are the bipolar limb leads?
   a. aVR, aVF, aVL
   b. V1, V2, V3
   c. V4, V5, V6
   d. I, II, III
4. Which of the following parts of the ECG is used to calculate the heart rate?
   a. RR interval
   b. PR interval
   c. QT interval
   d. ST segment
5. A healthy athlete has a heart rate of 50 beats per minute. What will be seen in his ECG?
   a. Sinus bradycardia
   b. Sinus tachycardia
   c. Sinus arrhythmia
   d. AV Block

Chapter 27:

1. Which of the following is true of the cardiac cycle at rest?
   a. Atrial systole is 0.3 secs
   b. Atrial diastole is 0.5 secs
   c. Ventricular systole is 0.3 secs
   d. Ventricular diastole is 0.7 secs
2. During which phase of the cardiac cycle does the second heart sound occur?
   a. Isovolumetric contraction
   b. Protodiastole
   c. Rapid filling
   d. Atrial systole
3. During which phase does blood flow out from the ventricles?
   a. Atrial systole
   b. Rapid ejection phase
   c. Rapid filling phase
   d. Isovolumetric relaxation
4. Which of the following define cardiac output?
   a. Blood ejected by both ventricles per contraction
   b. Blood ejected by both ventricles per minute
   c. Blood ejected per ventricle per contraction
   d. Blood ejected per ventricle per minute
5. In which of the following positions will venous return to the heart be increased?
   a. Standing
   b. Sitting
   c. Lying down
   d. Lying down with the legs elevated

Chapter 28:

1. Using Poiseuille's equation, the major determinant of blood flow through a blood vessel is:
   a. Radius of the blood vessel
   b. Viscosity of blood
   c. Length of the blood vessel
   d. Cardiac output
2. Pulse pressure is:
   a. The highest pressure during systole
   b. Lowest pressure during diastole
   c. Difference between systolic and diastolic BP
   d. Average blood pressure

3. Systolic blood pressure is determined mainly by:
   a. Total peripheral resistance
   b. Venous return
   c. Laminar blood flow
   d. Cardiac output
4. The stimulus for the baroreflex is:
   a. Decreased blood volume
   b. Rise in blood pressure
   c. Increased venous return
   d. Decreased cardiac output
5. Which of the following will increase blood pressure?
   a. Fall in cardiac output
   b. Decreased blood volume
   c. Increased peripheral resistance
   d. Decreased venous return

Chapter 29:

1. What is the normal coronary blood flow at rest?
   a. 100 mL/min
   b. 250 mL/min
   c. 500 mL/min
   d. 1000 mL/min
2. Which of the following is a feature of coronary circulation?
   a. Low capillary density
   b. Portal circulation
   c. Collaterals
   d. Not related to metabolic activity
3. Which of the following regional circulations does not show autoregulation of blood flow?
   a. Coronary
   b. Renal
   c. Cerebral
   d. Skeletal muscle
4. In which of the following circulations is Cushing's reflex seen?
   a. Coronary
   b. Renal
   c. Cerebral
   d. Skeletal muscle
5. Which of the following is a characteristic of the renal circulation?
   a. Collaterals
   b. High oxygen extraction
   c. Blood flow of 500 mL/min
   d. Portal circulation

Chapter 30:

1. During exercise, there is an increase in venous return to the heart. Which of the following increases the venous return most?
   a. Muscle pump
   b. Constriction of the veins
   c. Increased heart rate
   d. Increased peripheral resistance
2. Which of the following factors increase due to the increased cardiac output during exercise?
   a. Systolic blood pressure
   b. Diastolic blood pressure
   c. Total peripheral resistance
   d. Cerebral blood flow
3. Which of the following factors can result in syncope?
   a. Increased blood pressure
   b. Increased cardiac output
   c. Increased venous return
   d. Posture change – lying to standing

Chapter 31:

1. Which of the following changes are seen in the heart of elderly people?
   a. Increase in the number of cardiac muscle cells
   b. Increase in the number of pacemaker cells
   c. Thinning of the valves
   d. Hypertrophy of the left ventricle
2. Which of the following changes occur with ageing?
   a. Increase in the force of contraction of the heart
   b. Reduction in the maximum heart rate
   c. Decreased risk of developing arrhythmias
   d. Increase in diastolic filling of the ventricles
3. Which of the following changes occur in the blood vessels with ageing?
   a. Blood vessels get more elastic
   b. Blood vessels get more compliant
   c. Increased atherosclerotic plaques
   d. Fall in blood pressure

Chapter 32:

1. Starling's forces determine:
   a. Force of contraction of the heart
   b. Venous return
   c. Fluid movement in capillary beds
   d. Cardiac output
2. Which of the following nutrients are transported by the lymphatic system from the gastro-intestinal tract?
   a. Fats
   b. Glucose
   c. Amino acids
   d. Disaccharides
3. Which of the following is a special feature of lymphoedema compared to peripheral oedema?
   a. Seen with heart failure
   b. Nonpitting oedema
   c. Usually bilateral
   d. Due to poorly functioning venous valves

SHORT ANSWER QUESTIONS (FOR RAPID REVIEW)

1. State whether the following are true or false for the pulmonary circulation:
   a. The pulmonary circulation receives the same amount of cardiac output as the systemic circulation.
   b. The pressures in the pulmonary circulation are the same as that of the systemic circulation.
   c. The response of the pulmonary blood vessels to hypoxia is vasoconstriction.
   d. The pulmonary artery carries deoxygenated blood.

2. Give examples of each of the following blood vessels:
   a. Elastic vessels
   b. Resistance vessels
   c. Exchange vessels
   d. Capacitance vessels
3. Indicate whether the following statements which refer to properties of the cardiac muscle are true or false:
   a. The functioning of cardiac muscle as a single unit is called conductance.
   b. Autorhythmicity is a function of pacemaker cells located in the ventricle.
   c. The intercalated discs are low-resistance pathways for transmitting the cardiac impulse.
   d. Cardiac muscle is nonfatigable.
4. List four reasons why cardiac muscle does not fatigue.
   a.
   b.
   c.
   d.
5. Label the diagram of the conducting system of the heart.

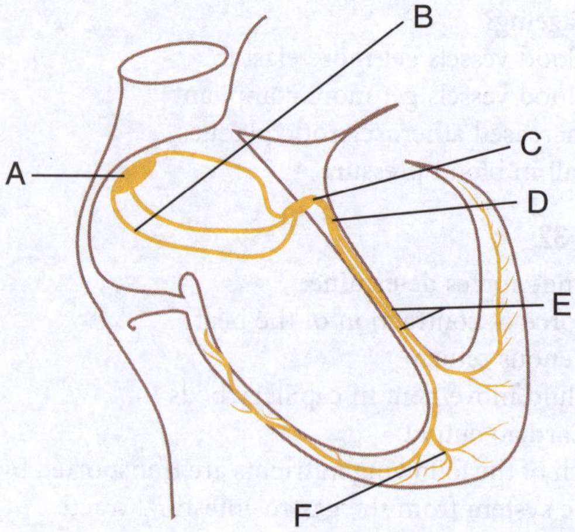

   a.
   b.
   c.
   d.
   e.
   f.
6. What is nodal delay and what is its function?

____

____

____

7. List three functions of the conducting system of the heart.
   a.
   b.
   c.
8. The following diagram shows a normal ECG with the waves P, Q, R, S and T:

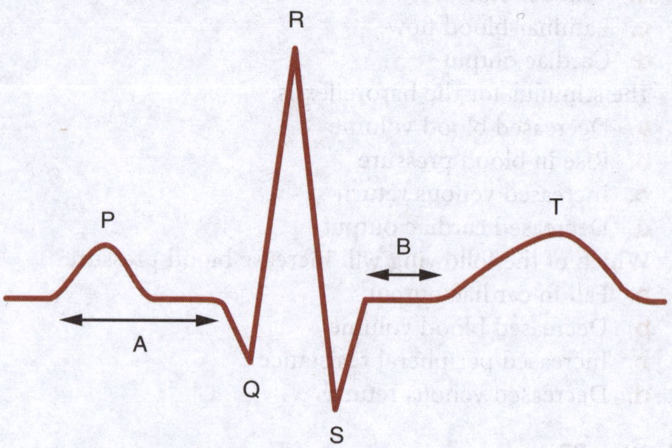

Indicate what the following represent:
- P wave
- QRS complex
- T wave
- Interval represented by 'A'
- Segment represented by 'B'

9. Match column A (which represents the 12 leads of the ECG) correctly with column B.

Column A	Column B
1. Leads I, II, III	A. Precordial leads
2. Leads aVR, aVF, aVL	B. Bipolar limb leads
3. Leads V1, V2, V3, V4, V5, V6	C. Augmented limb leads

10. State Einthoven's law.

____

____

11. Match column A (which represents variations in cardiac rhythm) with the column B.

Column A	Column B
1. Sinus bradycardia	A. Change in heart rate with respiration
2. Type I AV block	B. Slow heart rate – less than 60/min
3. Sinus tachycardia	C. Complete AV dissociation
4. Type II AV block	D. Prolonged PR interval
5. Sinus arrythmia	E. Fast heart rate – more than 100/min
6. Type III AV block	F. Some P waves are conducted into the ventricles

12. Rearrange the following phases of the cardiac cycle in the correct sequence starting from isovolumetric contraction:
    - Isovolumetric contraction
    - Rapid filling
    - Rapid ejection
    - Slow filling
    - Atrial systole
    - Protodiastole
    - Slow ejection
    - Isovolumetric contraction
13. Column A indicates specific heart sounds. Fill in the following table to indicate the reason for the heart sound.

First heart sound	
Second heart sound	
Third heart sound	
Fourth heart sound	

14. Indicate the reasons for the following waves of the jugular venous pressure (JVP). Fill in the following table to indicate the reason for the waves.
    'a' wave
    'c' wave
    'v' wave
15. Define cardiac output and give its normal resting value.
16. Define stroke volume and give its normal resting value.
17. The determinants of cardiac output are stroke volume and heart rate. List three factors which affect stroke volume.
    a.
    b.
    c.
18. List five factors that affect venous return.
    a.
    b.
    c.
    d.
    e.
19. Write down Poiseuille's law to represent the determinants of blood flow. What does each of the letters in the equation represent?
20. Two patterns of blood flow are:
    a.
    b.
21. The following figure represents the arterial pressure trace. Indicate the pressures labelled A to D, where C = B minus A and D = A + (1/3 of C).

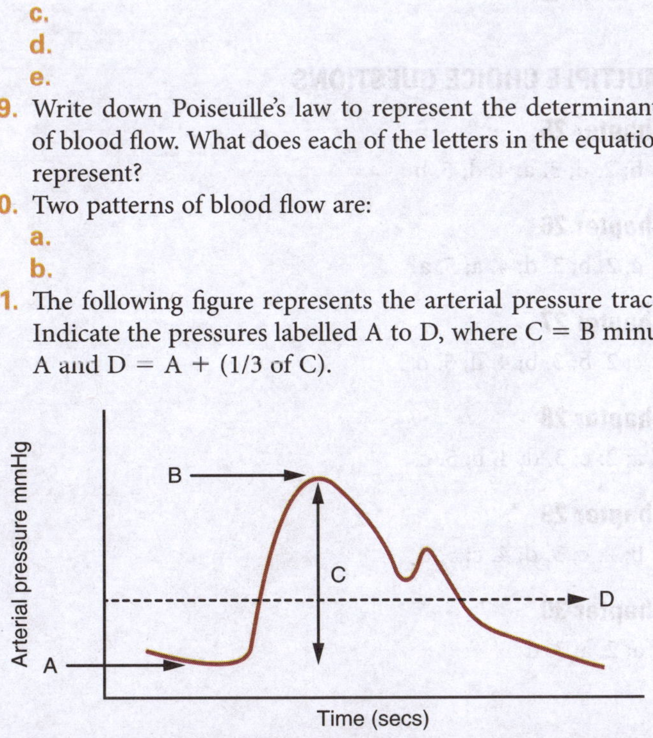

22. The baroreflex reflex regulates the blood pressure in the short term. Fill in the following table to describe the baroreflex.

Part of the Reflex Arc	Structures	Function
Stimulus		
Receptors		
Afferent nerves		
Integrating centre		
Effector nerves		
Effectors		

23. List two mechanisms by which blood pressure is regulated in the longer term.
    a.
    b.
24. What is autoregulation of blood flow?
25. List three regional circulations which show autoregulation.
    a.
    b.
    c.
26. List five features of the coronary circulation.
27. List the three phases of the triple response in the skin.
28. List five cardiovascular responses to whole-body isotonic exercise.
    a.
    b.
    c.
    d.
    e.
29. What is syncope?
30. Describe the mechanisms that help to prevent syncope on standing from a lying position.
31. List three cardiac changes that occur with ageing.
    a.
    b.
    c.
32. List three vascular changes that occur with ageing.
    a.
    b.
    c.
33. Describe how cardiovascular regulation changes with ageing.
34. See the following figure and then answer the following questions:

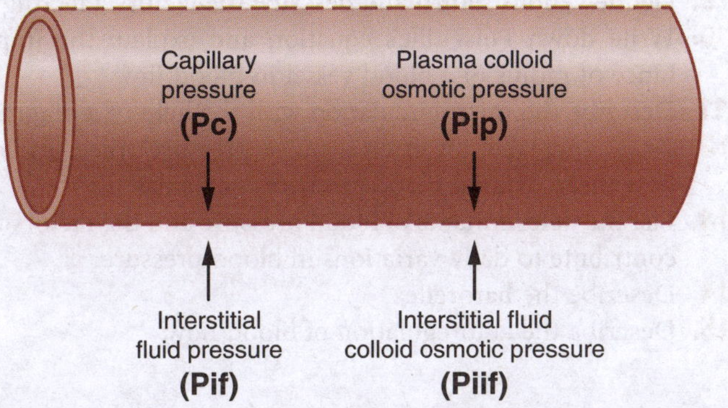

a) The pressures that have been shown are collectively called ____________.

b) The net effective pressure that pushes fluid from the capillary to the interstitium is given by ____________.

c) Movement of fluid to the interstitium will cause ____________.

35. List three functions of the lymphatic system.
a.
b.
c.

36. List three factors which affect lymphatic flow.
a.
b.
c.

37. Define shock.

38. Indicate in the following table the type of shock based on the clinical description provided:

Clinical Description	Type of Shock
1. Severe blood loss following a road traffic accident	
2. Severe allergic reaction following administration of penicillin injection without a test dose	
3. Patient brought into emergency following a severe head injury	
4. Patient comes following a massive heart attack	
5. Patient has a severe infection not responding to antibiotics	

SHORT ESSAY QUESTIONS

1. Differentiate between the pulmonary and systemic circulation.
2. Classify the vessels of the circulatory system and list their functions.
3. Describe the functional properties of cardiac muscle.
4. Describe the uses of the ECG.
5. Classify and describe the conduction defects of the heart.
6. Describe the ECG changes seen in myocardial ischaemia and infarction.
7. List the heart sounds. Indicate when they occur in the cardiac cycle and explain their basis.
8. Draw and explain the jugular venous pressure waves.
9. Define venous return and describe the factors affecting it.
10. Write down Poiseuille's equation and explain the importance of radius of a blood vessel in blood flow.
11. Describe the microcirculation with the help of a diagram.
12. Draw and label an arterial pulse pressure trace. Indicate how mean arterial blood pressure is calculated.
13. List the determinants of blood pressure and the factors that contribute to daily variations in blood pressure.
14. Describe the baroreflex.
15. Describe the autoregulation of blood flow.
16. Describe the functional features of the coronary circulation.
17. Describe the functional features of the cerebral circulation.
18. Describe the renal circulation.
19. Describe the blood flow to skeletal muscle.
20. Describe the function of the cutaneous circulation in temperature regulation.
21. Describe the cardiovascular changes during isotonic exercise.
22. Describe the cardiovascular changes during a change in posture (lying to standing).
23. What is syncope? Why does it occur? List some conditions when it is seen.
24. Describe the functions of the lymphatic system.
25. What is lymphoedema. Differentiate between peripheral vascular oedema and lymphoedema.
26. What is heart failure? Differentiate between left and right heart failure.

LONG ESSAY QUESTIONS

1. Draw a diagram of the conducting system of the heart and describe the sequence of events.
2. Draw a normal ECG. Label the waves, intervals and segments. Describe the physiological basis of the waves.
3. List the phases of the cardiac cycle and describe the pressure–volume changes in the ventricle during one cardiac cycle.
4. Define cardiac output. List its determinants and describe its regulation.
5. Describe the short- and long-term regulation of blood pressure.
6. Describe the cardiovascular changes that occur with ageing.
7. Define shock. List the types of shock and describe the phases of shock.

MULTIPLE CHOICE QUESTIONS

Chapter 25
1. b; 2. d; 3. a; 4. d; 5. b

Chapter 26
1. c; 2. b; 3. d; 4. a; 5. a

Chapter 27
1. c; 2. b; 3. b; 4. d; 5. d

Chapter 28
1. a; 2. c; 3. d; 4. b; 5. c

Chapter 29
1. b; 2. c; 3. d; 4. c; 5. d

Chapter 30
1. a; 2. a; 3. d

Chapter 31

1. d; 2. b; 3. c

Chapter 32

1. c; 2. a; 3. b

SHORT ANSWER QUESTIONS: ANSWER KEY

1. (a) True, (b) false, (c) true, (d) true.
2. (a) Large arteries, for example, aorta; (b) arterioles; (c) capillaries; (d) veins.
3. (a) False, (b) false, (c) true, (d) true.
4. See Chapter 25.
5. (A) SA node, (B) internodal pathways, (C) AV node, () bundle of His, (E) left and right bundle branches, (F) Purkinje's fibres.
6. See Chapter 26.
7. See Chapter 26.
8. P wave, atrial repolarization; QRS complex, ventricular depolarization; T wave, ventricular repolarization; interval represented by 'A', PR interval; segment represented by 'B', ST segment.
9. 1, B; 2, C; 3, A.
10. See Chapter 26.
11. 1, B; 2, D; 3, E; 4, F; 5, A; 6, C.
12. Isovolumetric contraction, rapid ejection, slow ejection, protodiastole, isovolumetric relaxation, rapid filling, slow filling, atrial systole.

13–18. See Chapter 27.

19. See Chapter 28.
20. (a) Laminar flow, (b) turbulent flow.
21. (A) Diastolic blood pressure, (B) systolic blood pressure, (C) pulse pressure, (D) mean blood pressure.
22. See Chapter 28.
23. See Chapter 28.
24. See Chapter 29.
25. Renal, coronary, cerebral.
26. See Chapter 29.
27. See Chapter 29.

28–30. See Chapter 30.

31–33. See Chapter 31.

34 (a) Starling's forces, (b) see Chapter 32, (c) oedema.

35 and 36. See Chapter 32.

37. See Chapter 33.
38. (1) Hypovolaemic, (2) anaphylactic, (3) neurogenic, (4) cardiogenic, (5) septic.

SECTION 5

Workbook: Blood

SPECIFIC LEARNING OBJECTIVES

At the end of this chapter, the student should be able to:

Chapter 34

- Distinguish between plasma and serum.
- Classify the cellular components of the blood.
- List the major plasma proteins and describe their functions.
- Describe the consequences of Rh incompatibility in the newborn.

Chapter 35

- Describe the steps in the formation of a red blood cell (RBC) (erythropoiesis) and the major changes that occur during this formation.
- List the factors that affect erythropoiesis.
- List the functions of haemoglobin.
- Describe the fate of RBCs.

Chapter 36

- Describe the formation of leucocytes (white blood cells).
- Classify white blood cells.
- Describe each type of white blood cell in terms of its morphology and function.

Chapter 37

- Describe the structure, formation and functions of platelets.
- Describe the sequence of events that stop bleeding in response to an injury.
- Describe the coagulation pathways.
- Classify anticoagulants and describe their mode of action.
- Briefly describe some common bleeding and clotting disorders, specifically:
  - Thrombocytopaenic purpura
  - Haemophilia

Chapter 38

- List the different blood groups.
- State Landsteiner's law and explain its application.
- Describe the process for screening a potential blood donor.
- List the changes with storage of blood.
- Describe potential transfusion reactions.
- Describe Rh incompatibility of the newborn.

Chapter 39

- Distinguish between innate and acquired immunity.
- Compare and contrast cellular and humoural immunity.
- Distinguish between the primary and secondary immune responses.
- Discuss the role of passive immunity.
- Discuss the mechanism and role of vaccination.
- Define inflammation and list its components.
- List the functions of the thymus.

Chapter 40

- Define and classify anaemia.
- Define and classify jaundice.
- Distinguish between bleeding disorders and clotting disorders.
- Describe the process of disseminated intravascular coagulation.
- List some common immune deficiency states.
- Describe the immune basis of transplantation.

GLOSSARY OF TERMS

Chapter 34

- **Plasma:** fluid portion of the blood obtained after centrifuging blood with anticoagulant
- **Serum:** plasma minus the clotting factors
- **Erythrocytes:** red blood cells
- **Leucocytes:** white blood cells
- **Thrombocytes:** platelets

Chapter 35

- **Erythropoiesis:** the process of formation of RBCs
- **Jaundice:** a yellowish discolouration of the skin and mucous membranes due to elevated levels of serum bilirubin
- **Anaemia:** a reduced oxygen-carrying capacity of the blood due to alterations in the quantity or quality of RBCs and haemoglobin

Chapter 36

- **Granulocytes:** those WBCs which have granules in the cytoplasm, that is, neutrophils, basophils and eosinophils
- **Agranulocytes:** those WBCs which do not have granules in the cytoplasm, that is, lymphocytes and monocytes
- **Cellular immunity:** an immune response that involves activation of the T lymphocytes and the release of cytokines

- **Humoral immunity:** an immune response that involves the production of antibodies from B lymphocytes and plasma cells
- **Cytokines:** proteins released by immune cells that affect cellular interactions and help mediate the immune response
- **Leukotrienes:** inflammatory molecules released by mast cells and basophils in response to allergens (molecules that trigger an allergic reaction)
- **Antigen:** a molecule or a part of a molecule that triggers an immune reaction

Chapter 37

- **Megakaryocyte:** a large bone marrow cell which gives rise to platelets
- **Thrombocyte:** platelet
- **Thrombocytopaenia:** a reduction in platelet count below 150,000/mm^3
- **Haemostasis:** stoppage of bleeding (not to be confused with homeostasis)
- **Platelet plug:** temporary haemostatic plug of aggregated platelets
- **Clot:** a permanent haemostatic plug with fibrin deposited into the platelet plug
- **Coagulation:** clotting
- **Fibrinolysis:** enzymatic degradation of a clot

Chapter 38

- **Agglutinogen:** antigen on the RBC cell membrane
- **Agglutinin:** antibody to an agglutinogen
- **Agglutination:** an antigen–antibody reaction visible microscopically
- **Major cross-matching:** mixing of donor's RBCs and recipient's plasma in a tube to check for agglutination
- **Minor cross-matching:** mixing of donor's plasma and recipient's RBCs in a tube to check for agglutination.

Chapter 39

- **Immunity:** the ability of an individual to resist or overcome an infection
- **Antigen:** any molecule that can stimulate an immune response
- **Antibody:** also called immunoglobulin, produced by transformed B lymphocytes called plasma cells – are responsible for humoural immunity
- **Innate immunity:** uses cells and molecules that are already present in the body to help get rid of pathogens
- **Acquired immunity:** specific body defence response on exposure to pathogens
- **Autoimmunity:** an immune response to the body's own cells (self-antigens), seen in a variety of autoimmune disorders
- **Vaccination:** stimulation of the immune system against a microbe using vaccines (vaccines are often, but not always, made from live, attenuated [weakened] microbes or dead microbes)

Chapter 40

- **Jaundice:** a yellowish discolouration of the skin and mucous membranes due to elevated levels of serum bilirubin
- **Anaemia:** a reduced oxygen-carrying capacity of the blood due to alterations in the quantity or quality of RBCs and haemoglobin
- **Transplantation:** the transfer of a tissue or an organ from one part of the body to another (e.g. skin grafts) or from one person to another

MULTIPLE CHOICE QUESTIONS

Chapter 34:

1. Which of the following will be absent from serum?
   a. Albumin
   b. Cholesterol
   c. Fibrinogen
   d. Globulins
2. Which of the following cells has a count of 150–400,000/cu mm?
   a. Red blood cells
   b. Platelets
   c. White blood cells
   d. Reticulocytes
3. Which of the following plasma proteins contributes most to the plasma osmotic pressure?
   a. Albumin
   b. Beta globulins
   c. Gamma globulins
   d. Fibrinogen
4. Which of the following cells is important in haemostasis?
   a. Red blood cells
   b. White blood cells
   c. Reticulocytes
   d. Platelets
5. Which cell carries carbon dioxide in blood?
   a. Red blood cell
   b. White blood cell
   c. Platelets
   d. Reticulocytes

Chapter 35:

1. Which of the following changes occur in the cells during erythropoiesis?
   a. They become bigger
   b. They develop more nuclei
   c. The nucleus condenses and is extruded
   d. The change from acidophilic to basophilic
2. Erythropoietin which increases erythropoiesis is formed mainly in the:
   a. Liver
   b. Kidney
   c. Spleen
   d. Lining of blood vessels
3. Vitamin B12 which is important in erythropoiesis is absorbed in the:
   a. Stomach
   b. Duodenum
   c. Jejunum
   d. Ileum

4. The lifespan of the RBC is approximately:
   a. 10 days
   b. 60 days
   c. 80 days
   d. 120 days
5. Iron is important for erythropoiesis. Which of the following are true for iron?
   a. It is present only in nonvegetarian foods
   b. It is absorbed in the large intestine
   c. Ferrous iron is better absorbed than ferric iron
   d. Stomach acid reduces the absorption of iron

Chapter 36:

1. Which of the following white blood cells is increased in an acute bacterial infection?
   a. Lymphocytes
   b. Neutrophils
   c. Basophils
   d. Eosinophils
2. Which of the following white blood cells is increased during allergies?
   a. Neutrophils
   b. Monocytes
   c. Eosinophils
   d. Lymphocytes
3. What is an increase in WBCs greater than the normal count called?
   a. Leucocytosis
   b. Leucopaenia
   c. Leukaemia
   d. Neutrophilia
4. Which of the following cells is without granules, the same size as an RBC with a large circular nucleus?
   a. Monocyte
   b. Lymphocyte
   c. Basophil
   d. Eosinophil
5. Which of the following WBCs is not phagocytic?
   a. Neutrophils
   b. Eosinophils
   c. Monocytes
   d. Lymphocytes

Chapter 37:

1. Which of the following functions of platelets helps to stop bleeding first?
   a. Formation of platelet plug
   b. Formation of clot
   c. Clot retraction
   d. Release of growth factors
2. Which of the following clotting factors is the main antihaemophilic factor?
   a. Factor I
   b. Factor V
   c. Factor VIII
   d. Factor XII
3. Which of the following anticoagulants acts by chelation of calcium ions?
   a. Heparin
   b. Dicoumarol
   c. Warfarin
   d. EDTA
4. Which of the following is a feature of the extrinsic clotting pathway?
   a. Due to injury inside the blood vessel
   b. Uses fewer clotting factors
   c. Slower clotting after activation
   d. Uses factor XII
5. The enzymatic breakdown of a clot is called:
   a. Clot retraction
   b. Haemostasis
   c. Fibrinolysis
   d. Haemophilia

Chapter 38:

1. Which of the following antibodies will a person with blood group A have?
   a. Anti A
   b. Anti B
   c. Anti A and anti B
   d. No antibodies
2. Which of the following antigens will a person with blood group AB have?
   a. A
   b. B
   c. A and B
   d. No antigens
3. Major cross-matching involves checking for an immune response with:
   a. Donor's red blood cells with recipient's plasma
   b. Donor's plasma and recipient's red blood cells
   c. Donor's plasma and donor's red blood cells
   d. Recipient's plasma and recipient's red blood cells
4. Which of following transfusions will result in a mismatched blood transfusion?
   a. Donor A− and recipient A+
   b. Donor B− and recipient B+
   c. Donor O− and recipient AB−
   d. Donor A− and recipient B−
5. Which of the following is true of Rh incompatibility of the newborn?
   a. Mother is Rh +, Child is Rh −
   b. Mother is Rh −, child is Rh +
   c. First pregnancy results in most severe disease
   d. Rh+ transfusions to mother prevents future disease

Chapter 39:

1. Which of the following is a part of the innate immunity of the body?
   a. Antibodies
   b. Helper T cells
   c. Suppressor T cells
   d. Skin

2. Which part of the acquired immunity is mediated by antibodies?
   a. Cell-mediated immunity
   b. Humoural immunity
   c. Complement system
   d. Phagocytosis
3. A secondary immune response with repeated infection is characterized by:
   a. A smaller response
   b. A slower response
   c. Mainly IgG antibodies
   d. Mainly IgM antibodies
4. The transfer of antibodies from the mother to baby via breast milk is an example of:
   a. Innate immunity
   b. Cell-mediated immunity
   c. Artificial passive immunity
   d. Natural passive immunity
5. Which of the following functions does the thymus gland have:
   a. Production of antibodies
   b. Development of B lymphocytes
   c. Maturation of T lymphocytes
   d. Production of complement proteins

SHORT ANSWER QUESTIONS (FOR RAPID REVIEW)

1. Indicate whether the following statements are true or false:
   a. When blood with an anticoagulant is centrifuged, we get serum.
   b. Serum is plasma without the clotting factors.
   c. When blood without an anticoagulant is allowed to stand, we get a straw-coloured fluid called serum.
2. Complete the following table to indicate the major plasma proteins and their concentration:

Type of Plasma Protein	Concentration (g%)
Albumin	

3. List five functions of plasma proteins.
   a.
   b.
   c.
   d.
   e.
4. List five functions of blood.
   a.
   b.
   c.
   d.
   e.
5. Indicate whether the following statements are true or false:
   a. Erythropoiesis takes place sequentially in the following sites: foetal liver, yolk sac and bone marrow.
   b. Haemopoietic stem cells show two properties: self-renewal and differentiation.
   c. Erythropoietin in the adult is secreted mainly from the liver.
   d. The mature RBC does not have a nucleus.
6. Rewrite the following stages of erythropoiesis in the correct sequence: early normoblast, reticulocyte, intermediate normoblast, pronormoblast, late normoblast, mature RBC.
7. Indicate three broad changes that occur in the cells as they mature during erythropoiesis.
   a.
   b.
   c.
8. List five factors which affect erythropoiesis.
   a.
   b.
   c.
   d.
   e.
9. Indicate whether the following statements about haemoglobin are true or false:
   a. Haemoglobin consists of haem and four globular chains.
   b. Calcium ion at the centre of haem is responsible for the binding of oxygen.
   c. Adult haemoglobin has two alpha and two beta chains.
   d. Foetal haemoglobin has two alpha and two gamma chains.
10. Give two reasons why normal haemoglobin levels are lower in females compared to males.
    a.
    b.
11. List three functions of haemoglobin.
    a.
    b.
    c.
12. List the three types of granulocytes.
    a.
    b.
    c.
13. List the two types of agranulocytes.
    a.
    b.

14. Match column B and C with the appropriate cell listed in column A.

Type of Cell	Structural Feature	Function
1. Neutrophil	a. Spectacle-shaped nucleus	i. Becomes a tissue macrophage
2. Monocyte	b. Fine azurophilic granules	ii. Cellular and humoral immunity
3. Eosinophil	c. May be small or large	iii. Contain histamine
4. Lymphocyte	d. Coarse blue granules	iv. Raised in allergic conditions
5. Basophil	e. Kidney-shaped nucleus	v. Phagocytosis

15. Identify the cell illustrated below and answer the questions.
   a. Identify the cell: ____________

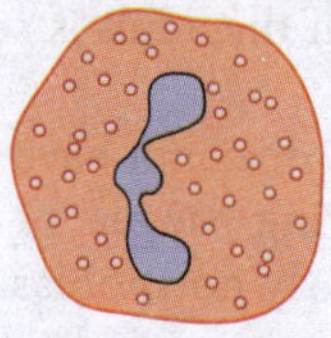

   b. Percentage of WBCs of this cell: ____________%
   c. List two reasons for your identification.
      i.
      ii.
   d. List two ways in which this cell has antimicrobial action.
      i.
      ii.

16. Identify the cell illustrated below and answer the questions.

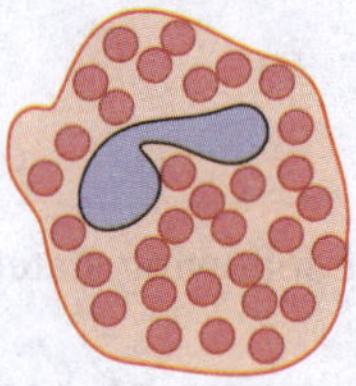

   a. Identify the cell: ____________
   b. Percentage of WBCs in a normal WBC count: ____________%
   c. List two features which help with the identification.
      i.
      ii.
   d. List two functions of this cell.
      i.
      ii.

17. With regard to monocytes:
   a. List two features of the cell.
      i.
      ii.
   b. List two functions.
      i.
      ii.

18. What is the normal WBC count:/mm^3

19. List two conditions associated with a reduced WBC count.
   a.
   b.

20. Indicate one condition associated with each of the following:
   a. Neutrophilia
   b. Eosinophilia
   c. Monocytosis
   d. Lymphocytosis

21. With regard to platelets (thrombocytes), answer the following:
   a. Normal platelet count: ____________/mm^3
   b. Two types of granules in platelets:
      i.
      ii.
   c. Three functions of platelets:
      i.
      ii.
      iii.
   d. A reduction in platelets is called ____________.
   e. A reduction in platelets is associated with:
      i. Pin-point haemorrhages on the skin called:
      ii. ____________bleeding time
      iii. ____________clotting time

22. The formation of the temporary platelet plug is associated with the following processes:
   a.
   b.
   c.

23. The two pathways for clotting are:
   a.
   b.

24. Indicate which of the statements about the coagulation cascade are true or false:
   a. Intrinsic pathway is activated by tissue factor.
   b. Extrinsic pathway has fewer steps.
   c. Extrinsic pathway is faster.
   d. Factor VII is involved in the intrinsic pathway.

25. Match column A (type of anticoagulant) with column B (mechanism of action).

Anticoagulant	Mechanism
1. EDTA	a. Prevents conversion of fibrinogen to fibrin
2. Dicoumarol	b. Calcium chelator (binds calcium)
3. Heparin	c. Vitamin K antagonist

26. Indicate which of the following statements are true or false:
   a. Classical haemophilia is X-linked recessive.
   b. Classical haemophilia is due to deficiency of factor VIII.
   c. Classical haemophilia is associated with pin-point haemorrhages in the skin.
   d. In classical haemophilia, men are the carriers and women have the disease.

27. Define fibrinolysis. ____________

28. In the following table, fill in the antigens (agglutinogens) and antibodies (agglutinins) for the blood groups specified.

Blood Group	Antigens	Antibodies
A		
B		
O		
AB		

29. ______________blood group is the universal donor and ______________the universal recipient.

30. State Landsteiner's laws (two parts).

a. ______________

b. ______________

31. Fill in the following table with the words 'Blood cells' or 'Plasma' to describe the two types of cross-matching.

Type of Cross-matching	Donor	Recipient
Major		
Minor		

32. Indicate the function of each component of the preservative listed as follows used to store blood:

Citrate	
Phosphate buffer	
Dextrose	

33. List the changes seen with each of the following cells with storage of blood in the blood bank:

a. RBCs:

b. WBCs:

c. Platelets:

34. List three types of transfusion reactions that may be seen clinically.

a.

b.

c.

35. Write a short note on erythroblastosis foetalis.

36. List three components of innate immunity.

a.

b.

c.

37. List the steps involved in phagocytosis.

____

38. List three functions of the complement system of proteins.

a.

b.

c.

39. Complete the following table:

Type of Immunity	Cells Involved	Mediators
Cell-mediated immunity		
Humoral immunity		

40. Indicate whether the following statements are true:

a. IgG crosses the placenta.

b. IgD is the largest antibody.

c. IgE is the antibody found in secretions.

d. IgM is seen in higher concentrations in allergic reactions.

41. Give two examples of passive immunity.

a.

b.

42. List the five classic signs of inflammation.

a.

b.

c.

d.

e.

43. List three functions of the thymus gland.

a.

b.

c.

44. Define anaemia. ______________

45. Indicate a cause for each of the following types of anaemia:

a. Microcytic hypochromic anaemia:

b. Macrocytic/megaloblastic anaemia:

c. Normocytic normochromic anaemia:

46. List two disorders of haemoglobin that can cause anaemia.

a.

b.

47. Define jaundice. ______________

48. Complete the following table to differentiate between prehepatic, hepatic and posthepatic jaundice.

	Prehepatic Jaundice	Hepatic Jaundice	Posthepatic Jaundice
Example			
Type of hyperbilirubinaemia			
Bilirubin in the urine			
Increased liver enzymes			
Increased biliary tract enzymes			
Urine urobilinogen			

49. What is disseminated intravascular coagulation and when is it seen?
50. List two causes of immune deficiency.
    a.
    b.

SHORT ESSAY QUESTIONS

1. Describe the factors that affect erythropoiesis.
2. Describe the functions of haemoglobin.
3. Discuss the variations in total and individual WBC counts.
4. Describe the formation of WBCs.
5. Describe the intrinsic coagulation pathway.
6. Describe the extrinsic coagulation pathway.
7. Differentiate between the intrinsic and extrinsic clotting pathways.
8. Describe the process and importance of fibrinolysis.
9. Classify anticoagulants and indicate their mechanism of action.
10. Differentiate between clotting and bleeding disorders.
11. Describe the basis and clinical features of haemophilia.
12. State Landsteiner's laws and describe with a table their application for the ABO blood group system.
13. Describe the basis and importance of cross-matching prior to a transfusion.
14. Describe the principles involved in the storage of blood and the changes that occur with prolonged storage.
15. Describe some common causes of immune deficiency.
16. Classify the types of transplantation. Describe transplant rejection.
17. Describe the mechanisms of innate immunity.
18. Differentiate between cellular and humoural immunity.
19. Describe the role of the thymus in immunity.

LONG ESSAY QUESTIONS

1. Classify plasma proteins. Indicate their normal concentrations and describe their functions.
2. Describe the steps involved in erythropoiesis and the cellular changes that occur.
3. Classify WBCs and describe the morphology of each cell.
4. Classify WBCs and list the functions of each cell.
5. Describe the structure, formation and functions of platelets.
6. Describe the coagulation pathways.
7. Describe the various types of transfusion reactions and their mechanism.
8. Describe the basis, clinical features and prevention of Rh incompatibility of the newborn.
9. Define anaemia. Classify anaemia based on aetiology and morphology using examples.
10. Define jaundice. Differentiate between the different types of jaundice.
11. Describe the processes involved in acquired immunity.

MULTIPLE CHOICE QUESTIONS ANSWERS

Chapter 34:

1-c; 2-b; 3-a; 4-d; 5-a

Chapter 35:

1-c; 2-b; 3-d; 4-d; 5-c

Chapter 36:

1-b; 2-c; 3-a; 4-b; 5-d

Chapter 37:

1-a; 2-c; 3-d; 4-b; 5-c

Chapter 38:

1-b; 2-c; 3-a; 4-d; 5-b

Chapter 39:

1-d; 2-b; 3-c; 4-d; 5-c

SHORT ANSWER QUESTIONS: ANSWER KEY

1. (a) False, (b) true, (c) true.
2. Check Chapter 34.
3. Check Chapter 34.
4. Check Chapter 34.
5. (a) False, (b) true, (c) false, (d) true.
6. Pronormoblast, early normoblast, intermediate normoblast, late normoblast, reticulocyte, mature RBC.
7. See Chapter 35.
8. See Chapter 35.
9. (a) True, (b) false, (c) true, (d) true.
10. See Chapter 35.
11. See Chapter 35.
12. Neutrophil; eosinophil; basophil.
13. Lymphocyte; monocyte.
14. 1 – b, v; 2 – e, i; 3 – a, iv; 4 – c, ii; 5 – d, iii.
15. (a) Neutrophil; (b) 40–60; (c) amoeboid shape, multilobed nucleus, fine granules; (d) phagocytosis, degranulation, neutrophil extracellular traps.
16. (a) Eosinophil; (b) 1–4; (c) spectacle-shaped nucleus, coarse eosinophilic granules; (d) mediating allergic reactions, fighting viral infections, antihelminthic, mildly phagocytic.
17. See Chapter 36.
18. 4000–11,000.
19. See Chapter 36.
20. See Chapter 36.
21. (a) 150–400,000; (b) alpha granules, dense bodies; (c) vasoconstriction, platelet plug, wound repair; (d) thrombocytopaenia; (e) petechiae/purpura, increased, normal.
22. Platelet adhesion; platelet activation; platelet aggregation.
23. Intrinsic pathway; extrinsic pathway.
24. (a) False, (b) true, (c) true, (d) false.
25. 1, b; 2, c; 3, a.
26. (a) True, (b) true, (c) false, (d) false.
27. See Chapter 37.
28. See Chapter 38.
29. O, AB.
30. See Chapter 38.
31. See Chapter 38.
32. See Chapter 38.
33. See Chapter 38.

34. See Chapter 38.
35. See Chapter 38.
36. See Chapter 39.
37. See Chapter 39.
38. See Chapter 39.
39. Cell-mediated immunity – T lymphocytes, cytokines; humoral immunity – B lymphocytes and plasma cells, antibodies.
40. (a) True, (b) false, (c) false, (d) false.
41. See Chapter 39.
42. See Chapter 39.
43. See Chapter 39.
44. See Chapter 40.
45. (a) Iron deficiency, (b) vitamin B_{12}/folate deficiency, (c) acute blood loss.
46. Sickle cell anaemia, thalassaemia.
47. See Chapter 40.
48. See Chapter 40.
49. See Chapter 40.
50. See Chapter 40.

SECTION 6

Workbook: The Endocrine System

SPECIFIC LEARNING OBJECTIVES

At the end of this chapter, the student should be able to:

Chapter 41

- List the characteristics of a hormone.
- Describe the relationship between the hypothalamus and the pituitary.
- List the hormones produced by the hypothalamus and state their functions.
- List the pituitary hormones and state their functions.
- Describe with an example 'negative feedback'.
- List the functions of the pineal gland.

Chapter 42

- List the hormones secreted by the thyroid gland.
- Describe the steps in the synthesis of T3 and T4.
- List the actions of thyroid hormones.
- Describe how the secretion of thyroid hormones is regulated.
- List and briefly describe disorders of thyroxine secretion.

Chapter 43

- List the basic functions of calcium in the body.
- Outline briefly the metabolism of calcium in the body.
- List the hormones involved in calcium balance and their respective roles. Specifically describe the formation and actions of:
  - Parathormone
  - Vitamin D
  - Calcitonin
- Explain the calcium–phosphate interrelationship.
- Describe the consequences of hypocalcaemia.
- Describe briefly disorders of the parathyroid gland.
- Explain briefly what rickets is.
- Write a short note on osteoporosis.

Chapter 44

- Describe the functional anatomy of the endocrine pancreas. List the hormones produced by the endocrine pancreas.
- Describe the actions of insulin.
- Describe the regulation of insulin secretion.
- Describe the actions of glucagon.
- Describe the role of somatostatin in relation to glucagon and insulin secretion.
- List the types of diabetes mellitus and describe their clinical features.

Chapter 45

- Describe the functional anatomy of the adrenal gland in relation to endocrine physiology.
- List the hormones that are produced by different parts of the adrenal gland.
- Describe the actions of mineralocorticoids.
- Describe the actions of glucocorticoids.
- Describe the control of secretion of glucocorticoids through the hypothalamo–hypophysial–adrenal axis.
- Describe the clinical features of Cushing's syndrome.
- Briefly describe the Addison's disease, Conn' syndrome and adrenogenital disease.
- Describe the actions of adrenaline.
- Briefly describe the features of pheochromocytoma.
- Define stress. Describe the body's response to stress.

Chapter 46

- Cardiovascular function
- Weight balance
- Foetal growth and development
- Ageing
- Stress

GLOSSARY OF TERMS

Chapter 41

- **Endocrine:** relating to hormones and the glands that synthesize or secrete them
- **Neuroendocrine reflex:** a reflex which is mediated by nerves and hormone (the sensory nerve typically conveys information of the stimulus which then results in the secretion of the hormone and an action)
- **Negative feedback:** a process in which the system responds in an opposite manner to the perturbation (stimulus) (with regard to hormones, an increase in the concentration of hormone results in effects which attempt to lower the concentration of the hormone)
- **Second messenger:** chemical released following the binding of a hormone with its receptor, which mediates the action of the hormone

Chapter 42

- **Hypothyroidism:** an underactive thyroid gland in which less thyroid hormone is secreted

- **Hyperthyroidism:** an overactive thyroid gland in which excessive thyroid hormone is secreted
- **Goitre:** an enlargement of the thyroid gland

Chapter 43

- **Hyperparathyroidism:** an increased secretion of parathormone from the parathyroid glands
- **Hypocalcaemia:** a reduction in circulating calcium levels (normal XX mg/dL)
- **Carpopedal spasm:** a spasm of the muscles of the hand and feet due to hypocalcaemia
- **Rickets:** a decrease in mineralization of bone in children due to the deficiency of vitamin D
- **Osteoporosis:** a condition commonly seen with increasing age characterized by brittle bones due to the loss of matrix in the bone

Chapter 44

- **Hypoglycaemia:** a condition characterized by an abnormally low level of blood glucose
- **Insulin resistance**
- **Diabetes:** two types of diabetes – diabetes insipidus due to a deficiency in secretion or action of antidiuretic hormone and diabetes mellitus characterized by an abnormal elevation in blood glucose due to inadequate secretion of insulin or due to resistance to insulin action

Chapter 45

- **Glucocorticoids**
- **Mineralocorticoids**
- **Hypernatraemia/hyponatraemia:** a rise/fall in circulating sodium concentrations
- **Hyperkalaemia/hypokalaemia:** a rise/fall in circulating potassium concentrations
- **Catecholamines:** a class of substances that includes epinephrine, norepinephrine and dopamine

Chapter 46

- **Hyperlipidaemia:** an increase in the circulating fat particles (i.e. in the blood) which include cholesterol and triglycerides
- **Palpitations:** an uncomfortable awareness of one's own heartbeat because of irregularity or rapid heart rate
- **Ventricular hypertrophy:** thickening of the wall of the ventricle due to an increase in its mass
- **Hypertension:** an abnormal increase in the systemic arterial blood pressure
- **Stress:** the response of the body to an increased demand which may be physical, social or psychological
- **Stressor:** an event or situation which evokes a stress response

MULTIPLE CHOICE QUESTIONS

Chapter 41:

1. Which of the following hypothalamic hormones stimulates the release of FSH from the anterior pituitary gland?
   a. Growth hormone releasing hormone
   b. Thyrotropin releasing hormone
   c. Corticotropin releasing hormone
   d. Gonadotropin releasing hormone
2. Which of the following is not a hormone of the anterior pituitary gland?
   a. Adrenocorticotropin (ACTH)
   b. Thyroid stimulating hormone (TSH)
   c. Oxytocin
   d. Prolactin
3. Which of the following statements are true for growth hormone?
   a. Produced by thyrotropes in the anterior pituitary
   b. Increase proteolysis
   c. Raise blood glucose levels
   d. Increase milk production during lactation
4. Which of the following hormones is responsible for milk ejection?
   a. Oxytocin
   b. Prolactin
   c. Growth hormone
   d. FSH
5. Which of the following hormones has an antidiuretic effect?
   a. Oxytocin
   b. Prolactin
   c. Vasopressin
   d. Growth hormone

Chapter 42:

1. Which of the following hormones is NOT produced in the thyroid gland?
   a. Thyroxine (T4)
   b. Triiodothyronine (T3)
   c. Calcitonin
   d. Calcitriol
2. Which of the following steps results in the synthesis of monoiodotyrosine (MIT)?
   a. Iodide trapping
   b. Oxidation of iodide
   c. Organification of thyroglobulin
   d. Coupling reaction
3. Which of the following is an action of thyroxine?
   a. Increase in heart rate
   b. Decreased food intake
   c. Decreased respiration
   d. Weight gain
4. Hypothyroidism in infancy results in:
   a. Myxoedema
   b. Thyrotoxicosis
   c. Cretinism
   d. Grave's disease
5. Which of the following features are seen in hyperthyroidism?
   a. Slow heart rate
   b. Intolerance to cold
   c. Weight loss
   d. Slowing of mental activity

Chapter 43:

1. Which of the following hormones decreases plasma calcium levels?

a. Parathormone
b. Vitamin D3
c. Calcitonin
d. Growth hormone

2. Which of the following hormones directly increases calcium absorption in the intestine?
a. Parathormone
b. Vitamin D3
c. Calcitonin
d. Thyroxine

3. Which of the following hormones decreases calcium excretion by the kidney?
a. Vitamin D3
b. Parathormone
c. Calcitonin
d. Cortisol

4. Which of the following clinical features is seen during hypocalcaemia?
a. Sustained contraction of muscles
b. Increased cardiac output
c. Reduced nerve irritability
d. Increased bone density

5. Deficiency of which of the following vitamins is associated with rickets?
a. A
b. D
c. E
d. K

Chapter 44:

1. Which of the following cells of the Islets of Langerhans secretes insulin?
a. Alpha
b. Beta
c. Delta
d. F

2. Which of the following hormones inhibits the alpha and beta cells of the Islets of Langerhans?
a. Insulin
b. Glucagon
c. Thyroxine
d. Somatostatin

3. Which of the following hormones is counter-regulatory to insulin?
a. Oxytocin
b. Vasopressin
c. Adrenaline
d. Motilin

4. Which of the following is true for Type I Diabetes mellitus?
a. Occurs mainly in older people
b. Patient is typically obese
c. Plasma insulin levels are low
d. May respond to increased physical activity and exercise

5. Which of the following is a metabolic effect of insulin?
a. Reduced uptake of glucose into muscle
b. Protein breakdown
c. Reduced plasma potassium levels
d. Lipolysis

Chapter 45:

1. The hormone that is produced by the zona glomerulosa of the adrenal cortex is:
a. Mineralocorticoids
b. Glucocorticoids
c. Androgens
d. Adrenaline

2. Which of the following is an action of glucocorticoids?
a. Increased protein synthesis
b. Increases the effect of insulin
c. Decreases gastric acid secretion
d. Anti-inflammatory

3. Which of the following hormones is increased in Cushing's syndrome?
a. Aldosterone
b. Growth hormone
c. Cortisol
d. Adrenaline

4. Which of the following hormones is creased in Conn's syndrome?
a. Androgens
b. Aldosterone
c. Adrenaline
d. Glucocorticoids

5. Which of the following is an action of adrenaline (epinephrine)?
a. Lipogenesis
b. Reduced plasma glucose
c. Anti-inflammatory
d. Increased heart rate

SHORT ANSWER QUESTIONS (FOR RAPID REVIEW)

1. List four characteristics of a hormone.
a.
b.
c.
d.

2. Name the three broad groups of hormones.
a.
b.
c.

3. List the three locations of hormone receptors in a cell.
a.
b.
c.

4. Name three second messengers.
a.
b.
c.

5. List five hormones released from the hypothalamus that regulate the anterior pituitary.
a.
b.
c.

d.
e.

6. List two hormones that are produced in the hypothalamus but released from the posterior pituitary gland.
a.
b.

7. List five hormones of the anterior pituitary gland.
a.
b.
c.
d.
e.

8. List five functions of growth hormone.
a.
b.
c.
d.
e.

9. Indicate the clinical condition in column B which reflects the description in column A.

Column A	Column B
Excess secretion of growth hormone in childhood resulting in increased height	i.
Excess secretion of growth hormone in adulthood associated with prognathism, spade-like hands and organomegaly, among others	ii.
Reduced secretion in growth hormone or somatomedins from birth or childhood	iii.

10. List two functions of oxytocin.
a.
b.

11. List two functions of vasopressin.
a.
b.

12. The hormone secreted by the pineal gland is ______________________ and three of its functions include:
a.
b.
c.

13. The five steps of synthesis and secretion of thyroxine are:
a.
b.
c.
d.
e.

14. What the secretions of the hypothalamus and anterior pituitary that regulate the secretion of T3 and T4?
a.
b.

15. List five actions of thyroxine.
a.
b.
c.
d.
e.

16. List five features of adult hyperthyroidism.
a.
b.
c.
d.
e.

17. List five features of adult hypothyroidism.
a.
b.
c.
d.
e.

18. Hypothyroidism in infancy is called ______________ and two features of this condition are:
a.
b.

19. There are three major hormones which regulate calcium levels in the blood. Fill in the following table to indicate the hormones, their source and their action on calcium levels in the blood.

Hormone	Source	Action on Calcium Levels in the Blood

20. The normal calcium level in blood is ______________ mg/dL, and five functions of calcium in the body are:
a.
b.
c.
d.
e.

21. Two features of hypocalcaemia are:
a.
b.

22. Two tests of hypocalcaemia are:
a.
b.

23. Fill in the following table to indicate the clinical condition involved.

Decreased vitamin D in children	
Decreased vitamin D in adults	

24. With regard to osteoporosis:
a. List three risk factors.
i.
ii.
iii.
b. List two clinical features.

i.
ii.

c. List three ways of preventing osteoporosis.
i.
ii.
iii.

25. Fill in the following table to describe the islets of Langerhans in the pancreas.

Type of Cell	Percentage of Cells in the Islets	Hormone Secreted

26. List four functions of insulin.
a.
b.
c.
d.

27. Four hormones which have opposite actions of insulin on glucose levels in the blood (counter-regulatory hormones) are:
a.
b.
c.
d.

28. Differentiate between type I and type II diabetes mellitus.

	Type I Diabetes Mellitus	Type II Diabetes Mellitus
Usual age of onset		
Insulin levels (low/high)		
Glucose levels (low/high)		
Pathogenesis (insulin secretion vs insulin resistance)		
Body weight (low/high)		

29. List three complications of longstanding, uncontrolled type II diabetes mellitus.
a.
b.
c.

30. With regard to the adrenal cortex and adrenal medulla, match column A (layer of cortex) with column B (hormone secreted) and column C (action of hormone).

Column A	Column B	Column C
Part of Adrenal Gland	Hormone Secreted	Action of Hormone
1. Cortex: zona glomerulosa	a. Aldosterone	i. Fight-or-flight response
2. Cortex: zona fasciculata	b. Adrenaline	ii. Sex steroids
3. Cortex: zona reticularis	c. Androgens	iii. Anti-inflammatory
4. Medulla	d. Cortisol	iv. Sodium and water retention

31. List two functions of mineralocorticoids (aldosterone).
a.
b.

32. List three metabolic actions of glucocorticoids.
a.
b.
c.

33. Briefly describe how cortisol is anti-inflammatory.

34. Cushing's syndrome is seen due to ______________ secretion of cortisol and features of the syndrome are:
a.
b.
c.
d.
e.

35. Addison's disease is due to ______________ and four features of the condition are:
a.
b.
c.
d.

36. The major hormone produced by the adrenal medulla is ______________. It acts through receptors which are of two broad categories: ______________ and ______________; and mediates the ______________ response.

SHORT ESSAY QUESTIONS

1. Describe the endocrine role of the hypothalamus.
2. List the hormones of the anterior pituitary gland. How are these controlled by the hypothalamus?
3. Describe the actions of growth hormone.
4. Describe disorders of excess and deficient secretion of growth hormone.
5. Describe the synthesis of thyroxine.
6. Describe the pathogenesis and clinical features of cretinism.
7. Compare and contrast hypothyroidism and hyperthyroidism.
8. State the normal serum calcium level. List the functions of calcium in the body.
9. Describe the features of hypocalcaemia.
10. Describe the disorders of the parathyroid gland.
11. Describe the features and risk factors of osteoporosis.
12. Differentiate between type I and type II diabetes mellitus.
13. List the counter-regulatory hormones of insulin. Describe the function of glucagon.

14. List the source, function and regulation of mineralocorticoids.
15. Describe the physiological basis of the clinical features of Cushing's syndrome.
16. Describe the physiological basis of the clinical features of Addison's disease.
17. Describe the actions of epinephrine.

LONG ESSAY QUESTIONS

1. List the characteristics of a hormone. Classify hormones and describe their mechanisms of action.
2. Describe the actions of hormones secreted from the posterior pituitary gland.
3. Describe the actions of thyroxine and its regulation.
4. Describe the hormonal regulation of calcium in the body.
5. Describe the actions and regulation of insulin.
6. Describe the source, functions and regulation of glucocorticoids.

MULTIPLE CHOICE QUESTIONS ANSWERS

Chapter 41:

1-d; 2-c; 3-c; 4-a; 5-c

Chapter 42:

1-d; 2-c; 3-a; 4-c; 5-c

Chapter 43:

1-c; 2-b; 3-b; 4-a; 5-b

Chapter 44:

1-b; 2-d; 3-c; 4-c; 5-c

Chapter 45:

1-a; 2-d; 3-c; 4-b; 5-d

SHORT ANSWER QUESTIONS: ANSWER KEY

1. See Chapter 41.
2. Peptide hormone, steroid hormones, amines.
3. Cell membrane, cytoplasm, nucleus.
4. See Chapter 41.
5. See Chapter 41.
6. Oxytocin, vasopressin.
7. See Chapter 41.
8. See Chapter 41.
9. (i) Gigantism, (ii) acromegaly, (iii) dwarfism.
10. Milk ejection, contraction of the pregnant uterus.
11. Retention of water in the kidney (antidiuresis), vasoconstriction.
12. Melatonin (see Chapter 41 for functions).
13. Iodide trapping, oxidation of iodide, organification of thyroglobulin, coupling reaction, secretion by exocytosis.
14. (a) TRH from the hypothalamus, (b) TSH from the pituitary.
15. See Chapter 42.
16. See Chapter 42.
17. See Chapter 42.
18. See Chapter 42.
19. (1) Parathormone – parathyroid glands – increases calcium; (2) vitamin D – skin/liver/kidney – increases calcium; (3) calcitonin – thyroid gland – decreases calcium.
20. 10 (see Chapter 43 for functions).
21. Increased nerve irritability, muscle spasm.
22. Chvostek's sign, Trousseau's sign.
23. Rickets, osteomalacia.
24. See Chapter 43.
25. See Chapter 44.
26. See Chapter 44.
27. Cortisol, glucagon, adrenaline, growth hormone.
28. See Chapter 44.
29. See Chapter 44.
30. 1 – a, iv; 2 – d, iii; 3 – c, ii; 4 – b, i.
31. See Chapter 45.
32. See Chapter 45.
33. See Chapter 45.
34. Excess (see Chapter 45 for features).
35. Adrenal insufficiency (see Chapter 45 for features).
36. Epinephrine (adrenaline), alpha-adrenergic receptors, beta-adrenergic receptors, fight-or-flight.

Workbook: The Sensory Organs

SPECIFIC LEARNING OBJECTIVES

At the end of this chapter, the student should be able to:

Chapter 47

- Describe the functional anatomy of the skin.
- List the functions of the skin.
- Describe each function of the skin in brief.
- List the changes that occur in the skin with ageing.

Chapter 48

- Draw and label a diagram of the cross-section of the eye.
- List the extraocular muscles and describe the movement that each performs.
- List the parts of the eye that light passes through in sequence before reaching the retina.
- Distinguish between rods and cones, the receptors in the eye.
- Distinguish between light and dark adaptations.
- Describe the features of accommodation.
- Trace the pathway for vision from the retina to the cortex and describe the common errors that are associated with disruptions of this pathway.
- Describe the effects of ageing on vision.
- Describe how visual function can be tested with regard to the following:
  - Visual fields
  - Visual acuity
  - Pupillary reflexes
  - Colour vision
  - Movements of the eye

Chapter 49

- Draw and label a diagram of the ear indicating the outer, middle and inner ear.
- List the functions of the middle ear.
- Describe how sound is sensed in the inner ear.
- Trace the auditory pathway.
- Describe the effects of ageing on hearing.
- Describe how hearing is tested using tuning forks and audiometry.

Chapter 50

- List the categories of taste.
- Indicate which cranial nerves are involved in transmitting taste sensation to the brain.
- Indicate which cranial nerve is involved in olfaction.
- Describe how you would test for taste and smell at the bedside of a patient.

Chapter 51

- Briefly describe the pathogenesis and consequences of burns.
- Describe the purpose and list the types of skin grafts.
- List some causes for the loss of sensation.
- Write a short note on hyperhidrosis.
- Describe and indicate corrections for the following refractory errors: myopia, hypermetropia, astigmatism and presbyopia.
- Briefly describe the following disorders: cataract, glaucoma and vitamin A deficiency (night blindness).
- Differentiate between conduction deafness and sensorineural deafness.
- Briefly describe the use of hearing aids.
- List the disorders of taste.
- List the disorders of smell.

GLOSSARY OF TERMS

Chapter 47

- **Epidermis:** the outermost layer of the skin
- **Dermis:** situated just below the epidermis, this layer contains a variety of structures including connective tissue, blood vessels, sebaceous and sweat glands, nerves and hair follicles
- **Piloerection:** hair 'stands on end'; the erection of hair that accompanies exposure to cold
- **Sensation:** in medicine, sensation is the registration of nerve signals that originates from sensory receptors (in the skin, these receptors include those of pain, temperature, touch and pressure)
- **Thermoregulation:** the maintenance or regulation of body temperature (normal temperature is 98.6°F [37°C])

Chapter 48

- **Accommodation:** changes that occur in the eye when a person focuses from a distant object to a nearby object
- **Light adaptation:** the process by which the eye adapts when a person moves from a dark area to bright light
- **Dark adaptation:** the process by which the eye adapts when a person moves from bright light to a darkened area
- **Strabismus:** a condition in which the eyes are not normally aligned – commonly called squint
- **Scotoma:** loss of a part of the visual field

Chapter 49

- **Audiometry:** a test which measures the ability of a person to hear sounds over a range of frequencies

Chapter 50

- **Olfactory:** refers to the sense of smell
- **Gustatory:** refers to the sense of taste

Chapter 51

- **Anaesthesia:** complete loss of sensation
- **Hypoaesthesia:** partial loss of sensation
- **Myopia:** short-sightedness – correctable by biconcave lens
- **Hypermetropia:** long-sightedness – correctable by biconvex lens
- **Astigmatism:** deviation from the spherical curvature of the cornea resulting in distorted images as rays of light cannot be focused at a single point on the retina
- **Presbyopia:** refractory error of ageing – difficulty in accommodation – correctable by a bifocal lens
- **Presbycusis:** hearing loss associated with ageing
- **Ageusia:** loss of taste sensation
- **Anosmia:** loss of smell

MULTIPLE CHOICE QUESTIONS

Chapter 47:

1. Most of the skin receptors are located in the:
   a. Epidermis
   b. Stratum corneum
   c. Dermis
   d. Subcutaneous adipose tissue
2. Which of the following in the skin is associated with hot weather?
   a. Piloerection
   b. Vasodilation
   c. Reduced sweating
   d. Insulation by fat
3. Which of the following hormones are partly synthesized in the skin?
   a. Melatonin
   b. Adrenaline
   c. Vitamin D
   d. Androgens
4. Which of the following changes are seen in the skin with ageing?
   a. Decrease in thickness of epidermis and dermis
   b. Increase in melanocyte density
   c. Increased sebum secretion from sebaceous glands
   d. Increased number of sweat glands

Chapter 48:

1. Which of the following is the outermost covering of the eye?
   a. Conjunctiva
   b. Cornea
   c. Sclera
   d. Retina
2. Which of the following features is true of the cones in the retina?
   a. More in number than rods
   b. Most active in dim light
   c. Contain rhodopsin
   d. Important for colour vision
3. With ageing, a person has to hold a book further way to read. This condition is called:
   a. Myopia
   b. Hypermetropia
   c. Presbyopia
   d. Astigmatism
4. A part of the optic nerve crosses over to the other cerebral hemisphere at:
   a. Optic chiasma
   b. Optic tract
   c. Optic radiation
   d. Lateral geniculate body
5. The visual fields of a person can be tested using:
   a. Snellen's chart
   b. Ishihara's charts
   c. Confrontation test
   d. Pupillary reflexes

Chapter 49:

1. Which of the following is NOT a function of the middle ear?
   a. Impedance matching
   b. Equalizing pressure in middle ear
   c. Attenuation reflex
   d. Conversion of sound into electrical signals
2. Which of the following is the receptor for hearing?
   a. Basilar membrane
   b. Organ of Corti
   c. Ossicles
   d. Round window
3. In which cerebral lobe is the auditory cortex located?
   a. Frontal lobe
   b. Temporal lobe
   c. Parietal lobe
   d. Occipital lobe
4. Which cranial nerve is involved in hearing?
   a. VII
   b. VIII
   c. IX
   d. X
5. Deafness that occurs due to excessive wax in the ear is:
   a. Conduction deafness
   b. Sensorineural deafness
   c. Peripheral presbycusis
   d. Central presbycusis

Chapter 50:

1. The cranial nerve that carries taste from the anterior two-thirds of the tongue is:
   a. VI
   b. VII

c. IX
d. X

2. Which taste sensation is best felt at the tip of the tongue?
   a. Sweet
   b. Sour
   c. Salty
   d. Bitter
3. With regard to olfaction, which of the following statements are true?
   a. Smell receptors are located in the lower nostril
   b. The olfactory nerve is the second cranial nerve
   c. The olfactory pathway passes through the thalamus
   d. The olfactory fibres pass the cribriform plate

SHORT ANSWER QUESTIONS (FOR RAPID REVIEW)

1. The three layers of the skin are:
   a.
   b.
   c.
2. List five functions of the skin.
   a.
   b.
   c.
   d.
   e.
3. List four ways in which the skin helps in thermoregulation.
   a.
   b.
   c.
   d.
4. List four ways in which ageing affects the skin.
   a.
   b.
   c.
   d.
5. The three cranial nerves that control the movements of the eye are:
   a.
   b.
   c.
6. The rods and cones are the sensory receptors of the retina; fill in the following table to differentiate between them.

	Rods	Cones
Number		
Most active		
Characteristics/functions		
Pigment		

7. The part of the retina which has the maximum density of cones is ____________.
8. The area of the retina which has no receptors is at the ____________ where the optic nerve arises and this absence of receptors gives rise to the __________.
9. The process by which the eye gets used to darkness after entering from an area of bright light is called ____________.
10. Accommodation occurs when we focus on a near object after looking into distance. The three changes of accommodation are:
    a.
    b.
    c.
11. Rearrange the following to correctly represent the visual pathway: occipital cortex, optic nerve, optical tract, optic radiation, lateral geniculate body, optic chiasma.
12. Complete the following table to indicate the visual defects that are found with lesions at different paths of the visual pathway.

Site of the Lesion (Assume a Complete Lesion)	Visual Field Defect
a. Left optic nerve	
b. Optic chiasma	
c. Left optic tract	
d. Left optic radiation	

13. List four changes which occur in vision with ageing.
    a.
    b.
    c.
    d.
14. Two ways in which visual fields can be tested are:
    a.
    b.
15. Visual acuity is tested by using ____________ chart; near vision is tested by using ____________ chart and colour vision by using ____________ charts.
16. When light is shone into an eye, constriction of the pupil on the same side is called the ____________ light reflex, while constriction of the pupil on the other side is called the ____________ light reflex.
17. List three functions of the external ear.
    a.
    b.
    c.
18. The three ossicles in the middle ear are:
    a.
    b.
    c.
19. The two muscles of the middle ear are:
    a.
    b.

20. Four functions of the middle ear are:
   a.
   b.
   c.
   d.
21. The sensory organ of hearing in the cochlea is the ________________ which rests on the ________________ membrane.
22. The human ear can hear sound with a frequency range of ________________ Hz.
23. The loss of hearing with ageing is called ________________ and two factors which contribute to this loss are:
   a.
   b.
24. Hearing can be assessed clinically by using ________________. More accurate information can be obtained by using ________________.
25. The five categories of taste are:
   a.
   b.
   c.
   d.
   e.
26. The three cranial nerves which are sensory for taste are:
   a. Anterior two-thirds of the tongue: ________________
   b. Posterior one-third of the tongue: ________________
   c. Posterior-most part: ________________
27. The cranial nerve responsible for smell is ________________.
28. In the following diagrams, indicate the refractory defect and the lens that will correct the defect:

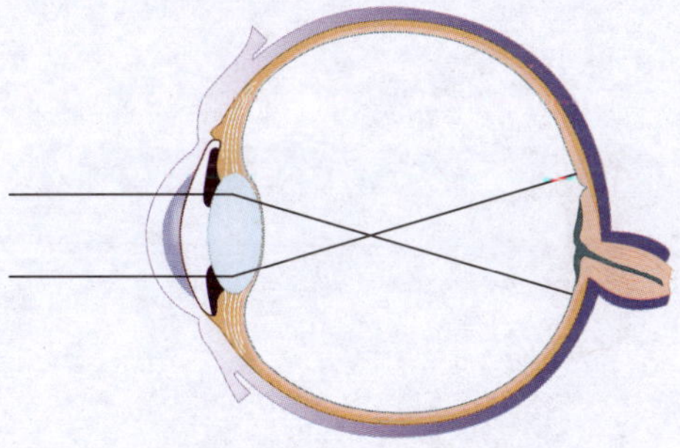

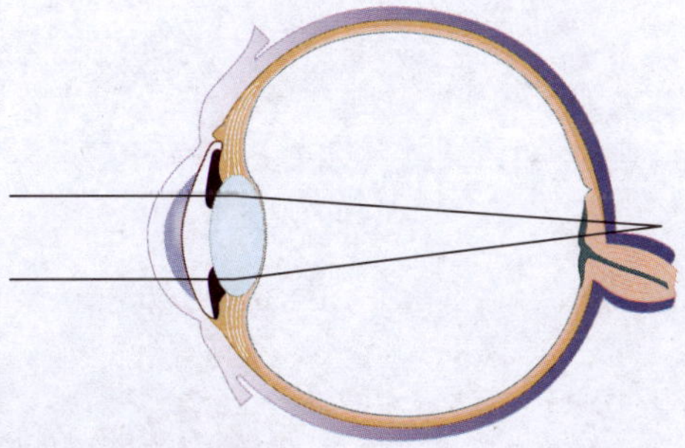

SHORT ESSAY QUESTIONS

1. Describe the changes in the skin with ageing.
2. Explain the role of the skin as a protective organ.
3. Distinguish between the rods and the cones.
4. List the extraocular muscles and explain their functions.
5. Describe the phenomenon of accommodation.
6. Describe the effects of ageing on vision.
7. Describe the effects of ageing on hearing.
8. Describe the tests of hearing.
9. Describe how smell is perceived. Trace the pathway for olfaction.
10. Distinguish between conduction and sensorineural deafness.

LONG ESSAY QUESTIONS

1. Describe the functions of the skin.
2. Explain the visual pathway with the help of a diagram.
3. What is the visual field? Describe the changes that occur in the visual fields with lesions in the visual pathway.
4. Describe the examination of the eye in relation to (a) visual fields, (b) visual acuity, (c) colour vision and (d) pupillary reflexes.
5. Draw a diagram of the middle ear and explain its functions.
6. Describe how sound is processed in the inner ear and trace the auditory pathway.
7. List the categories of taste. Indicate where in the tongue these are best sensed. Trace the taste pathway.
8. Describe with diagrams the various errors of refraction and indicate how they can be corrected.

MULTIPLE CHOICE QUESTIONS ANSWERS

Chapter 47:

1-c; 2-b; 3-c; 4-a

Chapter 48:

1-a; 2-d; 3-c; 4-a; 5-c

Chapter 49:

1-d; 2-b; 3-b; 4-b; 5-a

Chapter 50:

1-b; 2-a; 3-d

SHORT ANSWER QUESTIONS: ANSWER KEY

1. Epidermis, dermis, hypodermis.
2. See Chapter 47.
3. See Chapter 47.
4. See Chapter 47.
5. Cranial nerve III – oculomotor nerve; cranial nerve IV – trochlear nerve; cranial nerve VI – abducens nerve.
6. See Chapter 48.
7. Fovea.
8. Optic disc, blind spot.
9. Dark adaptation.
10. Convergence of the eyes, miosis (pupillary constriction), increased curvature of the lens.
11. Optic nerve, optic chiasma, optic tract, lateral geniculate body, optic radiation, occipital cortex.

12. (a) Complete blindness – left eye; (b) bitemporal hemianopia; (c) right-sided homonymous hemianopia; (d) right-sided homonymous hemianopia with macular sparing
13. See Chapter 48.
14. Confrontation test, perimeter.
15. Snellen's, Jaeger's, Ishihara's.
16. Direct, consensual.
17. See Chapter 49.
18. Incus, malleus, stapes.
19. Tensor tympani, stapedius.
20. Transmission of sound to the inner ear, impedance matching, equalization of pressures in the middle and outer ear, protection of the ear from loud sounds – attenuation reflex.
21. Organ of Corti, basilar membrane.
22. 20–20,000.
23. Presbycusis, see Chapter 49.
24. Tuning fork tests (Rinne, Weber), audiometry.
25. Sweet, salt, bitter, sour, umami.
26. Corda tympani branch of the facial nerve (VII), glossopharyngeal (IX), vagus (X).
27. Olfactory nerve (cranial nerve I).
28. (a) Myopia – correction, biconcave lens; (b) hypermetropia – correction, biconvex lens.

SECTION 8

Workbook: Musculo-Skeletal System

SPECIFIC LEARNING OBJECTIVES

At the end of this chapter, the student should be able to:

Chapter 52

- Draw a neuromuscular junction and label its parts.
- Describe the events that occur in the neuromuscular junction.
- Briefly indicate the types of drugs that act on the neuromuscular junction.
- Write a short note on myasthenia gravis.

Chapter 53

- Describe the structure of skeletal muscle with specific emphasis on the (1) motor unit, (2) sarcotubular system and (3) sarcomere.
- Explain the process of excitation–contraction coupling.
- List the molecular events associated with muscle contraction.
- Differentiate between isotonic and isometric muscle contractions.
- Describe the effect of increasing frequency of stimulus on muscle contraction.
- Describe briefly the different types of muscle fibres.
- Define muscle fatigue and list its causes.
- Describe the features of (1) muscular dystrophy and (2) disuse atrophy.

Chapter 54

- Define muscle tone.
- Describe how muscle tone is regulated.
- Distinguish between hypotonia and hypertonia.

Chapter 55

- Describe the location of skeletal, cardiac and smooth muscles.
- Distinguish between skeletal, cardiac and smooth muscles.

GLOSSARY OF TERMS

Chapter 52

- **Neuromuscular junction:** the junction between the motor nerve and the muscle
- **End-plate potential:** the membrane potential that is developed at the neuromuscular junction following the quantal release of acetylcholine
- **Ligand-gated channel:** a channel on the membrane that is opened by the binding of a chemical

Chapter 53

- **Excitation–contraction coupling:** the coupling of the electrical event in muscle (action potential on the sarcolemma) with a mechanical event (contraction) via a chemical mediator (calcium ions)
- **Sarcomere:** the portion of the myofibril contained between two Z lines
- **Motor unit:** a single motor nerve fibre together with the multiple muscle fibres that it innervates
- **Quantal summation:** the increase in amplitude of muscle contraction associated with a recruitment of motor units
- **Isotonic contraction:** muscle contraction associated with muscle shortening in which work is done
- **Isometric contraction:** muscle contraction in which the length of the muscle remains unchanged and no work is done
- **Muscle fatigue:** the inability of a muscle to sustain a given amplitude of contraction

Chapter 54

- **Muscle tone:** a state of sustained partial contraction of a muscle at rest
- **Hypertonia:** an increase in the muscle tone
- **Hypotonia:** a decrease in the muscle tone

Chapter 55

- **Syncytium:** functionally, the ability of muscle cells to work together due to the presence of communicating intercellular junctions (these are intercalated discs for cardiac muscle and gap junctions for smooth muscle)

MULTIPLE CHOICE QUESTIONS

Chapter 52:

1. The neurotransmitter and receptor at the neuromuscular junction is:
   a. Acetylcholine – muscarinic receptor
   b. Acetylcholine – nictonic receptor
   c. Norepinephrine – alpha adrenergic receptor
   d. Norepinephrine – beta adrenergic receptor
2. The potential that is formed at the neuromuscular junction is:
   a. Local response
   b. Action potential
   c. End plate potential
   d. Inhibitory postsynaptic potential

3. Botulinum toxin blocks:
   a. Exocytosis of neurotransmitter
   b. Voltage-gated calcium channels
   c. Postsynaptic receptors
   d. Action potential on sarcolemma
4. Bungarotoxin contained in the venom of the krait snake blocks:
   a. Exocytosis of neurotransmitter
   b. Voltage gated calcium channels
   c. Post-synaptic receptors
   d. Action potential on sarcolemma
5. In myasthenia gravis, auto-antibodies act against:
   a. Voltage-gated calcium channels
   b. Neurotransmitter vesicles
   c. Postsynaptic Ach receptors
   d. Sarcolemma

Chapter 53:

1. In the sarcomere, which of the following proteins makes the thick filament?
   a. Actin
   b. Troponin
   c. Tropomyosin
   d. Myosin
2. Which of the following is true of isotonic muscle contraction?
   a. Muscle shortens
   b. Tone increases
   c. No work is done
   d. Heat produced is minimum
3. Which of the following proteins does calcium bind to during muscle contraction?
   a. Actin
   b. Troponin
   c. Tropomyosin
   d. Myosin
4. Which of the following is true of red muscle fibres?
   a. Large muscle fibres
   b. Fatigue easily
   c. More in weight lifters
   d. Rich in mitochondria
5. Sustained contraction in muscle due to high rates of stimulation is called:
   a. Quantal summation
   b. Clonus
   c. Beneficial effect
   d. Tetanus

Chapter 54:

1. Which of the receptors in the muscle respond to stretch?
   a. Muscle spindle
   b. Golgi's tendon organs
   c. Touch receptors
   d. Pressure receptors
2. Which of the receptors in the muscle respond to increased muscle tone?
   a. Pressure receptors
   b. Muscle spindle
   c. Golgi's tendon organ
   d. Touch receptors

Chapter 55:

1. Which of the following muscles are striated and involuntary?
   a. Skeletal
   b. Cardiac
   c. Single unit smooth
   d. Multiunit smooth
2. Which of these muscles is most likely to fatigue?
   a. Skeletal
   b. Cardiac
   c. Single unit smooth
   d. Multiunit smooth
3. Which of the following muscles is supplied by motor nerves of the peripheral nervous system?
   a. Skeletal
   b. Cardiac
   c. Single unit smooth
   d. Multiunit smooth

SHORT ANSWER QUESTIONS (FOR RAPID REVIEW)

1. In the following diagram of the neuromuscular junction, label the parts A–E.

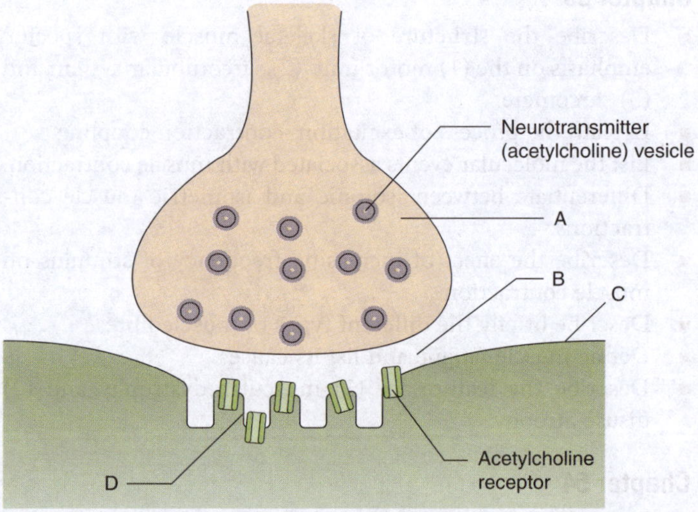

2. List the events at the neuromuscular junction.

3. Match column A (drug/toxin/poison) with column B (mode of action) to illustrate the actions of these substances on transmission at the neuromuscular junction.

Column A	Column B
1. Botulinum	A. Drug which binds to the nicotinic receptor
2. Nerve gas	B. Pesticide which inhibits cholinesterase
3. Bungarotoxin	C. Inhibits cholinesterase in the synaptic cleft
4. Organophosphorus poison	D. Prevents the release of acetylcholine from the nerve terminal
5. Succinylcholine	E. Poison which binds to the nicotinic receptor

4. With reference to myasthenia gravis, indicate whether the following statements are true (T) or false (F):
   1. Myasthenia gravis is an autoimmune disease.
   2. Antibodies are produced against acetylcholine receptors located on the presynaptic membrane.
   3. Neostigmine/physostigmine act by increasing the release of acetylcholine.
   4. Ptosis and easy fatigability are among the symptoms.
   5. There is blunting of the folds on the postsynaptic membrane.
5. The explanation in column A refers to a particular term. Fill in this term in column B.

Column A	Column B
1. A single nerve fibre with the muscle fibres that it innervates	
2. The space between two Z lines (discs)	
3. Transverse invaginations of the sarcolemma into the muscle fibre	
4. Process by which muscle contraction is coupled to the action potential by using calcium ions as a mediator	
5. Increasing strength of contraction due to recruitment of more motor units	
6. The higher amplitude of muscle contraction following a second stimulus soon after the first muscle contraction	

6. Label the diagram of the sarcomere.

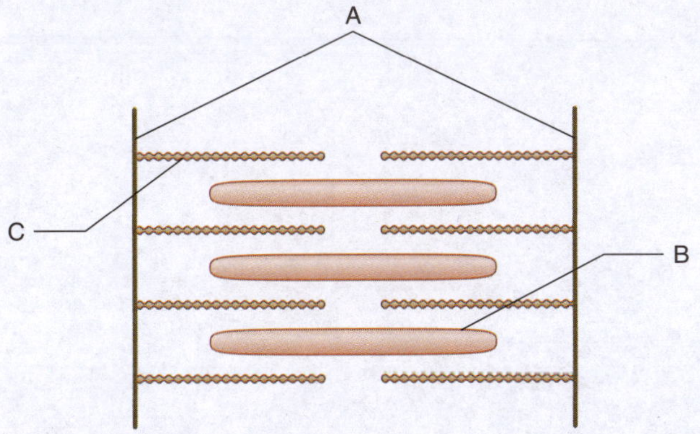

7. List the three molecules that make up the thin filament.
   a.
   b.
   c.
8. The thick filament is composed of ______________________ ______________________.
9. List the molecular events that occur with skeletal muscle contraction.
10. List two differences between isotonic and isometric contractions and give one example of each.

Isotonic Contraction	Isometric Contraction
Example:	Example:

11. Define muscle fatigue.
12. List three causes of muscle fatigue.
    a.
    b.
    c.
13. List five differences between red and white muscle fibres.

Red Muscle Fibres (Type I)	White Muscle Fibres (Type II)

14. Define rigor mortis and indicate its cause.
15. List the receptors in skeletal muscle which sense:
    a. Muscle length
    b. Muscle tension
16. In relation to cardiac, smooth and skeletal muscles, indicate:
    a. Which muscle does not function like a syncytium? ______________
    b. Which muscle is not fatigable? ______________
    c. Which muscle is spindle shaped? ______________
    d. Which muscle is found in the blood vessel wall? ______________
    e. Which muscle is striated and branched? ______________
    f. Which muscle is made up of red and white muscle fibres? ______________

SHORT ESSAY QUESTIONS

1. Describe some toxins/drugs that act at the neuromuscular junction. Classify them by site of action.
2. Define a motor unit. Describe the phenomenon of quantal summation.

3. Differentiate between isotonic and isometric contractions.
4. What is muscle fatigue? What are its causes?
5. Distinguish between the different types of skeletal muscle fibres.
6. Distinguish between muscular dystrophy and disuse atrophy.
7. Define muscle tone. How is it regulated and what are the variations in muscle tone?

LONG ESSAY QUESTIONS

1. Draw and label a typical neuromuscular junction (NMJ) and list the events that occur at the NMJ.
2. Describe the pathophysiological basis, clinical features and treatment of myasthenia gravis.
3. Draw and label a sarcomere. List the molecular events that occur during muscle contraction.
4. Compare and contrast skeletal, smooth and cardiac muscles.

MULTIPLE CHOICE QUESTIONS ANSWERS

Chapter 52:

1-b; 2-c; 3-a; 4-c; 5-c

Chapter 53:

1-d; 2-a; 3-b; 4-d; 5-d

Chapter 54:

1-a; 2-c

Chapter 55:

1-b; 2-a; 3-a

SHORT ANSWER QUESTIONS: ANSWER KEY

1. (A) Nerve terminal (bouton), (B) synaptic cleft, (C) sarcolemma (muscle membrane), (D) postsynaptic membrane, (E) presynaptic membrane.
2. See Chapter 52.
3. 1 – D; 2 – C; 3 – E; 4 – B; 5 – A.
4. (a) True, (b) false, (c) false, (d) true, (e) true (see Chapter 52 for details).
5. (a) Motor unit, (b) sarcomere, (c) T tubule, –(d) excitation–contraction coupling, (e) quantal summation, (f) beneficial effect.
6. (A) Z lines, (B) thick filament, (C) thin filament.
7. Actin, tropomyosin, troponin.
8. See Chapter 53.
9. See Chapter 53.
10. See Table 53.1.
11. See Chapter 53.
12. See Chapter 53.
13. See Chapter 53.
14. See Chapter 53.
15. (a) Muscle spindle, (b) Golgi's tendon organ.
16. (a) Skeletal, (b) cardiac, (c) smooth, (d) smooth, (e) cardiac, (f) skeletal.

SECTION 9

Workbook: Renal System

SPECIFIC LEARNING OBJECTIVES

At the end of this chapter, the student should be able to:

Chapter 57

- Describe the functional anatomy of the kidney.
- Draw a nephron and label its parts.
- Describe the juxtaglomerular apparatus and indicate its function.
- List the excretory and nonexcretory functions of the kidney.

Chapter 58

- Draw and label the filtration barrier (glomerular membrane).
- Define glomerular filtration rate and list the factors that affect it.
- Describe the relationship between the loop of Henle and the vasa recta.
- Describe the counter-current multiplier and its role.
- Describe the counter-current exchanger and its role.
- Describe the mechanism of glucose reabsorption in the kidney.
- Define the term 'clearance'.
- List the key elements of urine formation in the different parts of the nephron.

Chapter 59

- Describe the normal composition of urine.
- Describe the abnormal constituents of urine and their interpretation.
- List the tests in urine and blood which reflect kidney function.
- Briefly describe imaging tests specific to kidney function.
- Describe the pathophysiology of acute renal failure.
- Describe the pathophysiology of chronic renal failure.

GLOSSARY OF TERMS

Chapter 57

- **Nephron:** the structural and functional unit of the kidney (while numbers vary between people, there are on average about 1 million nephrons per kidney)
- **Ultrafiltration:** filtration which allows some (smaller) molecules to pass through while retaining other (usually larger) molecules
- **Juxtaglomerular apparatus (JGA):** structure in the kidney that consists of three different cells – (1) the juxtaglomerular (JG) cells of the afferent arteriole of the glomerulus, (2) mesangial (Lacis) cells and (3) macula densa cells of the distal convoluted tubule

Chapter 58

- **Counter-current multiplier:** the mechanism by which a concentration gradient is created in the medulla of the kidney
- **Counter-current exchanger:** the mechanism by which the concentration gradient in the medulla of the kidney is maintained
- **Transport maximum for glucose:** the maximum rate of glucose reabsorption at the proximal convoluted tubule of the kidney (expressed in mg/min)
- **Starling's forces:** the hydrostatic and osmotic pressures on either side of the capillary wall which determine the movement of fluid across it
- **Micturition:** the act of voiding urine
- **Cystometrogram:** a graphical depiction of the volume–pressure relationship in the urinary bladder obtained by cystometry (this test allows the evaluation of urinary bladder capacity, the pattern of bladder contractions and the ability to voluntarily control micturition)

Chapter 59

- **Urine culture:** a method to grow bacteria that may be present in the urine (typically, as part of this test, antibiotics are tested for the effectiveness against the bacteria that have been grown; this is called drug sensitivity testing)
- **Biopsy:** the removal of a piece of tissue from a living person to determine the presence and nature of disease

MULTIPLE CHOICE QUESTIONS

Chapter 57:

1. Which of the following is a characteristic of juxtamedullary nephrons?
   a. They are 85% of the nephrons in the kidney
   b. The glomeruli are located in the cortex
   c. They have long loops of Henle
   d. They secrete erythropoietin

2. In the juxtaglomerular apparatus, the substance that is secreted is:
   a. Renin
   b. Aldosterone
   c. Angiotensin
   d. Antidiuretic hormone
3. Which of the hormones is synthesized in the kidney?
   a. Aldosterone
   b. Angiotensin
   c. Cortisol
   d. Erythropoietin
4. An example of substance that is completely reabsorbed in the kidney is:
   a. Urea
   b. Creatinine
   c. Glucose
   d. Water
5. The major site of filtration of the kidney is:
   a. Proximal convoluted tubule
   b. Glomerulus
   c. Distal convoluted tubule
   d. Loop of Henle

Chapter 58:

1. The normal glomerular filtration rate is:
   a. 50 mL/min
   b. 125 mL/min
   c. 300 mL/min
   d. 600 mL/min
2. The major site of reabsorption of water in the nephron is:
   a. Proximal convoluted tubule
   b. Loop of Henle
   c. Distal convoluted tubule
   d. Collecting duct
3. Which of the following parts of the nephron is the site of the counter-current multiplier which creates the renal medullary osmotic gradient?
   a. Proximal convoluted tubule
   b. Loop of Henle
   c. Vasa recta
   d. Distal convoluted tubule
4. What is the role of the vasa recta?
   a. Counter-current exchanger
   b. Concentration of urine
   c. Production of vitamin D
   d. Production of erythropoietin
5. At which of the following sites does antidiuretic hormone act?
   a. Bowman's capsule
   b. Proximal convoluted tubule
   c. Loop of Henle
   d. Collecting duct

SHORT ANSWER QUESTIONS (FOR RAPID REVIEW)

1. Label the parts of the nephron indicated as follows:

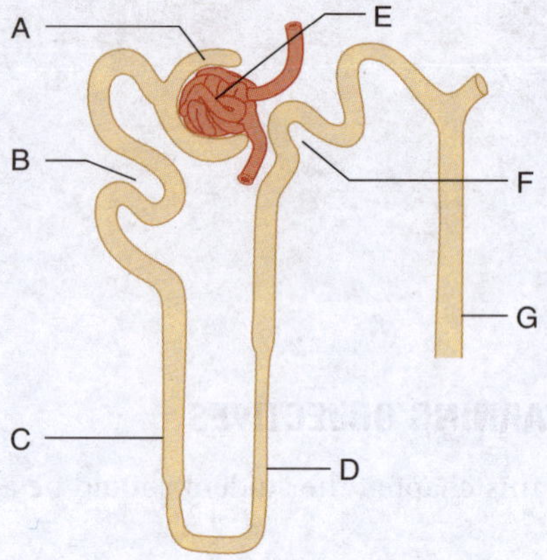

2. Match column A (site of the nephron) with the appropriate function (column B).

Column A	Column B
1. Glomerulus	A. Site of action of ADH
2. Bowman's capsule	B. Concentrating segment
3. Proximal convoluted tubule	C. Site of filtration
4. Descending limb of loop of Henle	D. Site of action of aldosterone
5. Ascending limb of loop of Henle	E. Receives filtrate
6. Distal convoluted tubule	F. Diluting segment
7. Collecting Duct	G. Reabsorption of solutes and glucose

3. There are two types of nephrons in the kidney – cortical and juxtamedullary. Indicate whether the following statements are true or false:
   a. Cortical nephrons are fewer and account for 15% of nephrons.
   b. Juxtamedullary nephrons have long loops of Henle.
   c. Cortical nephrons are more important for concentrating urine.
4. List the three cells which make up the juxtaglomerular apparatus (JGA).
   a.
   b.
   c.
5. List three functions of the JGA.
   a.
   b.
   c.

6. List three processes involved in the excretion of urine.
   a.
   b.
   c.
7. List four nonexcretory functions of the kidney.
   a.
   b.
   c.
   d.
8. Define glomerular filtration rate. ______
9. What is the normal GFR? ______
10. List the three layers that the glomerular filtrate passes through.
   a.
   b.
   c.
11. The pressures which determine the glomerular filtration rate are called Starling's forces. Indicate the three major pressures involved that determine net filtration rate and indicate whether they increase or decrease filtration.

Type of Pressure	Increase/Decrease Filtration

12. List four substances which are reabsorbed in the proximal convoluted tubule.
   a.
   b.
   c.
   d.
13. Define renal plasma threshold for glucose and give its normal value.
14. Define transport maximum for glucose (Tm_G) and give its normal value.
15. Indicate which structure is involved in the
   a. Counter-current multiplier: ______
   b. Counter-current exchanger: ______
16. Indicate the function of the
   a. Counter-current multiplier: ______
   b. Counter-current exchanger: ______
17. Indicate which part of the loop of Henle:
   a. Is permeable to water but not to solute and is the concentrating segment
   b. Is impermeable to water and transports sodium, potassium and chloride out of the loop of Henle
18. List two characteristics of the vasa recta.
   a.
   b.
19. ADH acts through aquaporin channels in the collecting duct.
   a. What is the name of the condition that results in the absence of ADH?
   b. List two features of the condition.
20. Fill in the following table to describe the micturition (voiding of urine) reflex.

Stimulus	
Afferent nerves	
Integrating centre	
Efferent nerves	
Actions of efferent nerves	

21. Explain the following terms:
   a. Anuria
   b. Oliguria
   c. Polyuria
22. List five abnormal constituents in urine and indicate for each, one condition in which they are found.

Abnormal Constituent	Condition

23. List two blood tests that are commonly used to evaluate renal function.
   a.
   b.
24. List three clinical features of chronic renal failure.
   a.
   b.
   c.

SHORT ESSAY QUESTIONS

1. Describe the functions of the juxtaglomerular apparatus.
2. Describe the nonexcretory functions of the kidney.

3. Describe the functions of the proximal convoluted tubule of the nephron. Describe the function of the collecting duct of the nephron.
4. Describe the nonurine tests of kidney function.
5. Describe the features of chronic renal failure.

LONG ESSAY QUESTIONS

1. Draw and label the juxtaglomerular apparatus and describe its functions.
2. Describe the excretory and nonexcretory functions of the kidney.
3. Define glomerular filtration. Describe the layers through which the filtrate needs to pass. What are the factors that affect glomerular filtration rate?
4. Describe the function of the counter-current multiplier and counter-current exchanger.
5. Describe the innervation of the bladder and the micturition reflex.
6. Describe the normal composition of urine.
7. List the abnormal constituents of urine and indicate when they are found.

MULTIPLE CHOICE QUESTIONS ANSWERS

Chapter 57:

1-c; 2-a; 3-d; 4-c; 5-b

Chapter 58:

1-b; 2-a; 3-b; 4-a; 5-d

SHORT ANSWER QUESTIONS: ANSWER KEY

1. (A) Bowman's capsule, (B) proximal convoluted tubule, (C) descending limb of loop of Henle, (D) ascending limb of loop of Henle, (E) glomerulus, (F) distal convoluted tubule, (G) collecting duct.
2. 1, C; 2, E; 3, G; 4, B; 5, F; 6, D; 7, A.
3. (a) False, (b) true, (c) false.
4. Juxtaglomerular (granular) cells, mesangial (Lacis) cells, macula densa cells.
5. See Chapter 57.
6. Ultrafiltration, reabsorption, secretion.
7. See Chapter 57.
8. See Chapter 58.
9. 125 mL/min.
10. See Chapter 58.
11. Glomerular hydrostatic pressure: increases; glomerular osmotic pressure: decreases; Bowman's capsule hydrostatic pressure: decreases.
12. Sodium, water, glucose, amino acids.
13. See Chapter 58.
14. See Chapter 58.
15. (a) Loop of Henle, (b) vasa recta.
16. (a) Generate the medullary osmotic gradient, (b) maintains the medullary osmotic gradient.
17. (a) Descending limb of the loop of Henle, (b) thick ascending limb of the loop of Henle.
18. Freely permeable to salute and water; flow is opposite in direction to the loop of Henle.
19. (a) Diabetes insipidus, (b) see Chapter 58.
20. See Chapter 58.
21. See Chapter 59.
22. See Chapter 59.
23. Blood urea nitrogen, serum creatinine.
24. See Chapter 59.

SECTION 10

Workbook: The Reproductive System

SPECIFIC LEARNING OBJECTIVES

At the end of this chapter, the student should be able to:

Chapter 60

- Describe with a diagram the functional anatomy of the female reproductive system.
- Define the following terms:
  - Menarche
  - Puberty
  - Menopause
- List the secondary sexual characteristics of the female which develop at puberty.
- Describe the factors which affect the onset of menarche and menopause.

Chapter 61

- List with a diagram the phases and durations of a typical menstrual cycle.
- Describe the changes that occur during the menstrual cycle in the:
  - Ovaries
  - Uterus (endometrium)
  - Cervix
- Describe the hormonal changes that occur during a menstrual cycle.
- Define ovulation and list the tests of ovulation.
- Define the following terms:
  - Amenorrhoea
  - Menorrhagia
  - Dysmenorrhoea
- Describe the sequence of the sexual act.
- List the actions of oestrogen and progesterone.

Chapter 62

- Define the following terms:
  - Fertilization
  - Implantation
- Describe the functions of the placenta.
- List the physiological changes that occur during pregnancy in the mother.
- List the tests of pregnancy.
- Define parturition and describe the process of birth.
- Define lactation and list the factors that affect lactation.
- Compare and contrast the composition of breast milk and formula/dairy milk.

Chapter 63

- Describe the process of sex differentiation during the development of the foetus.
- Describe the functional anatomy of the male reproductive system; specifically describe the function of:
  - Vas deferens
  - Seminal vesicle
  - Prostate gland
  - List the secondary sexual characteristics of the male which develop during puberty.
- List the actions of testosterone.
- List the steps of spermatogenesis with the help of a diagram.
- Define spermiogenesis.
- List the factors which affect and regulate spermatogenesis.
- List the actions of testosterone.
- List the features which are assessed during semen analysis.
- Define the following terms:
  - Oligospermia
  - Azoospermia

Chapter 64

- List some common variations/disorders of the menstrual cycle.
- List the methods of contraception in the male and female.
- Outline the broad principles of antenatal care during pregnancy.
- Describe prolonged and obstructed labour.
- Describe the basic parameters of a semen analysis.
- Outline the approach to an infertile couple coming to the hospital.

GLOSSARY OF TERMS

Chapter 60

- **Menarche:** the onset of menstruation
- **Menopause:** the complete stoppage of menstruation

Chapter 61

- **Ovulation:** the release of the ovum (egg) from the ovaries
- **Follicular phase:** the first phase of the menstrual cycle prior to ovulation

- **Luteal phase:** the second phase of the menstrual cycle after ovulation
- **Spinnbarkeit:** the 'stretchy' property of cervical mucus around the time of ovulation
- **Endometrium:** the epithelial lining of the uterus which is shed during menstruation

Chapter 62

- **Fertilization:** the union of the male and female gametes (i.e. sperm and ovum) with the exchange of nuclear material
- **Implantation:** the attachment of the fertilized ovum (actually, the blastocyst) to the lining of the uterus
- **Gestation:** the period of development in utero (i.e. inside the uterus)
- **Parturition:** process of childbirth
- **Lactation:** secretion of milk by the mammary glands (breasts)

Chapter 63

- **Puberty:** the age at which male and female adolescents achieve sexual maturity and are capable of reproduction (girls typically achieve puberty between 10 and 14 years and boys, 1–2 years later)
- **Secondary sexual characteristics:** the physical changes that occur at puberty which distinguish males from females, but which are not necessarily directly involved with reproduction

Chapter 64

- **Contraception:** prevention of pregnancy by interfering with ovulation, fertilization or implantation
- **Infertility:** failure to conceive by natural means in the absence of contraception
- **Sterility:** the inability to reproduce (i.e. have children)

MULTIPLE CHOICE QUESTIONS

Chapter 60:

1. Which of the following is associated with menarche?
   a. Appearance of first menstrual period
   b. Development of the breasts
   c. Development of the adrenal glands
   d. Oogenesis
2. Which of the following is not a secondary sexual characteristic in the female?
   a. Enlargement of breasts
   b. Deepening of the voice
   c. Widening of hips
   d. Growth of pubic hair
3. Which of the following is associated with menopause?
   a. Stage prior to onset of menstrual cycles
   b. Period when the woman is capable of bearing a child
   c. Variation in menstrual cycles as the woman grows older
   d. Permanent stoppage of the menstrual cycles
4. Which of the following is not a major determinant of onset of menarche?
   a. Climate
   b. Race
   c. Nutritional status
   d. Strenuous physical activity
5. Which of the following increases the age at which menopause occurs?
   a. Absence of childbirth
   b. Smoking
   c. High intakes of fat and cholesterol
   d. Giving birth to a child before 25 years

Chapter 61:

1. Which of the following stages of oogenesis occurs just prior to the release of the ovum?
   a. Primordial follicle
   b. Graafian follicle
   c. Preantral follicle
   d. Antral follicle
2. Which of the following hormones secreted from the corpus luteum helps to maintain pregnancy?
   a. Oestrogen
   b. Follicle stimulating hormone (FSH)
   c. Progesterone
   d. Lutenizing hormone (LH)
3. Surge of which of the following hormones occurs just before ovulation?
   a. Oestrogen
   b. LH
   c. FSH
   d. Progesterone
4. Which of the following is the correct order of the menstrual cycle?
   a. Menstrual bleeding – proliferative phase – ovulation– secretory phase
   b. Menstrual bleeding – ovulation – proliferative phase – secretory phase
   c. Ovulation – menstrual bleeding – proliferative phase – secretory phase
   d. Menstrual bleeding – secretory phase – ovulation – proliferative phase
5. Which of the following is not a test of ovulation?
   a. Spinnbarkeit test
   b. Measurement of basal body temperature
   c. Fern test
   d. Urinary hCG

Chapter 62:

1. Where does fertilization typically occur?
   a. Upper uterus
   b. Lower uterus
   c. Fallopian tube
   d. Cervix
2. Which of the following is true of the placenta?
   a. It is connected to the foetus by two umbilical veins and one umbilical artery
   b. Maternal and foetal blood mixes in the placenta
   c. It allows IgM antibodies to pass through
   d. It produces human chorionic gonadotropin (hCG)

3. The parturition reflex (birth of the baby) is an example of:
   a. Positive feedback
   b. Negative feedback
   c. Feedforward control
   d. Autoregulation
4. Following birth, the clamping of the umbilical cord results in:
   a. Closure of the ductus arteriosus
   b. Closure of the ductus venosus
   c. Closure of foramen ovale
   d. First cry of the baby
5. Which of the following hormones is involved in the milk ejection reflex?
   a. Prolactin
   b. Oestrogen
   c. Progesterone
   d. Oxytocin

Chapter 63:

1. The sex chromosomal pattern XO is associated with:
   a. Turner's syndrome
   b. Klinefelter's syndrome
   c. Down's syndrome
   d. Super female
2. Which of the following glands contributes most of the volume of the semen?
   a. Bulbourethral gland
   b. Seminal vesicle
   c. Prostate gland
   d. Testes
3. During which phase of the development of a sperm does the tail and acrosome develop?
   a. First meiotic division
   b. Second meiotic division
   c. Initial mitosis
   d. Spermiogenesis
4. Which of the following cells secretes testosterone?
   a. Sertoli's cells
   b. Leydig's cells
   c. Epithelial cells of epididymis
   d. Cells of seminal vesicle
5. Which of the following substances is produced by the Sertoli's cells?
   a. Testosterone
   b. Fructose in the semen
   c. Mucous
   d. Mullerian-inhibiting substance

SHORT ANSWER QUESTIONS (FOR RAPID REVIEW)

1. Define the following terms:
   a. Menarche
   b. Puberty
   c. Menopause
2. List the six stages of the reproductive cycle in the female in sequence.
   a.
   b.
   c.
   d.
   e.
   f.
3. List four secondary sexual characteristics in the female.
   a.
   b.
   c.
   d.
4. List four factors which affect the onset of menarche.
   a.
   b.
   c.
   d.
5. List five factors which affect the onset of menopause.
   a.
   b.
   c.
   d.
   e.
6. The following figure indicates the phases of a typical 28-day menstrual cycle. Label the boxes A and B (ovarian cycle) and C and D (uterine cycle).

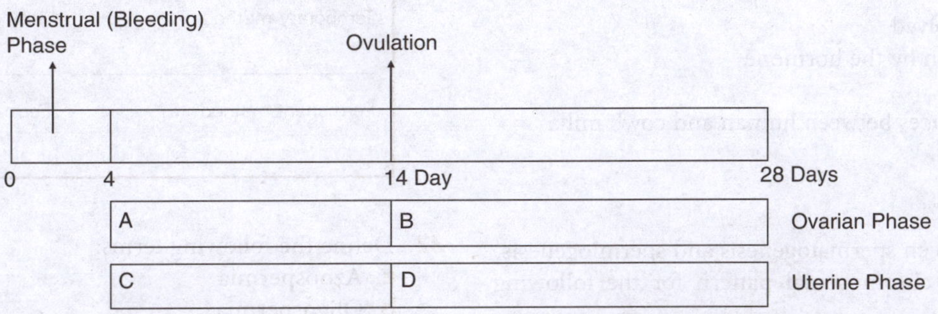

7. List the stages of oogenesis prior to ovulation.
   a.
   b.
   c.
   d.
8. Indicate when in the menstrual cycle, the following hormones achieve the peak values.
   a. Luteinizing hormone (LH)
   b. Progesterone

9. List three tests of ovulation.
a.
b.
c.

10. List four functions of oestrogen.
a.
b.
c.
d.

11. List two functions of progesterone.
a.
b.

12. Define the following terms:
a. Fertilization
b. Implantation

13. List four functions of the placenta.
a.
b.
c.
d.

14. List two tests of pregnancy.
a.
b.

15. With regard to the parturition reflex, indicate the following:
a. Stimulus for the reflex
b. Hormone involved
c. Effect of the hormone
d. Type of feedback

16. Apart from the role of the placenta and umbilical vessels, indicate four major characteristics of the foetal circulation.
a.
b.
c.
d.

17. List four hormones responsible for the enlargement of the breast and milk production.
a.
b.
c.
d.

18. With regard to the milk ejection reflex, indicate the following:
a. Stimulus
b. Hormone involved
c. Cell acted upon by the hormone
d. Type of reflex

19. List three differences between human and cow's milk.
a.
b.
c.

20. Distinguish between spermatogenesis and spermiogenesis.

21. Indicate the sex chromosomal pattern for the following conditions:
a. Turner's syndrome
b. Klinefelter's syndrome

22. List three functions of testosterone.
a.
b.
c.

23. List four secondary sexual characteristics in the male.
a.
b.
c.
d.

24. Rearrange the following to correctly describe the sequence of spermatogenesis:
Primary spermatocyte, spermatid, spermatogonium, secondary spermatocyte, spermatozoa

25. Indicate when the following steps occur during spermatogenesis:
a. Mitosis
b. First meiosis
c. Second meiosis

26. Indicate the functions of the following parts of the spermatozoa:
a. Acrosome
b. Midpiece
c. Tail

27. List four functions of Sertoli's cells.
a.
b.
c.
d.

28. Which hormone is secreted by the Leydig's cells?

29. List three factors which affect spermatogenesis.
a.
b.
c.

30. Define the following terms:
a. Amenorrhoea
b. Menorrhagia
c. Dysmenorrhoea

31. Fill in the following table to indicate the temporary and permanent methods of contraception in the male and female.

Male	Female
Temporary methods	Temporary methods
Permanent method	Permanent method

32. Define the following terms:
a. Azoospermia
b. Oligospermia
c. Cryptorchidism

SHORT ESSAY QUESTIONS

1. Describe the reproductive life cycle in the female.
2. What is menarche and what are the factors associated with its onset?
3. What is menopause and what are the factors associated with its onset?
4. Describe the normal menstrual cycle and list its phases in the ovary and uterus.
5. Describe the hormonal changes that occur in the normal menstrual cycle.
6. Describe the tests of ovulation.
7. Describe the actions of oestrogen.
8. Describe the actions of progesterone.
9. Describe the phases of penile–vaginal intercourse.
10. Describe the process of fertilization and implantation.
11. Describe the functions of the placenta.
12. Describe the parturition reflex.
13. Describe the stages of labour.
14. Describe the changes in the foetal circulation at birth.
15. Describe the milk ejection reflex.
16. Describe the composition of human milk.
17. Describe the process of sex differentiation in utero.
18. Describe some clinical problems related to sex differentiation.
19. Describe the functions of testosterone.
20. Describe the changes that occur with puberty in the male.
21. Describe the functions of the Sertoli's cells.
22. Describe the features of antenatal care.
23. Describe the characteristics of normal semen and list some disorders of sperm production.
24. Describe the clinical approach to an infertile couple.

LONG ESSAY QUESTIONS

1. Describe the internal reproductive organs of the female and their functions.
2. Describe the changes in the ovary, uterus and cervix during the normal menstrual cycle.
3. Describe the maternal changes during pregnancy.
4. List the parts of the male reproductive system and describe the function of each part.
5. Describe the steps of spermatogenesis and its regulation.
6. Describe the methods of contraception in the male and female.

MULTIPLE CHOICE QUESTIONS

Chapter 60
1. a; 2. b; 3. d; 4. a; 5. d

Chapter 61
1. b; 2. c; 3. b; 4. a; 5. d

Chapter 62
1. c; 2. d; 3. a; 4. b; 5. d

Chapter 63
1. a; 2. b; 3. d; 4. b; 5. d

SHORT ANSWER QUESTIONS: ANSWER KEY

1. See Chapter 60.
2. Premenarche, menarche, reproductive phase, perimenopausal phase, menopause, postmenopausal phase.
3. See Chapter 60.
4. See Chapter 60.
5. See Chapter 61.
6. (A) Follicular phase, (B) luteal phase, (C) proliferative phase, (D) secretory phase.
7. Primordial follicle, preantral follicle, antral follicle, Graafian follicle.
8. LH surge, at the time of ovulation; in the luteal phase, related to the formation of the corpus luteum.
9. See Chapter 61.
10. See Chapter 61.
11. See Chapter 61.
12. See Chapter 62.
13. See Chapter 62.
14. Urinary hCG, ultrasound.
15. (a) Stretch of the cervix, (b) oxytocin, (c) uterine contraction, (d) positive feedback.
16. Ductus venosus to bypass the liver, foramen ovale between right and left atria, shutdown of pulmonary circulation, ductus arteriosus between pulmonary artery and aorta.
17. Oestrogen, progesterone, prolactin, human chorionic somatomammotropin.
18. (a) Suckling, (b) oxytocin, (c) myoepithelial cells, (d) neuroendocrine reflex.
19. See Chapter 62.
20. See Chapter 63.
21. (a) XO, (b) XXY.
22. See Chapter 63.
23. See Chapter 63.
24. Spermatogonium, primary spermatocyte, secondary spermatocyte, spermatid, spermatozoa.
25. (a) Between spermatogonium and primary spermatocyte, (b) between primary spermatocyte and secondary spermatocyte, (c) between secondary spermatocyte and spermatid.
26. See Chapter 63.
27. See Chapter 63.
28. Testosterone.
29. See Chapter 63.
30. See Chapter 64.
31. See Chapter 64.
32. See Chapter 64.

Workbook: The Nervous System

SPECIFIC LEARNING OBJECTIVES

At the end of this chapter, the student should be able to:

Chapter 65

- Categorize the different components of the nervous system.
- List the three broad divisions of the brain.
- List the lobes of the cerebrum and indicate their functions.
- Describe the functions of the following:
- Cerebellum
- Midbrain
  - Pons
  - Medulla
  - Hypothalamus
  - Identify key 'centres' in the brain and indicate their functions.
  - Enumerate the different types of spinal nerves.

Chapter 66

- Draw and label a typical neuron.
- List the different types of neurons.
- Describe the different types of 'synapse'.
- List the supporting cells of the peripheral and central nervous system.
- Describe the functions of the supporting cells of the peripheral and central nervous system.

Chapter 67

- Define stimulus. List different kinds of stimuli.
- Explain the meaning of resting membrane potential.
- Briefly describe the ionic basis of resting membrane in nerve.
- Differentiate between a threshold and a subthreshold stimulus.
- Define the terms depolarization and repolarization.
- Describe the characteristics of a 'local response'.
- Draw an action potential and explain its ionic basis.
- State the 'all-or-none' law.
- Distinguish between an action potential and a local response.
- Define 'refractory period'.
- Explain how an impulse travels along a nerve and list the factors that influence it.

Chapter 68

- Describe the formation, circulation and functions of cerebrospinal fluid.

Chapter 69

- Classify sensory receptors.
- List the properties of receptors.
- Draw and label a diagram of a synapse.
- List the properties of synapses.
- Trace the major sensory pathways that convey information from the periphery to the brain.
- Distinguish between the different types of pain.
- Define referred pain and give some examples.
- Describe the role of the cortex in the perception of sensation.

Chapter 70

- Define muscle tone.
- Describe the structure and functions of receptors that convey information of the 'state' of the muscles.
- Describe the location and function of the motor cortex.
- Trace and describe the function of the pyramidal tract.
- Describe the role of the basal ganglia in motor control.
- Describe the function of the vestibular apparatus.
- Describe the function of the cerebellum.

Chapter 71

- Describe the functional anatomy of the autonomic nervous system.
- List the broad actions of the sympathetic nervous system.
- List the broad actions of the parasympathetic nervous system.
- List the receptors through which autonomic nervous effects are mediated.
- List the interactions between the sympathetic nervous system and the parasympathetic nervous system.
- Describe the salient features of autonomic failure.

Chapter 72

- List the major waves of the electroencephalogram (EEG) in terms of their amplitude and frequency.
- List the uses of EEG.
- Describe the physiology of sleep in relation to:
  - The stages of sleep
  - The difference between slow-wave and rapid eye movement (REM) sleep
- List some common disorders of sleep.
- List the areas involved with speech.
- Define aphasia and list the different types of aphasia.

- Define memory and learning.
- List the stages of memory.
- List some common disorders of memory.

Chapter 73

- Organization of the cranial nerves
- Functions of the cranial nerves
- Testing of the cranial nerves

Chapter 74

- List the components of the reflex arc with the help of a diagram.
- List the different types of reflexes.
- List the properties of reflexes.
- List the spinal reflexes and describe the components of the stretch reflex and inverse stretch reflex.
- List the major deep tendon reflexes used in clinical examination and state the spinal root values.
- List the different superficial reflexes tested during a clinical examination.

Chapter 75

- List the common types of nerve injury.
- Explain the term 'Wallerian degeneration'.
- List the common causes of peripheral neuropathy.
- Differentiate between an upper motor and a lower motor neuron lesion.
- Outline the salient features of:
  - Stroke and hemiplegia
  - Parkinsonism
  - Types of amnesia
  - Transection of the spinal cord
  - Brown-Séquard syndrome
  - Mental health disorders
- Outline the physiological basis of fever and chills.

GLOSSARY OF TERMS

Chapter 65

- **Gyrus:** ridges or folds on the surface of the brain
- **Sulcus:** grooves on the surface of the brain
- **Brainstem:** consists of the midbrain, pons and medulla (it is responsible for controlling the flow of information to and from the brain)
- **Brodmann's areas:** they are specific numbered areas of the brain typically associated with discrete functions (e.g. the motor speech areas = 44, 45; primary motor area = 4; primary sensory areas = 1, 2, 3)

Chapter 66

- **Myelination:** the process of the formation of a myelin sheath around nerves (this allows nerves to transmit nerve impulses faster)
- **Blood–brain barrier:** a barrier that separates the circulating blood from the extracellular fluid of the brain (it is primarily due to the endothelial lining of the blood vessels which have tight junctions, among other features; it is also partly contributed to by astrocytes which form a second layer around the endothelium)

Chapter 67

- **Stimulus:** a change in the environment that elicits a response
- **Resting membrane potential:** the potential of the cell membrane at rest, that is in its quiescent or unstimulated state
- **Gibbs–Donnan effect:** the ability of nondiffusible ions to affect the distribution of the diffusible ions across a cell membrane
- **Depolarization:** the conversion of the resting membrane potential from a negative to a less negative or positive potential
- **Repolarization:** the return of the cell membrane potential back to its resting state, that is from a more positive potential to the resting membrane potential
- **Action potential:** the cell membrane potential that develops in response to a threshold or suprathreshold stimulus
- **Local response:** the cell membrane potential that develops in response to a subthreshold stimulus
- **Nerve impulse:** the propagation of the action potential along a nerve membrane
- **All-or-none law:** when threshold or suprathreshold stimuli are applied to a nerve membrane, they elicit an action potential of the same amplitude
- **Summation of local responses:** subthreshold stimuli applied together close to each other or in quick succession at the same point of the membrane result in a higher cell membrane potential (when this achieves a critical firing level, an action potential will be elicited)
- **Refractory period:** the period of the action potential during which a second stimulus elicits no response
- **Synapse:** a junction between two nerves where information is transmitted through a neurotransmitter released into the synaptic cleft
- **Saltatory conduction:** conduction of the nerve impulse from one node of Ranvier to the next node of Ranvier (this 'jumping' ensures faster conduction)

Chapter 68

- **Cerebrospinal fluid (CSF):** fluid contained within the subarachnoid space of the brain and the spinal cord
- **Hydrocephalus:** an excessive accumulation of CSF in the brain
- **Cerebral lateralization:** some processes are better performed by one of the two cerebral hemispheres

Chapter 69

- **Sensory transduction:** the conversion of a sensory stimulus into an electrical signal in the sensory nerve
- **Receptor:** a sense organ (some receptors are specific, i.e. they can sense a single type of sensory stimulus, while others are 'polymodal', i.e. they can sense multiple types of sensory stimuli)
- **Synapse:** junction between two nerves

Chapter 70

- **Muscle tone:** tension in the muscle that occurs even when the muscle is relaxed

- **Flaccidity:** reduced muscle tone – muscle feels soft and limp
- **Rigidity:** increased muscle tone – muscle feels firm and stiff
- **Posture:** position of the body, for example, standing, sitting
- **Tremor:** involuntary, trembling movement of muscles, often seen in the hands

Chapter 71

- **Craniosacral outflow:** the collection of parasympathetic nerves that emerge from the central nervous system
- **Thoracolumbar outflow:** the collection of sympathetic nerves that emerge from the central nervous system
- **Preganglionic nerves:** the motor outflow of the autonomic nervous system (both sympathetic and parasympathetic) is formed by two neurons connected in series (i.e. separated by a synapse); the first neuron which originates in the brain or spinal cord is called a preganglionic neuron
- **Postganglionic nerves:** the second neuron that originates outside the central nervous system and supplies the organs

Chapter 72

- **EEG:** a record of the fluctuations of the electrical activity of large numbers of neurons in the brain, recorded with electrodes applied to the surface of the scalp
- **Coma:** a state of prolonged unconsciousness
- **Epilepsy:** fits or seizures triggered by abnormal electrical activity in the brain
- **Brain death:** irreversible loss of the neuronal functions of the brain (EEG shows absence of brain activity)
- **REM sleep:** rapid eye movement sleep, also called paradoxical sleep, characterized by beta waves, hypotonia, withdrawal of sympathetic tone and dreams, among other features
- **Aphasia:** a disorder of speech
- **Learning:** acquisition of new knowledge
- **Memory:** storage and retrieval of learned knowledge
- **Amnesia:** loss of memory

Chapter 73

- **Bell's palsy:** a sudden weakness in the facial muscles involving the facial nerve, and often following a viral infection (recovery is usually complete if detected early and treated)
- **Vertigo:** a sense of dizziness, 'spinning', unsteadiness, often accompanied by nausea or vomiting
- **Accommodation:** the response of the eye when it is required to suddenly focus on a nearby object after looking into the distance
- **Visual acuity:** the ability to see an object with clarity, sharpness and detail

Chapter 74

- **Reflex:** rapid, involuntary response to a stimulus mediated through a reflex arc
- **Deep tendon reflexes:** stretch reflexes elicited during clinical testing (the common deep tendon reflexes include biceps, triceps, brachioradialis, knee and ankle jerks)
- **Superficial reflexes:** clinical reflexes elicited by stroking the skin or mucous membrane and eliciting specific muscle contraction responses

Chapter 75

- **Paralysis:** the inability to move a part of the body (this may be complete or partial)
- **Hemiplegia:** paralysis of one side of the body
- **Hyperreflexia:** excessive or greater than normal reflexes
- **Amnesia:** loss of memory (this may be partial or complete)

MULTIPLE CHOICE QUESTIONS

Chapter 65:

1. Which of the following is true for the meninges of the brain?
   a. The arachnoid mater is the outermost membrane
   b. The pia mater is between the dura mater and arachnid mater
   c. The subarachnoid space is between arachnoid and pia mater
   d. The subarachnoid space contains plasma
2. The occipital lobe is important for:
   a. Speech
   b. Perception of touch and pressure
   c. Control of emotions and behaviour
   d. Control of vision
3. Which part of the hypothalamus is responsible for satiety?
   a. Ventromedial hypothalamus
   b. Lateral hypothalamus
   c. Suprachiasmatic nucleus
   d. Anterior hypothalamus
4. Which part of the hypothalamus controls circadian rhythms?
   a. Ventromedial hypothalamus
   b. Lateral hypothalamus
   c. Suprachiasmatic nucleus
   d. Posterior hypothalamus
5. Which part of the hindbrain is responsible for the control of balance and posture?
   a. Pons
   b. Medulla
   c. Thalamus
   d. Cerebellum

Chapter 66:

1. Which part of the neuron receives impulses?
   a. Nerve terminal
   b. Dendrites
   c. Axon hillock
   d. Axon
2. Which neurons carry information to the viscera?
   a. Autonomic
   b. Sensory
   c. Motor
   d. Peripheral
3. Which of the following is not a neurotransmitter?
   a. Norepinephrine
   b. Glycine
   c. Dopamine
   d. Thyroxine
4. Which of the following cells is responsible for myelination in peripheral nerves?

a. Microglia
b. Oligodendrocytes
c. Schwann's cells
d. Astrocytes

5. Which of the following cells helps to form the blood–brain barrier?
a. Microglia
b. Oligodendrocytes
c. Schwann's cells
d. Astrocytes

Chapter 67:

1. The resting membrane potential of a neuron is:
a. Always positive
b. Always negative
c. Dependent on the stimulus
d. Dependent on the type of nerve

2. A threshold stimulus to a nerve fibre results in:
a. Local response
b. Hyperpolarization
c. Action potential
d. Summation

3. Which phase of the action potential is due to the opening of voltage-gated sodium channels?
a. Depolarization
b. Repolarization
c. Hyperpolarization
d. Return to resting membrane potential

4. Which of the following is a characteristic of an action potential?
a. Graded response
b. Summation
c. No refractory period
d. Propagation as a nerve impulse

5. A nerve fibre responds with an action potential of the same amplitude to threshold and suprathreshold stimuli. This is called:
a. Summation
b. Refractory period
c. All or None Law
d. Propagation

Chapter 68:

1. Which of the following is true of cerebrospinal fluid?
a. More glucose than plasma
b. More protein than plasma
c. Lower osmotic pressure than plasma
d. Almost cell free

2. CSF is absorbed by:
a. Arachnoid villi
b. Choroid plexus
c. Third ventricle
d. Subarachnoid space

3. The left cerebral hemisphere is dominant for:
a. Emotions
b. Music
c. Creativity
d. Language

Chapter 69:

1. The surface area which inputs into a single sensory nerve fibre is called:
a. Dermatome
b. Receptive field
c. Sensory area
d. Epicritic sensation

2. Which of the following sensations is carried by the antero-lateral spinothalamic tract?
a. Two-point discrimination
b. Proprioception
c. Fine touch
d. Pain

3. Which of the following sensations is carried by the dorsal columns?
a. Vibration
b. Crude touch
c. Pain
d. Temperature

4. In which cerebral lobe is the primary sensory cortex located?
a. Frontal
b. Temporal
c. Parietal
d. Occipital

5. Pain that is felt in an area from where it does not originate is called:
a. Somatic pain
b. Visceral pain
c. Referred pain
d. Central pain

Chapter 70:

1. The nerve which supplies a muscle and originates from the ventral horn of the spinal cord is:
a. Alpha neuron
b. Beta neuron
c. Gamma neuron
d. Delta neuron

2. In which cerebral lobe is the motor cortex located?
a. Frontal
b. Parietal
c. Temporal
d. Occipital

3. The pyramidal tract crosses (decussates) at:
a. Pons
b. Internal capsule
c. Corona radiate
d. Medulla

4. A common disorder of the basal ganglia is:
a. Haemiplegia
b. Brown-Sequard syndrome
c. Parkinson's disease
d. Paraplegia

5. The part of the inner ear associated with equilibrium and balance is:
a. Cochlea
b. Auditory nerve

c. Organ of Corti
d. Vestibular apparatus

Chapter 71:

1. Which of the following cranial nerves are part of the parasympathetic nervous system?
   a. II, V, IX, X
   b. III, VI, IX, X
   c. III, VII, IX, X
   d. II, VII, IX, X
2. On which receptors does acetylcholine act postganglionically?
   a. Alpha 1 adrenergic
   b. Beta 1 adrenergic
   c. Muscarinic
   d. Nicotinic
3. Which of the following effects are associated with sympathetic nervous activation?
   a. Decrease in heart rate
   b. Fall in blood pressure
   c. Bronchodilation
   d. Constriction of pupils
4. Which of the following is due to sympathetic activity in the gastrointestinal tract?
   a. Increased pancreatic enzyme secretion
   b. Increased gastric acid secretion
   c. Increased peristalsis
   d. Contraction of sphincters

Chapter 72:

1. Which of the following EEG waves has the lowest frequency and highest amplitude?
   a. Alpha
   b. Beta
   c. Theta
   d. Delta
2. Which of the following features is characteristic of REM sleep?
   a. Delta waves
   b. Rapid eye movements
   c. Lack of dreams
   d. Hypertonia
3. Which of the following is an example of hypersomnia (excessive sleep)?
   a. Obstructive sleep apnoea
   b. Somnambulism
   c. Enuresis
   d. Nightmares
4. Motor aphasia involves:
   a. Wernicke's area
   b. Broca's area
   c. Arcus fasciculus
   d. Auditory area
5. In which form of learning are the number of neuronal synapses reduced?
   a. Sensitization
   b. Classical conditioning
   c. Habituation
   d. Operant conditioning

Chapter 73:

1. Which cranial nerve is involved in smell?
   a. I
   b. II
   c. III
   d. IV
2. Which of the cranial nerves forms a major part of the parasympathetic nervous system?
   a. III
   b. VII
   c. IX
   d. X
3. Which cranial nerve carries impulses from the vestibular apparatus?
   a. V
   b. VII
   c. VIII
   d. X
4. Which cranial nerve supplies the muscle of the tongue?
   a. VII
   b. IX
   c. X
   d. XII
5. Which cranial nerves supply the extraocular muscles of the eye?
   a. III, IV, VI
   b. II, IV, VI
   c. II, III, VI
   d. III, V, VI

Chapter 74:

1. Which of the following reflexes has a single synapse?
   a. Stretch
   b. Inverse stretch
   c. Withdrawal
   d. Crossed extensor
2. Which of the following is an autonomic reflex?
   a. Inverse stretch
   b. Deep tendon
   c. Baroreflex
   d. Withdrawal
3. Which reflex relates to the spinal segments C5, C6?
   a. Biceps
   b. Triceps
   c. Knee jerk
   d. Ankle jerk

SHORT ANSWER QUESTIONS (FOR RAPID REVIEW)

1. List the four lobes of the cerebrum.
   a.
   b.
   c.
   d.

2. List three functions of the frontal lobe.
   a.
   b.
   c.
3. List three functions of the parietal lobe.
   a.
   b.
   c.
4. List three functions of the temporal lobe.
   a.
   b.
   c.
5. Indicate one major sensory processing area located in the occipital lobe: ______________.
6. List six functions of the hypothalamus.
   a.
   b.
   c.
   d.
   e.
   f.
7. List three functions of the cerebellum.
   a.
   b.
   c.
8. There are 31 pairs of spinal nerves. Indicate the number of pairs of each of the following nerves:
   a. Cervical
   b. Thoracic
   c. Lumbar
   d. Sacral
   e. Coccygeal
9. List two functions of Schwann's cells.
   a.
   b.
10. List the types of glial cells.
    a.
    b.
    c.
    d.
11. List three functions of glial cells.
    a.
    b.
    c.
12. Define stimulus.
13. List four different kinds of stimulus.
    a.
    b.
    c.
    d.
14. The resting membrane potential (RMP) of the nerve is between −70 and −90 mV. Indicate three factors that contribute to the RMP.
    a.
    b.
    c.
15. Indicate the ionic basis for the following phases of the action potential:
    a. Depolarization
    b. Repolarization
16. List three differences between a local response and an action potential.
    a.
    b.
    c.
17. The conduction of a nerve impulse from one node of Ranvier to another node of Ranvier is called ______________.
18. List two factors which affect the speed of conduction of a nerve impulse.
    a.
    b.
19. In the following table, list three distinct difference between the function of the left and right cerebral hemispheres.

Left Hemisphere	**Right Hemisphere**

20. List four functions of CSF.
    a.
    b.
    c.
    d.
21. List three differences between CSF and blood.
    a.
    b.
    c.
22. Fill in the blanks:
    CSF is produced by the ______________ of the ventricles, circulates in the ______________ space and is absorbed by the ______________. Normal production of CSF is ______________ mL/day. About ______________ CSF is normally present; excess CSF gives rise to a clinical condition called ______________.
23. List three properties of a receptor.
    a.
    b.
    c.
24. List three properties of a synapse.
    a.
    b.
    c.

25. Fill in the following table to outline the features of the anterolateral spinothalamic tract and the dorsal columns:

	Spinothalamic Tract	Dorsal Column
Sensations carried		
Receptors		
Location where tract crosses to the opposite side		

26. The sensory cortex is located ____________ the central sulcus in the ____________ lobe. Representation of the body in the sensory cortex forms the ____________.

27. Pain is transmitted by the ____________ tract. The ____________ theory explains how pain can be controlled at the spinal cord. Central modulation of pain involves the actions of endogenous ____________ and the ____________ in the midbrain. Cardiac pain which is felt on the inner aspect of the arm is an example of ____________ pain.

28. Indicate the stimulus for the following sensory organs:
a. Muscle spindle
b. Golgi's tendon organ

29. The primary motor cortex is located ____________ of the central sulcus. It constitutes Brodmann's area ____________. Two other areas of the cortex which are involved in motor control are the ____________ and ____________.

30. With regard to the pyramidal (corticospinal) tract, indicate the following:
a. Origin of the tract
b. Site often affected by stroke
c. Site of decussation (crossing over)
d. Cells with which it synapses in the spinal cord

31. With regard to Parkinson's disease, indicate:
a. Area affected
b. Neurotransmitter affected
c. Three clinical features
i.
ii.
iii.

32. List three functions of the cerebellum.
a.
b.
c.

33. List three features of cerebellar dysfunction.
a.
b.
c.

34. Which parts of the autonomic nervous system describe the following?
a. Thoracolumbar outflow
b. Craniosacral outflow

35. The neurotransmitter at the parasympathetic and sympathetic ganglia is ____________ and the receptor is ____________.

36. Fill in the following table:

	Sympathetic Nervous System	Parasympathetic Nervous System
Postganglionic neuron neurotransmitter		
Receptors on target organs		
Condition associated with		
Effect on heart rate		
Effect on blood pressure		
Effect on gastrointestinal motility		
Effect on GIT sphincters		

37. Identify the EEG waves labelled a–d.

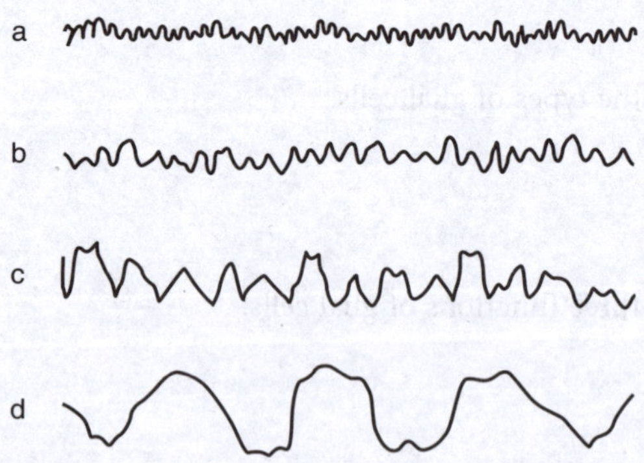

38. List three uses of the EEG.
a.
b.
c.

39. List five features of REM sleep.
a.
b.
c.
d.
e.

40. List four categories of sleep disorders.

a.
b.
c.
d.

41. Label area A involved in the production of speech and B involved in sensory processing for speech.

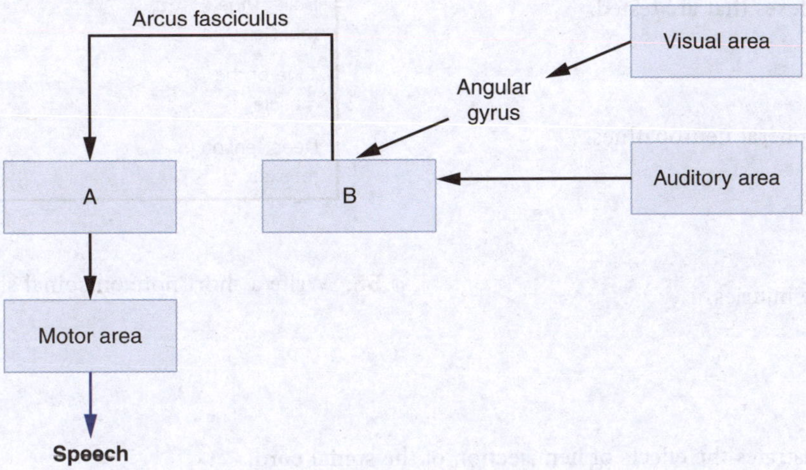

42. Disturbances in the production/comprehension of spoken/written language or speech are called ____________________. Two types of this disorder are

a.
b.

43. List the two types of conditioning.

a.
b.

44. What is amnesia? ____________________

a. List two types of amnesia.

i.
ii.

b. List three features of Alzheimer's disease.

i.
ii.
iii.

45. List three cranial nerves which are purely sensory.

a.
b.
c.

46. List four cranial nerves which are sensory and motor.

a.
b.
c.
d.

47. List four cranial nerves which have autonomic function.

a.
b.
c.
d.

48. List three properties of reflexes.

a.
b.
c.
d.

49. Label the parts of the reflex arc in the following diagram.

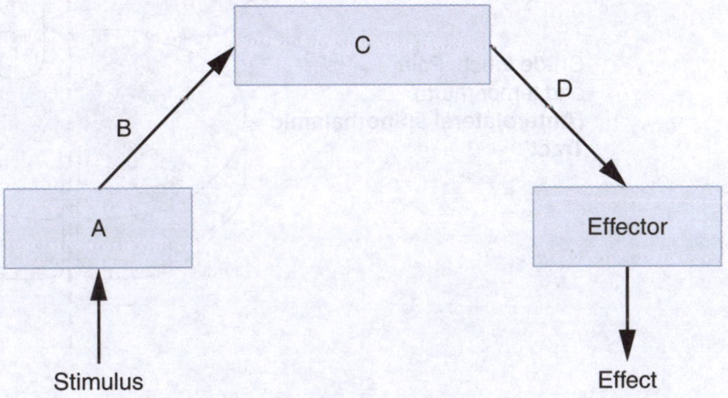

50. Complete the following table to indicate the features of the stretch, inverse stretch and withdrawal reflex:

	Stretch	Inverse Stretch	Withdrawal
Stimulus			
Receptor			
Sensory neuron			
Effector muscles			
Effect			

51. List five deep tendon reflexes that are commonly used clinically.

a.
b.
c.
d.
e.

52. List three superficial reflexes that are tested.

a.
b.
c.

53. List four causes for peripheral neuropathies.

a.
b.
c.
d.

54. List three types of nerve injuries.

a.
b.
c.

55. Complete the following table to distinguish between upper and lower motor neuron lesions:

	Upper Motor Neuron Lesion	Lower Motor Neuron Lesion
Bulk of the muscle		
Tone of the muscle		
Deep tenson reflexes		

56. Write a short note on spinal shock.

57. The following figure illustrates the effects of hemisection of the spinal cord.

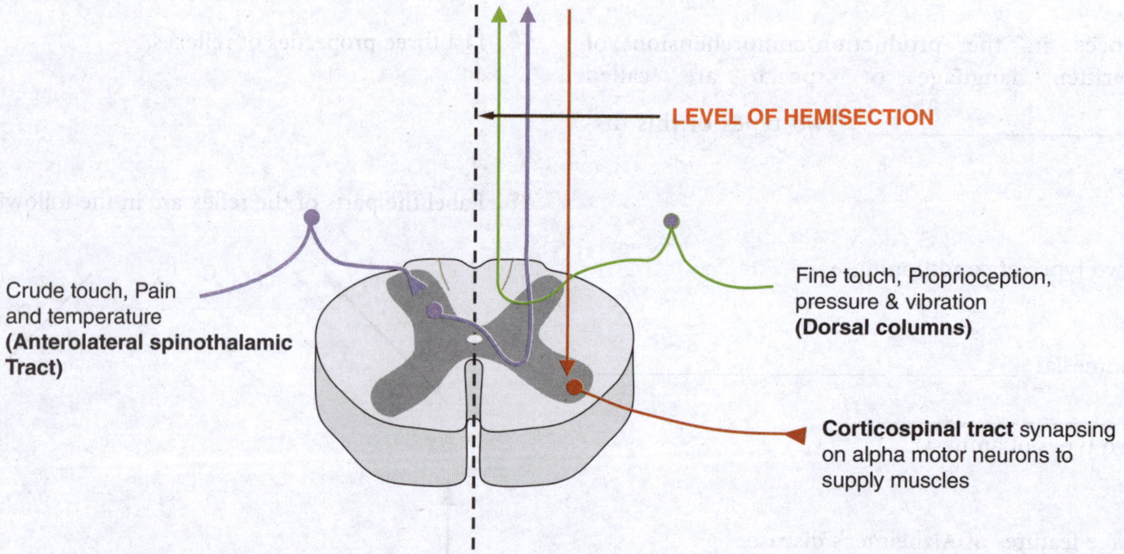

Indicate the side of loss of the following:

a. Crude touch, pain and temperature
b. Fine touch, vibration, pressure and proprioception
c. Muscle function

SHORT ESSAY QUESTIONS

1. Describe the composition and location of cerebrospinal fluid. What are its functions?
2. Describe the organization of the nerves in the spinal cord.
3. Describe the constituents and functions of the midbrain.
4. Describe the functions of the hindbrain.
5. Classify the different types of nerves. Draw and label a typical neuron.
6. Classify the different types of synapses.
7. List the different types of glial cells and describe their functions.
8. What is resting membrane potential and what is its genesis?
9. Describe how a nerve impulse is transmitted and the factors affecting transmission.
10. Distinguish between a local response and an action potential.
11. Compare the left and right cerebral hemisphere.
12. What is referred pain? Give examples and explain one theory used to explain it.
13. Describe the central modulation of pain.

14. List the receptors in skeletal muscle and muscle tendons and describe their function.
15. Describe the structure and functions of the vestibular apparatus.
16. Describe the stages of sleep.
17. Describe the features of rapid eye movement (REM) sleep.
18. Describe some disorders of sleep.
19. Describe the pathway involved in speech. What are aphasias?
20. Describe the different forms of learning.
21. Describe the stages of memory storage. What is amnesia?
22. List the functions of optic nerve. How is this cranial nerve tested?
23. What are the cranial nerves that supply the extraocular muscles? What are their functions and how are they tested?
24. What are the functions of the trigeminal nerve and how is it tested?
25. What are the functions of the facial nerve and how is it tested?
26. Describe the functions of the glossopharyngeal and vagus nerves. How are they tested?
27. Draw and label a reflex arc and list the properties of reflexes.
28. Describe the spinal reflexes.
29. What is peripheral neuropathy? List some common causes.
30. Describe the different types of nerve injury.
31. Distinguish between upper and lower motor neuron lesions.
32. Describe the basis and features of haemiplegia.
33. Describe the features following a complete transection of the spinal cord.
34. Describe Brown-Séquard syndrome.

LONG ESSAY QUESTIONS

1. List the cerebral lobes and describe their functions.
2. Describe the functions of the hypothalamus.
3. Draw and label the action potential and describe its ionic basis.
4. Classify sensory receptors and describe their properties.
5. Draw and label a typical synapse and list the events that occur at the synapse.
6. Trace the dorsal column pathways. What sensations does it carry?
7. Trace the anterolateral spinothalamic tract. What sensations does it carry?
8. Describe the origin and pathway of the pyramidal tract and its function.
9. Describe the components, functions and disorders of the basal ganglia.
10. Describe the components and functions of the cerebellum.
11. Describe the functional anatomy, neurotransmitter, receptors and functions of the sympathetic nervous system.
12. Describe the functional anatomy, neurotransmitter, receptors and functions of the parasympathetic nervous system.
13. List the major waves of the EEG. Describe their characteristics. List the functions of the EEG.
14. What are deep tendon reflexes? Give examples. How are they tested and graded?

MULTIPLE CHOICE QUESTIONS

Chapter 65:
1. c; 2. d; 3. a; 4. c; 5. d

Chapter 66:
1. b; 2. a; 3. d; 4. c; 5. d

Chapter 67:
1. b; 2. c; 3. a; 4. d; 5. c

Chapter 68:
1. d; 2. a; 3. d

Chapter 69:
1. b; 2. d; 3. a; 4. c; 5. c

Chapter 70:
1. a; 2. a; 3. d; 4. c; 5. d

Chapter 71:
1. c; 2. c; 3. c; 4. d

Chapter 72:
1. d; 2. b; 3. a; 4. b; 5. c

Chapter 73:
1. a; 2. d; 3. c; 4. d; 5. a

Chapter 74:
1. a; 2. c; 3. a

SHORT ANSWER QUESTIONS: ANSWER KEY

1. Frontal, parietal, temporal, occipital.
2. See Chapter 65.
3. See Chapter 65.
4. See Chapter 65.
5. Visual cortex.
6. See Chapter 65.
7. See Chapter 65.
8. 8, 12, 5, 5, 1.
9. See Chapter 66.
10. Microglia, macroglia, astrocytes, oligodendrocytes.
11. See Chapter 66.
12. See Chapter 67.
13. Mechanical, thermal, chemical electrical.
14. Permeability of K^+, permeability to Na^+, Na–K-ATPase pump (note that K^+ permeability is 100 times greater than N^+ permeability).
15. (a) Na^+ entry via fast voltage-gated channels, (b) K^+ efflux from the cell.
16. See Chapter 67.
17. Saltatory conduction.
18. Diameter, myelination.
19. See table in Chapter 68.
20. See Chapter 68.

21. See Chapter 68.
22. Choroid plexus, subarachnoid space, arachnoid villi, 500, 150 mL, hydrocephalus.
23. See Chapter 69.
24. See Chapter 69.
25. See Chapter 69.
26. Behind, parietal, sensory homunculus.
27. Anterolateral spinothalamic, gate control, opioids, periaqueductal grey, referred.
28. Muscle length (increased), muscle tension (increased).
29. In front, 4, premotor cortex, supplementary motor area.
30. (a) Motor cortex, (b) internal capsule, (c) medulla, (d) alpha motor neurons.
31. (a) Substantia nigra (nigrostriatal pathway), (b) dopamine, (c) see Chapter 70.
32. See Chapter 70.
33. See Chapter 70.
34. (a) Sympathetic nervous system, (b) parasympathetic nervous system.
35. Acetylcholine, nicotinic.
36.

	Sympathetic Nervous System	Parasympathetic Nervous System
Postganglionic neuron neurotransmitter	Norepinephrine	Acetylcholine
Receptors on target organs	Adrenergic; alpha/beta	Cholinergic; muscarinic
Condition associated with	Fight and flight	Rest and digest/fear
Effect on heart rate	Increased	Decreased
Effect on blood pressure	Increased	Decreased
Effect on gastrointestinal motility	Decreased	Increased
Effect on GIT sphincters	Contraction	Relaxation

37. (a) Beta, (b) alpha, (c) theta, (d) delta.
38. See Chapter 72.
39. See Chapter 72.
40. See Chapter 72.
41. (A) Broca's area, (B) Wernicke's area.
42. Aphasias; (a) motor, (b) sensory.
43. Classical (Pavlovian), operant (trial and error).
44. See Chapter 72.
45. Olfactory (I), optic (II), vestibulocochlear (VIII).
46. V, VII, IX, X.
47. III, VII, IX, X.
48. See Chapter 74.
49. (A) Receptor, (B) sensory (afferent nerve), (C) integrating centre, (D) motor (efferent nerve).
50. See Chapter 74 – tables.
51. Biceps, triceps, brachioradialis, knee, ankle.
52. See Chapter 74.
53. See Chapter 75.
54. See Chapter 75.
55. See Chapter 75.
56. See Chapter 75.
57. (a) Contralateral (opposite side), (b) ipsilateral (same side), (c) ipsilateral.

Index